Build1 room227

Human Anatomy and Physiology Laboratory Manual

Elaine N. Marieb, R.N., Ph.D.

Holyoke Community College

FOURTH EDITION

The Benjamin/Cummings Publishing Company, Inc.

Redwood City, California · Menlo Park, California
Reading, Massachusetts · New York · Don Mills, Ontario
Wokingham, U.K. · Amsterdam · Bonn · Sydney
Singapore · Tokyo · Madrid · San Juan

Sponsoring Editor: Melinda Adams
Production Coordinator: Andy Marinkovich
Manufacturing Coordinator: Casi Kostecki
Assistant Editor: Diane Honigberg
Editorial Assistant: Sami Iwata
Photo Research: Kelli West and Cecilia Mills
Cover and Book Design: Gary Head
Copy Editor: Anita Wagner
Proofreader: Christine Sabooni
Photomicrographs for Histology Atlas: Victor Eroschenko
Art to accompany photomicrographs: Linda McVay
Cover art: Top left: © David Wagner/PhotoTake; Bottom left: © CNRI/SPL/Photo Researchers, Inc.; Bottom right: © Michael Abbey/Photo Researchers, Inc.
Typesetter: GTS Graphics, Commerce, CA
Printer: Von Hoffman Press, Jefferson City, MO

The Author and Publisher believe that the lab experiments described in this publication, when conducted in conformity with the safety precautions described herein and according to the school's laboratory safety procedures, are reasonably safe for the students to whom this manual is directed. Nonetheless, many of the described experiments are accompanied by some degree of risk, including human error, the failure or misuse of laboratory or electrical equipment, mismeasurement, spills of chemicals, and exposure to sharp objects, heat, bodily fluids, blood, or other biologics. The Author and Publisher disclaim any liability arising from such risks in connection with any of the experiments contained in this manual. If students have any questions or problems with materials, procedures, or instructions on any experiment, they should *always* ask their instructor for help before proceeding.

ISBN 0-8053-4053-X

1 2 3 4 5 6 7 8 9 10-VH-96 95 94 93 92

The Benjamin/Cummings Publishing Company, Inc.
390 Bridge Parkway
Redwood City, California 94065

The Benjamin/Cummings Series in Human Anatomy and Physiology:

R. A. Chase
The Bassett Atlas of Human Anatomy (1989)

S. W. Langjahr and R. D. Brister
Coloring Atlas of Human Anatomy, Second Edition (1992)

E. N. Marieb
Human Anatomy and Physiology, Second Edition (1992)

E. N. Marieb
Human Anatomy and Physiology, Study Guide, Second Edition (1992)

E. N. Marieb
Human Anatomy and Physiology Laboratory Manual: Brief Version, Third Edition (1993)

E. N. Marieb
Human Anatomy and Physiology Laboratory Manual: Cat Version, Fourth Edition (1993)

E. N. Marieb
Essentials of Human Anatomy and Physiology, Third Edition (1991)

E. N. Marieb
The A & P Coloring Workbook: A Complete Study Guide, Third Edition (1991)

E. N. Marieb and J. Mallatt
Human Anatomy (1992)

A. P. Spence
Basic Human Anatomy, Third Edition (1991)

R. L. Vines and A. Hinderstein
California State University, Sacramento
Human Musculature Videotape (1989)

R. L. Vines and University Media Services,
California State University, Sacramento
Human Nervous System Videotape (1992)

Table of Contents

Exercises denoted by a red asterisk (*) contain physiology experiments.

Preface to the Instructor

Each new edition of this book brings a matured sensibility for the way teachers teach and students learn. This sensibility is achieved through years of teaching the subject and by listening to the suggestions of other instructors as well as those of students enrolled in multifaceted health-care programs. The fourth edition of *Human Anatomy and Physiology Laboratory Manual: Fetal Pig Version* has been developed to facilitate the A&P laboratory experience for both teachers and students.

As with previous editions of this manual, this edition is intended for students in introductory human anatomy and physiology courses. This manual presents a wide range of laboratory experiences for students concentrating in nursing, physical therapy, occupational therapy, respiratory therapy, dental hygiene, pharmacology, health and physical education, as well as biology and premedical programs. It differs from the Brief Version (Third Edition, 1993) in that the Fetal Pig Version contains: (1) detailed guidelines for dissecting a laboratory animal, (2) more experiments in the various exercises, and (3) more questions and diagrams to be labeled in the laboratory review sections. The manual's coverage is intentionally broad, allowing it to serve both one- and two-semester courses as well.

ORGANIZATION

The variety of both anatomical studies and physiological experiments provides flexibility that enables instructors to gear their courses to specific academic programs, or to their own teaching preferences. The manual is still independent of any textbook, so it contains the background discussions and terminology necessary to perform all experiments. Such a self-contained learning aid eliminates the need for students to bring a textbook into the laboratory.

Each of the 46 exercises leads students toward a coherent understanding of the structure and function of the human body. The manual begins with anatomical terminology and an orientation to the body, which provides the necessary tools for studying the various body systems. The exercises that follow reflect the dual focus of the manual—both anatomical and physiological aspects receive considerable attention. As the various organ systems of the body are introduced, the initial exercises focus on organization from the cellular to the organ level. As indicated by the Table of Contents, the anatomical exercises are followed by physiological experiments that familiarize students with various aspects of body functioning and promote an appreciation for the critical fact that function follows structure. Homeostasis is continually emphasized as a requirement for optimal health. Pathological conditions are viewed as a loss of homeostasis; these discussions can be recognized by the homeostasis imbalance logo ⅄ within the descriptive material of each exercise. This holistic approach ultimately gives students an integrated understanding of the human body.

NEW FEATURES

In this revision, I really tried to respond to reviewers' and users' feedback concerning trends that are having an impact on the anatomy and physiology laboratory experience, most importantly:

- the pedagogical advantage of using four-color histology photomicrographs and dissection photographs
- the growing reluctance of students to perform experiments using living laboratory animals and the declining popularity of animal dissection exercises
- the increased use of computers and other technology in the laboratory and, hence, the subsequent desire for more computer simulation exercises and technological equipment
- the demand for clearer safety guidelines for students, especially when working with blood and other body fluids.

Among the specific changes implemented to address these trends are the following:

1. With the addition of a new ten-page Histology Atlas, the number of colored histology plates in this edition totals sixty. Great care has been taken to select histology photomicrographs that will be the most helpful to students and that correspond closely with what they will view in the laboratory.

While most tissues are stained with hematoxylin and eosin (H&E), a few of those depicted in the Histology Atlas have special stains, such as the photomicrograph of a pancreatic islet of Langerhans that has been differentially stained to distinguish between its glucagon-producing alpha cells and its insulin-secreting beta cells. For some organs studied, a low-power view is presented first to orient the student to the tissue slide before presenting the anatomical detail of the high-power view.

New line drawings, corresponding exactly to the colored plates in the Histology Atlas, appear in the appropriate exercises in conjunction with text that instructs students to view the histologic preparations. This provision adds immeasurably to the utility and effectiveness of the Histology Atlas. Additionally, since these diagrams can be colored by the student to replicate the stained slides they are viewing, the line art will be an excellent student learning aid. The edges of the Histology Atlas are colored blue so that the Atlas can be quickly located.

2. A new ten plate Fetal Pig Anatomy Atlas has been provided in full color. These plates offer unique photographs of organ dissections not previously available in earlier versions of this manual. The edges of the Fetal Pig Anatomy Atlas are red for easy recognition.

3. A color photograph of a Beauchene skull is also a new feature in this edition. The Beauchene skull is an excellent learning tool for students because it clearly shows the relationship of the bones in the skull. The single view shown in the insert highlights the three-dimensional quality of each bone and its unique shape. The Beauchene Skull Photo Insert can be found between the Histology Atlas and the Fetal Pig Anatomy Atlas.

4. In response to the trend toward less animal dissection, a computer simulation exercise, Exercise 16B, Muscle Physiology (Computerized Simulations), has been added to this edition. This exercise provides an *alternative* method to studying skeletal muscle physiology for those who choose not to use frogs to conduct the traditional laboratory experiments. The standard frog gastrocnemius exercise (Exercise 16A) is still provided for the traditionalists among us.

In addition, Exercise 14, the Microscopic Anatomy, Organization, Classification of Skeletal Muscle, and Body Movements, now suggests using chicken meat purchased from the butcher shop for the study of skeletal muscle tissue histology rather than sacrificing a frog to obtain the needed fresh tissue.

5. Five logos, which are visual mnemonics to alert students to a special feature or instructions, appear in this edition.

 The dissection tray logo appears at the beginning of lab activities to be conducted by the students.

The homeostasis imbalance logo described on p. v directs the student's attention to conditions representing a loss of homeostasis.

A blood and body fluid logo appears when blood or other body fluids (saliva, urine) must be handled and signifies where special self-protective measures are to be taken.

A safety logo notifies students that specific safety precautions are to be observed when using certain equipment or conducting particular lab procedures (for example, a hood is to be used when working with ether, and so on).

The cooperative learning logo is seen before experiment heads or procedures where learning would be enhanced and/or time saved by having students work together (in pairs or teams).

6. Two new exercises are included—the computer simulation exercise for muscle physiology (Exercise 16B) mentioned above, and a new surface anatomy lab (Exercise 46) that invites students to apply the anatomical concepts that they have learned, involving them in active observation and manipulation of surface features of their own bodies and those of other students.

7. Barcodes, corresponding to images on any Slice of Life videodisc, provide immediate access to those images relating to topics being studied in the laboratory. These barcodes provide a useful pedagogical tool for both instructors (in demonstrations) and students (for self-study and review).

8. Several exercises have been expanded, modified, or rewritten:

- Exercise 13 on joints has been rewritten with a *structural classification* focus in response to users' requests.
- Exercise 18, Neurophysiology of Nerve Impulses, has been expanded to include an exercise using the oscilloscope to study properties of the nerve impulse.
- Exercise 29 on blood reflects current CDC guidelines for handling human blood. (Since it is important that nursing students, in particular, learn how to safely handle blood-stained articles, the human focus has been retained. In other cases, the use of animal blood for testing purposes is suggested.)

- Exercise 33, Human Cardiovascular Physiology, now has instructions for performing the Harvard step test and guidelines for numerical interpretation of the experimental results.
- Exercise 37 on respiratory physiology has been revised to include instructions for both nonrecording and recording spirometers.
- Exercise 39, on enzyme activity in the digestive system, has been entirely revised and is retitled Chemical and Physical Processes of Digestion. The experiments on chemical digestion (enzymatic activity) have been rewritten and simplified to provide greater student success in this difficult-to-conduct set of experiments. A new section on the physical aspects of digestion focuses on swallowing and gastrointestinal mobility (topics formerly found in the exercise on mechanisms of food propulsion and the physiology of smooth muscle).
- Exercise 41, Urinalysis, has been rewritten to provide for greater safety in handling human urine. In addition, the *Instructor's Guide* provides the source of a published "recipe" for making safe-to-handle artificial urine.

9. In response to user feedback, two infrequently used exercises—Kidney Regulation of Fluid and Electrolyte Balance, and Pregnancy Tests—have been deleted.
10. The anatomical terminology in this manual has been updated to match the updated terminology in *Human Anatomy and Physiology, Second Edition* (by this author) to avoid student confusion over conflicting terminology.
11. The questions in the laboratory review sheets are expanded and now include more labeling exercises.
12. Two new appendices have been added. Appendix A: The Metric System is a useful reference for the student, giving conversion factors to and from the English system to the metric system. Appendix B contains the two Predicted Vital Capacity tables used in computing student results for the spirometer recordings in Exercise 37, Respiratory Physiology.
13. All laboratory instructions and procedures have been revised to incorporate the latest precautions as recommended by the Centers for Disease Control (CDC), including recommendations for safely handling body fluids. These guidelines are reinforced by the laboratory safety procedures described in the inside front cover of this text and the *Instructor's Guide.*
14. Finally, because art plays such a critical role in helping students visualize anatomical and physiological concepts, every effort has been made in this manual to offer a figure, in either line art or photographs, for essentially everything students will examine in the laboratory.

SPECIAL FEATURES

Virtually all the special features appreciated by the adopters of the third edition are retained.

- Each exercise begins with learning objectives.
- Key terms appear in boldface print, and each term is defined when introduced.
- Illustrations are large and of exceptional quality. The use of full color highlights, differentiates and focuses student attention on important structures.
- Body structures are studied from simple-to-complex levels, and physiological experiments allow ample opportunity for student observation, manipulation, and experimentation.
- There are numerous physiological experiments for each organ system, ranging from simple experiments that can be performed without specialized tools to more complex experiments using laboratory equipment and instrumentation techniques.
- Tear-out laboratory review sheets, located toward the end of the manual, are designed to accompany the laboratory exercises. They require students to label diagrams and answer multiple-choice, short-answer, and review questions.
- Space is provided for recording and interpreting experimental results.
- In addition to the figures and instructions for using the major dissection animals, isolated animal organs such as the sheep heart and pig kidney are employed because of their exceptional similarity to human organs. If no major dissection animal is used, the Brief Version of this manual is recommended.
- The prologue, "Getting Started—What to Expect, The Scientific Method, Scientific Notation, and Metrics," explains the scientific method, the logical, practical, and reliable way of approaching and solving problems in the laboratory. It also reviews the use of exponents, metric units, and interconversions.

SUPPLEMENTS

The *Instructor's Guide* that accompanies the *Human Anatomy & Physiology Laboratory Manuals: Cat and Fetal Pig Versions* contains a wealth of information for anyone involved in teaching this course. Instructors can find help in planning the experiments, ordering equipment and supplies, anticipating pitfalls and problem areas, and locating audiovisual material. The probable in-class time required for each lab is indicated by a clock logo. Other useful resources are the updated Trends in Instrumentation section that describes the latest laboratory equipment and technological teaching tools available, and the Anatomy and Physiology Laboratory Safety Procedures section that incorporates current Centers for Disease Control (CDC) guidelines for handling body fluids and other precautions recommended by the CDC. These procedures, located in the front section of the *Instructor's Guide,* can be photo-copied and posted in the lab. By adhering to CDC-recommended measures, the students of this course will be well trained in laboratory safety.

The Mechanical Properties of Active Muscle soft-ware that accompanies Exercise 16B, Muscle Physiol-ogy (Computerized Simulations), is available only to qualified adopters.

ACKNOWLEDGMENTS

I wish to thank the following reviewers for their contri-butions to this edition: Edward DeSchuytner (Northern Essex Community College), Wayne Eshelman (Central Oregon Community College), Kathy McCann Evans (Alvernia College), Jerry Ross (Highline Community College), and Peter Zao (North Idaho College).

My continued thanks to my colleagues at Benja-min/Cummings who helped me in the production of this edition, especially Melinda Adams, my Sponsoring Ed-itor, and Andy Marinkovich, Production Coordinator. Also not to be forgotten is the diligent work of Diane Honigberg, Assistant Editor; the Editorial Assistant, Sami Iwata; and the team of Cecilia Mills and Kelli West, who were responsible for photo research. A spe-cial debt of gratitude is owed Peter Zao (North Idaho College) who adapted the software for the muscle phys-iology computer simulation exercise and catalogued the barcodes which appear in this manual.

Finally, since preparations for the next edition begin well in advance of its publication, I invite users of this edition to send me their comments and suggestions for subsequent editions.

Elaine N. Marieb
Department of Biology
Holyoke Community College
303 Homestead Avenue
Holyoke, MA 01040

Preface to the Student

With hope, your laboratory experiences will be exciting times for you. Like any unfamiliar experience, it really helps if you know in advance what to expect and what will be expected of you.

LABORATORY ACTIVITIES

The A&P laboratory exercises within this manual are designed to help you gain a broad understanding of both anatomy and physiology. So, you can anticipate that you will be examining models, dissecting isolated animal organs, and using a microscope to look at tissue slides (anatomical approaches). You will also investigate chemical conditions or observe changes in both living and nonliving systems, and conduct experiments that examine responses of living organisms, such as frogs or yourself, to various stimuli (physiological approaches).

Because some students question the use of animals in the laboratory setting, their concerns need to be addressed. Be assured that the commercially available major dissection animals and preserved organ specimens used in the A&P lab are *not* harvested from animals raised specifically for dissection purposes. Instead, fetuses or organs (such as the brain, heart, or lungs) that are of no use to the meat packing industry are sent from slaughterhouses to qualified biological supply houses, where they are prepared for laboratory use according to USDA guidelines.

Relative to using live animals for experimentation, every effort is being made to find alternative methods that do not use living animals to study physiological concepts. For example, new to this edition is Exercise 16B, a computer simulation that studies the properties of contracting muscles. This is provided as an alternative in addition to the traditional exercise (16A) that uses frogs. Without a doubt, computer simulations offer certain advantages: (1) they allow you to experiment at length without time constraints of traditional animal experiments, in which fragile living tissues need to be kept alive and viable for the duration of the experiment; and (2) they make it possible to investigate certain concepts (such as isometric versus isotonic contraction in this case) that would be difficult (or impossible) to explore in traditional exercises. Yet, the main disadvantage of computer simulations is that the real-life aspects of experimentation are sacrificed; an animated frog muscle or heart on a computer screen is not really a substitute for observing the responses of actual muscle tissue.

Although it might appear that the choice is simply to decide which approach offers fewer disadvantages, unfortunately adequate software applications are still unavailable. Consequently, living animal experiments remain an important part of the approach of this manual to the study of human A&P. However, wherever possible, the minimum number of animals needed to demonstrate a particular point are used. Furthermore, more instructor-delivered demonstrations of live animal experiments are suggested.

If you use living animals for experiments, you will be expected to handle them humanely. Inconsiderate treatment of laboratory animals will not be tolerated in your A&P laboratory.

BARCODES

The Slice of Life videodisc has become a very popular choice for providing enrichment images for the A&P laboratory. The barcodes sprinkled throughout this manual will allow you to access topic-related images from that videodisc as you work in the laboratory (provided your classroom has the appropriate equipment).

LOGOS/VISUAL MNEMONICS

I have tried to make this manual very easy for you to use, and to this end, five different types of logos (visual mnemonics) are described below:

 The **dissection tray logo** appears at the beginning of lab activities. Since most exercises have some explanatory background provided before the experiment(s), this visual cue alerts you that your involvement is imminent.

The **blood/body fluid logo** appears where blood or other body fluids (saliva, urine) must be handled, and it signifies that you should take special measures to protect yourself.

The **safety logo** alerts you to special precautions in handling lab equipment or conducting certain procedures, e.g., use a ventilating hood when using volatile chemicals.

The **cooperative learning logo** is seen before procedures where your learning will be enhanced (or time saved) if you work with a partner (or team).

The **homeostasis imbalance logo** appears where a clinical disorder is described to indicate what happens when there is a structural abnormality or physiological malfunction, i.e., a loss of homeostasis.

HINTS FOR SUCCESS IN THE LABORATORY

With the possible exception of those who have photographic memories, most students could use some helpful hints and guidelines to ensure that they have successful lab experiences. Since that is what this section provides, read on.

1. Perhaps the best bit of advice is to attend all your scheduled labs and to participate in all the assigned exercises. Learning is an *active* process.

2. Scan the scheduled lab exercise and the questions in the review section in the back of the manual that pertain to it *before* going to lab.

3. Be on time. Most instructors explain what the lab is about, pitfalls to avoid, and the sequence or format to be followed at the beginning of the lab session. If you are late, not only will you miss this information, you will not endear yourself to the instructor.

4. Review your lab notes after completing the lab session to help you focus on and remember the important concepts.

5. Keep your work area clean and neat. This reduces confusion and accidents.

6. Assume that all lab chemicals and equipment are sources of potential danger to you. Follow directions for equipment use and observe the laboratory safety guidelines provided inside the front cover of this manual.

7. Keep in mind the real value of the laboratory experience—a place for you to observe, manipulate, and experience "hands on" activities that will dramatically enhance your understanding of the lecture presentations.

I really hope that you enjoy your A&P laboratories and that this lab manual makes learning about intricate structures and functions of the human body a fun and rewarding process. I'm always open to constructive criticism and suggestions for improvement in future editions. If you have any, please write to me.

Elaine N. Marieb
Department of Biology
Holyoke Community College
303 Homestead Avenue
Holyoke, MA 01040

Getting Started—What to Expect, The Scientific Method, Scientific Notation, and Metrics

Two hundred years ago science was largely a plaything of wealthy patrons, but today's world is dominated by science and its technology. Whether or not we believe that such domination is desirable, we all have a responsibility to try to understand the goals and methods of science that have seeded this knowledge and technological explosion.

The biosciences are very special and exciting because they open the doors to an understanding of all the wondrous workings of living things. A course in human anatomy and physiology (a minute subdivision of bioscience) provides such insights in relation to your own body. Although some experience in scientific studies is helpful when beginning a study of anatomy and physiology, perhaps the single most important prerequisite is curiosity.

Gaining an understanding of science is a little like becoming acquainted with another person. Even though a written description can provide a good deal of information about the person, you can never really know another unless there is personal contact. And so it is with science—if you are to know it well, you must deal with it intimately.

The laboratory is the setting for "intimate contact" with science. It is where scientists test their ideas (do research), the essential purpose of which is to provide a basis from which predictions about scientific phenomena can be made. Likewise, it will be the site of your "intimate contact" with the subject of human anatomy and physiology as you are introduced to the methods and instruments used in biological research.

For many students, human anatomy and physiology is taken as an introductory-level course; and their scientific background exists, at best, as a dim memory. If this is your predicament, this prologue may be just what you need to fill in a few gaps and to get you started on the right track before your actual laboratory experiences begin. So—let's get to it!

THE SCIENTIFIC METHOD

Science would quickly stagnate if new knowledge were not continually derived from and added to it. The approach commonly used by scientists when they investigate various aspects of their respective disciplines is called the **scientific method.** This method is *not* a single rigorous technique that must be followed in a lockstep manner. It is nothing more or less than a logical, practical, and reliable way of approaching and solving problems of every kind—scientific or otherwise—to gain knowledge. It comprises five major steps.

Step 1: Observation of Phenomena

The crucial first step involves observation of some phenomenon of interest. In other words, before a scientist can investigate anything, he or she must decide on a *problem* or focus for the investigation. In most college laboratory experiments, the problem or focus has been decided for you. However, to illustrate this important step, we will assume that you want to investigate the true nature of apples, particularly green apples. In such a case you would begin your studies by making a number of different observations concerning apples.

Step 2: Statement of the Hypothesis

Once you have decided on a focus of concern, the next step is to design a significant question to be answered. Such a question is usually posed in the form of a **hypothesis,** an unproven conclusion that attempts to explain some phenomenon. (At its crudest level, a hypothesis can be considered to be a "guess" or an intuitive hunch that tentatively explains some observation.) Generally, scientists do not restrict themselves to a single hypothesis; instead, they usually pose several and then test each one systematically.

We will assume that, to accomplish step one, you go to the supermarket and randomly select apples from several bins. When you later eat the apples, you find that the green apples are sour, but the red and yellow apples are sweet. From this observation, you might conclude (*hypothesize*) that "green apples are sour." This statement would represent your current understanding of green apples. You might also reasonably predict that, if you were to buy more apples, any green ones you buy will be sour. Thus, you would have gone beyond your initial observation that "these" green apples are sour to the prediction that "all" green apples are sour.

Any good hypothesis must meet several criteria. First, *it must be testable.* This characteristic is far more important than its being correct. The tests may prove the hypothesis incorrect; or new information may require that the hypothesis be modified. Clearly the accuracy of a prediction in the green apple example or in any scientific study depends on the accuracy of the initial information on which it is based.

In our example, no great harm will come from an inaccurate prediction—that is, were we to find that some green apples are sweet. However, in some cases human life may depend on the accuracy of the prediction. Take the case of testing drugs for their effectiveness in treating disease. If one set of observations erroneously indicates that the drugs are risky but very effective, such a conclusion could lead to the death of the subsequent drug recipient(s). This illustrates two points: (1) Repeated testing of scientific ideas is important, particularly because scientists working on the same problem do not always agree in their conclusions. The studies on the use of saccharin and amino acid sweeteners are only two examples. (2) Conclusions drawn from scientific tests are only as accurate as the information on which they are based; therefore, careful observation is essential, even at the very outset of a study.

A second criterion is that, even though hypotheses are guesses of a sort, *they must be based on measurable, describable facts. No mysticism can be theorized.* We cannot conjure up, to support our hypothesis, forces that have not been shown to exist. For example, as scientists, we cannot say that the tooth fairy took Johnny's tooth unless we can prove that the tooth fairy exists!

Third, a hypothesis *must not be anthropomorphic.* Human beings tend to anthropomorphize—that is, to relate all experiences to human experience. Because man is a social animal influenced by culture, these two characteristics tend to promote biased thinking. Whereas we could state that bears instinctively protect their young, it would be anthropomorphic to say that bears love their young, because love is a human emotional response. Thus, the initial hypothesis must be stated without interpretation.

Step 3: Data Collection

Once the initial hypothesis has been stated, scientists plan experiments that will provide data (or evidence) to verify or disprove their hypotheses—that is, they *test* their hypotheses. Data are accumulated by making qualitative or quantitative observations of some sort. The observations are often aided by the use of various types of equipment such as cameras, microscopes, stimulators, or various electronic devices that allow chemical and physiologic measurements to be made.

Observations referred to as **qualitative** are those we can make with our senses—that is, by using our vision, hearing, or sense of taste, smell, or touch. The color of an object, its texture, the relationship of one part to another, and its relative size (large versus small) may all be part of a qualitative description. For some quick practice in qualitative observation, compare and contrast* an orange and an apple.

Whereas the differences between an apple and an orange are obvious, this is not always the case in biological observations. Quite often a scientist tries to detect very subtle differences that cannot be determined by qualitative observations; and data must be derived from measurements made using a variety of scientific equipment. Such observations based on precise measurements of one type or another are **quantitative observations.** Examples of quantitative observations include careful measurements of body or organ dimensions such as mass, size, and volume; measurement of volumes of oxygen consumed during metabolic studies; determination of the concentration of glucose and other chemicals in urine; and determination of the differences in blood pressure and pulse under conditions of rest and exercise. An apple and an orange could be compared quantitatively by performing chemical measurements of the relative amounts of sugar and water in a given volume of fruit flesh, by analyzing the pigments and vitamins present in the apple skin and orange peel, and so on.

A valuable part of data gathering is the use of experiments to verify or disprove a hypothesis. **An experiment** is a procedure designed to describe the factors in a given situation that affect one another (that is, to discover cause and effect) under certain conditions.

Two general rules govern experimentation. The first of these rules is that the experiment(s) should be conducted in such a manner that every **variable** (any factor that might affect the outcome of the experiment) is under the control of the experimenter. The experimenter manipulates the **independent variables** and observes the effects of this manipulation on the **dependent (or response) variable.** For example, if the goal is to determine the effect of body temperature on breathing rate, the value measured (breathing rate) is called the dependent variable because it "depends on" the value chosen for the independent variable (body temperature). The ideal way to perform such an experiment is to set up and run a series of tests that are all identical, except for one specific factor that is varied.

One specimen (or group of specimens) is used as the **control** against which all other experimental samples are compared. The importance of the control sample cannot be overemphasized. It is essential to know how the system you are investigating works under normal circumstances before you can be sure that the results obtained from experimentation are due solely to the manipulation of the independent variable(s). Taking our example one step further, if we wanted to investigate the effects of body temperature (the independent variable) on breathing rate (the dependent variable), we could collect data on the breathing rate of individuals with "normal" body temperature (the implicit control group), and compare these data to breathing-rate measurements obtained from groups of individuals with higher and lower body temperatures. The control group

---

* *Compare* means to emphasize the similarities between two things, whereas *contrast* means that the differences are to be emphasized.

would provide the "normal standard" against which all other samples would be compared relative to the dependent variable.

The second rule governing experimentation is that valid results require that testing be done on large numbers of subjects. It is essential to understand that it is nearly impossible to control all possible variables in biological tests. Indeed, there is a bit of scientific wisdom that mirrors this truth—that is, that laboratory animals, even in the most rigidly controlled and carefully designed experiments, "will do as they damn well please." Thus, stating that the testing of a drug for its pain-killing effects was successful after having tested it on only one postoperative patient would be scientific suicide. Large numbers of patients would have to receive the drug and be monitored for a decrease in postoperative pain before such a statement could have any scientific validity. Then, other researchers would have to be able to uphold those conclusions by running similar experiments. *Repeatability* is an important part of the scientific method, and is the primary basis for acceptance or rejection of many hypotheses.

During experimentation and observation, data must be carefully recorded. Usually, such initial, or raw, data are recorded in tabular (table) form. The table should be labeled to show the variables investigated and the results for each sample. At this point, *accurate recording* of observations is the primary concern. Later, these raw data will be reorganized and manipulated to show more explicitly the outcome of the experimentation.

Some of the observations that you will be asked to make in the anatomy and physiology laboratory will require that a drawing be made. Don't panic! The purpose of making drawings (in addition to providing a record) is to force you to observe things very closely. You need not be an artist (most biological drawings are simple outline drawings), but you do need to be neat and as accurate as possible. It is advisable to use a 4H pencil to do your drawings, because it is easily erased and doesn't smudge. Before beginning to draw, you should examine your specimen closely, studying it as though you were going to have to draw it from memory. For example, when looking at cells you should ask yourself questions such as "What is their shape—the relationship of length and width? How are they joined together?" Then decide precisely what you are going to show and how large the drawing must be to show the necessary detail. After making the drawing, add labels in the margins; and connect them, by straight lines (leader lines), to the structures being named.

Step 4: Manipulation and Analysis of Data

The form of the final data varies, depending on the nature of the data collected. Usually, the final data represent information converted from the original measured values (raw data) to some other form. This may mean that averaging or some other statistical treatment must be applied, or it may require conversions from one kind of units to another. In other cases, graphs may be needed to display the data.

ELEMENTARY TREATMENT OF DATA   Only very elementary statistical treatment of data is required in this manual. For example, you will be expected to understand and/or compute an average (mean), percentages, and a range.

Two of these statistics, the average and the range, are useful in describing the *typical* case among a large number of samples evaluated. Let us use a simple example. We will assume that the following heart rates (in beats/min) were recorded during an experiment: 64, 70, 82, 94, 85, 75, 72, 78. If you put these numbers in numerical order, the **range** is easily computed, because the range is the difference between the highest and lowest numbers obtained (highest number minus lowest number). What is the range of the set of numbers just provided?

1. _____ *

The **average,** or **mean,** is obtained by summing the items and dividing the sum by the number of items. Compute the average for the set of numbers just provided:

2. _____

The word *percent* comes from the Latin meaning "for 100"; thus *percent,* indicated by the percent sign, %, means parts per 100 parts. Thus, if we say that 45% of Americans have type O blood, what we are really saying is that among each group of 100 Americans, 45 (45/100) can be expected to have type O blood.

It is very easy to convert any number (including decimals) to a percent. The rule is to move the decimal point two places to the right and add the percent sign. If no decimal point appears, it is *assumed* to be at the end of the number; and zeros are added to fill any empty spaces. Two examples follow:

$$0.25 = 0.2\underset{\curvearrowright}{\ }5 = 25\%$$
$$5 = 5\underset{\curvearrowright}{\ } = 500\%$$

Change the following numbers to percents:

3. 38.2 = _____   5. 1.6 = _____

4. 402 = _____

Note that although you are being asked here to convert numbers to percents, percents by themselves are meaningless. We always speak in terms of a percentage *of* something.

To change a percent to a whole number (or decimal), remove the percent sign, and move the decimal point two places to the left. Change the following percents to whole numbers or decimals:

6. 36% = _____   8. 25777% = _____

7. 800% = _____   9. 0.05% = _____

* Answers are given on page xviii.

MAKING AND READING LINE GRAPHS For some laboratory experiments you will be required to show your data (or part of them) graphically. Simple line graphs allow relationships within the data to be shown interestingly and allow trends (or patterns) in the data to be demonstrated. An advantage of properly drawn graphs is that they save the reader's time because the essential meaning of large numbers of statistical data can be visualized at a glance.

To aid in making accurate graphs, graph paper (or a printed grid in the manual) is used. Line graphs have both horizontal and vertical scales. Each scale should have uniform intervals—that is, each unit measured on the scale should require the same distance along the scale as any other. Variations from this rule may be misleading and result in false interpretations of the data. By convention, the condition that is manipulated (the independent variable) in the experimental series is plotted on the X-axis (the horizontal axis); and the value that we then measure (the dependent variable) is plotted on the Y-axis (the vertical axis). To plot the data, a dot or a small *x* is placed at the precise point where the two variables (measured for each sample) meet; and then a line (this is called the **curve**) is drawn to connect the plotted points.

Sometimes, you will see the curve on a line graph extended beyond the last plotted point. This is (supposedly) done to predict "what comes next." When you see this done, be skeptical. The information provided by such a technique is only slightly more accurate than that provided by a crystal ball!

To read a line graph, pick any point on the line, and match it with the information directly below on the horizontal scale and with that directly to the left of it on the vertical scale. Figure G.1 is a graph that illustrates the relationship between breaths per minute (respiratory rate) and body temperature. Answer the following questions about this graph:

10. What was the respiratory rate at a body temperature of 96°F?_____

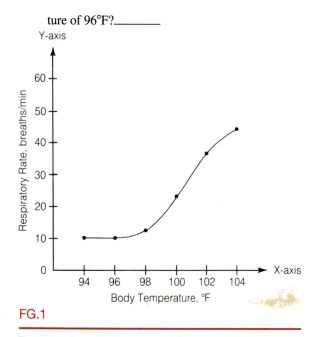

FG.1

Example of graphically presented data.

11. Between 98° and 102°F, the respiratory rate increased from

_____ to _____ breaths per minute.

12. Between which two body temperature readings was the increase in breaths per minute greatest?

_____

13. Are the intervals on each scale uniform?

_____

Step 5: Reporting Conclusions of the Study

Drawings, tables, and graphs alone do not suffice as the final presentation of scientific results. The final step requires that you provide a straightforward description of the conclusions drawn from your results. If possible, your findings should be compared to those of other investigators working on the same problem. (For laboratory investigations conducted by students, these comparative figures are provided by classmates.)

It is important to realize that scientific investigations do not always yield the anticipated results. If there are discrepancies between your results and those of others, or what you expected to find based on your class notes or textbook readings, this is the place to try to explain those discrepancies.

Results are often only as good as the observation techniques used. Depending on the type of experiment conducted, several questions may need to be answered. Did you weigh the specimen carefully enough? Did you balance the scale first? Was the subject's blood pressure actually as high as you recorded it, or did you record it hastily (and inaccurately)? If you did record it accurately, is it possible that the subject was emotionally upset about something, which (even though the matter of concern had nothing to do with the experiment) might have given falsely high data for the variable being investigated? Attempting to explain an unexpected result will often teach you more than you would have learned from anticipated results.

When the experiment produces results that are consistent with the hypothesis, then the hypothesis can be said to have reached a higher level of certainty. There is now a greater probability that the hypothesis is correct. A hypothesis that has been validated by many different investigators is called a **theory.** Theories are useful in two important ways. First, they link sets of data; and second, they make predictions that may lead to additional avenues of investigation. (Okay, we know this with a high degree of certainty; what's next?)

When a theory has been repeatedly verified and appears to have wide applicability in biology, it may assume the status of a **biological principle.** A principle is a statement that applies with a high degree of probability to a range of events. For example, "Living matter is made of cells or cell products" is a principle stated in many biology texts. It is a sound and useful principle, and will continue to be used as such—unless new findings prove it wrong.

We have been through quite a bit of background concerning the scientific method and what its use entails. Because it is important that you remember the phases of the scientific method, they are summarized here:

1. Observation of some phenomenon
2. Statement of a hypothesis (based on the observations)
3. Collection of data (testing the hypothesis with controlled experiments)
4. Manipulation and analysis of the data
5. Reporting of the conclusions of the study

SCIENTIFIC NOTATION AND METRICS

No matter how highly developed our ability to observe, observations have scientific value only if they can be communicated to others. This necessitates the use of scientific notation and the widely accepted system of metric measurements.

Scientific Notation

Because quantitative measurements often yield very large or very small numbers, you are quite likely to encounter numbers such as 3.5×10^{12} or 10^{-3}. It is important that you understand what this **scientific notation** means.

Scientific notation is dependent on the properties of exponents and on the movement of the decimal point when multiplying or dividing by 10. When you multiply 10 by itself, you get a product that is one followed by zeros. The number of zeros (two, in this case) in the product is equal to the number of times you have used 10 as a factor and is shown as an **exponent.** Thus, the following notation

$$\text{base} \to 10^2 \leftarrow \text{exponent}$$

translates to "the base 10 multiplied by itself (10×10)."

The powers of 10 are represented as follows:

$10^0 = 1$	(Any number followed by a zero exponent is one.)
$10^1 = 10$	($10 \times 1 = 10$)
$10^2 = 100$	($10 \times 10 = 100$)
$10^3 = 1000$	($10 \times 10 \times 10 = 1000$)
$10^4 = 10,000$	($10 \times 10 \times 10 \times 10 = 10,000$)

As you can see, each time the exponent is increased by one, another zero ($\times 10$) is added to the answer.

When you multiply any number by a power of 10 written with exponents, the decimal point is moved to the right the number of times shown in the exponent. Thus:

$$3.25 \times 10^1 = 3.2\,5 \qquad = 32.5$$
$$3.25 \times 10^3 = 3.2\,5 \qquad = 3250$$
$$3.25 \times 10^5 = 3.2\,5 \qquad = 325,000$$

By using such exponential notation, very large numbers may be written in far simpler form.

Write the following numbers using the proper scientific notation:

14. $140,000 = 1.4 \times \underline{10^5}$

15. $9,650,000 = 9.65 \times \underline{10^6}$

16. $852 = 8.52 \times \underline{10^2}$

17. $10 = 1.0 \times \underline{10^1}$

Notice that proper scientific notation entails only one number to the left of the decimal point. Thus 1.03×10^3 is correct, but 10.3×10^2 is not.

In the above examples, all of the numbers used were greater than one. Scientific notation can also be used to report numbers less than one. To do this, negative exponents are used. For example, in

$$3.25 \times 10^2$$

the positive exponent means that the decimal point is to be moved two places to the right, and the number designated is 325 ($3.25 \times 10 \times 10$). However, in

$$3.25 \times 10^{-2}$$

the negative exponent means that the number is to be divided by the power of 10 indicated by the exponent and the decimal point is to be moved two places to the left. The number so designated is 0.0325 [$3.25 \div (10 \times 10)$].

Thus, the rule for converting scientific notation (using powers of 10) to decimal notation is to move the decimal point the number of places indicated by the exponent. When the exponent is positive (with or without a plus sign), the decimal point is moved to the right. When the exponent is negative (always provided with a minus sign), the decimal point is moved to the left.

For a little practice, write the following numbers in scientific notation: (18–23)

$140,000 = 1.4 \times \underline{10^5}$ $\qquad$ $45,000 = 4.5 \times \underline{10^4}$

$0.0000063 = 6.3 \times \underline{10^{-6}}$ $\qquad$ $0.265 = 2.65 \times \underline{10^{-1}}$

$0.00054 = 5.4 \times \underline{10^{-4}}$ $\qquad$ $0.10 = 1.0 \times \underline{10^{-1}}$

Metrics

Without measurement, we would be limited to qualitative description. However, with a system of measurement, quantitative description becomes possible.

Anyone can establish a system of measurement. All that is required is a reference point; and, historically, much of our common (the British) system of measurement evolved from units based on objects everyone knew. For example, horses were measured in "hands," and a "fathom" was the distance between outstretched arms. However, the variability in such measurements is immediately apparent—for example, an infant's hand is substantially smaller than that of an adult. Therefore, for precise and repeatable communication of information, the agreed-upon system of measurement used by scientists is the **metric system,** a nonvarying standard of reference.

TABLE G.1   Commonly Used Units of the Metric System, and Their Fractions and Multiples

Measurement	Unit	Fraction or multiple		Prefix	Symbol
Length	Meter (m)	10^6	one million	mega	M
Volume	Liter (l)	10^3	one thousand	kilo	k
Mass	Gram (g)	10^{-1}	one tenth	deci	d
Time*	Second (s)	10^{-2}	one hundredth	centi	c
Temperature	Degree Celsius (°C)	10^{-3}	one thousandth	milli	m
		10^{-6}	one millionth	micro	μ
		10^{-9}	one billionth	nano	n

*The accepted standard for time is the second; and thus hours and minutes are used in scientific, as well as everyday, measurement of time. The prefixes used in the designation of units of length, mass, and volume are also used in specifying units of time. However, because minutes and hours are terms that indicate *multiples* of seconds, the only prefixes generally used are those indicating *fractional portions* of seconds—for example, millisecond and microsecond.

A major advantage of the metric system is that it is based on units of 10. This allows rapid conversion to workable numbers so that neither very large nor very small figures need be used in calculations. Fractions or multiples of the standard units of length, volume, mass, time, and temperature have been assigned specific names. Table G.1 shows the commonly used units of the metric system, along with the prefixes used to designate fractions and multiples thereof.

To change from smaller units to larger units, you must *divide* by the appropriate factor of 10 (because there are fewer of the larger units). For example, a milliunit (milli = one thousandth), such as a milliliter or millimeter, is one step smaller than a centiunit (centi = one hundredth), such as a centiliter or centimeter. Thus to change milliunits to centiunits, you must divide by 10. On the other hand, when converting from larger units to smaller ones, you must *multiply* by the appropriate factor of 10 (because there will be more of the smaller units). A partial scheme for conversions between the metric units is shown below.

Students studying a science or preparing for a profession in the health-related fields find that certain of the metric units are encountered and dealt with more frequently than others. Thus, the objectives of the sections that follow are to provide a brief overview of these most-used measurements and to help you gain some measure of confidence in dealing with them. (A listing of the most frequently used conversion factors, for conversions between British and metric system units, is provided in Appendix A.)

LENGTH MEASUREMENTS The metric unit of length is the **meter (m)**. In addition to measuring things in meters, you will be expected to measure smaller objects in centimeters or millimeters. Subcellular structures are measured in micrometers.

To help you picture these units of length, some equivalents follow:

One meter (m) is slightly longer than one yard (1 m = 39.37 in.).

One centimeter (cm) is approximately the width of a piece of chalk. (Note: there are 2.54 cm in 1 in.)

One millimeter (mm) is approximately the thickness of the wire of a paper clip or of a mark made by a No. 2 pencil lead.

One micrometer (μm) is extremely tiny and can be measured only microscopically.

Make the following conversions between metric units of length: (24–28)

352 cm = _3520_ mm   12 cm = _120_ mm

150 km = _150,000_ m   1 mm = _.001_ m

2000 μm = _2_ mm

Now, circle the answer that would make the most sense in each of the following statements:

29. A match (in a matchbook) is (0.3, 3, 30) cm long.
30. A standard-size American car is about 4 (mm, cm, m, km) long.
31. John pole-vaults a height of 5 meters, whereas Gerry vaults a height of 5 yards. Does John or Gerry make the more difficult vault?

_____

microunit ⇌ milliunit ⇌ centiunit ⇌ unit ⇌ kilounit

÷ 1000 / × 1000   ÷ 10 / × 10   ÷ 100 / × 100   ÷ 1000 / × 1000

smallest ⇌ largest

VOLUME MEASUREMENTS   The metric unit of volume is the liter (l). A liter (l) is slightly more than a quart (1 l = 1.057 quarts). Liquid products, measured in liters, are becoming more common, and laboratory solutions are often prepared in 1-liter quantities. Liquid volumes measured out for laboratory experiments are usually measured in milliliter (ml) volumes. (The terms *ml* and *cc,* cubic centimeter, are used interchangeably in laboratory and medical settings.)

To help you visualize metric volumes, the equivalents of some common substances follow:

A 12-oz can of soda is just slightly more than 360 ml.
A cup of coffee is approximately 180 ml.
A fluid ounce is 30 ml (cc).
A teaspoon of vanilla is about 5 ml (cc), and many drug injections are given in 5-ml volumes.

Compute the following:

32. How many 5-ml injections can be prepared from 1 liter of a medicine? $1 lt = 1000 ml$

   200   $1000 \div 5 = 200$

33. A 450-ml volume of alcohol is __.45__ l.

34. The volume of one grape is approximately 0.004 l. What is the volume of the grape in milliliters?

   __4 ml__

MASS MEASUREMENTS   Although many people use the terms *mass* and *weight* interchangeably, this usage is inaccurate. Mass is the amount of matter in an object; and an object has a constant mass, regardless of where it is—that is, at sea level, on a mountaintop, or in outer space. However, weight varies with gravitational pull; the greater the gravitational pull, the greater the weight. Thus, our astronauts are said to be weightless* when in outer space, but they still have the same mass as they do on earth.

The metric unit of mass is the gram (g), and most objects weighed in the laboratory will be measured in terms of this unit or fractions thereof. Medical dosages are usually prescribed in milligrams (mg) or micrograms (μg); and, in the clinical agency, body weight (particularly of infants) is typically specified in kilograms (kg) (1 kg = 2.2 lb).

The following examples are provided to help you become familiar with the masses of some common objects:

Two aspirin tablets have a mass of approximately 1 g.
A nickel has a mass of 5 g.
The mass of an average woman (132 lb) is 60 kg.

* Astronauts are not *really* weightless. It is just that they and their surroundings are being pulled toward the earth at the same speed; and so, in reference to their environment, they appear to float.

Make the following conversions:

35. 300 g = __3×10^5__ mg = __3×10^8__ μg

36. 4000 μg = __4__ mg = __4×10^{-3}__ g

37. A nurse must administer to her patient, Mrs. Smith, 5 mg of a drug per kg of body mass. Mrs. Smith weighs 140 lb. How many grams of the drug should the nurse administer to her patient?

   __.32__ g $\frac{140 lb}{2.2} = 63.63 Kg \times 5 mg = 318 mg$

TEMPERATURE MEASUREMENTS   In the laboratory and in the clinical agency, temperature is measured both in metric units (degrees Celsius, °C) and in British units (degrees Fahrenheit, °F). Thus it helps to be familiar with both temperature scales.

The temperatures of boiling and freezing water can be used to compare the two scales:

The boiling point of water is 100°C and 212°F.
The freezing point of water is 0°C and 32°F.

As you can see, the range from the freezing point to the boiling point of water on the Celsius scale is 100 degrees, whereas the comparable range on the Fahrenheit scale is 180 degrees. Hence, one degree on the Celsius scale represents a greater change in temperature. Normal body temperature is approximately 98.6°F and 37°C.

To convert from the Fahrenheit scale to the Celsius scale (or vice versa), the following equation is used:

$$°C = 5(°F − 32)/9$$

For example, to convert 180°C to °F: $°C \rightarrow °F$

$$°C = 5(°F − 32)/9$$
$$180 = 5(°F − 32)/9$$
$$1620 = 5(°F − 32)$$
$$1620 = 5(°F) − 160$$
$$1780 = 5(°F)$$
$$356 = °F$$

and to convert 72°F to °C:

$$°C = 5(°F − 32)/9$$
$$°C = 5(72 − 32)/9$$
$$°C = 5(40)/9$$
$$°C = 200/9$$
$$°C = 22.2$$

Perform the following temperature conversions:

38. Convert 38°C to °F: __100.4__

39. Convert 158°F to °C: __70__

Answers

1. range of 94–64; 30 beats/min

2. average 77.5

3. 3820%

4. 40200%

5. 160%

6. 0.36

7. 8

8. 257.77

9. 0.0005

10. 10 breaths/min

11. 12 to 36

12. interval between 100–102° (went from 22 to 36 breaths/min)

13. yes

14. 10^5

15. 10^6

16. 10^2

17. 10^1

18. 1.4×10^5

19. 6.3×10^{-6}

20. 5.4×10^{-4}

21. 4.5×10^4

22. 2.65×10^{-1}

23. 1.0×10^{-1}

24. cm = 3520 mm

25. km = 150,000 m

26. μm = 2 mm

27. cm = 120 mm

28. mm = 0.001 m

29. 3 cm

30. m long

31. John

32. 200

33. 0.45 l

34. 4 ml

35. 300 g = 3×10^5 mg = 3×10^8 μg

36. 4000 μg = 4 mg = 4×10^{-3} g (0.004)

37. 0.32 g

38. 100.4°F

39. 70°C

The Language of Anatomy

<table>
<tr><td colspan="1">

OBJECTIVES

1. To describe the anatomical position verbally or by demonstration.
2. To use proper anatomical terminology to describe body directions, planes, and surfaces.
3. To name the body cavities and note the important organs in each.

</td><td>

MATERIALS

Human torso model (dissectible)
Human skeleton
Demonstration: sectioned and labeled kidneys (three separate kidneys uncut or cut so that (a) entire, (b) transverse section, and (c) longitudinal sectional views are visible)

</td></tr>
</table>

Most of us have a natural curiosity about our bodies. This fact is amply demonstrated by infants, who early in life become fascinated with their own waving hands or their mother's nose. The study of the gross anatomy of the human body elaborates on this fascination. Unlike the infant, however, the student of anatomy must learn to identify and observe the dissectible body structures formally. The purpose of any gross-anatomy experience is to examine the three-dimensional relationships of body structures—a goal that can never completely be achieved by using illustrations and models, regardless of their excellence.

When beginning the study of any science, the student is often initially overcome by the jargon unique to the subject. The study of anatomy is no exception. But without this specialized terminology, confusion is inevitable. For example, what do *over, on top of, superficial to, above,* and *behind* mean in reference to the human body? Anatomists have an accepted set of reference terms that are universally understood. These allow body structures to be located and identified with a minimum of words and a high degree of clarity. Thus it is not surprising that physicians' orders and progress notes, therapists' records, and nurses' notes use anatomical terminology to describe body parts, regions, positions, and activities. The ability to understand and use correct anatomical terminology is a skill that distinguishes health care personnel who are successful and comfortable in their chosen profession from those perpetually unsure of just what is expected of them.

This unit presents some of the most important anatomical terminology used to describe the body and introduces you to basic concepts of **gross anatomy,** the study of body structures visible to the naked eye.

ANATOMICAL POSITION

When anatomists or doctors discuss the human body, they refer to specific areas in accordance with a universally accepted standard position called the **anatomical position.** It is essential to understand this position, because much of the body terminology employed in this book refers to this body positioning, regardless of the position the body happens to be in. In the anatomical position the human body is erect, with feet together, head and toes pointed forward, and arms hanging at the sides with palms facing forward (Figure 1.1).

Assume the anatomical position, and note that it is not particularly comfortable. The hands are held unnaturally forward rather than hanging partially cupped toward the thighs.

BODY ORIENTATION AND DIRECTION

Study the terms below, referring to Figure 1.2. Note that certain terms have a different connotation for a four-legged animal than they do for a human.

Superior/inferior (*above/below*): These terms refer to placement of a body structure along the long axis of the body. Superior structures always appear above other structures. For example, the nose is superior to the mouth, and the abdomen is inferior to the chest region.

Anterior/posterior (*front/back*): In humans the most anterior structures are those that are most forward—the face, chest, and abdomen. Posterior

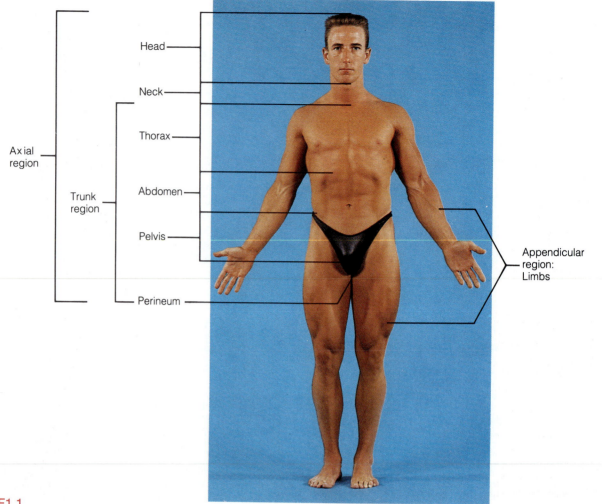

Head

Neck

Thorax

Abdomen

Pelvis

Perineum

Axial region

Trunk region

Appendicular region: Limbs

F1.1

Anatomical position.

structures or surfaces are those toward the backside of the body. For instance, the spine is posterior to the heart.

Medial/lateral (*toward the midline/away from the midline or median plane*): The ear is lateral to the bridge of the nose; the sternum (breastbone) is medial to the ribs.

The terms of position described above are dependent on an assumption of anatomical position. The next four term pairs, however, are more absolute; that is, their applicability is not relative to a particular body position, and they consistently have the same meaning in all vertebrate animals.

Cephalad/caudal (*toward the head/toward the tail*): In humans these terms are used interchangeably with *superior* and *inferior*. But in four-legged animals they are synonymous with *anterior* and *posterior* respectively.

Dorsal/ventral (*backside/belly side*): These terms are used chiefly in discussing the comparative anatomy

of animals, assuming the animal is standing. *Dorsum* is a Latin word meaning "back"; thus *dorsal* refers to the backside of the animal's body or of any other structures. For instance, the posterior surface of the leg is its dorsal surface. The term *ventral* derives from the Latin term *venter*, meaning "belly," and thus always refers to the belly side of animals. In humans the terms *ventral* and *dorsal* may be used interchangeably with the terms *anterior* and *posterior*, but in four-legged animals *ventral* and *dorsal* are synonymous with *inferior* and *superior* respectively.

Proximal/distal (*nearer the trunk or attached end/farther from the trunk or point of attachment*): These terms are used primarily to locate various areas of the body limbs. For example, the fingers are distal to the elbow; the knee is proximal to the toes.

Superficial/deep (*toward or at the body surface/away from the body surface or more internal*): These terms locate body organs according to their *relative* closeness to the body surface. For example, the lungs are deep to the rib cage, and the skin is superficial to the skeletal muscles.

Before continuing, use a human torso model, a skeleton, or your own body to specify the relationship between the following structures. Use the correct anatomical terminology:

The wrist is ___proximal___ to the hand.

The trachea (windpipe) is ___ventral___ to the spine.

The brain is ___superior___ to the spinal cord.

The kidneys are ___posterior___ to the liver.

The tip of the nose is ___anterior___ to the cheekbones.

SURFACE ANATOMY

Body surfaces provide visible landmarks for study of the body.

Anterior Body Landmarks

Note the following regions in Figure 1.3a:

Oral: pertaining to the mouth
Orbital: pertaining to the bony eye socket (orbit)
Buccal: pertaining to the cheek
Cervical: pertaining to the neck region
Thoracic: pertaining to the chest
Axillary: pertaining to the armpit
Brachial: pertaining to the arm (region of upper limb between the shoulder and elbow)
Antecubital: pertaining to the anterior surface of the elbow
Umbilical: pertaining to the navel
Abdominal: pertaining to the anterior body trunk region inferior to the ribs
Inguinal: pertaining to the area where the thigh meets the body trunk
Femoral: pertaining to the thigh
Pubic: pertaining to the genital region
Patellar: pertaining to the anterior knee (kneecap) region
Digital: pertaining to the fingers or toes

Surface Anatomy,   # 18644
Anterior Chest/Arms

Surface Anatomy,   # 18646
Face

Surface Anatomy,   # 18668
Arm, Medial View

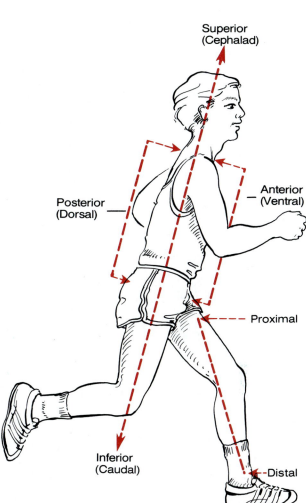

(a)

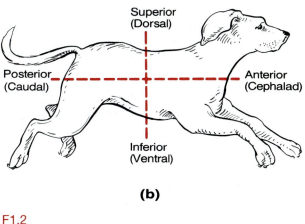

(b)

F1.2

Anatomical terminology describing body orientation and direction. (a) With reference to a human. (b) With reference to a four-legged animal.

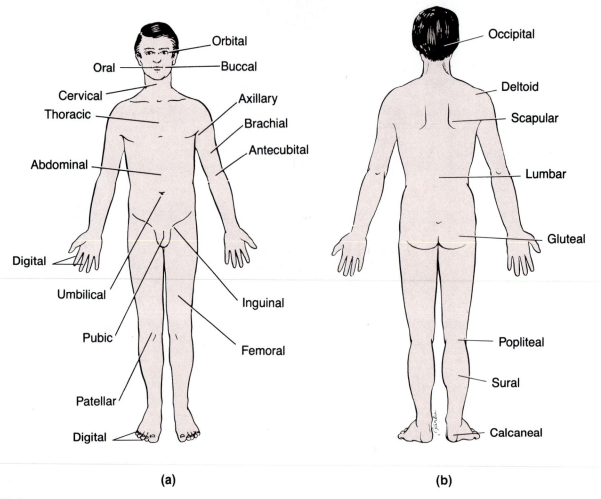

Orbital

Oral — Buccal

Cervical

Thoracic — Axillary

Brachial

Antecubital

Abdominal

Digital

Umbilical

Pubic — Inguinal

Femoral

Patellar

Digital

Occipital

Deltoid

Scapular

Lumbar

Gluteal

Popliteal

Sural

Calcaneal

(a)   (b)

F1.3

Surface anatomy. (a) Anterior body landmarks. (b) Posterior body landmarks.

Surface Anatomy, Leg, Anterior View	# 18653	
Surface Anatomy, Back	# 18641	
Surface Anatomy, PosteriorThigh/Leg	# 18657	
Surface Anatomy, Arm, Posterior View	# 18660	

Posterior Body Landmarks

Note the following body surface regions in Figure 1.3b:

Occipital: pertaining to the posterior surface of the head or base of skull

Deltoid: pertaining to the curve of the shoulder formed by the large deltoid muscle

Scapular: pertaining to the scapula or shoulder blade area

Lumbar: pertaining to the area of the back between the ribs and hips

Gluteal: pertaining to the buttocks or rump

Popliteal: pertaining to the posterior knee region

Sural: pertaining to the posterior surface of the leg

Calcaneal: pertaining to the heel of the foot

 Locate the anterior and posterior body landmarks on yourself, your lab partner, and a torso model before continuing.

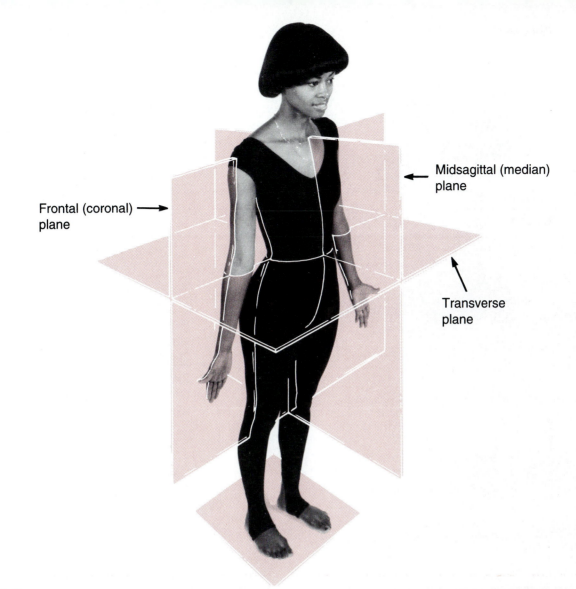

Frontal (coronal) plane →

→ Midsagittal (median) plane

Transverse plane

F1.4

Planes of the body.

BODY PLANES AND SECTIONS

The body is three-dimensional and, in order to observe its internal structures, it is often helpful and necessary to make use of a **section, or cut.** When the section is made through the body wall or through an organ, it is made along an imaginary surface or line called a **plane.** Anatomists commonly refer to three planes (Figure 1.4) or sections which lie at right angles to one another.

Sagittal plane: A plane that runs longitudinally, dividing the body into right and left parts, is referred to as a sagittal plane. If it divides the body into equal parts, right down the median plane of the body, it is called a **midsagittal, or median, plane.** All other planes are referred to as **parasagittal planes.**

Frontal plane: Sometimes called a **coronal plane,** the frontal plane is a longitudinal plane that divides the body (or an organ) into anterior and posterior parts.

Transverse plane: A transverse plane runs horizontally, dividing the body into superior and inferior parts.

When organs are sectioned along the transverse plane, the sections are commonly called **cross sections.**

As shown in Figure 1.5, a sagittal or frontal plane section of an organ provides quite a different view than a transverse section.

Go to the demonstration area and observe the transversely and longitudinally cut organ specimens. Pay close attention to the different details of structure in the samples.

BODY CAVITIES

The body has two sets of cavities, which provide different degrees of protection to the organs within them (Figure 1.6).

5

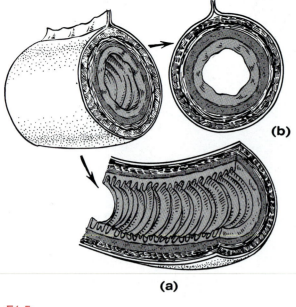

(b)

(a)

F1.5

Segment of the small intestine. (a) Cut longitudinally.
(b) Cut transversely.

Right upper quadrant | Left upper quadrant

Right lower quadrant | Left lower quadrant

(a)

F1.7

Abdominopelvic surface and cavity. (a) The four quadrants.
(b) Nine regions delineated by four planes. The superior
horizontal plane is just inferior to the ribs; the inferior
horizontal plane is at the superior aspect of the hip bones.
The vertical planes are just medial to the nipples. (c) Anterior
view of the abdominopelvic cavity showing superficial
organs.

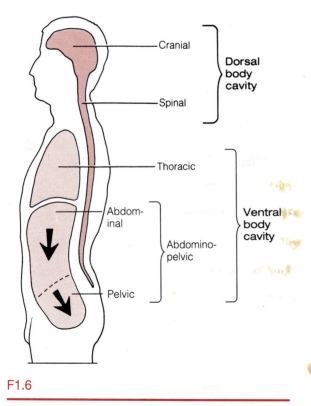

Cranial

Spinal

Dorsal body cavity

Thoracic

Abdom-inal

Abdomino-pelvic

Pelvic

Ventral body cavity

F1.6

Body cavities. The angle of the relationship between the
abdominal and pelvic cavities is shown here with arrows.

Dorsal Body Cavity

The dorsal body cavity can be subdivided into the **cranial cavity,** in which the brain is enclosed within the rigid skull, and the **spinal cavity,** within which the delicate spinal cord is protected by the bony vertebral column. Because the cord is a continuation of the brain, these cavities are continuous with each other.

Ventral Body Cavity

Like the dorsal cavity, the ventral body cavity is subdivided. The superior **thoracic cavity** is separated from the rest of the ventral cavity by the dome-shaped diaphragm. The heart and lungs, located in the thoracic cavity, are afforded some measure of protection by the bony rib cage. The cavity inferior to the diaphragm is often referred to as the **abdominopelvic cavity,** since there is no further physical separation of the ventral cav-

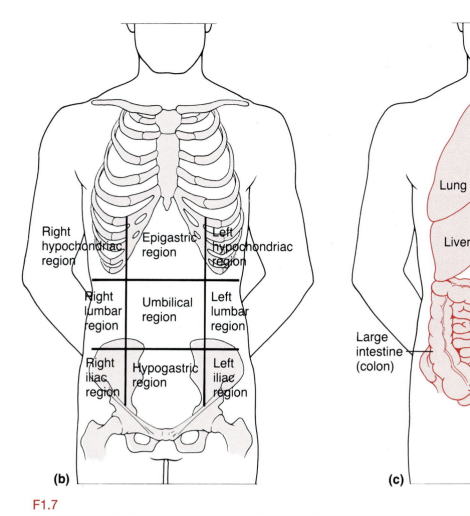

(b)

(c)

(continued)

ity. Some prefer to subdivide the abdominopelvic cavity into a superior **abdominal cavity,** which houses the stomach, intestines, liver, and other organs, and an inferior **pelvic cavity,** partially enclosed by the bony pelvis and containing the reproductive organs, bladder, and rectum. Notice in Figure 1.6 that the abdominal and pelvic cavities are not continuous with each other in a straight plane but that the pelvic cavity is tipped away from the perpendicular.

ABDOMINOPELVIC QUADRANTS AND REGIONS   Because the abdominopelvic cavity is quite large and contains many organs, it is helpful to divide it up into smaller areas for discussion or study. The scheme used by most physicians and nurses divides the abdominal surface (and the abdominopelvic cavity deep to it) into four approximately equal regions called **quadrants.** These quadrants are named according to their relative position—that is, *right upper quadrant, right lower quadrant, left upper quadrant,* and *left lower quadrant* (see Figure 1.7a).

Another scheme, commonly used by anatomists, divides the abdominal surface and abdominopelvic cavity into nine separate regions by four planes, as shown in Figure 1.7b. Although the names of these nine regions

are unfamiliar to you now, with a little patience and study they will become easier to remember. As you read through the descriptions of these nine regions below and locate them in the figure, notice the organs they contain by referring to Figure 1.7c.

Umbilical region: the centermost region, which includes the umbilicus
Epigastric region: immediately above the umbilical region; overlies most of the stomach
Hypogastric region: immediately below the umbilical region; encompasses the pubic area
Iliac regions: lateral to the hypogastric region and overlying the hip bones
Lumbar regions: between the ribs and the flaring portions of the hip bones
Hypochondriac regions: flanking the epigastric region and overlying the lower ribs

Locate the regions of the abdominal surface on a torso model and on yourself before continuing.

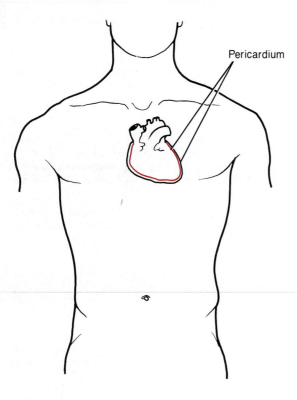

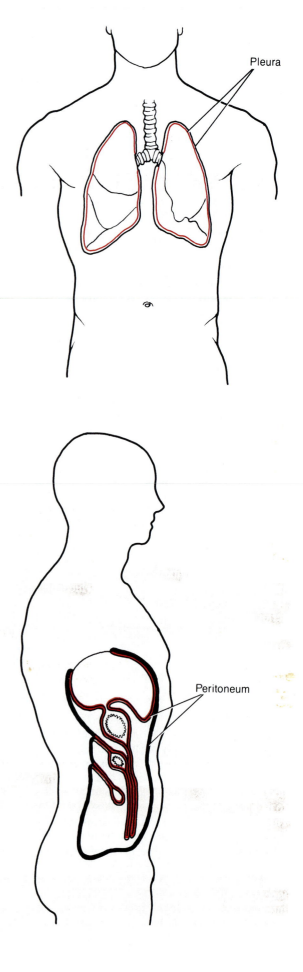

F1.8

Serous membranes. The visceral layer is shown in color; the parietal layer is shown in black.

SEROUS MEMBRANES OF THE VENTRAL BODY CAVITY   The walls of the ventral body cavity and the outer surfaces of the organs it contains are covered with an exceedingly thin, double-layered membrane called the **serosa,** or **serous membrane.** The part of the membrane lining the cavity walls is referred to as the **parietal serosa,** and it is continuous with a similar membrane, the **visceral serosa,** covering the external surface of the organs within the cavity. These membranes produce a thin lubricating fluid that allows the visceral organs to slide over one another or to rub against the body wall without friction. Serous membranes also act to compartmentalize the various organs so that infection of one organ is prevented from spreading to others.

The specific names of the serous membranes depend on the structures they envelop. Thus the serosa lining the abdominal cavity and covering its organs is the **peritoneum,** that enclosing the lungs is the **pleura,** and that around the heart is the **pericardium** (Figure 1.8).

Organ Systems Overview

OBJECTIVES

1. To name the human organ systems and state the major functions of each.
2. To list two or three organs of each system, and categorize the various organs by organ system.
3. To identify these organs in a dissected rat or on a dissectible human torso model or human cadaver.
4. To identify the correct organ system for each organ when presented with a list of organs (as studied in the laboratory).

MATERIALS

Freshly killed or preserved rat predissected by instructor as a demonstration or for student dissection (one for every two to four students), or dissected human cadaver
Dissecting pans and pins
Scissors
Forceps
Twine
Disposable plastic gloves
Human torso model (dissectible)

The basic unit or building block of all living things is the **cell.** Cells fall into four different categories according to their structures and functions. Each of these corresponds to one of the four **tissue** types: epithelial, muscular, nervous, and connective. An **organ** is a structure composed of two or more tissue types that performs a specific function for the body. For example, the small intestine, which digests and absorbs nutrients, is composed of all four tissue types. An **organ system** is a group of organs that act together to perform a particular body function. For example, the organs of the digestive system work together to assure that food moving through the digestive system is properly broken down and that the end products are absorbed into the bloodstream to provide nutrients and fuel for all the body's cells. In all, there are ten organ systems, which are described in Table 2.1. In addition to the organ systems, there is a *functional system,* the immune system, which is composed of an army of mobile *cells* (rather than organs) that act to protect the body from foreign substances. Read through this summary before beginning the rat dissection.

RAT DISSECTION

Now you will have a chance to observe the size, shape, location, and distribution of the organs and organ systems. Many of the external and internal structures of the rat are quite similar in structure and function to those of the human, so a study of the gross anatomy of the rat should help you understand your own physical structure.

The following instructions have been written to complement and direct the student's dissection and ob-

servation of a rat, but the descriptions for organ observations from procedure 4 (p. 11) apply as well to superficial observations of a previously dissected human cadaver. In addition, the general instructions for observation of external structures can easily be extrapolated to serve human cadaver observations.

Note that four of the organ systems listed in Table 2.1 will not be studied at this time (integumentary, skeletal, muscular, and nervous), as they require microscopic study or more detailed dissection.

External Structures

1. Obtain a preserved or freshly killed rat (one for every two to four students), a dissecting pan, dissecting pins, scissors, forceps, and disposable gloves.

2. Don the gloves before beginning your observations. This precaution is particularly important when handling freshly killed animals, which may harbor internal parasites.

3. Observe the major divisions of the animal's body—head, trunk, and extremities. Compare these divisions to those of humans.

Oral Cavity

Examine the structures of the oral cavity. Identify the teeth and tongue. Observe the extent of the hard palate (the portion underlain by bone) and the soft palate (immediately posterior to the hard palate, with no bony support). Note that the posterior end of the oral cavity leads into the throat, or pharynx. The pharynx is a passageway used by both the digestive and respiratory systems.

TABLE 2.1   Overview of Organ Systems of the Body

Organ system	Major component organs	Function
Integumentary (Skin)	Epidermal and dermal regions; cutaneous sense organs and glands	· Protects deeper organs from mechanical, chemical, and bacterial injury, and desiccation (drying out) · Excretion of salts and urea · Aids in regulation of body temperature · Produces vitamin D
Skeletal	Bones, cartilages, tendons, ligaments, and joints	· Body support and protection of internal organs · Provides levers for muscular action · Cavities provide a site for blood cell formation
Muscular	Muscles attached to the skeleton	· Primarily function to contract or shorten; in doing so, skeletal muscles allow locomotion (running, walking, etc.), grasping and manipulation of the environment, and facial expression · Generates heat
Nervous	Brain, spinal cord, nerves, and sensory receptors	· Allows body to detect changes in its internal and external environment and to respond to such information by activating appropriate muscles or glands · Helps maintain homeostasis of the body via rapid transmission of electrical signals
Endocrine	Pituitary, thyroid, parathyroid, adrenal, and pineal glands; ovaries, testes, and pancreas	· Helps maintain body homeostasis, promotes growth and development; produces chemical "messengers" (hormones) that travel in the blood to exert their effect(s) on various "target organs" of the body
Cardiovascular	Heart, blood vessels, and blood	· Primarily a transport system that carries blood containing oxygen, carbon dioxide, nutrients, wastes, ions, hormones, and other substances to and from the tissue cells where exchanges are made; blood is propelled through the blood vessels by the pumping action of the heart · Antibodies and other protein molecules in the blood act to protect the body
Lymphatic	Lymphatic vessels, lymph nodes, spleen, thymus, tonsils, and scattered collections of lymphoid tissue	· Picks up fluid leaked from the blood vessels and returns it to the blood · Cleanses blood of pathogens and other debris · Houses lymphocytes that act in body immunity
Respiratory	Nasal passages, pharynx, larynx, trachea, bronchi, and lungs	· Keeps the blood continuously supplied with oxygen while removing carbon dioxide
Digestive	Oral cavity, esophagus, stomach, small and large intestines, and accessory structures (teeth, salivary glands, liver, and pancreas)	· Acts to break down ingested foods to minute particles, which can be absorbed into the blood for delivery to the body cells · Undigested residue removed from the body as feces
Urinary	Kidneys, ureters, bladder, and urethra	· Rids the body of nitrogen-containing wastes (urea, uric acid, and ammonia), which result from the breakdown of proteins and nucleic acids by body cells · Maintains water, electrolyte, and acid–base balance of blood
Reproductive	Male: testes, scrotum, penis, and duct system, which carries sperm to the body exterior	· Provides germ cells (sperm and eggs) for perpetuation of the species
	Female: ovaries, uterine tubes, uterus, and vagina	· Female uterus houses the developing fetus until birth
Immune (functional system)	Major components are cells (lymphocytes and macrophages) that inhabit the lymphoid tissues and circulate in blood and lymph	· Protects the body via the immune response from foreign substances (antigens)

Ventral Body Cavity

1. Pin the animal to the wax of the dissecting pan by placing its dorsal side down and securing its extremities to wax. If the dissecting pan is not waxed, you will need to secure the animal with twine as shown in Figure 2.1a. (Some may prefer this method in any case.) Obtain the roll of twine. Make a loop knot around one upper limb, pass the twine under the pan, and secure the opposing limb. Repeat for the lower extremities.

2. Lift the abdominal skin with a forceps, and cut through it with the scissors (Figure 2.1b). Close the scissor blades and insert them under the cut skin. Moving in a cephalad direction, open and close the blades to loosen the skin from the underlying connective tissue and muscle. Once this skin-freeing procedure has been completed, cut the skin along the body midline, from the pubic region to the lower jaw (Figure 2.1c). Make a lateral cut about halfway down the ventral surface of each limb. Complete the job of freeing the skin with the scissor tips, and pin the flaps to the tray (Figure 2.2a). The underlying tissue that is now exposed is the skeletal musculature of the body wall and limbs. It allows voluntary body movement. Notice that the muscles are packaged in sheets of pearly white connective tissue (fascia), which protect the muscles and bind them together.

3. Carefully cut through the muscles of the abdominal wall in the pubic region, avoiding the underlying organs. Remember, *to dissect* means "to separate"—not mutilate! Now, hold and lift the muscle layer with a forceps and cut through the muscle layer from the pubic region to the bottom of the rib cage. Make two lateral cuts through the rib cage (Figure 2.2b). A thin membrane attached to the inferior boundary of the rib cage should be obvious; this is the **diaphragm,** which separates the thoracic and abdominal cavities. Cut the diaphragm away to loosen the rib cage. You can now lift the ribs to view the contents of the thoracic cavity.

4. Examine the structures of the thoracic cavity, starting with the most superficial structures and working deeper. As you work, refer to Figure 2.3 (p. 13), which shows the superficial organs.

Thymus: an irregular mass of glandular tissue overlying the heart.

Push the thymus to the side to view the heart.

Heart: median oval structure enclosed within the pericardium (serous membrane sac).
Lungs: flanking the heart on either side.

Now observe the throat region.

Trachea: tubelike "windpipe" running medially down the throat; part of the respiratory system.

Follow the trachea into the thoracic cavity; note where it divides. These are the bronchi.

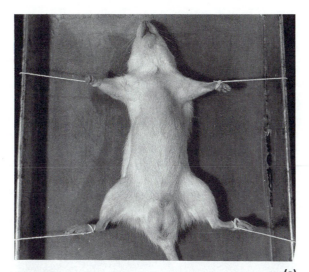

(a)

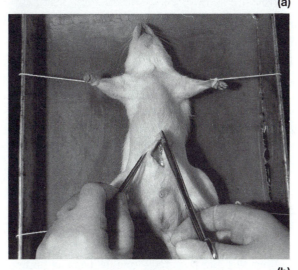

(b)

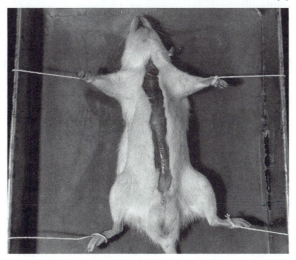

(c)

F2.1

Rat dissection: Securing and the initial incision.
(a) Securing the rat to the dissection tray. (b) Using scissors to make the incision on the median line of the abdominal region. (c) Completed incision from the pelvic region to the lower jaw.

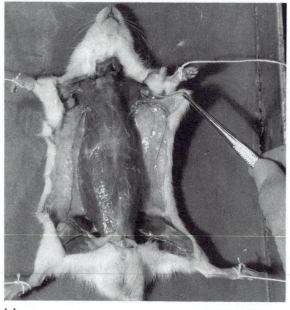

(a)

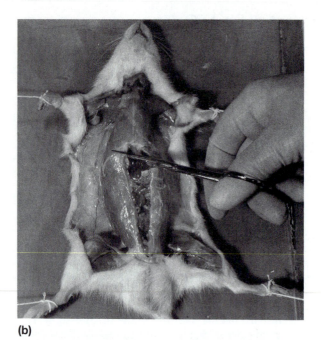

(b)

F2.2

Rat dissection. (a) Reflection (folding back) of the skin to expose the underlying muscles. (b) Making lateral cuts at the base of the rib cage.

Bronchi: two passageways that plunge laterally into the tissue of the two lungs.

Now push the trachea to one side to expose the esophagus.

Esophagus: a food chute; the part of the digestive system that transports food from the pharynx (throat) to the stomach.

Follow the esophagus through the diaphragm to its junction with the stomach.

Stomach: a C-shaped organ important in food digestion and temporary food storage.

5. Examine the superficial structures of the abdominopelvic cavity. Beginning with the stomach, trace the rest of the digestive tract.

Small intestine: connected to the stomach and ending just before a large saclike cecum.
Cecum: the initial portion of the large intestine.
Large intestine: a large muscular tube coiled within the abdomen.

Follow the course of the large intestine to the rectum, which is partially covered by the urinary bladder.

Rectum: terminal part of the large intestine; continuous with the anal canal.
Anus: the opening of the digestive tract (anal canal) to the exterior.

Now lift the small intestine with the forceps to view the mesentery.

Mesentery: an apronlike serous membrane; suspends many of the digestive organs in the abdominal cavity. Notice that it is heavily invested with blood vessels and, more likely than not, riddled with large fat deposits.

Locate the remaining abdominal structures.

Pancreas: a diffuse gland; rests dorsal to and in the mesentery between the first portion of the small intestine and the stomach.
Spleen: a dark red organ curving around the left lateral side of the stomach; considered part of the lymphatic system and often called the red blood cell graveyard.
Liver: large and brownish red; the most superior organ in the abdominal cavity, directly beneath the diaphragm.

6. To locate the deeper structures of the abdominopelvic cavity, cut through the superior margin of the stomach and the distal end of the large intestine and lay them aside. (Refer to Figure 2.4 as you work.)

Examine the posterior wall of the abdominal cavity to locate the two kidneys.

Kidneys: bean-shaped organs; retroperitoneal (behind the peritoneum).
Adrenal glands: large glands that sit astride the superior margin of each kidney; considered part of the endocrine system.

Carefully strip away part of the peritoneum and attempt to follow the course of one of the ureters to the bladder.

Ureter: tube running from the indented region of a kidney to the urinary bladder.

Urinary bladder: the sac that serves as a reservoir for urine.

7.   In the midline of the body cavity lying between the kidneys are the two principal abdominal blood vessels. Identify each.

Inferior vena cava: the large vein that returns blood to the heart from the lower regions of the body.

Descending aorta: deep to the inferior vena cava; the largest artery of the body; carries blood away from the heart down the midline of the body.

8.   Only a cursory examination of reproductive organs will be done. First determine if the animal is a male or female. Observe the ventral body surface beneath the tail. If a saclike scrotum and a single body opening are visible, the animal is a male. If three body openings are present, it is a female. (See Figure 2.4.)

MALE ANIMAL   Make a shallow incision into the **scrotum.** Loosen and lift out the oval **testis.** Exert a gentle pull on the testis to identify the slender **vas deferens,** or sperm duct, which carries sperm from the testis

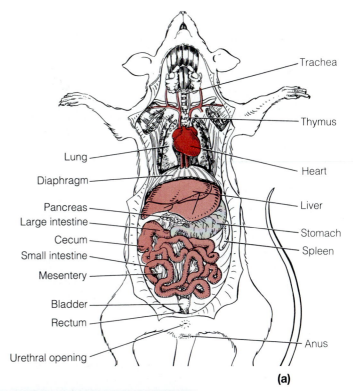

(a)

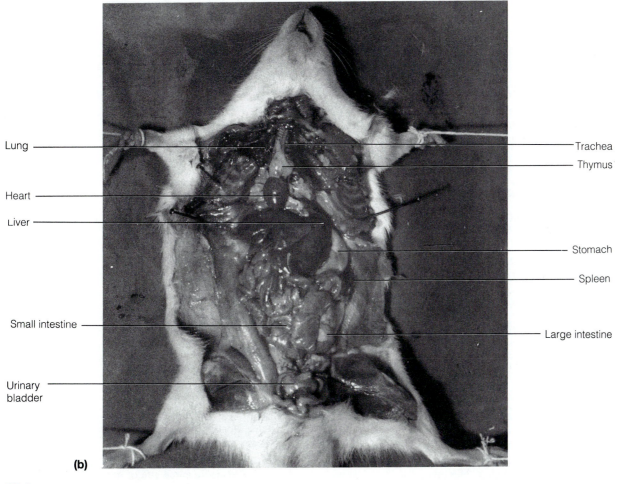

(b)

F2.3

Rat dissection: superficial organs of the thoracic and abdominal cavities. (a) Diagrammatic view. (b) Photograph.

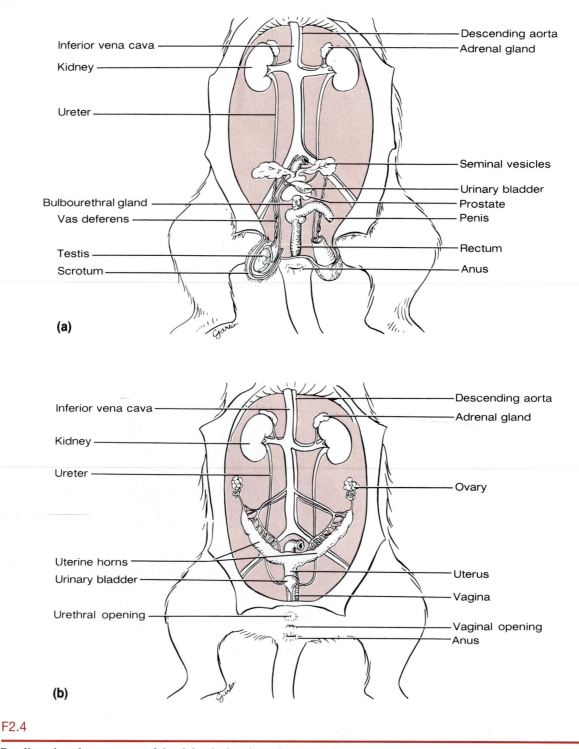

Inferior vena cava

Kidney

Ureter

Bulbourethral gland

Vas deferens

Testis

Scrotum

Descending aorta
Adrenal gland

Seminal vesicles

Urinary bladder
Prostate
Penis

Rectum

Anus

(a)

Inferior vena cava

Kidney

Ureter

Uterine horns

Urinary bladder

Urethral opening

Descending aorta
Adrenal gland

Ovary

Uterus

Vagina

Vaginal opening
Anus

(b)

F2.4

Rat dissection: deeper organs of the abdominal cavity and the reproductive structures. (a) Male. (b) Female.

superiorly into the abdominal cavity and joins with the urethra. The urethra runs through the penis of the male and carries both urine and sperm out of the body. Identify the **penis,** extending from the bladder to the ventral body wall. Figure 2.4a indicates other glands of the male reproductive system, but they need not be identified at this time.

FEMALE ANIMAL   Inspect the pelvic cavity to identify the Y-shaped **uterus** lying against the dorsal body wall and beneath the bladder (Figure 2.4b). Follow one of the uterine horns superiorly to identify an **ovary,** a small oval structure at the end of the uterine horn. (The rat uterus is quite different from the uterus of a human female, which is a single-chambered organ about the size and shape of a pear.) The inferior undivided part of the rat uterus is continuous with the vagina, which leads to the body exterior. Identify the **vaginal orifice** (external vaginal opening).

9.   When you have finished your observations, store or dispose of the rat according to your instructor's directions. Wash the dissecting pan and tools with laboratory detergent. Dispose of the gloves. Then wash and dry your hands before continuing with the examination of the torso model described next.

EXAMINING THE HUMAN TORSO MODEL

Examine a human torso model to identify the organs listed below. (Note: If a torso model is not available, Figure 2.5 may be used for this part of the exercise.)

Dorsal cavity: brain, spinal cord
Thoracic cavity: heart, lungs, bronchi, trachea, esophagus, diaphragm
Abdominopelvic cavity: liver, stomach, pancreas, *~inferior to stomach* spleen, small intestine, large intestine, rectum, kidneys, ureters, bladder, adrenal gland, descending aorta, inferior vena cava
posterior to stomach~

As you observe these structures, locate the nine abdominopelvic areas studied earlier and determine which organs would be found in each area.

Umbilical region: _Lge intest._

Epigastric region: _Liver, gallbladder_

Hypogastric region: _small intestine_

Right iliac region: _sml intest., Lge intest._

Left iliac region: _″   ″   ″ ″_

Right lumbar region: _Kidney, Lge intest_

Left lumbar region: _Kidney, Lge intest_

Right hypochondriac region: _Liver_

Left hypochondriac region: _Stomach, spleen_

Would you say that the shape and location of the human organs are similar or dissimilar to those of the rat?:

_____

Assign each of the organs just identified to one of the organ system categories below.

Digestive: _trachea, esophagus, stomach, Lge + sml intest + rectum_

Urinary: _Kidneys, ureters, bladder_

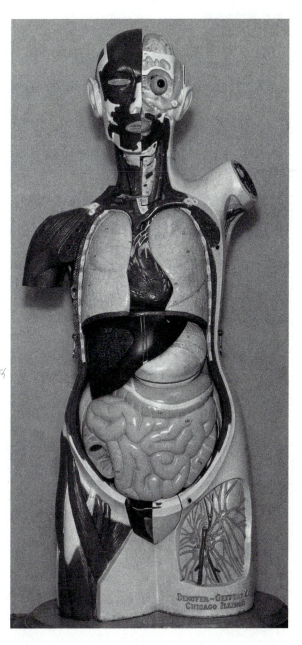

F2.5

Human torso model.

Cardiovascular: _heart, desc. aorta, inferior vena cava_

Reproductive: _ovaries, testes, penus,_

Respiratory: _trachea, lungs_

Lymphatic: _adrenal gland_

Nervous: _spinal cord, br_

Thorax, Abdomen   # 11954

Thorax, Model   # 11955

The Microscope

3 EXERCISE

OBJECTIVES

1. To identify the parts of the microscope and list the function of each.
2. To describe and demonstrate the proper techniques for care of the microscope.
3. To define *total magnification* and *resolution.*
4. To demonstrate the proper focusing technique.
5. To define *parfocal, field,* and *depth of field.*
6. To estimate the size of objects in a field.

MATERIALS

Compound microscope
Millimeter ruler
Prepared slides of the letter *e* or newsprint
Immersion oil
Lens paper
Prepared slide of grid ruled in millimeters (grid slide)
Prepared slide of 3 crossed colored threads
Clean microscope slide and cover slip
Toothpicks (flat-tipped)
Physiologic saline in a dropper bottle
Methylene blue stain (dilute) in a dropper bottle
Filter paper
Forceps
Beaker containing fresh 10% household bleach solution for wet mount disposal
Disposable autoclave bag

Note to the Instructor: The slides and coverslips used for viewing cheek cells are to be soaked for two hours (or longer) in 10% bleach solution and then drained. The slides, coverslips, and disposable autoclave bag (containing used toothpicks) are to be autoclaved for 15 min at 121°C and 15 pounds pressure to insure sterility. After autoclaving, the disposable autoclave bag may be discarded in any disposal facility and the glassware washed with laboratory detergent and reprepared for use. These instructions apply as well to any blood-stained glassware or disposable items used in other experimental procedures.

With the invention of the microscope, biologists gained a valuable tool to observe and study structures (like cells) that are too small to be seen by the unaided eye. As a result, many of the theories basic to the understanding of biologic sciences have been established. Microscopes range in magnification from the 3× hand lens to the 1,000,000× electron microscope. This exercise will familiarize you with the workhorse of microscopes—the compound microscope—and provide you with the necessary instructions for its proper use.

CARE AND STRUCTURE OF THE COMPOUND MICROSCOPE

The compound microscope is a precision instrument and should always be handled with care. At all times you must observe the following rules for its transport, cleaning, use, and storage:

- When transporting the microscope, hold it in an upright position with one hand on its arm and the other supporting its base. Avoid jarring the instrument when setting it down.

- Use only special grit-free lens paper to clean the lenses. Clean all lenses before and after use.
- Always begin the focusing process with the lowest-power objective lens in position, changing to the higher-power lenses if necessary.
- *Never* use the coarse adjustment knob with the high-power or oil immersion lenses.
- A cover slip must always be used with temporary (wet-mount) preparations.
- Before putting the microscope in the storage cabinet, remove the slide from the stage, rotate the lowest-power objective lens into position, and replace the dust cover.
- Never remove any parts from the microscope; inform your instructor of any mechanical problems that arise.

1. Obtain a microscope and bring it to the laboratory bench. (Use the proper carrying technique!) Compare your microscope with the illustration in Figure 3.1 and identify the following microscope parts:

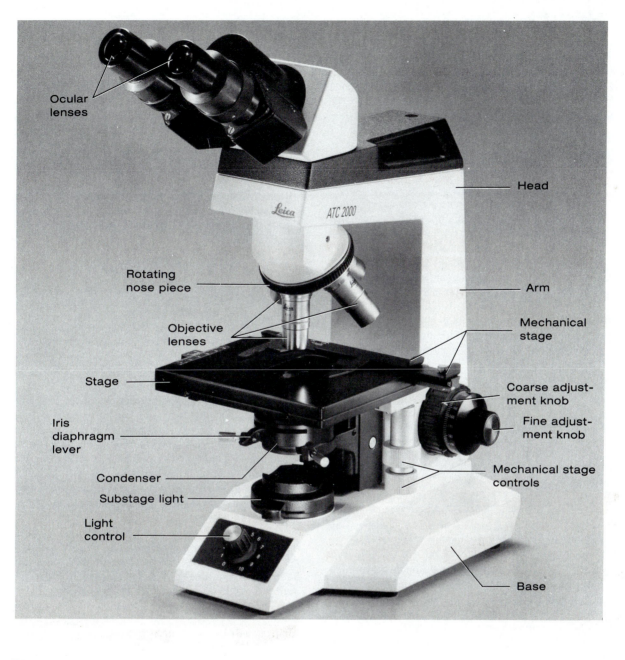

F3.1

Compound microscope and its parts. (Courtesy of Leica, Inc.)

Base: supports the microscope. (Note: Some microscopes are provided with an inclination joint, which allows the instrument to be tilted backward for viewing dry preparations.)

Substage light (or *mirror*): located in the base. In microscopes with a substage light source, the light passes directly upward through the microscope. If a mirror is used, light must be reflected from a separate free-standing lamp.

Stage: the platform the slide rests on while being viewed. The stage always has a hole in it to permit light to pass through both it and the specimen.

Some microscopes have a stage equipped with *spring clips;* others have a clamp-type *mechanical stage* as shown in Figure 3.1. Both hold the slide in position for viewing; in addition, the mechanical stage permits precise movement of the specimen.

Condenser: concentrates the light on the specimen. The condenser may be equipped with a height-adjustment knob that raises and lowers the condenser to vary the delivery of light. Generally, the best position for the condenser is close to the inferior surface of the stage.

Iris diaphragm lever: arm attached to the condenser

that regulates the amount of light passing through the condenser. The iris diaphragm permits the best possible contrast when viewing the specimen.

Coarse adjustment knob: used to focus the specimen.

Fine adjustment knob: used for precise focusing once coarse focusing has been completed.

Head or **body tube:** supports the objective lens system (which is mounted on a movable nosepiece), and the ocular lens or lenses.

Arm: vertical portion of the microscope connecting the base and head.

Ocular (or *eyepiece*): depending on the microscope, there will be one or two lenses at the superior end of the head or body tube. Observations are made through the ocular(s). An ocular lens has a magnification of 10× (it increases the apparent size of the object by ten times or ten diameters). If your microscope has a *pointer* (used to indicate a specific area of the viewed specimen), it is attached to the ocular and can be positioned by rotating the ocular lens.

Nosepiece: generally carries three objective lenses and permits the sequential positioning of these lenses over the light beam passing through the hole in the stage.

Objective lenses: adjustable lens system that permits the use of a **low-power lens,** a **high-power lens,** or an **oil immersion lens.** The objective lenses have different magnifying and resolving powers.

2.   Examine the objectives carefully, noting their relative lengths and the numbers inscribed on their sides. On most microscopes, the low-power (l.p.) objective is the shortest and generally has a magnification of 10×. The high-power (h.p.) objective is of intermediate length and has a magnification range from 40× to 50×, depending on the microscope. The oil immersion objective is usually the longest of the objectives and has a magnifying power of 95× to 100×. (Note: some microscopes lack the oil immersion lens but have a very low magnification lens called the **scanning lens,** which is a very short objective with a magnification of 4× to 5×.) Record the magnification of each objective lens in the chart below. If your microscope has a scanning lens instead of the oil

immersion lens, cross out "oil immersion" and substitute "scan" on the chart.

3.   Rotate the low-power objective into position, and turn the coarse adjustment knob about 180 degrees. Notice how far the stage (or objective) travels during this adjustment. Move the fine adjustment knob 180 degrees, noting again the distance that the stage (or the objective) moves.

Magnification and Resolution

The microscope is an instrument of magnification. In the compound microscope, magnification is achieved through the interplay of two lenses—the ocular lens and the objective lens. The objective lens magnifies the specimen to produce a **real image** that is projected to the ocular. This real image is magnified by the ocular lens to produce the **virtual image** seen by your eye (Figure 3.2).

The **total magnification** of any specimen being viewed is equal to the power of the ocular lens multiplied by the power of the objective lens used. For example, if the ocular lens magnifies 10× and the objective lens being used magnifies 45×, the total magnification is 450×.

Determine the total magnification you may achieve with each of the objectives on your microscope and record the figures on the chart below. At this time, also cross out the column relating to the lens that your microscope does not have, and record the number of your microscope at the top of the chart.

The compound light microscope has certain limitations. Although the level of magnification is almost limitless, the **resolution** (or resolving power), the ability to discriminate two close objects as separate, is not. The human eye can resolve objects about 100 μm apart, but the compound microscope has a resolution of 0.2 μm under ideal conditions. Objects closer than 0.2 μm are seen as a single fused image.

Resolving power (*RP*) is determined by the amount and physical properties of the visible light that enters the microscope. In general, the greater the amount of light

Summary Chart for Microscope # ___21___

	Scanning	Low Power	High Power	Oil Immersion
Magnification of objective lens	4 ×	10 ×	40 ×	×
Total magnification	40 ×	100×	400 ×	×
Detail observed				
Field size (diameter)	mm μm	mm μm	mm μm	mm μm
Working distance		mm	mm	mm

delivered to the objective lens, the greater the resolution. The size of the objective lens aperture (opening) decreases with increasing magnification, allowing less light to enter the objective. Thus, you will probably find it necessary to increase the light intensity at the higher magnifications.

VIEWING OBJECTS THROUGH THE MICROSCOPE

1. Obtain a millimeter ruler, a prepared slide of the letter *e* or newsprint, a dropper bottle of immersion oil, and some lens paper. Secure the slide on the stage so that the letter *e* is centered over the hole, and switch on the light source. (If the light source is not built into the base, use the curved surface of the mirror to reflect the light up into the microscope.) The condenser should be in its highest position.

2. With your lowest power (scanning or low-power) objective in position over the stage, use the coarse adjustment knob to bring the objective and stage as close together as possible.

3. Looking through the ocular, adjust the light for comfort. Now use the coarse adjustment knob to focus slowly away from the *e* until it is as clearly focused as possible. Complete the focusing with the fine adjustment knob.

4. Sketch the letter in the circle just as it appears in the **field** (the area you see through the microscope).

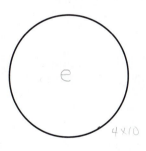

4×10

What is the total magnification? ___40___ × (scanning objective)

How far is the bottom of the objective from the specimen? In other words, what is the **working distance**?

_____ mm

Use a millimeter ruler to make this measurement and record it in the chart on page 18. How has the apparent orientation of the *e* changed top to bottom, right to left, and so on?

_____

_____

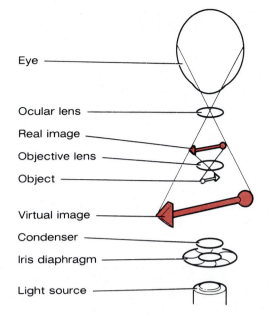

Eye

Ocular lens

Real image

Objective lens

Object

Virtual image

Condenser

Iris diaphragm

Light source

F3.2

Optical system of the compound microscope. Note the real and virtual images.

5. Move the slide slowly away from you on the stage as you look through the ocular. In what direction does the image move?

_____

Move the slide to the left. In what direction does the image move?

_____

At first this change in orientation will confuse you, but with practice you will learn to move the slide in the desired direction with no problem.

6. Without touching the focusing knobs, increase the magnification by rotating the next higher magnification lens (low-power or high-power) into position over the stage. Using the fine adjustment only, sharpen the focus.* What new details become clear?

_____

_____

What is the total magnification now? ___100___ × (low power objective)

---

* Today most good laboratory microscopes are parfocal; that is, the slide should be in focus (or nearly so) at the higher magnifications once you have properly focused in 1.p. If you are unable to swing the objective into position without raising the objective, your microscope is not parfocal. Consult your instructor.

As best you can, measure the distance between the objective and the slide (the working distance) and record it on the chart.

→ ?

Why should the coarse focusing knob *not* be used when focusing with the higher-powered objective lenses?

_____

_____

Is the image larger or smaller? ___*larga*___

Approximately how much of the letter *e* is visible now?

_____1/3_____

Is the field larger or smaller? ___*smaller*___

→ ?

Why is it necessary to center your object (or the portion of the slide you wish to view) before changing to a higher power?

_____

Move the iris diaphragm lever while observing the field. What happens?

_____

Is it more desirable to increase *or* decrease the light when changing to a higher magnification?

___increase___ Why? ___because the opening of the objective decreases with increasing magnification___

7.   If you have just been using the low-power objective, repeat the steps given in direction 6 using the high-power objective lens. Record the total magnification, approximate working distance, and information on detail observed on the chart on p. 18.

8.   Without touching the focusing knob, rotate the high-power lens out of position so that the area of the slide over the opening in the stage is unobstructed. Place a drop of immersion oil over the *e* on the slide and rotate the immersion lens into position. Adjust the fine focus and the light for the best possible resolution. Is the field again decreased in size?

NO hacer estos

_____

What is the total magnification with the immersion lens?

_____ ×

Is the working distance less or greater than it was when the high-power lens was focused?

_____

Compare your observations on the relative working distances of the objective lenses with the illustration in Figure 3.3. Explain why it is desirable to begin the focusing process in low power.

_____

_____

_____

9.   Rotate the immersion lens slightly to the side and remove the slide. Clean the oil immersion lens carefully with lens paper and then clean the slide in the same manner.

DETERMINING THE SIZE OF THE MICROSCOPE FIELD

By this time you should know that the size of the microscope field decreases with increasing magnification. For future microscope work, it will be useful to determine the diameter of each of the microscope fields. This information will allow you to make a fairly accurate estimate of the size of the objects you view in any field. For example, if you have calculated the field diameter to be 4 mm and the object being observed extends across half this diameter, you can estimate the length of the object to be approximately 2 mm.

Microscopic specimens are usually measured in micrometers and millimeters, both units of the metric system. You can get an idea of the relationship and meaning of these units from Table 3.1 on page 21.

1.   Return the letter *e* slide and obtain a grid slide, a slide prepared with graph paper ruled in millimeters. Each of the squares in the grid is 1 mm on each side. Use your lowest power objective to bring the grid lines into focus.

2.   Move the slide so that one grid line touches the edge of the field on one side, and then count the number of squares you can see across the diameter of the field. If you can see only part of a square, as in the accompanying diagram, estimate the part of a millimeter that the partial square represents.

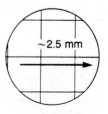

~2.5 mm

For future reference, record this figure in the appropriate space marked "field size" on the summary chart on page 18. (If you have been using the scanning lens, repeat the procedure with the low-power objective lens.) Complete the chart by computing the approximate diameter of the high-power and immersion fields. Say the diameter of the low-power field (total magnification of 50×) is 2 mm. You would compute the diameter of a high-power field with a total magnification of 100× as follows:

$$2 \text{ mm} \times 50 = Y \text{ (diameter of h.p. field)} \times 100$$

$$100 \text{ mm} = 100Y$$

$$1 \text{ mm} = Y \text{ (diameter of the h.p. field)}$$

The formula is:
Diameter of the l.p. field (mm) × Total magnification of the l.p. field = Diameter of field Y × Total magnification of field Y

3. Estimate the length (longest dimension) of the following microscopic objects. *Base your calculations on the field sizes you have determined for your microscope.*

Object seen in low-power field:

approximate length:

_____ mm.

Object seen in high-power field:

approximate length:

_____ mm,

or _____ μm.

Object seen in oil immersion field:

approximate length:

_____ μm.

4. If an object viewed with the oil immersion lens looked like the field depicted here, could you determine its approximate size from this view?

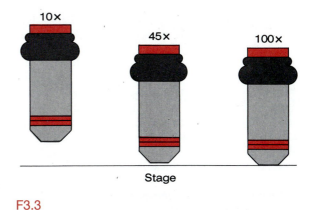

Stage

F3.3

Relative working distance of the 10×, 45×, and 100× objectives.

If not, then how could you determine it? _____

_____

_____

PERCEIVING DEPTH

Any specimen mounted on a slide has depth as well as length and width; it is rare indeed to view a tissue slide with just one layer of cells. Normally you can see two or three cell thicknesses. Therefore, it is important to learn how to determine relative depth with your microscope.*

---

* In microscope work the **depth of field** (the depth of the specimen clearly in focus) is greater at lower magnifications.

TABLE 3.1   Comparison of Metric Units of Length

Metric unit	Abbreviation	Equivalent
Meter	m	(about 39.3 in.)
Centimeter	cm	10^{-2} m
Millimeter	mm	10^{-3} m
Micrometer (or micron)	μm (μ)	10^{-6} m
Nanometer (or millimicrometer, or millimicron)	nm (mμ)	10^{-9} m
Angstrom	Å	10^{-10} m

1. Return the grid slide and obtain a slide of colored crossed threads. Focusing at low magnification, locate the point where the three threads cross each other.

2. Use the iris diaphragm lever to greatly reduce the light, thus increasing the contrast. Focus down with the coarse adjustment until the threads are out of focus, then slowly focus upward again, noting which thread comes into clear focus first. This one is the lowest or most inferior thread. (Note: you will see two or even all three threads, so you must be very careful in determining which one comes into clear focus first.) Record your observations:

_____red_____ thread is on top of _____blue_____

Continue to focus upward until the uppermost thread is clearly focused. Again record your observation.

_____red_____ thread is on top of _____yellow_____

Which thread is uppermost? _____red_____

Lowest? _____blue_____

PREPARING AND OBSERVING A WET MOUNT

1. Obtain the following: a clean microscope slide and cover slip, a flat-tipped toothpick, a dropper bottle of physiologic saline, a dropper bottle of methylene blue stain, forceps, and filter paper.

2. Place a drop of physiologic saline in the center of the slide. Using the flat end of the toothpick, gently scrape the inner lining of your cheek. Agitate the end of the toothpick containing the cheek scrapings in the drop of saline (Figure 3.4a).

Immediately dispose of the used toothpick in the disposable autoclave bag provided at the supplies area.

3. Add a small drop of the methylene blue stain to the preparation. (These epithelial cells are nearly transparent and thus difficult to see without the stain, which colors the nuclei of the cells and makes them look much darker than the cytoplasm.) Stir again.

4. Hold the cover slip with the forceps so that its bottom edge touches one side of the fluid drop (Figure 3.4b), then *carefully* lower the cover slip onto the preparation (Figure 3.4c). *Do not just drop the cover slip,* or you will trap large air bubbles under it, which will obscure the cells. *A cover slip should always be used with a wet mount* to prevent soiling the lens if you should misfocus.

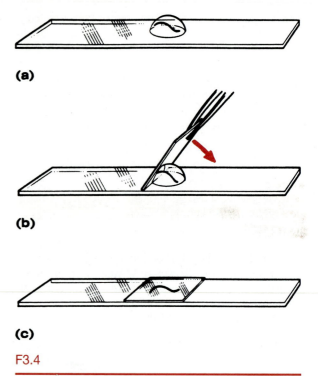

(a)

(b)

(c)

F3.4

Procedure for preparation of a wet mount. (a) The object is placed in a drop of water (or saline) on a clean slide, (b) a cover slip is held at a 45° angle with forceps, and (c) it is lowered carefully over the water and the object.

5. Examine your preparation carefully. The cover slip should be closely apposed to the slide. If there is excess fluid around its edges, obtain a piece of filter paper. Fold the filter paper in half, and use the folded edge to absorb the excess fluid.

Before continuing, dispose of the filter paper in the disposable autoclave bag.

6. Place the slide on the stage and locate the cells in low power. You will probably want to dim the light with the iris diaphragm to provide more contrast for viewing the lightly stained cells. (Furthermore, a wet mount will dry out quickly in bright light, because a bright light source is hot.)

7. Cheek epithelial cells are very thin, six-sided cells. In the cheek, they provide a smooth, tilelike lining, as shown in Figure 3.5.

8. Make a sketch of the epithelial cells that you observed.

Approximately how wide are the cheek epithelial cells?

_____ mm

Why do *your* cheek cells look different than those illustrated in Figure 3.5? (Hint: what did you have to *do* to your cheek to obtain them?)

_____

_____

9.   When you have completed your observations, dispose of your wet mount preparation in the beaker of bleach solution.

10.   Before leaving the laboratory, make sure all other materials are properly discarded or returned to the proper laboratory station. Clean the microscope lenses and put the dust cover on the microscope before you return it to the storage cabinet.

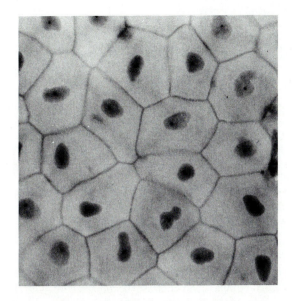

F3.5

Epithelial cells of the cheek cavity (surface view, 472×).

The Cell—Anatomy and Division

The **cell,** defined as the structural and functional unit of all living things, is a very complex entity. The cells of the human body are highly diverse; and their differences in size, shape, and internal composition reflect their specific roles in the body. Yet cells do have many common anatomical features, and there are some functions that all must perform to sustain life. For example, all cells have the ability to maintain their boundaries, to metabolize, to digest nutrients and dispose of wastes, to grow and reproduce, to move, and to respond to a stimulus. Most of these functions are considered in detail in later exercises. This exercise focuses on structural similarities that typify the "composite," or "generalized," cell and considers only the function of cell reproduction (cell division). Transport mechanisms (the means by which substances cross the plasma membrane) are dealt with separately in Exercise 5.

ANATOMY OF THE COMPOSITE CELL

In general, all cells have three major regions, or parts, that can readily be identified with a light microscope: the **nucleus,** the **plasma membrane,** and the **cytoplasm.** The nucleus is usually seen as a round or oval structure near the center of the cell. It is surrounded by cytoplasm, which in turn is enclosed by the plasma membrane. Since the advent of the electron microscope,

even smaller cell structures—organelles—have been identified. Figure 4.1a is a diagrammatic representation of the fine structure of the composite cell; Figure 4.1b depicts cellular structure as revealed by the electron microscope.

Nucleus

The nucleus is often described as the control center of the cell and is necessary for cell reproduction. A cell that has lost or ejected its nucleus (for whatever reason) is literally programmed to die because the nucleus is the site of the "genes," or genetic material—DNA.

When the cell is not dividing, the genetic material is loosely dispersed throughout the nucleus in a thread-like form called **chromatin.** When the cell is in the process of dividing to form daughter cells, the chromatin coils and condenses to form dense, darkly staining rod-like bodies called **chromosomes**—much in the way a stretched spring becomes shorter and thicker when relaxed. (Cell division is discussed later in this exercise.) Notice the appearance of the nucleus carefully—it is somewhat nondescript when a cell is healthy. When the nucleus appears dark and the chromatin becomes clumped, this is an indication that the cell is dying and undergoing degeneration.

The nucleus also contains one or more small round bodies, called **nucleoli,** composed primarily of proteins and ribonucleic acid (RNA). The nucleoli are believed to be storage sites for RNA and/or assembly sites for

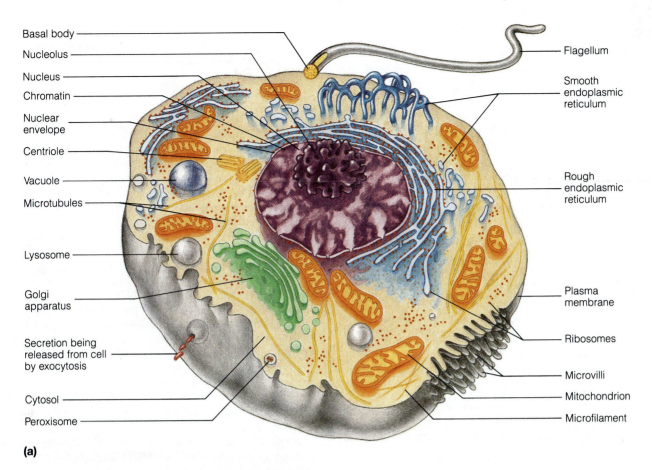

Basal body
Nucleolus
Nucleus
Chromatin
Nuclear envelope
Centriole
Vacuole
Microtubules
Lysosome
Golgi apparatus
Secretion being released from cell by exocytosis
Cytosol
Peroxisome

Flagellum
Smooth endoplasmic reticulum
Rough endoplasmic reticulum
Plasma membrane
Ribosomes
Microvilli
Mitochondrion
Microfilament

(a)

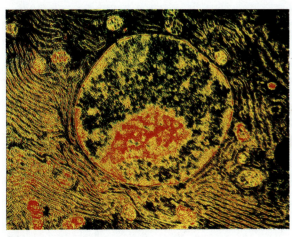

(b)

ribosomal particles (particularly abundant in the cytoplasm), which are the actual protein synthesizing "factories."

The nucleus is bound by a double-layered porous membrane, the **nuclear membrane** (or nuclear envelope), which is similar in composition to other cellular membranes.

● Identify the nuclear membrane, chromatin, and nucleoli in Figure 4.1a and b.

F4.1

Anatomy of the composite animal cell. (a) Diagrammatic view. (b) Transmission electron micrograph (10,000×).

Plasma Membrane

The **plasma membrane** separates cell contents from the surrounding environment. It is made up of protein and lipid (fat) and appears to have a bimolecular lipid core that protein molecules float in (see Figure 4.2). Besides providing a protective barrier for the cell, the plasma membrane plays an active role in determining which substances may enter or leave the cell and in what quantity. In some cells the membrane is thrown into minute fingerlike projections or folds called **microvilli,** which greatly increase the surface area of the cell available for absorption or passage of materials.

● Identify the phospholipid and protein portions of the plasma membrane in Figure 4.2 and the microvilli in Figure 4.1.

Cytoplasm and Organelles

The cytoplasm consists of the cell contents outside the nucleus. It is the major site of most activities carried out by the cell. Suspended in the *cytosol,* the fluid cytoplasmic material, are many small structures called **organelles** (literally, small organs). The organelles are the metabolic machinery of the cell, and they are highly organized to carry out specific functions for the cell as a

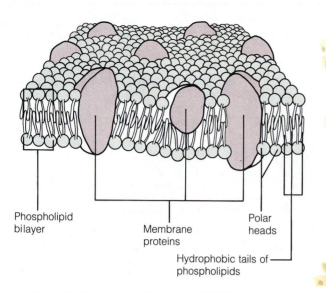

Phospholipid
bilayer

Membrane
proteins

Polar
heads

Hydrophobic tails of
phospholipids

F4.2

Structural details of the plasma membrane.

whole. The organelles include the ribosomes, endoplasmic reticulum, Golgi apparatus, lysosomes, mitochondria, centrioles, and cytoskeletal elements.

● Each organelle type is summarized in Table 4.1 and described briefly next. Read through this material and then, as best you can, locate the organelles on both Figure 4.1a and b.

The **ribosomes** are tiny spherical bodies composed of RNA and protein. They are the actual sites of protein synthesis. They are seen floating free in the cytoplasm or attached to a membranous structure. When they are attached, the whole ribosome-membrane complex is called the granular or rough endoplasmic reticulum.

The **endoplasmic reticulum** (**ER**) is a highly folded membranous system of tubules that extends throughout the cytoplasm. The ER has been observed to be continuous with the Golgi apparatus, nuclear membrane, and plasma membrane. Thus it is assumed that the ER provides a system of channels for the transport of cellular substances (primarily proteins) from one part of the cell to another or to the cell exterior. The ER exists in two forms; a particular cell may have both or only one, depending on its specific functions. The granular or **rough ER,** as noted earlier, is studded with ribosomes. Its cisternae store proteins and deliver them to other areas of the cell; the external face of the rough ER is involved in phospholipid and cholesterol synthesis. The amount of rough ER is closely correlated with the amount of protein a cell manufactures and is especially abundant in cells that make protein products for export—for example, pancreas cells, which produce digestive enzymes destined for the small intestine. The agranular or **smooth ER** has no protein synthesis–related function but is present in conspicuous amounts in cells that produce steroid-based hormones—for exam-

ple, the interstitial cells of the testes, which produce testosterone, and in cells that are highly active in lipid metabolism and drug detoxification activities—liver cells, for instance.

The **Golgi apparatus** is a stack of flattened sacs (accompanied by bulbous ends and small vesicles) and is generally found close to the nucleus. It is now known to have a role in packaging proteins destined for incorporation into cellular membranes or lysosomes, or for export (the proteins are delivered to it by the rough ER) and perhaps in attaching carbohydrate groups to some of them. As the proteins accumulate in the Golgi apparatus, the sacs swell, and little vesicles filled with protein pinch off. These vesicles containing secretory products travel to the plasma membrane, fuse with it, and eject their contents to the cell exterior.

The **lysosomes,** which appear in various sizes, are membrane-bound sacs containing an array of powerful digestive enzymes. Believed to arise from the packaging activities of the Golgi apparatus, the lysosomes contain enzymes capable of digesting worn-out cell structures and foreign substances that enter the cell through phagocytosis or pinocytosis (see Exercise 5). Lysosomes also bring about some of the changes that occur during menstruation, when the uterine lining is sloughed off. Since they have the capacity of total cell destruction, the lysosomes are often referred to as the "suicide sacs" of the cell.

The **mitochondria** are generally rod-shaped bodies with a double-membrane wall; the inner membrane is thrown into folds, or *cristae*. Oxidative enzymes on or within the mitochondria catalyze the reactions of the Krebs cycle and the electron transport chain (collectively called oxidative respiration), in which foods are broken down to produce energy. The released energy is captured in the bonds of ATP (adenosine triphosphate) molecules, which then diffuse out of the mitochondria to provide a ready energy supply to power the cell. Every living cell requires a constant supply of ATP for its many activities. Since the mitochondria provide the bulk of this ATP, they are referred to as the powerhouses of the cell.

The paired **centrioles** lie close to the nucleus in all animal cells capable of reproducing themselves. They are rod-shaped bodies that lie at right angles to each

Pinocytotic Vesicles	# 09121	
Mitochondria	# 46436	
Ribosomes	# 17351	
Rough Endoplasmic Reticulum	# 09061	
Golgi Apparatus, Lysosome, Vesicles	# 44151	

TABLE 4.1   Cytoplasmic Organelles

Organelle	Location and function
Ribosomes	Tiny spherical bodies composed of RNA and protein; actual sites of protein synthesis; seen floating free or attached to a membranous structure (the rough ER) in the cytoplasm
Endoplasmic reticulum (ER)	Membranous system of tubules that extends throughout the cytoplasm; two varieties: rough or granular ER—studded with ribosomes (tubules of the rough ER provide an area for storage and transport of the proteins made on the ribosomes to other cell areas; external face synthesizes phospholipids and cholesterol); smooth or agranular ER—no protein synthesis–related function (believed to be a site of lipid metabolism and for synthesis of lipids and steroid-based hormones)
Golgi apparatus	Stack of flattened sacs with bulbous ends and associated small vesicles; found close to the nucleus; role in packaging proteins or other substances for export from the cell or incorporation into the plasma membrane and in packaging lysosomal enzymes
Lysosomes	Various-sized membranous sacs containing powerful digestive enzymes; function to digest worn-out cell organelles and foreign substances that enter the cell; since they have the capacity of total cell destruction if ruptured, referred to as "suicide sacs of the cell"
Mitochondria	Generally rod-shaped bodies with a double membrane wall; inner membrane is thrown into folds, or cristae; contain enzymes that oxidize foodstuffs to produce cellular energy (ATP); often referred to as "powerhouses of the cell"
Centrioles	Paired, cylindrical bodies lying at right angles to each other, close to the nucleus; direct the formation of the mitotic spindle during cell division
Cytoskeletal elements: microtubules, intermediate filaments, and microfilaments*	Provide cellular support; function in intracellular transport; microtubules form the internal structure of the centrioles and help determine cell shape; intermediate filaments, stable elements composed of a variety of proteins, resist mechanical forces acting on cells; microfilaments are formed largely of contractile proteins, and thus are important in cell mobility (particularly in muscle cells)

*Cytoskeletal elements are *not* depicted in Figure 4.1.

other; internally they consist of a system of fine tubules. During cell division, the centrioles direct the formation of the mitotic spindle. Centrioles also form the basis for cell projections called cilia and flagella (described below).

The **cytoskeletal elements** are extremely important in cellular support and movement of substances within the cell. **Microtubules** are basically slender tubules formed of proteins called *tubulins*. Since tubulins can aggregate spontaneously to form microtubules and then disaggregate just as quickly, the microtubules have been difficult to study. Microtubules are the basis of the spindle formed by the centrioles during cell division; they act in the transport of substances down the length of elongated cells (such as neurons), and form part of the internal cytoskeleton, providing rigidity to the soft cellular substance. **Intermediate filaments** are *stable* proteinaceous cytoskeletal elements that are important in resisting mechanical forces acting on cells. **Microfilaments,** ribbon or cordlike elements, are formed of contractile proteins. Because of their ability to shorten and then relax to assume a more elongated form, these are important in cell mobility and are very conspicuous in cells that are highly specialized to contract (such as muscle cells).

The cytoskeletal structures are labile and minute. With the exception of the microtubules of the spindle, which are very obvious during cell division (see p. 29), and the microfilaments of skeletal muscle cells (see p. 106), they are rarely seen, even in electron micrographs, and are not depicted in Figure 4.1. However, special stains can reveal the plentiful supply of these very important organelles (see plate 5 in the Histology Atlas).

In addition to these cell structures, some cells have projections called **flagella,** which propel the cells, or **cilia,** which allow cells to sweep substances along a tract. Identify the cilium in Figure 4.1a.

The cell cytoplasm contains various other substances and structures, including stored foods (glycogen granules and lipid droplets), pigment granules, crystals of various types, water vacuoles, and ingested foreign materials. But these are not part of the active metabolic machinery of the cell and are therefore called **inclusions.**

- Once you have located all of these structures in Figure 4.1a, examine the cell model (or cell chart) to reinforce your identifications.

OBSERVING DIFFERENCES AND SIMILARITIES IN CELL STRUCTURE

1.   Obtain prepared slides of simple squamous epithelium, sperm, smooth muscle cells (teased), and human blood.

2.   Observe each slide under the microscope, carefully noting similarities and differences in the cells. (The oil immersion lens will be needed to observe blood and sperm.) Distinguish the limits of the individual cells, and note the shape and position of the nucleus in each case. When you look at the human blood smear, direct your attention to the red blood cells, the pink-stained cells that are most numerous. The color photomicrographs illustrating a blood smear (Plate 55) and sperm (Plate 50) that appear in the Histology Atlas may be helpful in this cell structure study. Sketch your observations in the circles provided.

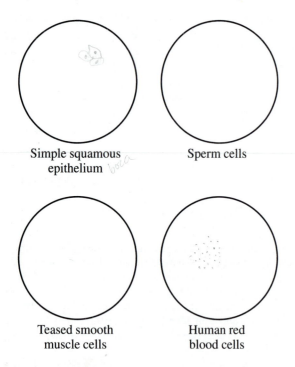

Simple squamous epithelium   Sperm cells

Teased smooth muscle cells   Human red blood cells

3.   How do these four cell types differ in shape and size?

_____

_____

_____

_____

_____

How might cell shape affect cell function?

_____

_____

_____

_____

_____

Which cells have visible projections?

_____

How do these projections relate to the function of this cell?

_____

_____

_____

Do any of these cells lack a cell membrane? _____

A nucleus? _____

In the cells with a nucleus, can you discern nucleoli?

_____

Were you able to observe any of the organelles in these

cells? _____ Why or why not?

_____

_____

_____

CELL DIVISION: MITOSIS AND CYTOKINESIS

Cell division in all cells other than bacteria consists of a series of events collectively called mitosis and cytokinesis. **Mitosis** is nuclear division; **cytokinesis** is the division of the cytoplasm, which begins after mitosis is nearly complete. Although mitosis is usually accompanied by cytokinesis, in some instances cytoplasmic division does not occur, leading to the formation of binucleate (or multinucleate) cells. This is relatively common in the human liver and during embryonic development of skeletal muscle cells.

The process of **mitosis** results in the formation of two daughter nuclei that are genetically identical to the mother nucleus. This distinguishes mitosis from **meiosis,** a specialized type of nuclear division that occurs only in the reproductive organs (testes or ovaries). Meiosis, which yields four daughter nuclei that differ genetically and in composition from the mother nucleus, is used only for the production of eggs and sperm (gametes) for sexual reproduction. The function of cell division, including mitosis and cytokinesis in the body, is to increase the number of cells for growth and repair while maintaining their genetic heritage.

In cells about to divide, an important event precedes cell division. The genetic material (the DNA molecules composing part of the chromatin strands) is replicated (duplicated exactly) during the portion of the cell's life cycle called **interphase.** Interphase is *not* part of mitosis; it represents the time when a cell is not actively involved in cell division. Although some people refer to interphase as the cell's resting period, this is an inaccurate description because the cell is quite active in its daily activities and is resting only from cell division. The stages of mitosis diagrammed in Figure 4.3 include the following events:

Prophase: At the onset of cell division, the chromatin threads coil and shorten to form densely staining, short, barlike **chromosomes.** By the middle of pro-

phase the chromosomes appear as double-stranded structures (each strand is a **chromatid**) connected by a small median body called a **centromere.** The centrioles separate from one another and act as focal points for the assembly of a system of microtubules called the **mitotic spindle** which forms between them. The spindle acts as a scaffolding for the attachment and movement of the chromosomes during later mitotic stages. The nuclear membrane and the nucleolus break down and disappear, and the chromosomes randomly attach to the spindle fibers by their centromeres.

Metaphase: A brief stage, during which the chromosomes migrate to the central plane or equator of the spindle and align along that plane in a straight line from the superior to the inferior region of the spindle (lateral view). Viewed from the poles of the cell (end view), the chromosomes appear to be arranged in a "rosette," or circle, around the widest dimension of the spindle.

Mitosis, Metaphase   # 50401

Mitosis, Anaphase   # 50403

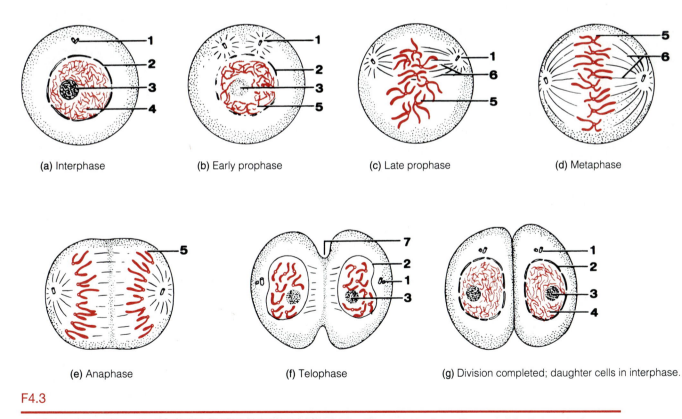

(a) Interphase   (b) Early prophase   (c) Late prophase   (d) Metaphase

(e) Anaphase   (f) Telophase   (g) Division completed; daughter cells in interphase.

F4.3

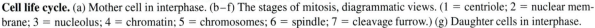

Cell life cycle. (a) Mother cell in interphase. (b–f) The stages of mitosis, diagrammatic views. (1 = centriole; 2 = nuclear membrane; 3 = nucleolus; 4 = chromatin; 5 = chromosomes; 6 = spindle; 7 = cleavage furrow.) (g) Daughter cells in interphase.

Anaphase: During anaphase, the centromeres break, and the chromatids (now called chromosomes again) separate from one another and then progress slowly toward opposite ends of the cell. The chromosomes appear to be pulled by their centromere attachment, with their "arms" dangling behind them. Anaphase is complete when poleward movement ceases.

Telophase: During telophase, the events of prophase are essentially reversed. The chromosomes at the poles begin to uncoil and resume the chromatin form, the spindle disappears, a nuclear membrane forms around each chromatin mass, and nucleoli appear in each of the daughter nuclei.

Mitosis is essentially the same in all animal cells, but depending on the type of tissue, it takes from 5 minutes to several hours to complete. In most cells, centriole replication is deferred until interphase of the next cell cycle.

Cytokinesis, or the division of the cytoplasmic mass, begins during telophase and provides a good guideline for where to look for the mitotic figures of telophase. In animal cells, a *cleavage furrow* begins to form approximately over the equator of the spindle, and eventually splits or pinches the original cytoplasmic mass into two portions. Thus at the end of cell division two daughter cells exist, each smaller in cytoplasmic mass than the mother cell but genetically identical to it. The daughter cells grow and carry out the normal spectrum of metabolic processes until it is their turn to divide.

Cell division is extremely important during the body's growth period. Most cells (excluding nerve cells) undergo mitosis until puberty, when normal body size is achieved and overall body growth ceases. After this time in life, only certain cells routinely carry out cell division—for example, cells subjected to abrasion (epithelium of the skin and lining of the gut). Other cell populations—such as liver cells—stop dividing but retain this ability should some of them be removed or damaged. Skeletal muscle and nervous tissue completely lose this ability to divide and thus are severely handicapped by injury. Throughout life, the body retains its ability to repair cuts and wounds and to replace some of its aged cells.

Obtain a prepared slide of whitefish blastulae to study the stages of mitosis. The cells of each *blastula* (a stage of embryonic development consisting of a hollow ball of cells) are at approximately the same mitotic stage, so it may be necessary to observe more than one blastula to view all the mitotic stages. The exceptionally high rate of mitosis observed in this tissue is typical of embryos, but if occurring in specialized tissues, it can be an indication of cancerous cells, which also have an extraordinarily high mitotic rate. Examine the slide carefully, identifying the four mitotic stages and the process of cytokinesis. Compare your observations with Figure 4.4, and verify your identifications with your instructor. Then sketch your observations of each stage in the circles provided here.

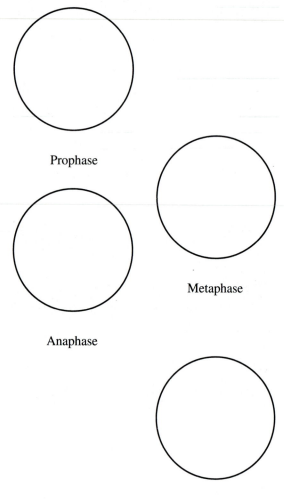

Prophase

Metaphase

Anaphase

Telophase

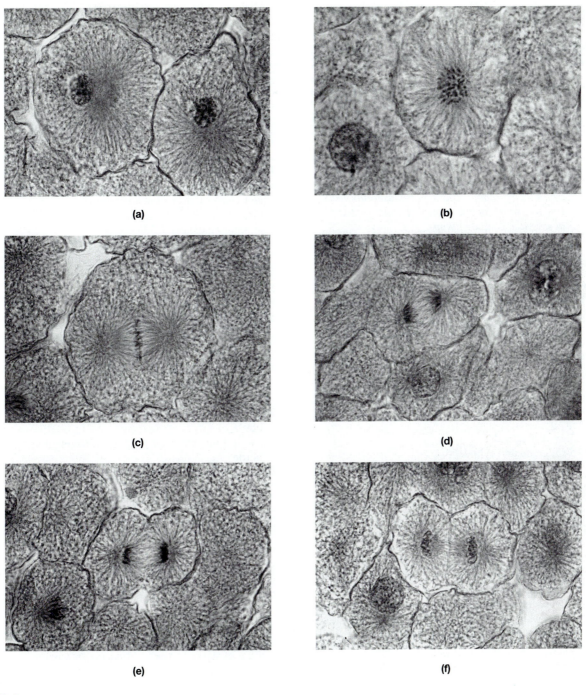

(a)

(b)

(c)

(d)

(e)

(f)

F4.4

Photomicrograph of mitotic stages in whitefish blastula (570×). (a) Early prophase. (b) Late prophase. (c) Metaphase. (d) Anaphase. (e) Early telophase. (f) Late telophase.

The Cell—
Transport Mechanisms
and Cell Permeability

OBJECTIVES

1. To define *differential,* or *selective, permeability; diffusion* (*dialysis* and *osmosis*); *Brownian motion; isotonic, hypotonic,* and *hypertonic solutions; passive transport; active transport; pinocytosis; phagocytosis;* and *solute pumps.*

2. To explain the processes that account for the movement of substances across the plasma membrane and to indicate the driving force for each.

3. To determine which way substances will move passively through a selectively permeable membrane (given appropriate information on concentration differences).

MATERIALS

For Passive Transport Experiments:
Clean slides and coverslips
Forceps
Glass stirring rods
15-ml graduated cylinders
Compound microscopes
Hot plate and large beaker for hot water bath

Brownian motion:
Milk in dropper bottles

Diffusion:

Demonstration 1: Diffusion of a dye through water
Prepared the morning of the laboratory session with setup time noted. Potassium permanganate crystals placed in a 1000-ml graduated cylinder, and distilled water slowly added with as little turbulence as possible to fill to the 1000-ml mark.

Demonstration 2: Osmometer
Just before the laboratory begins, the broad end of a thistle tube is closed with a selectively permeable dialysis membrane, and the tube is secured to a ring stand. Molasses is added to approximately 5 cm above the thistle tube bulb and the bulb is immersed in a beaker of distilled water. At the beginning of the lab session, the level of the molasses in the tube is marked with a wax pencil.

Petri plate containing 12 ml of 1.5% agar-agar
Methylene blue dye crystals
Potassium permanganate dye crystals
Millimeter rulers

Four dialysis sacs or small Hefty "alligator" sandwich bags
Beakers (250 ml)
40% glucose solution
Fine twine or dialysis tubing clamps
10% NaCl solution, boiled starch solution
Laboratory balance
Benedict's solution in dropper bottle
Test tubes in racks, test tube holder
Wax marker
Small funnel
Silver nitrate ($AgNO_3$) in dropper bottle
Lugol's iodine solution in dropper bottle

Lancets, alcohol swabs
Filter paper
Animal (mammalian) blood (in vials) obtained from an animal hospital or veterinary school—at option of instructor
Physiologic (mammalian) saline solution in dropper bottle
1.5% sodium chloride (NaCl) solution in dropper bottle
Distilled water in dropper bottle
Medicine dropper
Basin containing 10% household bleach solution
Disposable autoclave bag
Disposable plastic gloves

Filtration:
Ring stand, ring, clamp
Filter paper, funnel
Solution containing a mixture of uncooked starch, powdered charcoal, and copper sulfate ($CuSO_4$)

Active Transport:
Culture of starved amoeba (*Amoeba proteus*)
Depression slide
Coverslip (glass)
Tetrahymena pyriformis culture
Compound microscope

Note to the Instructor: See directions for handling wet mount preparations and disposable supplies on page 16, Exercise 3.

Because of its molecular composition, the plasma membrane is selective about what passes through it. It allows nutrients to enter the cell but keeps out undesirable substances. By the same token, valuable cell proteins and other substances are kept within the cell, and excreta or wastes pass to the exterior. This property is known as **selective permeability.** Transport through the plasma membrane occurs in two basic ways. In one, the cell must provide energy (ATP) to power the transport process (active transport); in the other, the transport process is driven by concentration or pressure differences (passive transport).

PASSIVE TRANSPORT

All molecules vibrate randomly (because of their inherent kinetic energy) at all temperatures above absolute zero (about $-460°F$). In general, the smaller the particle, the greater the kinetic energy it possesses and the faster its molecular motion. This random movement (Figure 5.1) may be detected indirectly by observing a suspension like milk. The larger particles can be seen moving randomly as they are hit and deflected by the smaller, more rapidly moving particles. The zigzag movement of the larger particles is known as **Brownian motion.**

1.   Make a wet mount of milk; that is, place a small drop of milk on a slide and cover carefully with a cover slip. Allow the slide to stand on the microscope stage for about 10 minutes before observing.

2.   Keeping the light low, observe the slide with high power and then with the oil immersion lens. Keep the light as dim as possible to increase the contrast. As the minute solvent (water) molecules collide with the fat globules of the milk, you can see the larger fat globules ricochet in an erratic manner (Brownian motion).

3.   Place the preparation on a warm hot plate for a few seconds. Observe again. How has the *rate* of Brownian motion changed?

_____

_____

What would you conclude about the effect of increased temperature on the kinetic energy of molecules?

_____

_____

_____

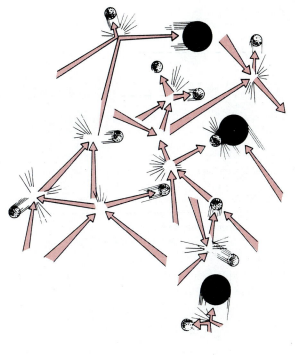

Random movement and numerous collisions cause molecules to become evenly distributed. The small spheres represent water molecules; the large spheres represent glucose molecules.

Diffusion

If a **concentration gradient** (difference in concentration) exists, molecules eventually become evenly distributed through random molecular motion (Figure 5.1). **Diffusion** is the movement of molecules from a region of their higher concentration to a region of their lower concentration. The driving force is the kinetic energy of the molecules themselves. There are many examples of diffusion in nonliving systems. For example, if a bottle of ether was uncorked at the front of the laboratory, very shortly thereafter you would be nodding, as the ether molecules become distributed throughout the room. The ability to smell a friend's cologne shortly after he or she has approached is another such example.

   The diffusion of particles into and out of cells is modified by the plasma membrane, which constitutes a physical barrier. In general, molecules diffuse passively through the plasma membrane if they are small enough to pass through its pores (and are aided by an electrical gradient), or if they can dissolve in the lipid portion of the membrane (as in the case of CO_2 and O_2). The diffusion of solutes (particles dissolved in water) through a semipermeable membrane is called **dialysis;** the diffusion of water through a semipermeable membrane is called **osmosis.** Both dialysis and osmosis, examples of diffusion phenomena, involve the movement of a substance from an area of its higher concentration to one of its lower concentration, i.e., down its concentration gradient.

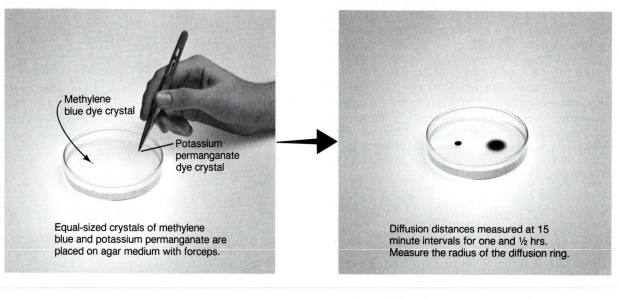

Methylene blue dye crystal

Potassium permanganate dye crystal

Equal-sized crystals of methylene blue and potassium permanganate are placed on agar medium with forceps.

Diffusion distances measured at 15 minute intervals for one and ½ hrs. Measure the radius of the diffusion ring.

F5.2

Setup for comparing the diffusion rates of molecules of methylene blue and potassium permanganate through an agar gel.

DIFFUSION OF A DYE THROUGH AN AGAR GEL

The relationship between molecular weight and the rate of diffusion can be examined simply by observing the diffusion of the molecules of two different types of dye through an agar gel. The dyes used in this experiment are methylene blue, which has a molecular weight of 320 and is deep blue in color, and potassium permanganate, a purple dye with a molecular weight of 158. Although the agar gel appears quite solid, it is primarily (98.5%) water and allows free movement of the diffusing dye molecules through it.

Time (min)	Diffusion of Methylene Blue (mm)	Diffusion of Potassium Permanganate (mm)
15		
30		
45		
60		
75		
90		

1.   Obtain a petri dish containing agar gel, a forceps, a millimeter ruler, and containers of methylene blue crystals and potassium permanganate crystals, and bring them to your bench.

Avoid contact between your skin and the dye crystals by using the forceps to pick up the crystals.

2.   Select approximately equal-size crystals of each dye, and place them gently on the agar gel surface, approximately 10 centimeters apart (Figure 5.2). Record the time.

_____

3.   At 15-minute intervals, use the millimeter ruler to measure the distance the dye has diffused from each crystal. These observations should be continued for 1½ hours, and the results recorded in the chart to the right.

Which dye diffused more rapidly? _____

What is the relationship between molecular weight and rate of molecular movement (diffusion)?

_____

Why did the dye molecules move? _____

_____

Compute the rate of diffusion of the potassium permanganate molecules in millimeters per minute (mm/min) and record.

_____ mm/min

Compute the rate of diffusion of the methylene blue molecules in mm/min and record.

_____ mm/min

DIFFUSION OF A DYE THROUGH WATER

Make a mental note to yourself to go to demonstration area 1 at the end of the laboratory session to observe the extent of diffusion of the potassium permanganate dye through water. At that time, follow the directions given next.

1.   Measure the number of millimeters from the bottom of the graduated cylinder the dye has diffused and record.

_____ mm

2.   Note the time the demonstration was set up and the time of your observation, and then compute the rate of the dye's diffusion through water and record below.

Time of set up _____

Time of observation _____

Rate of diffusion _____ mm/min

3.   Does the potassium permanganate dye move (diffuse) more rapidly through water or the agar gel? (Explain your answer.)

_____

_____

_____

_____

DIFFUSION THROUGH NONLIVING MEMBRANES

A diffusion experiment providing information on the passage of water and solutes through semipermeable membranes, which may be applied to the study of transport mechanisms in living membrane-bound cells, is outlined next.

1.   Obtain four dialysis sacs,* a small funnel, a graduated cylinder, and four beakers (250 ml). Number the beakers 1 to 4 with a wax marker, and half fill all of them with distilled water except beaker 2, to which you should add 40% glucose solution.

2.   Prepare the dialysis sacs one at a time. Using the funnel, half fill each with 20 ml of the specified liquid. Press out the air, fold over the open end of the sac, and

* Dialysis sacs are selectively permeable membranes with pores of a particular size. The selectivity of living membranes depends on more than just pore size, but using the dialysis sacs will allow you to examine selectivity due to this factor.

tie it securely with fine twine. Before proceeding to the next sac, quickly and carefully blot the sac dry by rolling it on a paper towel, and weigh it with a laboratory balance. Record the weight, and then drop the sac into the corresponding beaker. Be sure the sac is completely covered by the beaker solution, adding more solution if necessary.

• Sac 1: 40% glucose solution. Weight: _____ g

• Sac 2: 40% glucose solution. Weight: _____ g

• Sac 3: 10% NaCl solution. Weight: _____ g

• Sac 4: boiled starch solution. Weight: _____ g

Allow sacs to remain undisturbed in the beakers for 1 hour. (Use this time to continue with other experiments.)

3.   After an hour, get a beaker of water boiling on the hot plate and then quickly and gently blot sac 1 dry and weigh it. (Note: Do not squeeze the sac during the blotting process.)

_____ g

Has there been any change in weight? _____

Conclusions? _____

_____

_____

Place 5 ml of Benedict's solution in each of two test tubes. Put 4 ml of the beaker fluid into one test tube and 4 ml of the sac fluid into the other. Mark the tubes for identification and then place them in a beaker containing boiling water. Boil 2 minutes. Cool slowly. If a green, yellow, or rusty red precipitate forms, the test is positive, meaning that glucose is present. If the solution remains the original blue color, the test is negative.

Was glucose still present in the sac? _____

Was glucose present in the beaker? _____

Conclusions? _____

_____

_____

4.   Blot gently and weigh sac 2: _____ g

Was there an _increase_ or _decrease_ in weight? _____

With 40% glucose in the sac and 40% glucose in the beaker, would you expect to see any net movements of water (osmosis) or of glucose molecules (dialysis)?

_____ Why or why not? _____

_____

_____

5.   Blot gently and weigh sac 3: _____ g

Was there any change in weight? _____

Conclusions? _____

_____

Take a 5 ml sample of beaker 3 solution and put it in a test tube. Add a drop of silver nitrate. The appearance of a white precipitate or cloudiness indicates the presence of AgCl, which is formed by the reaction of $AgNO_3$ with NaCl (sodium chloride).

Results? _____

Conclusions? _____

_____

6.   Blot gently and weigh sac 4: _____ g

Was there any change in weight? _____

Conclusions? _____

_____

Take a 5 ml sample of beaker 4 solution and add a couple of drops of Lugol's iodine solution. The appearance of a black color is a positive test for the presence of starch. Did any starch diffuse from the sac into the beaker?

_____ Explain: _____

_____

_____

7.   In which of the test situations did net osmosis occur?

_____

In which of the test situations did net dialysis occur?

_____

What conclusions can you make about the relative size of glucose, starch, NaCl, and water molecules?

_____

_____

_____

With what cell structure can the dialysis sac be compared?

_____

_____

8.   Before leaving the laboratory, observe the _osmometer demonstration_ set up before the laboratory session to follow the movement of water through a membrane (osmosis). Measure the distance the water column has moved during the laboratory period and record below. (The position of the meniscus in the thistle tube at the beginning of the laboratory period is marked with wax pencil.)

Distance the meniscus has moved: _____ mm

DIFFUSION THROUGH LIVING MEMBRANES

To examine permeability properties of cell membranes, conduct the following two experiments.

 Experiment 1:   1.   Obtain a clean slide and cover slip, lancets, an alcohol swab, physiologic saline, 1.5% sodium chloride solution, 3 test tubes, test tube rack, glass stirring rod, 15 ml graduated cylinder, filter paper, and plastic gloves.
   If animal blood is to be used, also obtain a vial of animal blood and a medicine dropper.

2.   Label 3 test tubes A, B, and C, and prepare them as follows:

- A: add 2 ml physiologic saline
- B: add 2 ml 1.5% sodium chloride solution
- C: add 2 ml distilled water

If you are using your own blood, follow step 3a; if you are using animal blood provided by your instructor, follow the directions in step 3b.

3a.   Clean a fingertip with an alcohol swab, puncture it with a lancet, and add five drops of blood to each test tube. Stir each test tube with the glass rod, rinsing between each sample.

 Dispose of the used lancet in the autoclave bag before continuing.

3b.   Don plastic gloves, and use a medicine dropper to add 5 drops of animal blood to each test tube. Stir each test tube with the glass rod, rinsing between each sample.

4.   Hold each test tube in front of this printed page. _Record_ the clarity of print seen through the fluid in each tube.

Test tube A _____

Test tube B _____

Test tube C _____

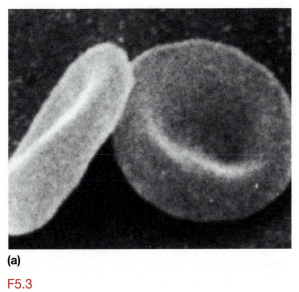

(a)

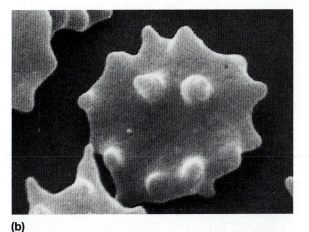

(b)

F5.3

Influence of hypertonic and hypotonic solutions on red blood cells. (a) Red blood cells suspended in an isotonic solution, where the cells retain their normal size and shape. (b) Red blood cells suspended in a hypertonic solution. As the cells lose water to the external environment, they shrink and become prickly; this phenomenon is called crenation. (c) Red blood cells suspended in a hypotonic solution. Notice their spherical bloated shape, a result of excessive water intake.

(c)

Experiment 2: Now you will conduct a microscope study of red blood cells suspended in the same three solutions. The objective is to determine if these solutions have any effect on cell shape by promoting net osmosis.

1. Place a very small drop of physiologic saline on a slide. As instructed above, clean your fingertip with an alcohol swab, puncture it with a lancet, and touch a small drop of blood to the saline on the slide *or* add a small drop of animal blood to the saline on the slide. Tilt the slide to mix, cover with a cover slip, and immediately examine the preparation under the high-power lens. Notice that the red blood cells retain their normal smooth disclike shape (see Figure 5.3a). This is because the physiologic saline is **isotonic** to the cells. That is, it contains a concentration of nonpenetrating solutes equal to that in the cells (same solute-solvent ratio). Consequently, the cells neither gain nor lose water by osmosis.

2. Prepare another wet mount of blood, but this time use 1.5% saline solution as the suspending medium. After 5 minutes, carefully observe the red blood cells under high power. What is happening to the normally smooth disc shape of the red blood cells?

_____

_____

_____

This crinkling-up process, called **crenation,** is due to the fact that the 1.5% sodium chloride solution is slightly hypertonic to the cell sap of the red blood cell. A **hypertonic** solution contains more nonpenetrating solutes (thus less water) than are present in the cell. Under these circumstances, water tends to leave the cells by osmosis. Compare your observations to Figure 5.3b.

3. Add a drop of distilled water to the edge of the cover slip. Fold a piece of filter paper in half and place its folded edge at the opposite edge of the cover slip; it will absorb the saline solution and draw the distilled water across the cells. Watch the red blood cells as they float across the field. After about 5 minutes have passed, describe the change in their appearance.

_____

_____

_____

Distilled water contains *no* solutes (it is 100% water). Distilled water and *very* dilute solutions (that is, those containing less than 0.9% nonpenetrating solutes) are **hypotonic** to the cell. In a hypotonic solution, the red blood cells first "plump up" (Figure 5.3c) but then they suddenly start to disappear. The red blood cells burst as the water floods into them, leaving "ghosts" in their wake. This phenomenon is called **hemolysis.**

How do your observations of test tube C in Experiment 1 correlate with what you have just observed under the microscope?

_____

_____

_____

 4. Dispose of your slides and test tube in the bleach-containing basin. Put your lancets and gloves (if used) into the disposable autoclave bag.

Filtration

Filtration is a physical process by which water and solutes pass through a membrane from an area of higher hydrostatic (fluid) pressure into an area of lower hydrostatic pressure. Like diffusion, it is a passive process. For example, fluids and solutes filter out of the capillaries in the kidneys into the kidney tubules because the blood pressure in the capillaries is greater than the fluid pressure in the tubules. Filtration is not a selective process. The amount of filtrate (fluids and solutes) formed depends almost entirely on the difference in pressure on the two sides of the membrane and on the size of the membrane pores.

1. Obtain the following equipment: a ring stand, ring, and ring clamp; a piece of filter paper; a beaker; and a solution of uncooked starch, powdered charcoal, and copper sulfate. Attach the ring to the ring stand with the clamp.

2. Fold the filter paper in half twice, open it into a cone, and place it in a funnel. Place the funnel in the ring of the ring stand and place a beaker under the funnel. Shake the starch solution, and fill the funnel with it to just below the top of the filter paper. When the steady stream of filtrate changes to countable filtrate drops, count the number of drops formed in 10 seconds and record.

_____ drops

When the funnel is half empty, again count the number of drops formed in 10 seconds and record the count.

_____ drops

3. After all the fluid has passed through the filter, check the filtrate and paper to see which materials were retained by the paper. (Note: If the filtrate is blue, the copper sulfate passed. Check both the paper and filtrate for black particles to see if the charcoal passed. Finally, add Lugol's iodine to a 2 ml filtrate sample in a test tube. If the sample turns blue/black when iodine is added, starch is present in the filtrate.)

Passed: _____

Retained: _____

What does the filter paper represent? _____

During which counting interval was the filtration rate

greatest? _____

Explain: _____

_____

_____

_____

What characteristic of the three solutes determined whether or not they passed through the filter paper?

_____

_____

ACTIVE TRANSPORT

Whenever a cell expends cellular energy (ATP) to move substances across its boundaries, the process is referred to as an active transport process. Substances moved by active means are generally unable to pass by diffusion. They may be too large to pass through the pores; they may not be lipid-soluble; or they may have to move against rather than with a concentration gradient.

In one type of active transport, substances move across the membrane by combining with a protein carrier molecule; the process resembles an enzyme-substrate interaction. ATP is required, and in many cases the substances move against concentration or electrochemical gradients or both. Some of the substances that are moved into the cells by such carriers (commonly called **solute pumps**) are amino acids and some sugars. Neither solute is lipid-soluble, and both are too large to pass through the pores but are necessary for cell life. On the other hand, sodium ions (Na^+) are moved out of cells by active transport. There is more Na^+ outside the cell than there is inside, so the Na^+ tends to remain in the cell unless actively transported out. Pinocytosis and phagocytosis also require ATP.

In **pinocytosis** (cell drinking), the cell membrane seems to sink beneath the material to form a small vesicle, which then pinches off into the cell interior (see Figure 5.4). Pinocytosis is most common for taking in liquids containing protein or fat.

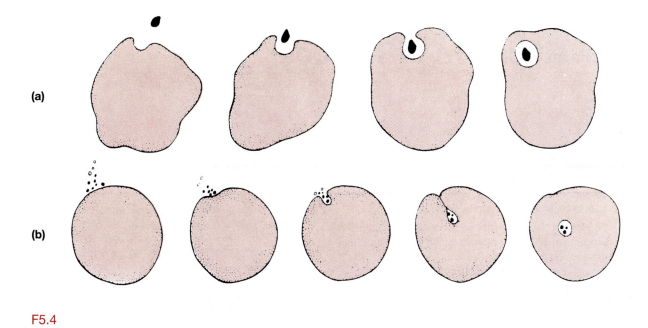

Phagocytosis and pinocytosis. (a) In phagocytosis, extensions of the plasma membrane (pseudopodia) flow around the external particle and enclose it within a vacuole. (b) In pinocytosis, dissolved proteins gather on the surface of the cell membrane, causing the membrane to invaginate and to incorporate the protein.

Pinocytotic Vesicles   # 09121

In **phagocytosis** (cell eating), parts of the plasma membrane flow around a relatively large or solid material (for example, bacteria or cell debris) and engulf it, enclosing it within a sac (Figure 5.4). The contents of the phagocytic vesicle are then digested by fusion with a lysosome. This is a rather uncommon phenomenon in the human body except for certain phagocytic or scavenger cells, such as some white blood cells and macrophages.

 1.   Obtain a drop of starved *Amoeba proteus* culture and place it on a coverslip. Add a drop of *Tetrahymena pyriformis* culture (an amoeba "meal") to the amoeba-containing drop, and then quickly but gently invert the coverslip over the well of a depression slide.

2.   Locate an amoeba under low power. Keep the light as dim as possible; otherwise the amoeba will "ball up" and begin to disintegrate.

3.   Observe as the amoeba phagocytizes the *Tetrahymena* by forming pseudopods that engulf it. In unicellular organisms like the amoeba, phagocytosis is an important food-getting mechanism, but in higher organisms, it is more important as a protective device, as noted above.

4.   Return all equipment to the appropriate supply areas and rinse glassware used.

Classification of Tissues

1. To name the four major types of tissues in the human body and the major subcategories of each.

2. To identify the tissue subcategories through microscopic inspection or inspection of an appropriate diagram or projected slide.

3. To state the location of the various tissue types in the body.

4. To state the general functions and structural characteristics of each of the four major tissue types.

Compound microscope
Prepared slides of simple squamous, simple cuboidal, simple columnar, stratified squamous (nonkeratinized), stratified cuboidal, stratified columnar, pseudostratified ciliated columnar, and transitional epithelium
Prepared slides of mesenchyme; of adipose, areolar, reticular, and dense (both regular [tendon] and irregular [dermis]) connective tissues; of elastic connective tissue (in wall of large artery); of hyaline and elastic cartilage; of fibrocartilage; of bone (cross section); and of blood
Prepared slides of skeletal, cardiac, and smooth muscle (longitudinal sections)
Prepared slide of nervous tissue (spinal cord smear)

Exercise 4 describes cells as the building blocks of life and the all-inclusive functional units of unicellular organisms. But in higher organisms cells do not ordinarily operate as isolated, independent entities. In humans and other multicellular organisms, cells depend on one another and cooperate to maintain homeostasis in the body.

With a few exceptions (parthenogenic organisms), even the most complex animal starts out as a single cell, the fertilized egg, which divides almost endlessly. The trillions of cells that result become specialized for a particular function; some become supportive bone, others the transparent lens of the eye, still others skin cells, and so on. Thus a division of labor exists, with certain groups of cells highly specialized to perform functions that benefit the organism as a whole.

Cell specialization brings about great sophistication of achievement but carries with it certain hazards. When a small specific group of cells is indispensable, any inability to function on its part can paralyze or destroy the entire body. For example, the action of the heart depends on a highly differentiated group of cells in the heart muscle. If they cease functioning, the heart no longer operates efficiently and the whole body suffers or dies from lack of oxygen. The jack-of-all-trades amoeba faces no such danger.

Groups of cells that are similar in structure and function are called **tissues.** The four primary tissue types—epithelium, connective tissue, nervous tissue, and muscle—have distinctive structures, patterns, and functions. The four primary tissues are further divided into subcategories.

To perform specific body functions, the tissues are organized into such **organs** as the heart, kidneys, and lungs. Most organs contain several representatives of the primary tissues, and the arrangement of these tissues determines the organ's structure and function. Thus **histology,** the study of tissues, complements a study of gross anatomy and provides the structural basis for a study of organ physiology.

The main objective of this exercise is to familiarize you with the major similarities and dissimilarities of the primary tissues, so that when the tissue makeup of an organ is described, you will be able to more easily understand (and perhaps even predict) the organ's major function. Because epithelium and some types of connective tissue will not be considered again, they are emphasized more than muscle, nervous tissue, and bone (a connective tissue), which are covered in more depth in later exercises.

EPITHELIAL TISSUE

Epithelial tissue, or **epithelium,** covers surfaces, and since glands almost invariably develop from epithelial membranes, they too are logically classed as epithelium. Epithelium covers the external body surface (as the epidermis), lines its cavities and tubules, and composes the

(a)

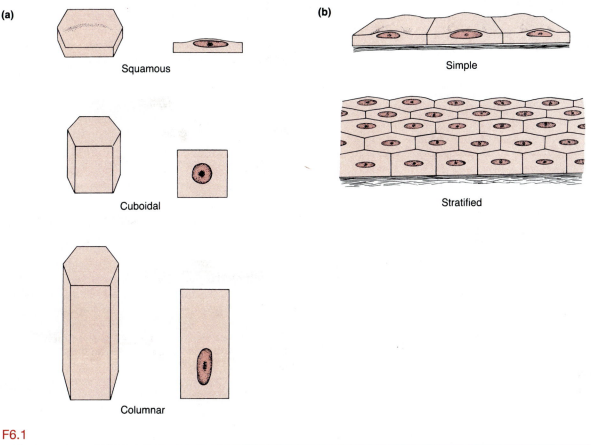

Squamous

Cuboidal

Columnar

(b)

Simple

Stratified

F6.1

Classification of epithelia. (a) Classification on the basis of cell shape. For each category, a whole cell is shown on the left and a longitudinal section is shown on the right. (b) Classification on the basis of arrangement (relative number of layers).

various endocrine (hormone-producing) and exocrine glands of the body.

Epithelial functions include protection, absorption, filtration, and secretion. For example, the epithelium covering the body protects against bacterial invasion and chemical damage; that lining the respiratory tract is ciliated to sweep dust and other foreign particles away from the lungs. Epithelium specialized to absorb substances lines the stomach and small intestine. In the kidney tubules, the epithelium absorbs, secretes, and filters. Secretion is a specialty of the glands.

Epithelium generally exhibits the following characteristics:

- Cells fit closely together to form membranes, or sheets of cells, and are bound together by specialized junctions.
- The membranes always have one free surface, called the *apical surface.*
- The cells are attached to an adhesive **basement membrane,** an amorphous material secreted partly by the epithelial cells (*basal lamina*) and connective tissue cells (*reticular lamina*) that lie adjacent to each other.

- Epithelial tissues have no blood supply of their own (are avascular), but depend on diffusion of nutrients from the underlying connective tissue.
- If well nourished, epithelial cells can easily regenerate themselves. This is an important characteristic because many epithelia are subjected to a good deal of friction.

The covering and lining epithelia are classified according to two criteria—cell shape and arrangement or relative number of layers (Figure 6.1). **Squamous** (scalelike), **cuboidal** (cubelike), and **columnar** (column-shaped) epithelial cells are the general types based on shape. On the basis of arrangement, there are **simple** epithelia, consisting of one layer of cells attached to the basement membrane, and **stratified** epithelia, consisting of more than one layer of cells. The terms denoting shape and arrangement of the epithelial cells are combined to describe the epithelium fully. *Stratified epithelia are named according to the cells at the apical surface of the epithelial membrane,* not those resting on the basement membrane.

There are, in addition, two less easily categorized types of epithelia. **Pseudostratified epithelium** is actually a simple columnar epithelium (one layer of cells),

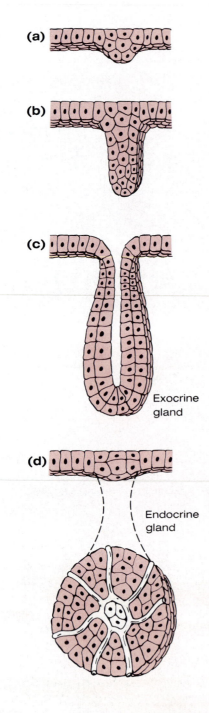

(a)

(b)

(c)

Exocrine
gland

(d)

Endocrine
gland

F6.2

Formation of endocrine and exocrine glands from epithelial sheets. (a) Epithelial cells grow and push into the underlying tissue. (b) A cord of epithelial cells forms. (c) In an exocrine gland, a lumen (cavity) forms. The inner cells form the duct, the outer cells produce the secretion. (d) In the formation of an endocrine gland, the connecting cells forming the duct atrophy, leaving the secretory cells with no connection to the epithelial surface. However, they do become heavily invested with blood and lymphatic vessels that receive the secretions.

but because its cells extend varied distances from the basement membrane, it gives the false appearance of being stratified. This epithelium is often ciliated. **Transitional epithelium** is a rather peculiar stratified squamous epithelium formed of rounded, or "plump," cells with the ability to slide over one another to allow the organ to be stretched. Transitional epithelium is found only in urinary system organs subjected to periodic distension, such as the bladder. The superficial cells are flattened (like true squamous cells) when the organ is distended and rounded when the organ is empty.

The most common types of epithelia, their most common locations in the body, and their functions are described in Figure 6.3.

Epithelial cells forming glands are highly specialized to remove materials from the blood and to manufacture them into new materials, which they then secrete. There are two types of glands, as shown in Figure 6.2. **Endocrine glands** lose their surface connection (duct) as they develop; thus they are referred to as ductless glands. Their secretions (all hormones) are extruded directly into the blood or the lymphatic vessels that weave through the glands. **Exocrine glands** retain their ducts, and their secretions empty through these ducts to an epithelial surface. The exocrine glands—including the sweat and oil glands, liver, and pancreas—are both external and internal; they will be discussed in conjunction with the organ systems to which their products are functionally related.

 Obtain slides of simple squamous, simple cuboidal, simple columnar, stratified squamous (nonkeratinized), pseudostratified ciliated columnar, stratified cuboidal, stratified columnar, and transitional epithelia. Examine each carefully, and notice how the epithelial cells fit closely together to form intact sheets of cells, a necessity for a tissue that forms linings or covering membranes. Compare your observations with the photomicrographs in Figure 6.3. Scan each epithelial type for modifications for specific functions, such as cilia (motile cell projections that help to move substances along the cell surface), and microvilli, which increase the surface area for absorption. Also be alert for goblet cells, which secrete lubricating mucus (see Plate 1 of the Histology Atlas).

While working, check the questions in the laboratory review section for this exercise. A number of the questions there refer to some of the observations you are asked to make during your microscopic study.

Epithelium, Simple Cuboidal	# 12454	‖‖‖‖‖‖‖
Epithelium, Pseudostratified	# 12456	‖‖‖‖‖‖‖
Epithelium, Stratified Squamous	# 12455	‖‖‖‖‖‖‖

(text continues on p. 47)

(a) Simple squamous epithelium

Description: Single layer of flattened cells with disc-shaped central nuclei and sparse cytoplasm; the simplest of the epithelia.

Location: Air sacs of lungs; kidney glomeruli; lining of heart, blood vessels, and lymphatic vessels; lining of ventral body cavity (serosae).

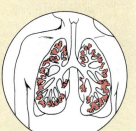

Function: Allows passage of materials by diffusion and filtration in sites where protection is not important; secretes lubricating substances in serosae.

Photomicrograph: Simple squamous epithelium forming walls of alveoli (air sacs) of the lung (280×).

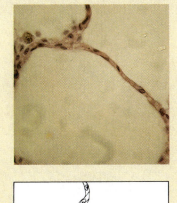

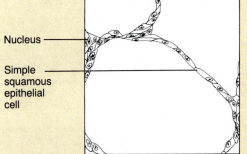

Nucleus

Simple squamous epithelial cell

(b) Simple cuboidal epithelium

Description: Single layer of cubelike cells with large, spherical central nuclei.

Location: Kidney tubules; ducts and secretory portions of small glands; ovary surface.

Function: Secretion and absorption.

Photomicrograph: Simple cuboidal epithelium in kidney tubules (260X)

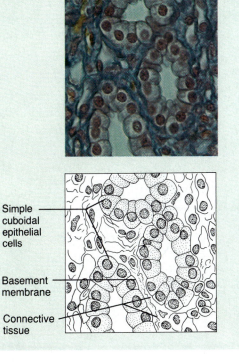

Simple cuboidal epithelial cells

Basement membrane

Connective tissue

Epithelial tissues. Simple epithelia (a and b).

(c) Simple columnar epithelium

Description: Single layer of tall cells with *oval* nuclei; some cells bear cilia; layer may contain mucus-secreting glands (goblet cells).

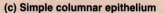

Location: Nonciliated type lines most of the digestive tract (stomach to anal canal), gallbladder and excretory ducts of some glands; ciliated variety lines small bronchi, uterine tubes, and some regions of the uterus.

Function: Absorption; secretion of mucus, enzymes, and other substances; ciliated type propels mucus (or reproductive cells) by ciliary action.

Photomicrograph: Simple columnar epithelium of the stomach mucosa (280×).

Connective tissue

Simple columnar epithelial cell

Basement membrane

(d) Pseudostratified columnar epithelium

Description: Single layer of cells of differing heights, some not reaching the free surface; nuclei seen at different levels; may contain goblet cells and bear cilia.

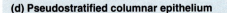

Location: Nonciliated type in ducts of large glands, parts of male urethra; ciliated variety lines the trachea, most of the upper respiratory tract.

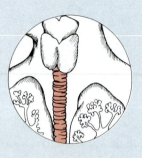

Function: Secretion, particularly of mucus; propulsion of mucus by ciliary action.

Photomicrograph: Pseudostratified ciliated columnar epithelium lining the human trachea (430×).

Cilia

Pseudo-stratified epithelial layer

Basement membrane

Connective tissue

F6.3 *(continued)*

Simple epithelia (c and d).

(e) Stratified squamous epithelium

Description: Thick membrane composed of several cell layers; basal cells are cuboidal or columnar and metabolically active; surface cells are flattened (squamous); in the keratinized type, the surface cells are full of keratin and dead; basal cells are active in mitosis and produce the cells of the more superficial layers.

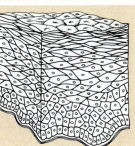

Location: Nonkeratinized type forms the moist linings of the esophagus, mouth, and vagina; keratinized variety forms the epidermis of the skin, a dry membrane.

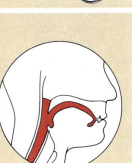

Function: Protects underlying tissues in areas subjected to abrasion.

Photomicrograph: Stratified squamous epithelium lining of the esophagus (173×).

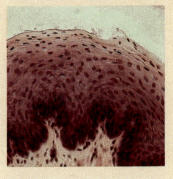

Stratified squamous epithelium —

Nuclei

Basement membrane

Connective tissue

(f) Stratified cuboidal epithelium

Description: Generally two layers of cube-like cells.

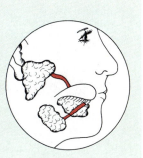

Location: Largest ducts of sweat glands, mammary glands, and salivary glands.

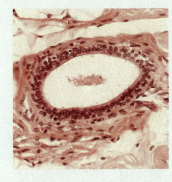

Function: Protection.

Photomicrograph: Stratified cuboidal epithelium forming a salivary gland duct (400×).

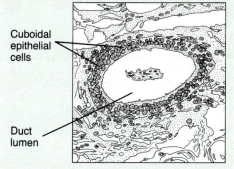

Cuboidal epithelial cells

Duct lumen

F6.3 *(continued)*

Stratified epithelia (e and f).

(g) Stratified columnar epithelium

Description: Several cell layers; basal cells usually cuboidal; superficial cells elongated and columnar.

Location: Rare in the body; small amounts in male urethra and in large ducts of some glands.

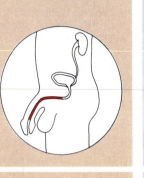

Function: Protection; secretion.

Photomicrograph: Stratified columnar epithelium lining of the male urethra (360×).

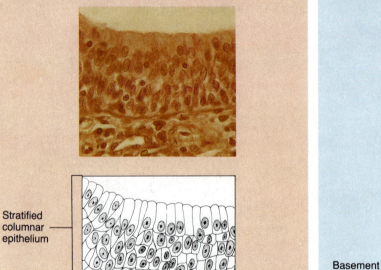

Stratified columnar epithelium

Underlying connective tissue

Basement membrane

(h) Transitional epithelium

Description: Resembles both stratified squamous and stratified cuboidal; basal cells cuboidal or columnar; surface cells dome-shaped or squamous-like, depending on degree of organ stretch.

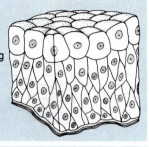

Location: Lines the ureters, bladder, and part of the urethra.

Function: Stretches readily and permits distension of urinary organ by contained urine.

Photomicrograph: Transitional epithelium lining of the bladder, relaxed state (170×); note the bulbous, or rounded, appearance of the cells at the surface; these cells flatten and become elongated when the bladder is filled with urine.

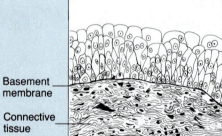

Basement membrane

Connective tissue

Transitional epithelium

F6.3 (continued)

Stratified epithelia (g and h).

CONNECTIVE TISSUE

Connective tissue is found in all parts of the body as discrete structures or as part of various body organs. It is the most abundant and widely distributed of the tissue types.

The connective tissues perform a variety of functions, but they primarily protect, support, and bind together other tissues of the body. For example, bones are composed of connective tissue (**bone** or **osseous tissue**), and they protect and support other body tissues and organs. The ligaments and tendons (**dense connective tissue**) bind the bones together or bind skeletal muscles to bones.

Areolar connective tissue is a soft packaging material that cushions and protects body organs. Fat (**adipose**) tissue provides insulation for the body tissues and a source of stored food. Blood-forming (**hematopoietic**) tissue replenishes the body's supply of red blood cells. In addition, connective tissue also serves a vital function in the repair of all body tissues since many wounds are repaired by connective tissue in the form of scar tissue.

The characteristics of connective tissue include the following:

- With a few exceptions (cartilages, tendons, and ligaments), connective tissues are well vascularized.
- Connective tissues are composed of many types of cells.
- There is a great deal of noncellular, nonliving material (matrix) between the cells of connective tissue.

The nonliving material between the cells—the **extracellular matrix**—deserves a bit more explanation. It is produced by the cells and then extruded. The matrix is primarily responsible for the strength associated with connective tissue, but there is variation. At one extreme, hematopoietic and adipose tissues are composed mostly of cells. At the opposite extreme, bone and cartilage have very few cells and large amounts of matrix.

The matrix has two components—ground substance and fibers. The **ground substance** is composed chiefly of glycoproteins and large charged polysaccharide molecules. Depending on its specific composition, the ground substance may be liquid, semisolid, gel-like, or very hard. When the matrix is firm, as in cartilage and bone, the connective tissue cells reside in cavities in the matrix called *lacunae*. The fibers include **collagenic** (white) **fibers, elastic** (yellow) **fibers,** and **reticular** (fine collagenic) **fibers.** Of these, the collagen fibers are most abundant.

Generally speaking, the ground substance functions as a molecular sieve, or medium through which nutrients and other dissolved substances can diffuse between the blood capillaries and the cells. The fibers in the matrix hinder diffusion somewhat and make the ground substance less pliable. The characteristic durability and strength of the various connective tissues depend on the relative firmness of their ground substance and the number and kinds of fibers deposited in it.

There are four main types of adult connective tissue, all of which typically have large amounts of matrix. These are connective tissue proper (which includes areolar, adipose, reticular, and dense [fibrous] connective tissues), cartilage, bone, and blood. All of these derive from an embryonic tissue called *mesenchyme*. Figure 6.4 lists the general characteristics, location, and function of some of the connective tissues found in the body.

Obtain prepared slides of mesenchyme; of adipose, areolar, reticular, dense regular and irregular connective tissue; of elastic connective tissue; of hyaline and elastic cartilage and fibrocartilage; and of osseous connective tissue (bone). Compare your observations with the views in Figure 6.4.

Distinguish between the living cells and the matrix and pay particular attention to the denseness and arrangement of the matrix. For example, notice how the matrix of the dense fibrous connective tissues, making up tendons and the dermis of the skin, is chock full of collagenic fibers, and that in the regular variety (tendon), the fibers are all running in the same direction, whereas in the dermis they appear to be running in many directions.

While examining the areolar connective tissue, a soft "packing tissue," notice how much empty space there appears to be, and distinguish between the collagen fibers and the coiled elastic fibers. Also, try to locate a **mast cell,** which has large darkly staining granules in its cytoplasm. This cell type releases histamine that makes capillaries quite permeable during inflammatory reactions and allergies and thus is partially responsible for that "runny nose" of allergies.

In adipose tissue, locate a cell (signet ring cell) in which the nucleus can be seen pushed to one side by the large fat-filled vacuole which appears to be a large empty space, and notice how little matrix there is in fat or adipose tissue.

Distinguish between the living cells and the matrix in the dense fibrous, bone, and hyaline cartilage preparations.

Collagen Fibers, Loose CT	# 14550
Elastic Fibers In Loose CT	# 14553
Fibroblast, Collagen Scanning EM	# 14556
Tissue, Reticular	# 12459
AdiposeTissue (White Fat)	# 14568

(text continues on p. 54)

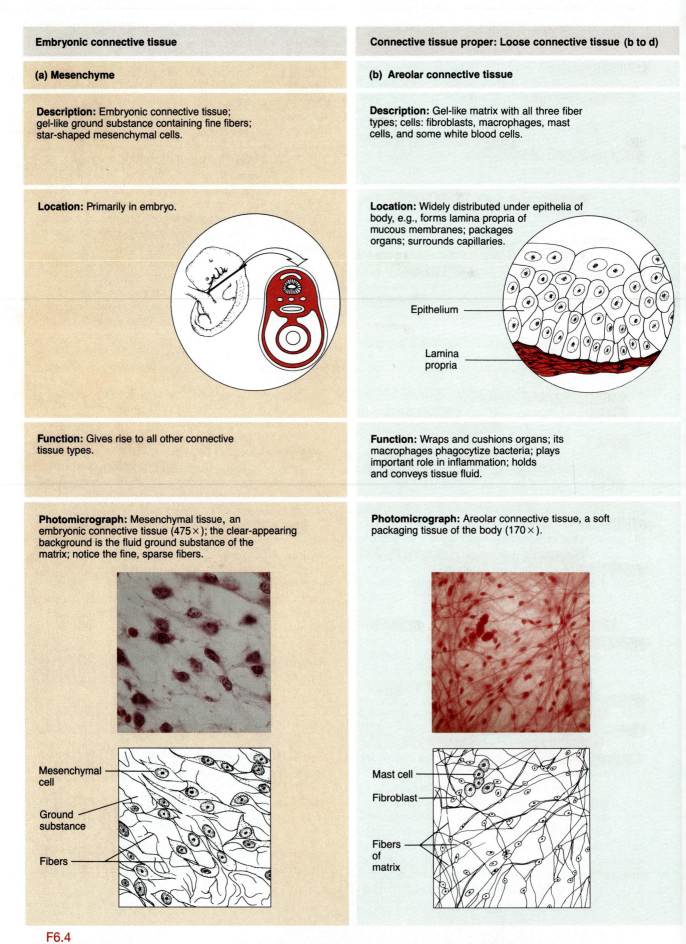

Embryonic connective tissue

(a) Mesenchyme

Description: Embryonic connective tissue; gel-like ground substance containing fine fibers; star-shaped mesenchymal cells.

Location: Primarily in embryo.

Function: Gives rise to all other connective tissue types.

Photomicrograph: Mesenchymal tissue, an embryonic connective tissue (475×); the clear-appearing background is the fluid ground substance of the matrix; notice the fine, sparse fibers.

Mesenchymal cell

Ground substance

Fibers

Connective tissue proper: Loose connective tissue (b to d)

(b) Areolar connective tissue

Description: Gel-like matrix with all three fiber types; cells: fibroblasts, macrophages, mast cells, and some white blood cells.

Location: Widely distributed under epithelia of body, e.g., forms lamina propria of mucous membranes; packages organs; surrounds capillaries.

Epithelium

Lamina propria

Function: Wraps and cushions organs; its macrophages phagocytize bacteria; plays important role in inflammation; holds and conveys tissue fluid.

Photomicrograph: Areolar connective tissue, a soft packaging tissue of the body (170×).

Mast cell

Fibroblast

Fibers of matrix

F6.4

Connective tissues.

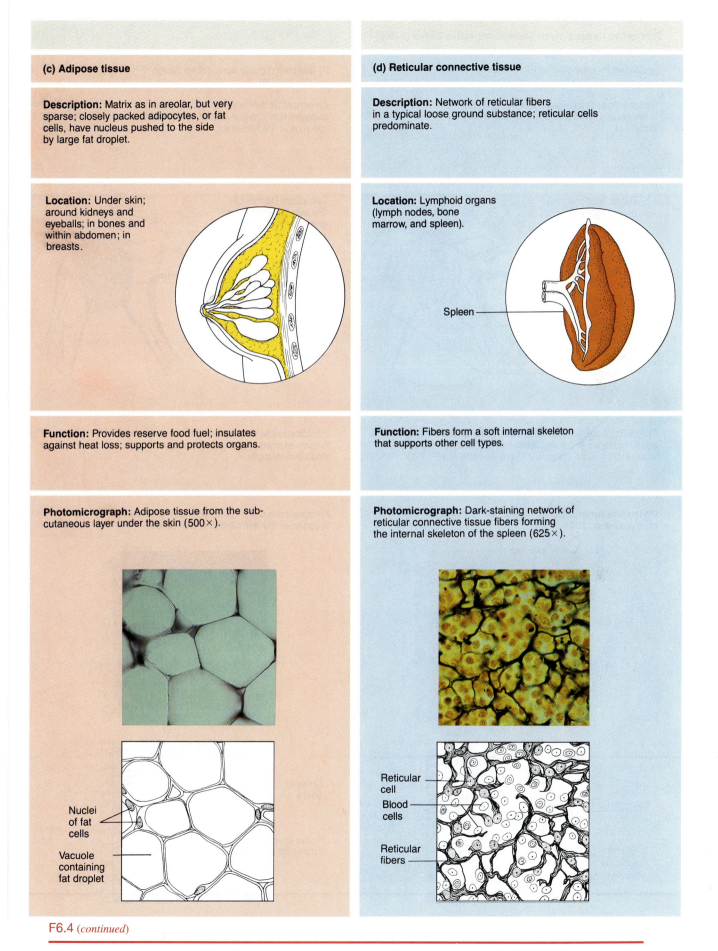

(c) Adipose tissue

Description: Matrix as in areolar, but very sparse; closely packed adipocytes, or fat cells, have nucleus pushed to the side by large fat droplet.

Location: Under skin; around kidneys and eyeballs; in bones and within abdomen; in breasts.

Function: Provides reserve food fuel; insulates against heat loss; supports and protects organs.

Photomicrograph: Adipose tissue from the subcutaneous layer under the skin (500×).

Nuclei of fat cells

Vacuole containing fat droplet

(d) Reticular connective tissue

Description: Network of reticular fibers in a typical loose ground substance; reticular cells predominate.

Location: Lymphoid organs (lymph nodes, bone marrow, and spleen).

Spleen

Function: Fibers form a soft internal skeleton that supports other cell types.

Photomicrograph: Dark-staining network of reticular connective tissue fibers forming the internal skeleton of the spleen (625×).

Reticular cell

Blood cells

Reticular fibers

F6.4 (continued)

Tendon, Dense Regular CT	# 14563								
Cartilage, Hyaline	# 12460								
Elastic Cartilage, Normal	# 14636								
Cartilage, Fibrous	# 44443								

MUSCLE TISSUE

Muscle tissue is highly specialized to contract (shorten) in order to produce movement of some body parts. As you might expect, muscle cells tend to be quite elongated, providing a long axis for contraction. The three basic types of muscle tissue are described briefly here; skeletal muscle is treated more completely in a later exercise.

Skeletal muscle, the "meat," or flesh, of the body, is attached to the skeleton. It is under voluntary control (consciously controlled), and its contraction moves the limbs and other external body parts. The cells of skeletal muscles are long, cylindrical, and multinucleate (several nuclei per cell); they have obvious *striations* (stripes).

Cardiac muscle is found only in the heart. As it contracts, the heart acts as a pump, propelling the blood through the blood vessels. Cardiac muscle, like skeletal muscle, has striations. But cardiac cells are branching uninucleate (or occasionally binucleate) cells that interdigitate (fit together) at tight junctions called **intercalated discs.** These structures allow the cardiac muscle to act as a unit. Cardiac muscle is under involuntary control, which means that we cannot voluntarily or consciously control the operation of the heart.

Smooth muscle, or *visceral muscle,* is found in the walls of hollow organs and blood vessels. Typically there are two layers that run at right angles to each other; consequently its contraction can constrict or dilate the lumen (cavity) of an organ and propel substances along predetermined pathways. Smooth muscle cells are quite different in appearance from those of skeletal or cardiac muscle. No striations are visible, and the uninucleate smooth muscle cells are spindle-shaped.

 Obtain and examine prepared slides of skeletal, cardiac, and smooth muscle. Notice their similarities and dissimilarities in both your observations and in the illustrations in Figure 6.5.

| Skeletal Muscle | # 14614 | ||||||| |
| Smooth Muscle,
Normal | # 14620 | ||||||| |

(a) Skeletal muscle

Description: Long, cylindrical, multinucleate cells; obvious striations.

Location: In skeletal muscles attached to bones or occasionally to skin.

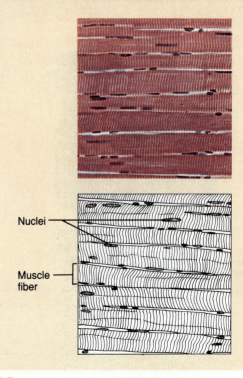

Function: Voluntary movement; locomotion; manipulation of the environment; facial expression. Voluntary control.

Photomicrograph: Skeletal muscle (approx. 30x). Notice the obvious banding pattern and the fact that these large cells are multinucleate.

Nuclei

Muscle fiber

F6.5

Muscle tissues.

(b) Cardiac muscle

Description: Branching, striated, generally uninucleate cells that interdigitate at specialized junctions (intercalated discs).

Location: The walls of the heart.

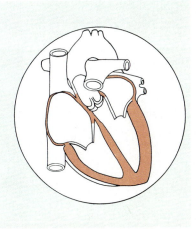

Function: As it contracts, it propels blood into the circulation; involuntary control.

Photomicrograph: Cardiac muscle (250x); notice the striations, branching of fibers, and the intercalated discs.

Inter-calated disc

Nucleus

(c) Smooth muscle

Description: Spindle-shaped cells with central nuclei; cells arranged closely to form sheets; no striations.

Location: Mostly in the walls of hollow organs.

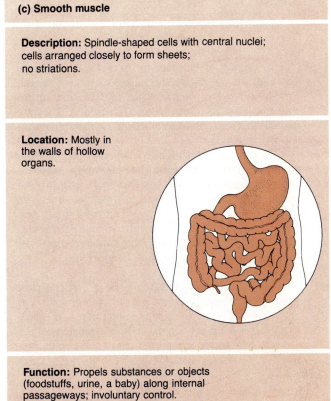

Function: Propels substances or objects (foodstuffs, urine, a baby) along internal passageways; involuntary control.

Photomicrograph: Sheet of smooth muscle (approx. 300x).

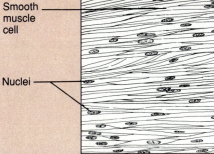

Smooth muscle cell

Nuclei

F6.5 *(continued)*

NERVOUS TISSUE

Nervous tissue is composed of two major cell populations. The **neuroglia** are special supporting cells that protect, support, and insulate the more delicate neurons. The **neurons** are highly specialized to receive stimuli (irritability) and to conduct waves of excitation, or impulses, to all parts of the body (conductivity). They are the cells that are most often associated with nervous system functioning.

The structure of neurons is markedly different from that of all other body cells. They all have a nucleus–containing cell body, and their cytoplasm is drawn out into long extensions (axons and dendrites)—sometimes as long as 3 feet (about 1 m), which allows a single neuron to conduct an impulse over relatively long distances. More detail about the anatomy of the different classes of neurons and neuroglia appears in Exercise 17.

Obtain a prepared slide of a spinal cord smear. Locate a neuron and compare it to Figure 6.6. Keep the light dim—this will help you see the cellular extensions of the neurons. Also see plates 4 and 5 in the histology atlas.

Dendrite, Neuron   # 00612
in Cerebral Cortex

Astrocyte,   # 14588
Glial Cells

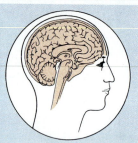

Description: Neurons are branching cells; cell processes that may be quite long extend from the nucleus-containing cell body; also contributing to nervous tissue are nonirritable supporting cells (not illustrated).

Cell body

Neuron

Location: Brain, spinal cord, and nerves.

Function: Transmit electrical signals from sensory receptors and to effectors (muscles and glands) which control their activity.

Photomicrograph: Neuron (170×).

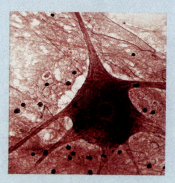

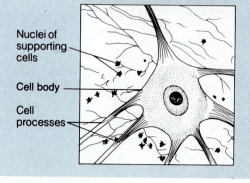

Nuclei of supporting cells

Cell body

Cell processes

F6.6

Nervous tissue.

The Integumentary System

The **skin,** or **integument,** is often considered an organ system because of its extent and complexity. It is much more than an external body covering; architecturally, the skin is a marvel. It is tough yet pliable, a characteristic that enables it to withstand constant insult from outside agents.

The skin has many functions, most (but not all) concerned with protection. It insulates and cushions the underlying body tissues and protects the entire body from mechanical damage (bumps and cuts), chemical damage (acids, alkalis, and the like), thermal damage (heat), and bacterial invasion (by virtue of its acid mantle and continuous surface). The hardened uppermost layer of the skin (the cornified layer) prevents water loss from the body surface. The skin's abundant capillary network (under the control of the nervous system) plays an important role in regulating heat loss from the body surface.

The skin has other functions as well. For example, it acts as a mini-excretory system; urea, salts, and water are lost through the skin pores in sweat. The skin is also the site of vitamin D synthesis for the body. Finally, the cutaneous sense organs are located in the dermis.

BASIC STRUCTURE OF THE SKIN

The skin has two distinct regions—the superficial *epidermis* composed of epithelium and an underlying connective tissue *dermis*. These layers are firmly "ce-

mented" together along an undulating border. But friction, such as the rubbing of a poorly fitting shoe, may cause them to separate, resulting in a blister. Immediately deep to the dermis is the **hypodermis** or **superficial fascia** (primarily adipose tissue), which is not considered part of the skin. The main skin areas and structures are described below.

As you read, locate the following structures on Figure 7.1 and on a skin model.

Skin, Model	# 11815	
Skin, Thick, Stratum Granulosa	# 20918	
Skin, Thick, Stratum Spinosum	# 20919	
Skin, Thick, Stratum Basalis	# 20920	
Skin, Thick, Stratum Corneum	# 20921	

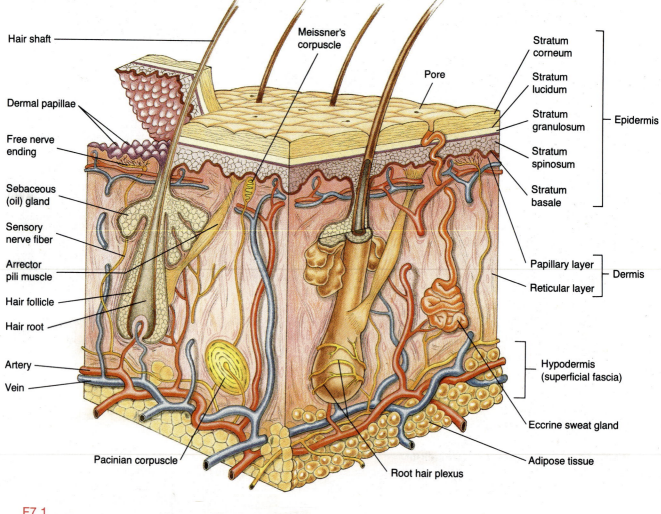

Hair shaft

Dermal papillae

Free nerve ending

Sebaceous (oil) gland

Sensory nerve fiber

Arrector pili muscle

Hair follicle

Hair root

Artery

Vein

Meissner's corpuscle

Pore

Stratum corneum

Stratum lucidum

Stratum granulosum

Stratum spinosum

Stratum basale

Epidermis

Papillary layer

Reticular layer

Dermis

Hypodermis (superficial fascia)

Eccrine sweat gland

Adipose tissue

Pacinian corpuscle

Root hair plexus

F7.1

Skin structure. Three-dimensional view of the skin and the underlying hypodermis. The epidermis and dermis have been pulled apart at the left corner to reveal the dermal papillae.

Epidermis

Structurally, the avascular epidermis is a keratinized stratified squamous epithelium consisting of 4 distinct cell types and 4 or 5 distinct layers.

CELLS OF THE EPIDERMIS   Most epidermal cells are **keratinocytes** (literally, keratin cells), epithelial cells that function mainly to produce keratin fibrils. **Keratin** is a fibrous protein that gives the epidermis its durability and protective capabilities.

Far less abundant are the following types of epidermal cells (Figure 7.2):

- **Melanocytes**—spidery black cells that produce the brown-to-black pigment called **melanin.** The skin tans because melanin production increases when the skin is exposed to sunlight. The melanin provides a protective pigment umbrella over the nuclei of the cells in the deeper epidermal layers, thus shielding their genetic material (DNA) from the damaging ef-

fects of ultraviolet radiation. A concentration of melanin in one spot is called a *freckle.*
- **Langerhans cells**—phagocytic cells (macrophages) that play a role in immunity.
- **Merkel cells**—in conjunction with sensory nerve endings, Merkel cells form sensitive touch receptors called *Merkel discs.*

LAYERS OF THE EPIDERMIS   From deep to superficial, the layers of the epidermis are the stratum basale, stratum spinosum, stratum granulosum, stratum lucidum, and stratum corneum (Figure 7.1).

The **stratum basale** (basal layer) is a single row of cells immediately adjacent to the dermis. Its cells are constantly undergoing mitotic cell division to produce millions of new cells daily, hence its alternate name *stratum germinativum.* About a quarter of the cells in this stratum are melanocytes, whose processes thread their way through this and the adjacent layers of keratinocytes (see Figure 7.2).

The **stratum spinosum** (spiny layer) is a stratum consisting of several cell layers immediately superficial to the basal layer. Its cells contain *tonofilaments,* thick bundles of intermediate filaments made of keratin protein. The stratum spinosum cells appear spiky (hence their name) because they shrink but their desmosomes hold tight as the skin tissue is prepared for histological examination. Cells divide fairly rapidly in this stratum, but less so than in the stratum basale. Cells in the basal and spiny layers are the only ones to receive adequate nourishment (via diffusion of nutrients from the dermis). So as their daughter cells are pushed upward and away from the source of nutrition, they gradually die.

The **stratum granulosum** (granular layer) is a thin layer named for the abundant granules its cells contain. These granules are of two types: (1) *laminated granules,* which contain a waterproofing lipid that is secreted into the extracellular space; and (2) *keratohyalin granules,* which combine with the tonofilaments in the more superficial layers to form the keratin fibrils. At the upper border of this layer, the cells are beginning to die.

The **stratum lucidum** (clear layer) is a very thin translucent band of flattened cells. It is not present in thin skin. The outermost epidermal layer, the **stratum corneum** (horny layer), consists of some 20 to 30 cell layers, and accounts for the bulk of the epidermal thickness. Cells in this layer, like those in the stratum lucidum (where it exists), are dead and their flattened scale-like remnants are fully keratinized. They are constantly rubbing off and being replaced by division of the deeper cells.

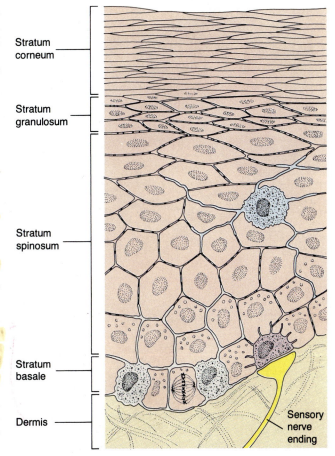

Stratum corneum

Stratum granulosum

Stratum spinosum

Stratum basale

Dermis

Sensory nerve ending

Dermis

The dense irregular connective tissue making up the dermis consists of two principal regions—the papillary and reticular areas. Like the epidermis, the dermis varies in thickness. For example, the skin is particularly thick on the palms of the hands and soles of the feet and is quite thin on the eyelids.

The **papillary layer** is the more superficial dermal region. It is very uneven and has fingerlike projections from its superior surface, the **dermal papillae,** which attach it to the epidermis above. These projections produce unique patterns of ridges that remain unchanged throughout life, which are reflected in fingerprints. Abundant capillary networks in the papillary layer furnish nutrients for the epidermal layers and allow heat to radiate to the skin surface. The pain and touch receptors (Meissner's corpuscles) are also found here.

The **reticular layer** is the deepest skin layer. It contains many arteries and veins, sweat and sebaceous glands, and pressure receptors.

Both the papillary and reticular layers are heavily invested with collagenic and elastic fibers. The elastic fibers give skin its exceptional elasticity in youth, but in old age, their number decreases and the subcutaneous layer loses fat, which leads to wrinkling and inelasticity of the skin. Fibroblasts, adipose cells, various types of macrophages (which are important in the body's defense), and other cell types are found throughout the dermis.

F7.2

Diagram showing the main features—layers and relative numbers of the different cell types—in epidermis of thin skin. The keratinocytes (pink) form the bulk of the epidermis. Less numerous are the melanocytes (gray), which produce the pigment melanin; Langerhans cells (blue), which function as macrophages; and Merkel cells (purple). A sensory nerve ending (yellow), extending to the Merkel cell from the dermis, is depicted in association with the Merkel cell forming a Merkel disc (touch receptor). Notice that the keratinocytes, but not the other cell types, are joined by numerous desmosomes.

The dermis has an abundant blood supply, which allows it to play a role in the regulation of body temperature. When body temperature is high, the arterioles dilate, and the capillary network of the dermis becomes engorged with the heated blood. Thus body heat is allowed to radiate from the skin surface. If the environment is cool and body heat must be conserved, the arterioles constrict so that blood bypasses the capillary networks.

Any restriction of the normal blood supply to the skin results in cell death and, if severe enough, skin

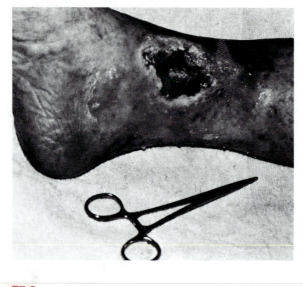

F7.3

A decubitus ulcer on the ankle of a patient.

ulcers (Figure 7.3). **Bedsores (decubitus ulcers)** occur in bedridden patients who are not turned regularly enough. The weight of the body exerts pressure on the skin, especially over bony projections, which leads to restriction of the blood supply and death of tissue. ■

The dermis is also richly provided with lymphatic vessels and a nerve supply. Many of the nerve endings bear highly specialized receptor organs that, when stimulated by environmental changes, transmit messages to the central nervous system for interpretation. Some of these receptors are shown in Figure 7.1. (These receptors are discussed in depth in Exercise 21.)

Skin Color

Skin color is a result of three factors—the relative amount of two pigments (melanin and carotene) and the degree of oxygenation of the blood. People who produce large amounts of melanin have brown-toned skin. In light-skinned people, who have less melanin, the dermal blood supply flushes through the rather transparent cell layers above, giving the skin a rosy glow. *Carotene* is a yellow-orange pigment present primarily in the stratum corneum and in the adipose tissue of the hypodermis.

Skin color may be an important diagnostic tool. For example, flushed skin may indicate hypertension, fever, or embarrassment, whereas pale skin is typically seen in anemic individuals. When the blood is inadequately oxygenated, as during asphyxiation and serious lung disease, the skin takes on a bluish or cyanotic cast. **Jaundice,** in which the tissues become yellowed, is almost always diagnostic for liver disease, whereas a bronzing of the skin hints that a person's adrenal cortex is hypoactive (**Addison's disease**). ■

APPENDAGES OF THE SKIN

The appendages of the skin—hair, nails, and cutaneous glands—are all derivatives of the epidermis, but they reside in the dermis. They originate from the stratum basale and grow downward into the deeper skin regions.

Cutaneous Glands

The cutaneous glands fall primarily into two categories: the sebaceous glands and the sweat glands. The **sebaceous glands** are found nearly all over the skin, with the exception of the palms of the hands and the soles of the feet. Their ducts usually empty into a hair follicle, but some open directly onto the skin surface.

The product of the sebaceous glands, called **sebum,** is a mixture of oily substances and fragmented cells. The sebum is a lubricant that keeps the skin soft and moist (a natural skin cream) and keeps the hair from becoming brittle. The sebaceous glands become particularly active during puberty; thus, the skin tends to become oilier during this period of life. *Blackheads* are accumulations of dried sebum and bacteria; *acne* is due to active infection of the sebaceous glands.

Epithelial openings, called pores, are the outlets for the **sweat (sudoriferous) glands.** These exocrine glands are widely distributed in the skin. Sweat glands are subcategorized on the basis of the composition of their secretions. The **eccrine glands,** which are distributed all over the body, produce clear perspiration, consisting primarily of water, salts (NaCl), and urea. The **apocrine glands,** found predominantly in the axillary and genital areas, secrete a milky protein-based substance (also containing water, salts, and urea) that is an excellent nutrient medium for microorganisms generally found on the skin.

The sweat glands, under the control of the nervous system, are an important part of the body's heat-regulating apparatus. They secrete perspiration when the external temperature or body temperature is high. When this water-based substance evaporates, it carries excess body heat with it. Thus evaporation of greater amounts of perspiration provides an efficient means of ridding the body of excess heat when the capillary cooling system is not sufficient or is unable to maintain body temperature homeostasis.

Skin, Thin,   # 15307
Apocrine Gland

Skin, Thin,   # 15309
Eccrine Gland

Hair

Hairs are found over the entire body surface, except for the palms of the hands, the soles of the feet, parts of the external genitalia, the nipples, and the lips. A hair, enclosed in a hair **follicle,** is also an epithelial structure.

The portion of the hair enclosed within the follicle is called the **root;** the portion projecting from the scalp surface is called the **shaft.** The hair is formed by mitosis of the well-nourished germinal epithelial cells at the basal end of the follicle (the hair **bulb**). As the daughter cells are pushed farther away from the growing region, they die and become keratinized; thus the bulk of the hair shaft, like the bulk of the epidermis, is dead material.

A hair consists of a central region (medulla) surrounded first by a protective cortex and then by the cuticle. Abrasion of the cuticle results in "split ends." Hair color is a manifestation of the amount and kind of melanin pigment within the hair cortex.

If you look carefully at the structure of the hair follicle (see Figure 7.1), you will see that it generally is slanted. Small bands of smooth muscle cells—**arrector pili**—connect each hair follicle to the papillary layer of the dermis. When these muscles contract (during cold or fright), the hair follicle (normally in a slanted position) is pulled upright, dimpling the skin surface with "goose bumps." This phenomenon is especially dramatic in a scared cat, whose fur actually stands on end to increase its apparent size. The activity of the arrector pili muscles also exerts pressure on the sebaceous glands surrounding the follicle, causing a small amount of sebum to be released.

Hair, Sebaceous Gland	# 44470
Nail, Epidermis Skin	# 44473

Nails

Nails, the hornlike derivatives of the epidermis, consist of a *free edge,* a *body* (visible attached portion), and a *root* (embedded in the skin and adhering to an epithelial **nail bed**).The borders of the nail are overlapped by skin folds called **nail folds;** the thick proximal nail fold is the **eponychium,** commonly called the cuticle (Figure 7.4).

The germinal cells in the **nail matrix,** the thickened proximal part of the nail bed, are responsible for nail growth. As the nail cells are produced by the matrix, they become heavily keratinized and die. Thus, nails, like hairs, are mostly nonliving material.

Nails are transparent and nearly colorless, but appear pink because of the blood supply in the underlying dermis. The exception to this is the proximal region of the thickened nail matrix which appears as a white crescent called the *lunula.* When someone is cyanotic due to a lack of oxygen in the blood, the nail beds take on a blue cast.

Identify the nail structures shown in Figure 7.4 on yourself or your lab partner.

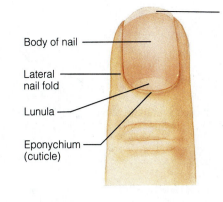

F7.4

Structure of a nail.

EXAMINATION OF THE MICROSCOPIC STRUCTURE OF THE SKIN

Obtain a prepared slide of human skin, and study it carefully under the microscope. Compare your tissue slide to the view shown in Figure 7.5, and identify as many of the structures diagrammed in Figure 7.1 as possible.

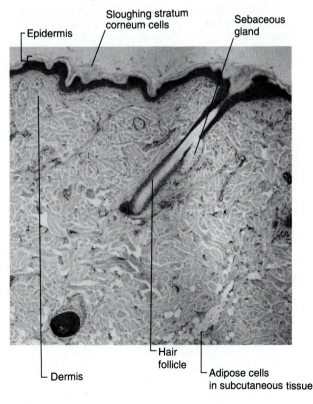

F7.5

Photomicrograph of skin (20×).

How is this stratified squamous epithelium different from that observed in Exercise 6?

_____

_____

How do these differences relate to the functions of these two similar epithelia?

_____

_____

_____

PLOTTING THE DISTRIBUTION OF SWEAT GLANDS

1. For this simple experiment you will need two squares of bond paper (each 1 cm × 1 cm), adhesive tape, and a beta-dine (iodine) swab *or* Lugol's iodine and a cotton-tipped swab. (The bond paper has been preruled in cm^2—just cut along the lines to obtain the required squares.)

2. Paint the medial aspect of your left palm (avoid the crease lines) and a region of your left forearm with the iodine solution, and allow it to dry thoroughly. The painted area in each case should be slightly larger than the paper squares to be used.

3. Have your lab partner *securely* tape a square of bond paper over each iodine-painted area, and leave them in place for 20 minutes. (If it is very warm in the laboratory while this test is being conducted, good results may be obtained within 10 to 15 minutes.)

4. After 20 minutes, remove the paper squares, and count the number of blue-black dots on each square. The presence of a blue-black dot on the paper indicates an active sweat gland. (The iodine in the pore is dissolved in the sweat and reacts chemically with the starch in the bond paper to produce the blue-black color.) Thus "sweat maps" have been produced for the two skin areas.

5. Which skin area tested has the greater density of sweat glands?

_____

_____

Classification of Body Membranes

The body membranes, which cover surfaces, line body cavities, and form protective (and often lubricating) sheets around organs, fall into two major categories. These are the so-called *epithelial membranes* and the *synovial membranes*.

EPITHELIAL MEMBRANES

The term "epithelial membrane" is used in various ways. Here we will define an **epithelial membrane** as a simple organ consisting of an epithelial sheet bound to an underlying layer of connective tissue. Most of the covering and lining epithelia take part in forming one of the three common varieties of epithelial membranes: cutaneous, mucous, or serous.

The **cutaneous membrane** is the skin, a dry membrane with a keratinizing epithelium (the epidermis). Since the skin is discussed in some detail in Exercise 7, the mucous and serous membranes will receive our attention here.

Mucous Membranes

The **mucous membranes** (**mucosae**) are composed of epithelial cells resting on a layer of loose connective tissue called the **lamina propria.** They line all body cavities that open to the body exterior—the respiratory, digestive, and urinary tracts. All mucosae are "wet" membranes because they are continuously bathed by secretions (or, in the case of urinary tract mucosae, urine). Although mucous membranes often secrete mucus, this is not a requirement. The mucous membranes of both the digestive and respiratory tracts secrete mucus, but that of the urinary tract does not.

Using Plates 31 and 36 of the Histology Atlas as guides, examine a slide made from a cross section of the trachea and another of the small intestine. Draw the mucosa of each in the appropriate circle, and fully identify each epithelial type. Remember to look for the epithelial cells at the free surface, and search the epithelial sheets for goblet cells.

Goblet cells are columnar epithelial cells with a large mucus-containing vacuole (goblet) in the cytoplasm. Which of these mucous membranes contains goblet cells?

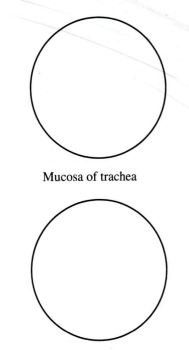

Mucosa of trachea

Mucosa of small intestine

How do the roles of these two mucous membranes differ?

_____

_____

_____

How are they the same?

_____

_____

_____

Would you say that mucous membranes have a high regenerative capacity? _____ Why or why not?

_____

_____

_____

Serous Membranes

The **serous membranes** (**serosae**) are also epithelial membranes. They are composed of a layer of simple squamous epithelium on a scant amount of loose connective tissue. The serous membranes generally occur in twos. The parietal layer lines a body cavity, and the visceral layer covers the outside of the organs in that cavity (see Figure 1.8, p. 8). In contrast to the mucous membranes, which line open body cavities, the serous membranes line body cavities that are closed to the exterior (with the exception of the female peritoneal cavity and the dorsal body cavity). The serosae secrete a thin fluid (serous fluid), which lubricates the organs and body walls and thus reduces friction as the organs slide across one another and against the body cavity walls. A serous membrane also lines the interior of blood vessels (endothelium) and the heart (endocardium). In capillaries, the entire wall is composed of serosa that serves as a selectively permeable membrane between the blood and the tissue fluid of the body.

 Examine a prepared slide of a serous membrane and diagram it in the circle provided here.

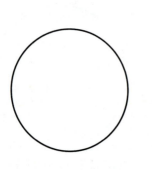

  What kind of cells that you have seen many times before are these shaped like?

_____

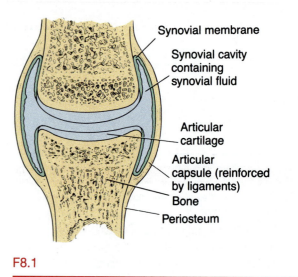

F8.1

A typical synovial joint.

What are the specific names of the serous membranes covering the heart and lining the cavity in which it resides (respectively)?

_____

The lungs and thoracic cavity (respectively)?

_____

The abdominal viscera and visceral cavity (respectively)?

_____

SYNOVIAL MEMBRANES

Synovial membranes, unlike the mucous and serous membranes, are composed entirely of connective tissue; they contain no epithelial cells. These membranes line the cavities surrounding the joints, providing a smooth surface and secreting a lubricating fluid. They also line smaller sacs of connective tissue (bursae) and tendon sheaths, both of which cushion structures moving against each other, as during muscle activity. Figure 8.1 illustrates the positioning of a synovial membrane in the joint cavity.

 If a freshly sawed beef joint is available, visually examine the interior surface of the joint capsule to observe the smooth texture of the synovial membrane.

Overview of the Skeleton: Classification and Structure of Bones and Cartilages

The skeleton is constructed of two of the most supportive tissues found in the human body—cartilage and bone. In embryos, the skeleton is predominantly composed of hyaline cartilage, but in the adult, most of the cartilage is replaced by more rigid bone. Cartilage persists only in such isolated areas as the bridge of the nose, the larynx, the trachea, the joints, and parts of the rib cage.

Besides supporting and protecting the body as an internal framework, the skeleton also provides a system of levers with which the skeletal muscles work to move the body. In addition, the bones store such substances as lipids and many minerals (most importantly calcium). Finally, the red marrow cavities of bones provide a site for hematopoiesis (blood cell formation).

The skeleton is made up of bones that are connected at joints, or articulations. The skeleton is subdivided into two divisions: the **axial skeleton** (those bones that lie around the body's center of gravity) and the **appendicular skeleton** (bones of the limbs, or appendages) (Figure 9.1).

Before beginning your study of the skeleton, imagine for a moment that your bones have turned to putty. What if you were running when this metamorphosis took place? Now imagine your bones forming a continuous metal framework within your body, somewhat like a network of plumbing pipes. What problems could you envision with this arrangement? These images should help you understand how well the skeletal system provides support and protection, as well as facilitating movement.

BONES: CLASSIFICATION AND MARKINGS

The 206 bones of the adult skeleton are composed of two basic kinds of osseous tissue that differ in their texture. **Compact** bone looks smooth and homogeneous; **spongy** (or *cancellous*) bone is composed of small spicules (bars) of bone and lots of open space.

Classification of Bones

Bones may be classified further on the basis of their relative gross anatomy into four groups: long, short, flat, and irregular bones.

Long bones, such as the femur, humerus, and metatarsals (see Figure 9.1), are generally longer than wide, consisting of a shaft with heads at either end. Long bones are composed predominantly of compact bone. **Short bones** are typically cube-shaped, and they contain more spongy bone than compact bone. See the tarsals and carpals in Figure 9.1.

Flat bones are generally thin and flattened, with two thin layers of compact bone sandwiching a layer of spongy bone between them. Although the name "flat bone" implies a structure that is level or horizontal, many flat bones are curved (for example, the bones of the skull). Bones that do not fall into one of the preceding categories are classified as **irregular bones.** The vertebrae are irregular bones (see Figure 9.1).

Some anatomists also recognize two other subcategories of bones. **Sesamoid bones** are small bones the spine (vertebrae); and (7) the cartilage supporting the external ear.

The skeletal cartilages consist of some variety of *cartilage tissue,* which typically consists primarily of water and is fairly resilient. Additionally, cartilage tissues are distinguished by the fact that they contain no nerves or blood vessels. Like bones, each cartilage is surrounded by a covering of dense connective tissue, called a *perichondrium* (rather than a periosteum). The perichondrium acts like a girdle to resist distortion of the cartilage when the cartilage is subjected to pressure. It also plays a role in the growth and repair of the cartilage.

Classification of Cartilage

The skeletal cartilages have representatives from each of the three cartilage tissue types—hyaline, elastic, and fibrocartilage. Although you have already studied cartilage tissues (Exercise 6), some of that information will be recapped briefly here. As you read through the descriptions of these cartilage types, keep in mind that the bulk of cartilage tissue consists of a nonliving *matrix* (containing a jellylike ground substance and fibers) secreted by chondrocytes.

Hyaline cartilage looks like frosted glass when viewed by the unaided eye. Its chondrocytes, snugly housed in lacunae, appear spherical (see Figure 6.4h, p. 51), and collagen fibers are the only fiber type in its matrix. Hyaline cartilage provides sturdy support with some resilience or "give." As easily seen in Figure 9.4, most skeletal cartilages are composed of hyaline cartilage.

Elastic cartilage can be envisioned as "hyaline cartilage with more elastic fibers" (see Figure 6.4i, p. 52). Consequently, it is much more flexible than hyaline cartilage and it tolerates repeated bending better. Essentially, only the cartilages of the external ear and the epiglottis (which flops over and covers the larynx when we swallow) are made of elastic cartilage.

Fibrocartilage consists of rows of chondrocytes alternating with rows of thick collagen fibers (see Figure 6.4j, p. 52). This tissue looks like a cartilage-dense regular connective tissue hybrid, and it is always found where hyaline cartilage joins a tendon or ligament. Fibrocartilage has great tensile strength and can withstand heavy compression. Hence, its use to construct the intervertebral discs and the cartilages within the knee joint makes a lot of sense (see Figure 9.4).

Haversian System   # 14655

In Formation

The Axial Skeleton

The **axial skeleton** (the green portion of Figure 9.1 on p. 66) can be divided into three parts: the skull, the vertebral column, and the bony thorax.

THE SKULL

The **skull** is composed of two sets of bones: the **cranium,** or **cranial vault,** encloses and protects the fragile brain tissue; the **facial bones** present the eyes in an anterior position and form the base for the facial muscles, which make it possible for us to present our feelings to the world. All but one of the bones of the skull are joined by interlocking joints called *sutures;* the mandible, or lower jawbone, is attached to the rest of the skull by a freely movable joint.

Cranium, Anterior, Exploded	# 01054	
Cranium, Lateral, Exploded	# 01055	
Skull, Inferior, Reversed	# 18603	
Skull View of Base	# 17920	
Frontal Sinus	# 47004	

The bones of the skull, shown in Figures 10.1 through 10.4, are described below. As you read through this material, identify each bone on an intact (and/or Beauchene) skull. Note that important bone markings are listed beneath the bones on which they appear and that a color-coding dot before each bone name indicates its color in the figures.

The Cranium

The cranium is composed of eight large flat bones. *With the exception of two paired bones (the parietals and the temporals), all are single bones.* Sometimes the six ossicles of the middle ear are also considered part of the cranium. Because the ossicles are functionally part of the hearing apparatus, their consideration is deferred to Exercise 25, Special Senses: Hearing and Equilibrium.

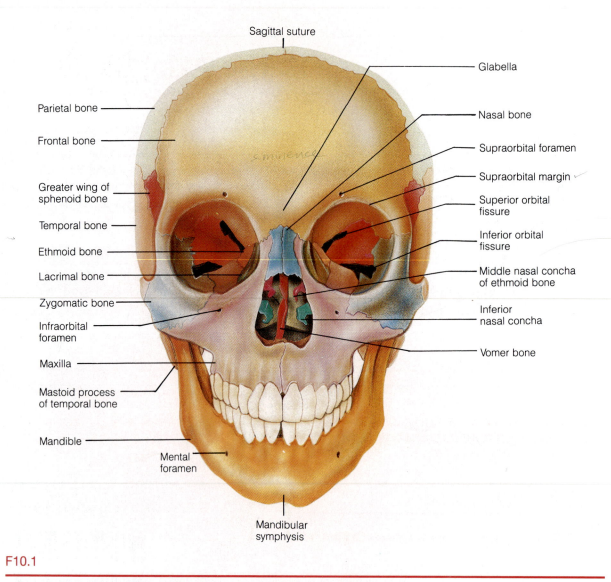

Sagittal suture

Glabella

Parietal bone

Frontal bone

Greater wing of
sphenoid bone

Temporal bone

Ethmoid bone

Lacrimal bone

Zygomatic bone

Infraorbital
foramen

Maxilla

Mastoid process
of temporal bone

Mandible

Mental
foramen

Nasal bone

Supraorbital foramen

Supraorbital margin

Superior orbital
fissure

Inferior orbital
fissure

Middle nasal concha
of ethmoid bone

Inferior
nasal concha

Vomer bone

Mandibular
symphysis

F10.1

Anatomy of the anterior aspect of the skull.

○ **FRONTAL**   See Figures 10.1, 10.2, and 10.4. Anterior portion of cranium; forms the forehead, superior part of the orbit, and floor of anterior cranial fossa.

Supraorbital foramen: opening above each orbit allowing blood vessels and nerves to pass.
Glabella: smooth area between the eyes.

○ **PARIETAL**   See Figures 10.1 and 10.2. Posterolateral to the frontal bone, forming sides of cranium.

Sagittal suture: midline articulation point of the two parietal bones.
Coronal suture: point of articulation of parietals with frontal bone.

○ **TEMPORAL**   See Figures 10.1 through 10.4. Inferior to parietal bone on lateral skull. The temporals can be divided into two major parts: the **squa-**

mous portion adjoins the parietals; the **petrous portion** forms the lateral inferior aspect of the skull.

Squamous suture: point of articulation of temporal bone (squamous region) with parietal bone.
External auditory meatus: canal leading to eardrum and middle ear.
Styloid (*stylo*=stake, pointed object) **process:** needle-like projection inferior to external auditory meatus; attachment point for muscles and ligaments. This process is often missing from (broken off) demonstration skulls.
Zygomatic process: bridgelike projection joining the zygomatic bone (cheekbone) anteriorly. Together these two bones form the *zygomatic arch.*
Mastoid process: rough projection inferior and posterior to external auditory meatus; attachment site for muscles.

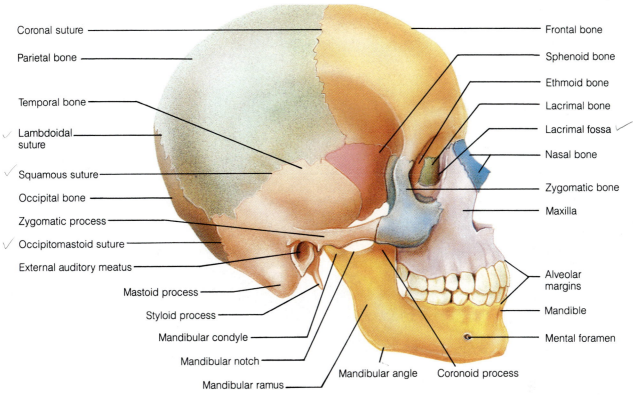

Coronal suture — Frontal bone

Parietal bone — Sphenoid bone

Ethmoid bone

Temporal bone — Lacrimal bone

Lambdoidal suture — Lacrimal fossa

Nasal bone

Squamous suture — Zygomatic bone

Occipital bone — Maxilla

Zygomatic process —

Occipitomastoid suture —

External auditory meatus — Alveolar margins

Mastoid process — Mandible

Styloid process — Mental foramen

Mandibular condyle —

Mandibular notch —

Mandibular ramus — Mandibular angle   Coronoid process

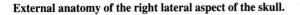

F10.2

External anatomy of the right lateral aspect of the skull.

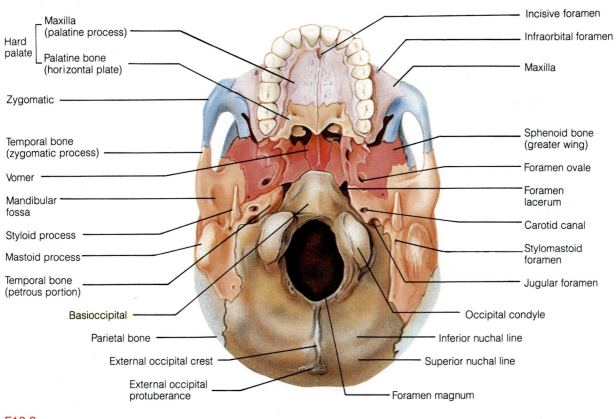

Hard palate — Maxilla (palatine process) — Incisive foramen

Infraorbital foramen

Palatine bone (horizontal plate) — Maxilla

Zygomatic —

Temporal bone (zygomatic process) — Sphenoid bone (greater wing)

Vomer — Foramen ovale

Mandibular fossa — Foramen lacerum

Carotid canal

Styloid process —

Mastoid process — Stylomastoid foramen

Temporal bone (petrous portion) — Jugular foramen

Basioccipital — Occipital condyle

Parietal bone — Inferior nuchal line

External occipital crest — Superior nuchal line

External occipital protuberance — Foramen magnum

F10.3

Anatomy of the inferior superficial view of the skull; mandible removed.

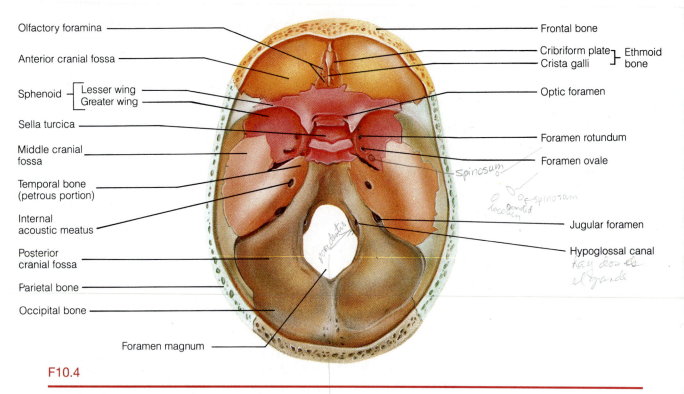

Olfactory foramina
Anterior cranial fossa
Sphenoid — Lesser wing / Greater wing
Sella turcica
Middle cranial fossa
Temporal bone (petrous portion)
Internal acoustic meatus
Posterior cranial fossa
Parietal bone
Occipital bone
Foramen magnum

Frontal bone
Cribriform plate ⎤ Ethmoid
Crista galli ⎦ bone
Optic foramen
Foramen rotundum
Foramen ovale
Jugular foramen
Hypoglossal canal

F10.4

Anatomy of the superior view of the floor of the cranial cavity; calvaria has been removed.

The mastoid process is full of air cavities and is so close to the middle ear, a trouble spot for infections, that it often becomes infected too, a condition referred to as **mastoiditis.** Should this troublesome condition persist, the mastoid process may be surgically removed. Because this area is separated from the brain by only a very thin layer of bone, an ear infection that has spread to the mastoid process can inflame the brain coverings or the meninges. The latter condition is known as **meningitis.** ■

Mandibular fossa: rounded depression anterior to external auditory meatus; forms the socket for the mandibular condyle, the point where the mandible (lower jaw) joins the cranium.

Jugular foramen: opening medial to styloid process through which blood vessels and cranial nerves IX, X, and XI pass.

Carotid canal: opening, medial to the styloid process, through which the internal carotid artery passes into the petrous portion of the temporal bone.

Stylomastoid foramen: tiny opening between the mastoid and styloid processes through which the seventh cranial nerve leaves the cranium.

Internal acoustic meatus: opening on posterior aspect (petrous portion) of temporal bone allowing passage of cranial nerves VII and VIII (see Figure 10.4).

● OCCIPITAL   See Figures 10.2, 10.3, 10.4. Most posterior bone of cranium—forms floor and back wall. Joins sphenoid bone anteriorly via its narrow basioccipital region.

Lambdoidal suture: site of articulation of occipital bone and parietal bones.
Foramen magnum: large opening in base of occipital, which allows the spinal cord to join with the brain.
Occipital condyles: rounded projections lateral to the foramen magnum, which articulate with the first cervical vertebra (atlas).
Hypoglossal canal: opening medial and superior to the occipital condyle through which the hypoglossal nerve (cranial nerve XII) passes.
External occipital crest and protuberance: midline prominences posterior to the foramen magnum.

● SPHENOID   See Figures 10.1 through 10.4. Bat-shaped bone forming the anterior plateau of the middle cranial fossa across the width of the skull.

Greater wings: portions of the sphenoid seen exteriorly anterior to the temporal and forming a portion of the orbits of the eyes.
Superior orbital fissures: jagged openings in orbits providing passage for cranial nerves III, IV, V, and VI to enter the orbit where they serve the eye.

The sphenoid bone can be seen in its entire width if the top of the cranium (calvaria) is removed (see Figure 10.4).

Sella turcica (Turk's saddle): small depression in sphenoid midline in which the pituitary gland rests in the living person.
Lesser wings: bat-shaped portion of sphenoid anterior to sella turcica.

Optic foramina: openings in the base of the lesser wings through which the optic nerves enter the orbits to serve the eyes.

Foramen rotundum: opening lateral to sella turcica providing passage for a branch of the fifth cranial nerve. (This foramen is not visible on an inferior view of the skull.)

Foramen ovale: opening posterior to the sella turcica providing passage for a branch of the fifth cranial nerve.

Foramen lacerum: a jagged opening between the temporal bone and the sphenoid providing passage for a number of small nerves, and for the internal carotid artery to enter the middle cranial fossa (after it passes through part of the temporal bone).

● **ETHMOID** See Figures 10.1, 10.2, and 10.4. Irregularly shaped bone anterior to the sphenoid. Forms the roof of the nasal cavity, upper nasal septum, and part of the medial orbit walls.

Crista galli (cock's comb): vertical projection providing a point of attachment for the dura mater (outermost membrane covering of the brain).

Cribriform plates: bony plates lateral to the crista galli through which olfactory fibers pass to the brain from the nasal mucosa.

Superior and middle nasal conchae (turbinates): thin plates of bone extending medially from the lateral masses of the ethmoid into the nasal cavity. The shelf-like conchae provide for a more efficient air flow through the nasal cavity and greatly increase the surface area of the mucosa that covers them, thus increasing the ability of the mucosa to warm and humidify the incoming air.

Facial Bones

There are 14 bones composing the face, and 12 of these are paired. *Only the mandible and vomer are single bones.* An additional bone, the hyoid bone, although not a facial bone, is considered here because of its location. Refer to Figures 10.1 through 10.4 to find the structures described below.

○ **MANDIBLE** See Figures 10.1 and 10.2. The lower jaw bone, which articulates with the temporal bones, providing the only freely movable joints of the skull.

Body: horizontal portion; forms the chin.

Ramus: vertical extension of the body on either side.

Mandibular condyle: point of articulation of the mandible with the mandibular fossa of the temporal bone.

Coronoid process: jutting anterior portion of the ramus; site of muscle attachment.

Angle: posterior point at which ramus meets the body.

Mental foramen: prominent opening on the body (lateral to the midline) that transmits the mental blood vessels and nerve to the lower jaw.

Mandibular foramen: open the lower jaw of the skull to identify this prominent foramen on the medial aspect of the mandibular ramus. This foramen permits passage of the nerve involved with tooth sensation (mandibular branch of cranial nerve V) and is the site where the dentist injects Novocain to prevent pain while working on the lower teeth.

Alveoli: sockets on superior margin of mandible in which the teeth lie.

Mandibular symphysis: anterior median depression indicating point of mandibular fusion.

● **MAXILLAE** See Figures 10.1, 10.2, and 10.3. Two bones fused in a median suture, which form the upper jawbone and part of the orbits. All facial bones, with the exception of the mandible, join the maxillae. Thus they are the main, or keystone, bones of the face.

Alveoli: sockets on the inferior margin in which teeth lie.

Palatine processes: form the anterior parts of the hard palate.

Infraorbital foramen: opening under the orbit carrying the infraorbital nerves and blood vessels to the nasal region.

Incisive foramen: large bilateral foramen located posterior to the central incisor tooth of the maxilla and piercing the hard palate; transmits the nasopalatine arteries and blood vessels.

○ **PALATINE** See Figure 10.3. Paired bones posterior to the palatine processes; form posterior hard palate and part of the orbit.

○ **ZYGOMATIC** See Figures 10.1, 10.2, and 10.3. Lateral to the maxilla; forms the portion of the face commonly called the cheekbone, and forms part of the lateral orbit. Its three processes are named for the bones with which they articulate.

● **LACRIMAL** See Figures 10.1 and 10.2. Fingernail-sized bones forming a part of the medial orbit walls between the maxilla and the ethmoid. Each lacrimal bone is pierced by an opening, the **lacrimal fossa,** which serves as a passageway for tears (*lacrima* means "tear").

● **NASAL** See Figures 10.1 and 10.2. Small rectangular bones forming the bridge of the nose.

● **VOMER** (*vomer* = plow) See Figure 10.1. Irregularly shaped bone in median plane of nasal cavity that forms the posterior and inferior nasal septum.

● **INFERIOR NASAL CONCHAE** (turbinates) See Figure 10.1. Thin curved bones protruding medially from the lateral walls of the nasal cavity; serve the same purpose as the turbinate portions of the ethmoid bone (described earlier).

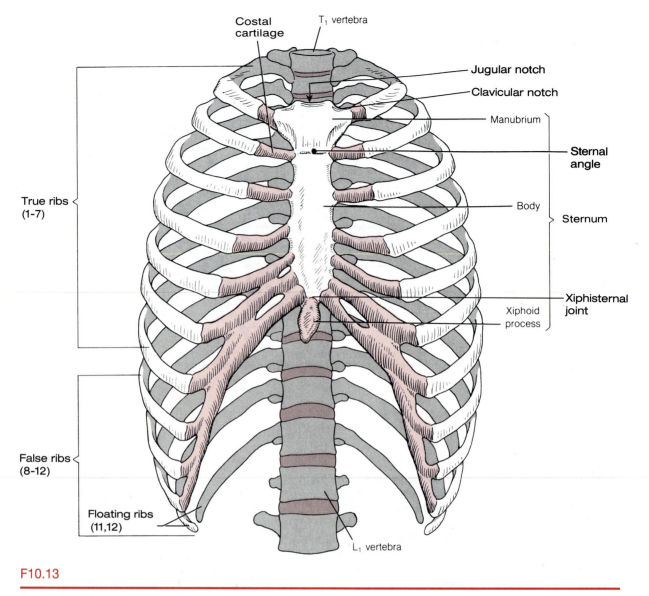

Costal cartilage

T₁ vertebra

Jugular notch

Clavicular notch

Manubrium

Sternal angle

True ribs (1-7)

Body

Sternum

Xiphisternal joint

Xiphoid process

False ribs (8-12)

Floating ribs (11,12)

L₁ vertebra

F10.13

Bony thorax, anterior view.

THE BONY THORAX

The **bony thorax** is composed of the sternum, ribs, and thoracic vertebrae (Figure 10.13). It is also referred to as the **thoracic cage** because of its appearance and because it forms a protective cone-shaped enclosure around the organs of the thoracic cavity (heart and lungs, for example).

The Sternum

The **sternum** (breastbone), a typical flat bone, is a result of the fusion of three bones—the manubrium, body, and xiphoid process. It is attached to the first seven pairs of ribs. The superiormost **manubrium** looks like the knot

of a tie; it articulates with the clavicle (collarbone) laterally. The **body (gladiolus)** forms the bulk of the sternum. The **xiphoid process** constructs the inferior end of the sternum and lies at the level of the fifth intercostal space. Although it is made of hyaline cartilage in children, it is usually ossified in adults.

In some people, the xiphoid process projects dorsally. This may present a problem because physical trauma to the chest can push such a xiphoid into the heart or liver (both immediately deep to the process), causing massive hemorrhage. ■

The sternum has two important bony landmarks—the jugular notch and the sternal angle. The **jugular notch** (concave upper border of the manubrium) can be

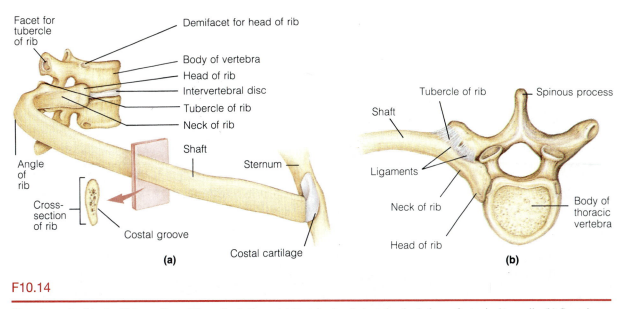

F10.14

Structure of a "typical" true rib and its articulations. (a) Vertebral and sternal articulations of a typical true rib. (b) Superior view of the articulation between a rib and a thoracic vertebra.

palpated easily; generally it is at the level of the third thoracic vertebra. The **sternal angle** is a result of the manubrium and body meeting at a slight angle to each other, so that a transverse ridge is formed at the level of the second ribs. It provides a handy reference point for counting ribs to locate the second intercostal space for listening to certain heart valves, and is an important anatomical landmark for thoracic surgery. The **xiphisternal joint,** the point where the sternal body and xiphoid process fuse, lies at the level of the ninth thoracic vertebra.

• Palpate your sternal angle and jugular notch.

Because of its accessibility, the sternum is a favored site for obtaining samples of blood-forming (hematopoietic) tissue for the diagnosis of suspected blood diseases. A needle is inserted into the marrow of the sternum and the sample withdrawn (sternal puncture).

The Ribs

The 12 pairs of **ribs** form the walls of the thoracic cage (see Figures 10.13 and 10.14). All of the ribs articulate posteriorly with the vertebral column via their heads and tubercles and then curve downward and toward the anterior body surface. The first seven pairs, called the *true ribs,* attach directly to the sternum by their "own" costal cartilages. The next five pairs, called *false ribs,* have indirect cartilage attachments to the sternum or no sternal attachment at all, as in the case of the last two pairs (which are also called *floating ribs*).

 First take a deep breath to expand your chest. Notice how your ribs seem to move outward and how your sternum rises. Then examine an articulated skeleton to observe the relationship between the ribs and the vertebrae.

Rib   # 18625

Pectoral Girdle   # 53887
and Rib Cage

EXERCISE

The Appendicular Skeleton

<table>
<tr><td>

1. To identify on an articulated skeleton the bones of the shoulder and pelvic girdles and their attached limbs.

2. To arrange unmarked, disarticulated bones in their proper relative position to form the entire skeleton.

3. To differentiate between a male and a female pelvis.

4. To discuss the common features of the human appendicular girdles (pectoral and pelvic), and to note how their structure relates to their specialized functions.

5. To identify specific bone markings in the appendicular skeleton.

</td><td>

Articulated skeletons
Disarticulated skeletons (complete)
Articulated pelves (male and female for comparative study)

</td></tr>
</table>

The **appendicular skeleton** (the gold-colored portion of Figure 9.1) is composed of the 126 bones of the appendages and the pectoral and pelvic girdles, which attach the limbs to the axial skeleton.

 Carefully examine each of the bones described and identify the characteristic bone markings of each. The markings aid in determining whether a bone is the right or left member of its pair. *This is a very important instruction because, before completing this laboratory exercise, you will be constructing your own skeleton.*

BONES OF THE SHOULDER GIRDLE AND UPPER EXTREMITY

The Shoulder Girdle

The paired **shoulder**, or **pectoral, girdles** (Figure 11.1) each consist of two bones—the anterior clavicle and the posterior scapula. The shoulder girdles function to attach the upper limbs to the axial skeleton. In addition, the bones of the shoulder girdles serve as attachment points for many trunk and neck muscles.

The **clavicle,** or collarbone, is a slender doubly curved bone. It is rounded on its medial end, which attaches to the sternal manubrium, and flattened on the lateral end, where it articulates with the scapula to form part of the shoulder joint. The clavicle serves as an anterior brace, or strut, to hold the arm away from the top of the thorax.

The **scapulae,** or shoulder blades, are generally triangular and are commonly called the "wings" of humans. Each scapula has a flattened body and two important processes—the **acromion** (the enlarged end of the spine of the scapula) and the beaklike **coracoid process** (*corac* = crow, raven). The suprascapular notch at the base of the coracoid process allows nerves to pass. The acromion connects with the clavicle; the coracoid process points anteriorly over the tip of the shoulder joint and serves as a point of attachment for some of the muscles of the upper limb. The scapula has no direct attachment to the axial skeleton but is loosely held in place by trunk muscles.

The scapula has three angles: superior, inferior, and lateral. The inferior angle provides a landmark for auscultating (listening to) lung sounds. The scapula also has three named borders: the superior; the medial (vertebral); and the lateral (axillary). Several shallow depressions (fossae) appear on both sides of the scapula and are named according to location; i.e., there are the anterior subscapular fossa and the posterior infraspinous and supraspinous fossae. The **glenoid cavity,** a shallow socket that receives the head of the arm bone, is located in the lateral angle.

The shoulder girdle is exceptionally light and allows the upper limb a degree of mobility not seen anywhere else in the body. This is due to the following factors:

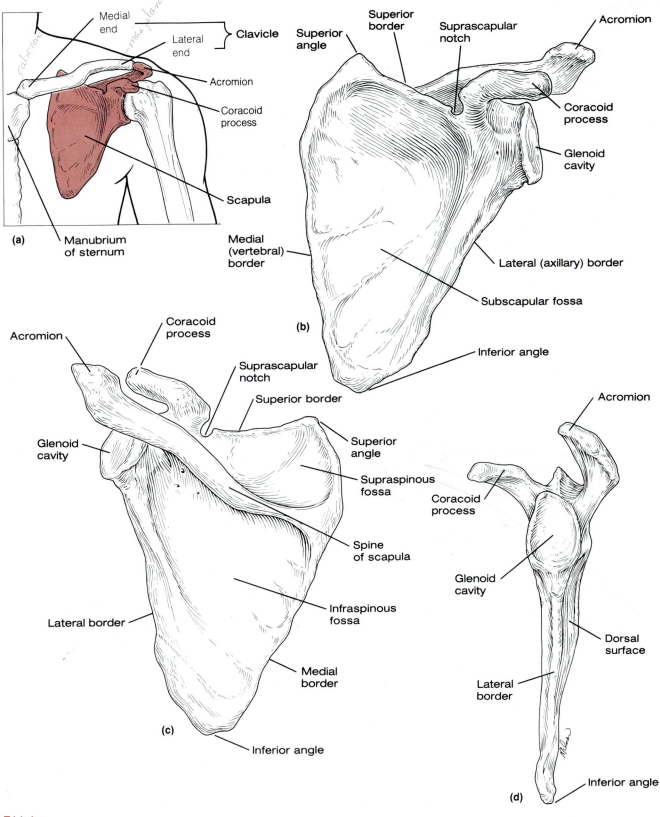

(a)

Medial end

Lateral end

Clavicle

Acromion

Coracoid process

Scapula

Manubrium of sternum

Superior angle

Superior border

Suprascapular notch

Acromion

Coracoid process

Glenoid cavity

Medial (vertebral) border

Lateral (axillary) border

Subscapular fossa

(b)

Inferior angle

Acromion

Coracoid process

Suprascapular notch

Superior border

Superior angle

Supraspinous fossa

Glenoid cavity

Spine of scapula

Lateral border

Infraspinous fossa

Medial border

(c)

Inferior angle

Acromion

Coracoid process

Glenoid cavity

Dorsal surface

Lateral border

(d)

Inferior angle

F11.1

Bones of the shoulder girdle. (a) Left shoulder girdle articulated to show the relationship of the girdle to the bones of the thorax and arm. (b) Left scapula, anterior view. (c) Left scapula, posterior view. (d) Left scapula, lateral view.

- The sternoclavicular joints are the *only* site of attachment of the shoulder girdles to the axial skeleton.
- The relative looseness of the scapular attachment allows it to slide back and forth against the thorax with muscular activity.
- The glenoid cavity is shallow, and does little to stabilize the shoulder joint.

However, this exceptional flexibility exacts a price: the arm bone (humerus) is very susceptible to dislocation, and fracture of the clavicle disables the entire upper limb.

Scapula, Anterior View	# 18626
Scapula, Posterior View	# 18627
Scapula, Lateral View	# 18628

The Arm

The arm (Figure 11.2) consists of a single bone—the **humerus,** a typical long bone. At its proximal end is the rounded head, which fits into the shallow glenoid cavity of the scapula. The head is separated from the shaft by the anatomical neck and the more constricted surgical neck, which is a common site of fracture. Opposite the head are two prominences, the **greater** and **lesser tubercles** (from lateral to medial aspect), separated by a groove (the **intertubercular** or **bicipital groove**) that guides the tendon of the biceps muscle to its point of attachment (the superior rim of the glenoid cavity). In the midpoint of the shaft is a roughened area, the **deltoid tuberosity,** where the large fleshy shoulder muscle, the deltoid, attaches. Just inferior to the deltoid tuberosity is the **radial groove,** which indicates the pathway of the radial nerve.

At the distal end of the humerus are two condyles—the medial **trochlea** (looking rather like a spool), which articulates with the ulna, and the lateral **capitulum,** which articulates with the radius of the forearm. This condyle pair is flanked medially by the **medial epicondyle** and laterally by the **lateral epicondyle.**

The medial epicondyle is commonly referred to as the "funny bone." The large ulnar nerve runs in a groove beneath the medial epicondyle, and when this region is sharply bumped, we are quite likely to experience a temporary, but excruciatingly painful, tingling sensation. This event is called "hitting the funny bone," a strange expression, because it is certainly *not* funny!

Above the trochlea on the anterior surface is a depression, the **coronoid fossa;** on the posterior surface is the **olecranon fossa.** These two depressions allow the corresponding processes of the ulna to move freely when the elbow is flexed and extended. A small **radial fossa,** lateral to the coronoid fossa, receives the head of the radius when the elbow is flexed.

The Forearm

Two bones, the radius and the ulna, compose the skeleton of the forearm, or antibrachium (see Figure 11.2c). When the body is in the anatomical position, the **radius** is in the lateral position in the forearm and the radius and ulna are parallel. Proximally, the disc-shaped head of the radius articulates with the capitulum of the humerus. Just below the head, on the medial aspect of the shaft, is a prominence called the **radial tuberosity,** the point of attachment for the tendon of the biceps muscle of the arm.

The **ulna** is the medial bone of the forearm. Its proximal end bears the anterior **coronoid process** and the posterior **olecranon process,** which are separated by the **trochlear notch.** Together these processes grip the trochlea of the humerus in a plierslike joint. The small **radial notch** on the lateral side of the coronoid process articulates with the head of the radius. The slimmer distal end of the ulna bears a small medial **styloid process,** which serves as a point of attachment for the ligaments of the wrist.

The Wrist

The wrist is referred to anatomically as the **carpus,** and the eight bones composing it are the **carpals.** The carpals are arranged in two irregular rows of four bones each, which are illustrated in Figure 11.3. In the proximal row (lateral to medial) are the scaphoid, lunate, triangular, and pisiform bones; the scaphoid and lunate articulate with the distal end of the radius. In the distal row are the trapezium, trapezoid, capitate, and hamate. The carpals are bound closely together by ligaments, which restrict movements between them.

The Hand

The hand, or manus (see Figure 11.3), consists of two groups of bones: the **metacarpals** (bones of the palm) and the **phalanges** (bones of the fingers). The metacarpals are numbered 1 to 5 from the thumb side of the hand toward the little finger. When the fist is clenched, the heads of the metacarpals become prominent as the knuckles. Each hand contains 14 phalanges. There are 3 phalanges in each finger except the thumb, which has only proximal and distal phalanges.

Humerus, Posterior View	# 18633
Humerus, Anterior View	# 18634
Radius and Ulna, Anterior View	# 18636
Hand, Anterior View, Skeleton	# 53890
Wrist Cross Sectional Series	# 38125

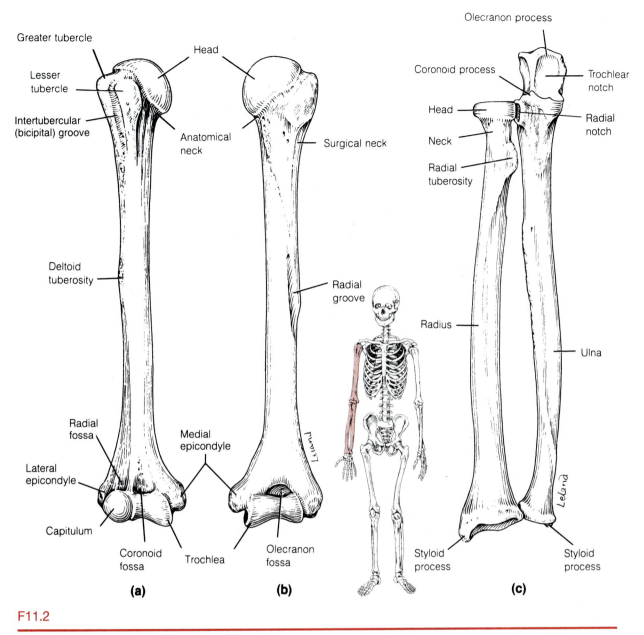

F11.2

Bones of the right arm and forearm. (a) Humerus, anterior view. (b) Humerus, posterior view. (c) Radius and ulna, anterior view.

 ## Surface Anatomy of the Pectoral Girdle and the Upper Limb

Before continuing on to study the bones of the pelvic girdle, take the time to identify the following bone markings related to the upper appendage on the skin surface. It is usually preferable to observe and palpate the bone markings on your lab partner, particularly since many of these markings can only be seen from the dorsal aspect.

- Clavicle: Palpate the clavicle along its entire length from sternum to shoulder.

- Acromioclavicular joint: The high point of the shoulder, which represents the junction point between the clavicle and the acromion of the scapular spine.
- Spine of the scapula: Extend your arm at the shoulder so that your scapula is moved posteriorly. As you do this, your scapular spine will be seen as a winglike protrusion on your dorsal thorax and can be easily palpated by your lab partner.
- Lateral epicondyle of the humerus: The inferiormost projection at the lateral aspect of the distal humerus. After you have located the epicondyle, run your finger posteriorly into the hollow immediately dorsal to the epicondyle. This is the site where the

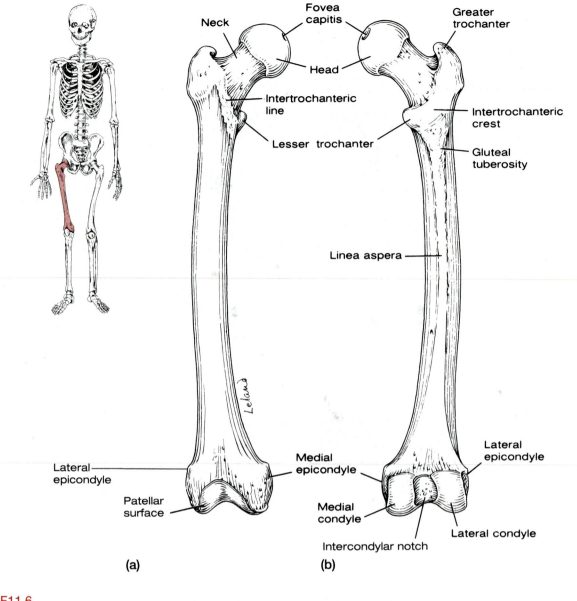

F11.6

Bone of the right thigh. (a) Femur, anterior view. (b) Femur, posterior view.

Distally, the femur terminates in the **lateral** and **medial condyles,** which articulate with the tibia below, and the **patellar surface,** which forms a joint with the patella anteriorly. The **lateral** and **medial epicondyles,** just superior to the condyles, are separated by the **intercondylar notch**.

The trochanters and trochanteric crest, as well as the **gluteal tuberosity** and the **linea aspera** located on the shaft, serve as sites for muscle attachment.

The Leg

Two bones, the tibia and the fibula, form the skeleton of the leg (see Figure 11.7). The **tibia,** or *shinbone,* is the larger and more medial of the two leg bones. At the proximal end, the **medial** and **lateral condyles** (separated by the **intercondylar eminence**) receive the distal end of the femur to form the knee joint. The **tibial tuberosity,** a roughened protrusion on the anterior tibial surface (just below the condyles), is the site of attachment of the patellar (kneecap) ligament. Small facets on its superior and inferior lateral surface articulate with the fibula. Distally, a process called the **medial malleolus** forms the inner (medial) bulge of the ankle, and the smaller distal end articulates with the talus bone of the foot. The anterior surface of the tibia is a sharpened ridge (anterior crest) that is relatively unprotected by muscles. It is easily felt beneath the skin.

The **fibula,** which lies parallel to the tibia, takes no part in forming the knee joint. Its proximal head articulates with the lateral condyle of the tibia. The fibula is thin and sticklike with a sharp anterior crest. It terminates distally in the **lateral malleolus,** which forms the outer part, or lateral bulge, of the ankle.

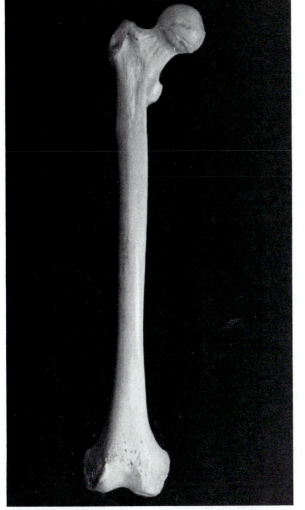
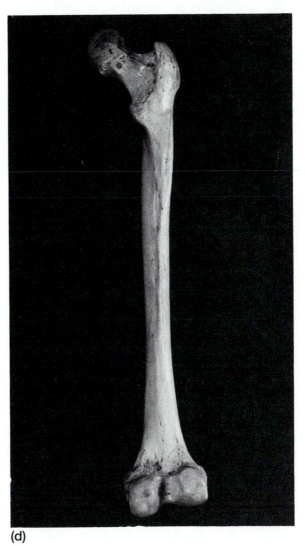

(c)

(d)

F11.6 (*continued*)

(c) Photo of femur, anterior view. (d) Photo of femur, posterior view.

| Patella, Both Sides, Skeleton | # 44651 |
| Foot, Inferior View of Foot Bones | # 18619 |

The Foot

The bones of the foot include the 7 **tarsal** bones, 5 **metatarsals,** which form the instep, and 14 **phalanges,** which form the toes (see Figure 11.8). Body weight is concentrated on the two largest tarsals which form the posterior aspect of the foot, the *calcaneus* (heel bone) and the *talus,* which lies between the tibia and the calcaneus. The other tarsals are named and identified in Figure 11.8. Like the fingers of the hand, each toe has 3 phalanges except the great toe, which has 2.

The bones in the foot are arranged to produce three strong arches—two longitudinal arches (medial and lateral) and one transverse arch (Figure 11.9). Ligaments, binding the foot bones together, and tendons of the foot muscles hold the bones firmly in the arched position but still allow a certain degree of give. Weakened arches are referred to as fallen arches or flat feet.

Surface Anatomy of the Pelvic Girdle and Lower Limb

Locate and palpate the following bone markings on yourself and/or your lab partner.

● Iliac crest and anterior superior iliac spine: Rest your hands on your hips— they will be overlying the iliac crests.

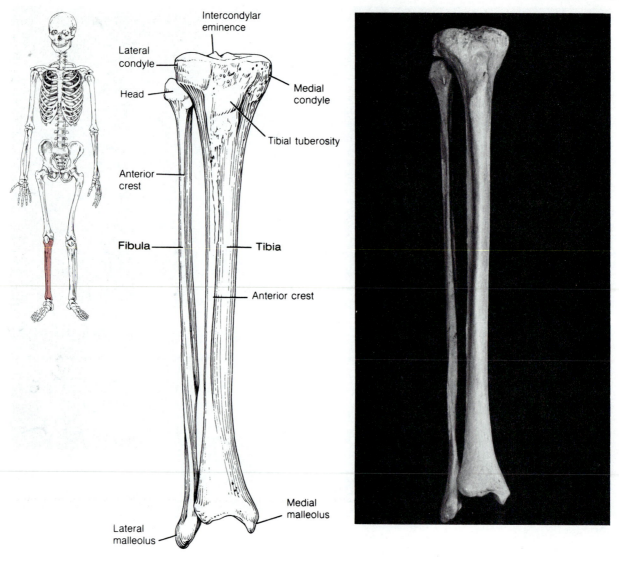

Intercondylar eminence

Lateral condyle

Head

Medial condyle

Tibial tuberosity

Anterior crest

Fibula — Tibia

Anterior crest

Medial malleolus

Lateral malleolus

F11.7

Bones of the right leg. Tibia and fibula, anterior view.

Trace the crest as far posteriorly as you can and then follow it anteriorly to its terminus at the anterior superior iliac spine. This latter bone marking is fairly easily felt in almost everyone, and is clearly visible through the skin (and perhaps the clothing) of very slim people. (The posterior superior iliac spine is much less obvious and is usually indicated only by a dimple in the overlying skin. Check it out in the mirror tonight.)

- Greater trochanter of the femur: This is usually easier to locate in females than in males because of the wider female pelvis and the fact that it is more likely to be clothed by bulky muscles in males. Try to locate it on yourself as the most lateral point of the proximal femur. It typically lies about 6–8 inches below the iliac crest.
- Patella and tibial tuberosity: Feel your kneecap and palpate the ligaments attached to its superior and in-

ferior aspects. Follow the inferior ligament to the tibial tuberosity to which it attaches.
- Medial and lateral condyles of the femur and tibia: As you move from the patella inferiorly on the medial (and then the lateral) knee surface, you will feel first the femoral and then the tibial condyle.
- Medial malleolus: Feel the medial protrusion of your ankle, which is the medial malleolus of the distal tibia.
- Lateral malleolus: Feel the bulge of the lateral aspect of your ankle, which is the lateral malleolus of the fibula.
- Calcaneus: Attempt to follow the extent of your calcaneus or heel bone.

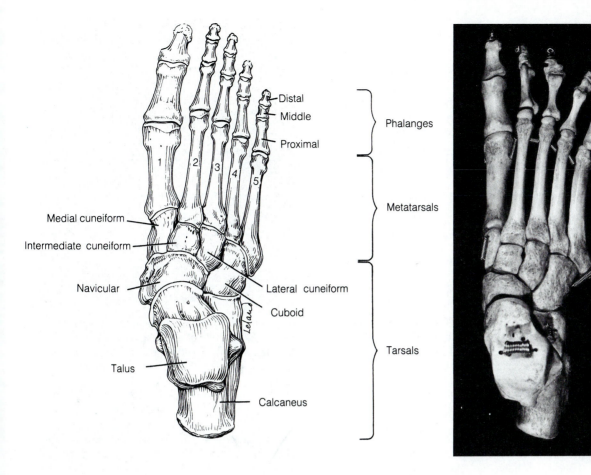

F11.8

Bones of the right ankle and foot, superior view.

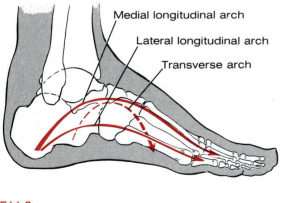

F11.9

Arches of the foot.

APPLYING KNOWLEDGE: CONSTRUCTING A SKELETON

1. When you have finished examining the disarticulated bones of the appendicular skeleton and yourself, work with your lab partner to arrange the disarticulated bones on the laboratory bench in their proper relative positions to form an entire skeleton. Careful observations of the bone markings should help you distinguish between right and left members of bone pairs.

2. When you believe that you have correctly accomplished this task, ask the instructor to check your arrangement to ensure that it is correct. If it is not, go to the articulated skeleton and check your bone arrangements. Also review the descriptions of the bone markings as necessary to correct your bone arrangement.

The Fetal Skeleton

OBJECTIVES	MATERIALS
1. To define *fontanel* and discuss its function and fate in the fetus. **2.** To demonstrate important differences between the fetal and adult skeletons.	Isolated fetal skull Fetal skeleton Adult skeleton

A human fetus about to be born has 275 bones, many more than the 206 bones found in the adult skeleton. This is because many of the bones described as single bones in the adult skeleton (for example, the coxal bone, sternum, and sacrum) have not yet fully ossified and fused in the fetus.

1. Obtain a fetal skull and study it carefully. Make observations as needed to answer the following questions. Does it have the same bones as the adult skull? How does the size of the fetal face relate to the cranium? How does this compare to what is seen in the adult?

2. Indentations between the bones of the fetal skull, called **fontanels,** are fibrous membranes. These areas will become bony (ossify) as the fetus ages, completing the process by the age of 20 to 22 months. The fontanels allow the fetal skull to be compressed slightly during birth and also allow for brain growth during late fetal life. Locate the following fontanels on the fetal skull with the aid of Figure 12.1: anterior (or frontal) fontanel, mastoid fontanel, sphenoidal fontanel, and posterior (or occipital) fontanel.

3. Note that some of the cranial bones have conical protrusions. These are growth centers. Notice also that the frontal bone is still bipartite, and the temporal bone is incompletely ossified, little more than a ring of bone in the fetus.

4. Obtain a fetal skeleton and examine it carefully, noting differences between it and an adult skeleton. Pay particular attention to the vertebrae, sternum, frontal bone of the cranium, patellae (kneecaps), coxal bones, carpals and tarsals, and rib cage.

5. Check the questions in the review section before completing this study to ensure that all of the necessary observations have been made.

Fontanel   # 44583

Skeleton, Newborn   # 44584

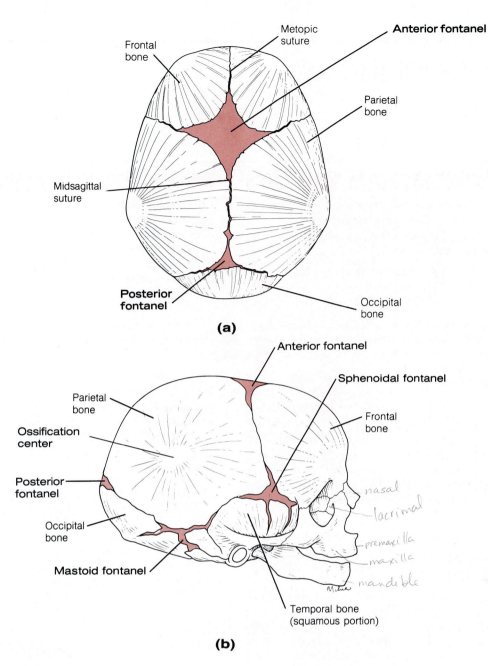

Frontal
bone

Metopic
suture

Anterior fontanel

Parietal
bone

Midsagittal
suture

**Posterior
fontanel**

Occipital
bone

(a)

Anterior fontanel

Sphenoidal fontanel

Parietal
bone

Ossification
center

Frontal
bone

Posterior
fontanel

Occipital
bone

nasal

lacrimal

premaxilla

maxilla

Mastoid fontanel

mandible

Temporal bone
(squamous portion)

(b)

F12.1

The fetal skull. (a) Superior view. (b) Lateral view.

cartilaginous bones
occipital
temporal
Ethmoid
auditory ossicles
Foramen magnum
anterior
sphenoidal } fontanelle
mastoid

EXERCISE

Articulations

OBJECTIVES	MATERIALS
1. To name the three structural categories of joints, and to compare their structure and mobility. **2.** To identify the types of movement seen in synovial joints. **3.** To define *origin* and *insertion* of muscles.	Articulated skeleton, skull Diarthrotic beef joint (fresh or preserved), preferably a knee joint Disposable gloves Anatomical chart of joint types (if available) X-rays of normal and arthritic joints (if available)

With rare exceptions, every bone in the body is connected to, or forms a joint with, at least one other bone. Joints, or articulations, perform two functions for the body. They (1) hold the bones together and (2) allow the rigid skeletal system some flexibility so that gross body movements can occur.

TYPES OF JOINTS

Joints may be classified structurally or functionally. The *structural classification* is based on whether there is connective tissue fiber, cartilage, or a joint cavity between the articulating bones. Structurally, there are *fibrous, cartilaginous,* and *synovial joints.*

The functional classification focuses on the amount of movement allowed at the joint. On this basis, there are **synarthroses,** or immovable joints; **amphiarthroses,** or slightly movable joints; and **diarthroses,** or freely movable joints. Freely movable joints predominate in the limbs, whereas immovable and slightly movable joints are largely restricted to the axial skeleton, where firm bony attachments and protection of enclosed organs are a priority.

As a general rule, fibrous joints are immovable, and synovial joints are freely movable. Cartilaginous joints offer both rigid and slightly movable examples. Since the structural categories are more clear-cut, we will use the structural classification here and indicate functional properties as appropriate.

Fibrous Joints

In **fibrous joints,** the bones are joined by fibrous tissue. No joint cavity is present. The amount of movement allowed depends on the length of the fibers uniting the bones. Although some fibrous joints are slightly moveable, most are synarthrotic and permit virtually no movement.

The two major types of fibrous joints are sutures and syndesmoses. In **sutures** (Figure 13.1d) the irregular edges of the bones interlock and are united by very short connective tissue fibers, as in most joints of the skull. In **syndesmoses** the articulating bones are connected by short ligaments of dense fibrous tissue; the bones do not interlock. The joint at the distal end of the tibia and fibula is an example of a syndesmosis (Figure 13.1e). Although this syndesmosis allows some give, it is classed functionally as a synarthrosis.

 Examine a human skull again. Notice that adjacent bone surfaces do not actually touch but are separated by fibrous connective tissue. Also examine a skeleton and anatomical chart of joint types for examples of fibrous joints.

Skull, Sutures   # 01075

Cartilaginous Joints

In **cartilaginous joints,** the articulating bone ends are connected by a plate or pad of cartilage. No joint cavity is present. The two major types of cartilaginous joints are synchondroses and symphyses. Although there is variation, most cartilaginous joints are *slightly movable* (amphiarthroses) functionally. In **symphyses** (*symphysis* means "a growth together") the bones are connected by a broad, flat disc of **fibrocartilage.** The intervertebral joints and the pubic symphysis of the pelvis are symphyses (see Figure 13.1b and c). In **synchondroses** the bony portions are united by hyaline cartilage. The articulation of the costal cartilage of the first rib with the sternum (Figure 13.1a) is a synchondrosis, but perhaps the best examples of synchondroses are the epiphyseal

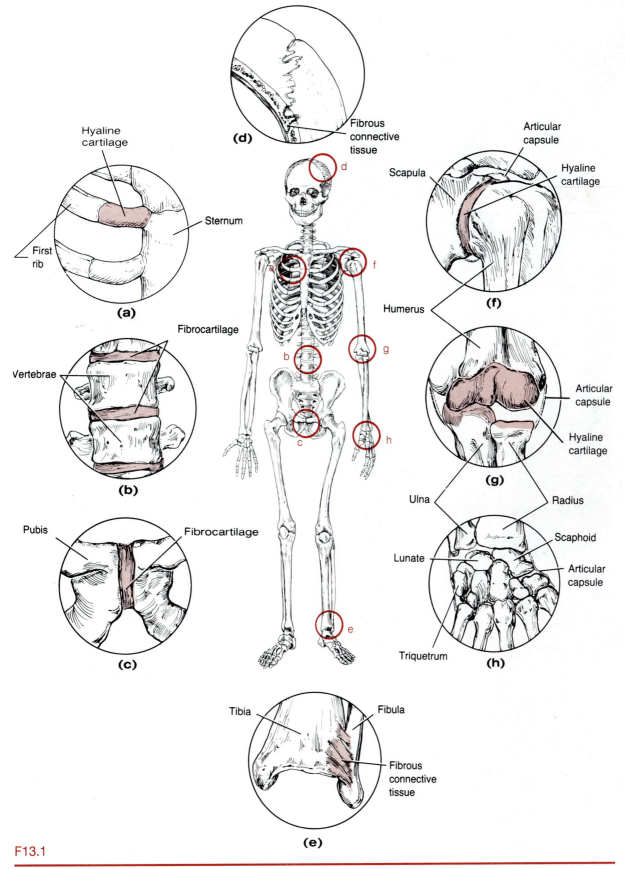

F13.1

Types of joints. Joints to the left of the skeleton are cartilaginous joints; joints above and below the skeleton are fibrous joints; joints to the right of the skeleton are synovial joints. (a) Synchondrosis (joint between costal cartilage of rib 1 and the sternum. (b) Symphysis (intervertebral discs of fibrocartilage connecting adjacent vertebrae). (c) Symphysis (fibrocartilaginous pubic symphysis connecting the pubic bones anteriorly). (d) Suture (fibrous connective tissue connecting interlocking skull bones). (e) Syndesmosis (fibrous connective tissue connecting the distal ends of the tibia and fibula. (f) Synovial joint (multiaxial shoulder joint). (g) Synovial joint (uniaxial elbow joint). (h) Synovial joints (biaxial intercarpal joints of the hand).

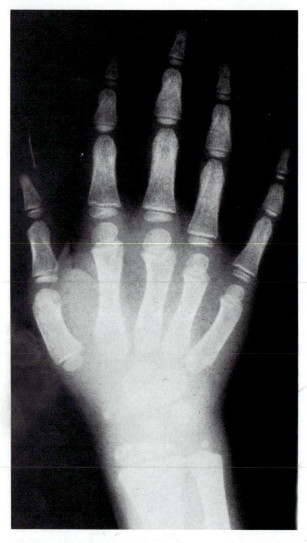

F13.2

X-ray of the hand of a child. Notice the cartilaginous epiphyseal plates, examples of temporary synchondroses.

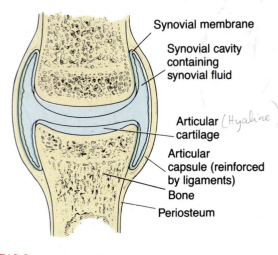

F13.3

Major structural features of a synovial joint.

Labels in figure F13.3:
- Synovial membrane
- Synovial cavity containing synovial fluid
- Articular (Hyaline) cartilage
- Articular capsule (reinforced by ligaments)
- Bone
- Periosteum

plates seen in the long bones of growing children (Figure 13.2). The epiphyseal plates are flexible during childhood but they are eventually totally ossified.

 Identify the cartilaginous joints on a human skeleton and on an anatomical chart of joint types.

Synovial Joints

Synovial joints are those in which the articulating bone ends are separated by a joint cavity containing synovial fluid (see Figure 13.1f–h). This arrangement allows a great deal of mobility and all synovial joints are diarthroses, or freely movable joints. This flexibility varies, however; some synovial joints can move in only one plane, and others can move in several directions (multiaxial movement). Most joints in the body are synovial joints.

All synovial joints are characterized by the following structural characteristics (Figure 13.3):

- The joint surfaces are enclosed by an *articular capsule* (a sleeve of fibrous connective tissue).
- The interior of this capsule is lined with a smooth connective tissue membrane, called *synovial membrane*, which produces a lubricating fluid (synovial fluid) that reduces friction.
- Articulating surfaces of the bones forming the joint are covered with hyaline (*articular*) cartilage.
- The articular capsule is typically reinforced with ligaments and may or may not contain bursae (fluid-filled sacs that reduce friction where tendons cross bone).
- Fibrocartilage pads may or may not be present within the capsule.

1. Examine a beef joint to identify the general structural features of diarthrotic joints.

⚠️ If the joint is freshly obtained from the slaughterhouse and you will be handling it, don plastic gloves before beginning your observations.

Because there are so many types of synovial joints, they have been divided into the following subcategories on the basis of movements allowed:

- Gliding: Articulating surfaces are flat or slightly curved, allowing sliding movements in one or two planes. Examples are the intercarpal and intertarsal joints and the vertebrocostal joints.
- Hinge: The rounded process of one bone fits into the concave surface of another to allow movement in one plane (uniaxial), usually flexion and extension. Examples are the elbow and interphalangeal joints.
- Pivot: The rounded or conical surface of one bone articulates with a shallow depression or foramen in

another bone to allow uniaxial rotation, as in the joint between the atlas and axis (C$_1$ and C$_2$).

- Condyloid: The oval condyle of one bone fits into an ellipsoidal depression in another bone, allowing biaxial (two-way) movement. The wrist joint and the metacarpal-phalangeal joints (knuckles) are examples.
- Saddle: Articulating surfaces are saddle-shaped; the articulating surface of one bone is convex, and the reciprocal surface is concave. Saddle joints, which are biaxial, include the joint between the thumb metacarpal and the trapezium of the wrist.
- Ball and socket: The ball-shaped head of one bone fits into a cuplike depression of another. These are multiaxial joints, allowing movement in all directions and pivotal rotation. Examples are the shoulder and hip joints.

2.   Examine the articulated skeleton, anatomical charts, and yourself to identify the subcategories of synovial joints. Make sure you understand the terms *uniaxial, biaxial,* and *multiaxial.*

3.   Compare and contrast the structure of the hip and knee joints (Figure 13.4). Both of these joints are large weight-bearing joints of the lower limb but they differ substantially in their security. Read through the questions in the review section that pertain to this exercise before beginning your comparison.

Hip Replacement	# 45172
Elbow Joint	# 44607
Dislocation	# 45322

JOINT DISORDERS

Most of us don't think about our joints until something goes wrong with them. Joint pains and malfunctions may be caused by a variety of things. For example, a hard blow to the knee can cause a painful **bursitis,** known as "water on the knee," due to damage to, or inflammation of, the patellar bursa. Slippage of a fibrocartilage pad or the tearing of a ligament may result in a painful condition that persists over a long period, since these poorly vascularized structures heal so slowly.

Sprains and dislocations are other types of joint problems. In a **sprain,** the ligaments reinforcing a joint are damaged by excessive stretching or are torn away from the bony attachment. Since both ligaments and tendons are cords of dense connective tissue with a poor blood supply, sprains heal slowly and are quite painful. **Dislocations** occur when bones are forced out of their normal position in the joint cavity. They are normally

accompanied by torn or stressed ligaments and considerable inflammation. The process of returning the bone to its proper position, called *reduction,* should be done only by a physician. Attempts by the untrained person to "snap the bone back into its socket" are often more harmful than helpful.

Advancing years also take their toll on joints. Weight-bearing joints in particular eventually begin to degenerate. *Adhesions* (fibrous bands) may form between the surfaces where bones join, and extraneous bone tissue (*spurs*) may grow along the joint edges. Such degenerative changes lead to the complaint so often heard from the elderly: "My joints are getting so stiff. . . ."

- If possible compare an X-ray of an arthritic joint to one of a normal joint. ■

Rheumatoid Arthritis	# 10313
Osteoarthritis, Vertebra	# 10946
Arthritis, Gouty; Tophus & Hands	# 25521

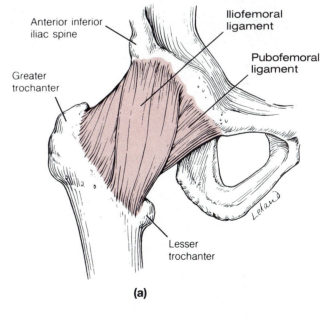

(a)

F13.4

Comparative anatomy of the hip and knee joints.
(a) Ligamentous reinforcements of right hip joint, anterior view. (Figure continued on following page.)

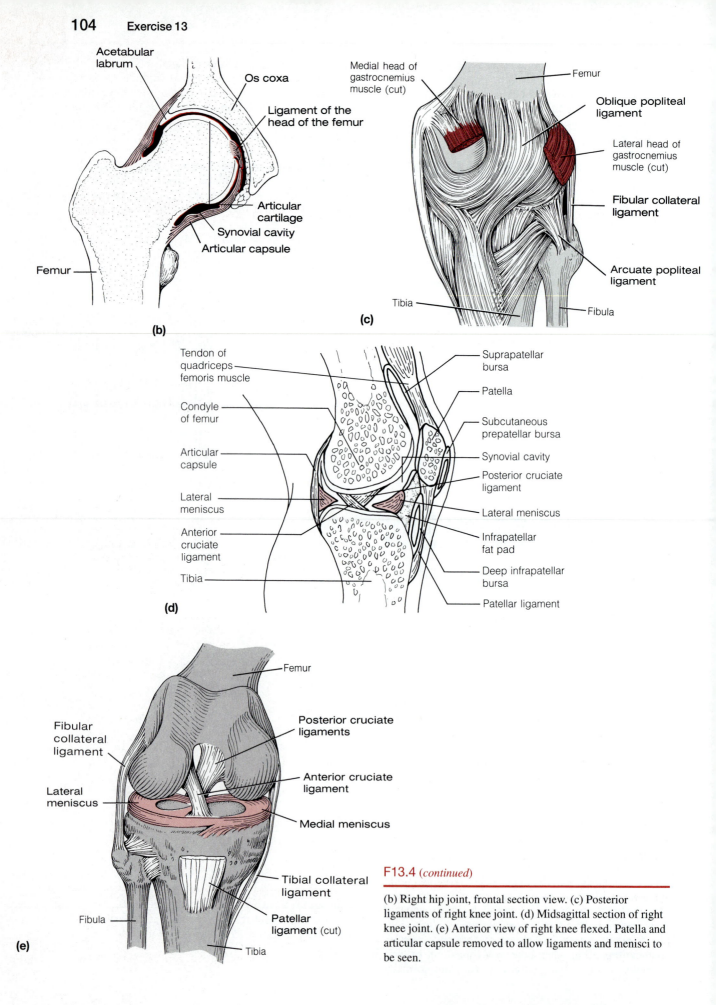

(b) Acetabular labrum, Os coxa, Ligament of the head of the femur, Articular cartilage, Synovial cavity, Articular capsule, Femur

(c) Medial head of gastrocnemius muscle (cut), Femur, Oblique popliteal ligament, Lateral head of gastrocnemius muscle (cut), Fibular collateral ligament, Arcuate popliteal ligament, Tibia, Fibula

(d) Tendon of quadriceps femoris muscle, Condyle of femur, Articular capsule, Lateral meniscus, Anterior cruciate ligament, Tibia, Suprapatellar bursa, Patella, Subcutaneous prepatellar bursa, Synovial cavity, Posterior cruciate ligament, Lateral meniscus, Infrapatellar fat pad, Deep infrapatellar bursa, Patellar ligament

(e) Femur, Fibular collateral ligament, Posterior cruciate ligaments, Anterior cruciate ligament, Lateral meniscus, Medial meniscus, Tibial collateral ligament, Patellar ligament (cut), Fibula, Tibia

F13.4 *(continued)*

(b) Right hip joint, frontal section view. (c) Posterior ligaments of right knee joint. (d) Midsagittal section of right knee joint. (e) Anterior view of right knee flexed. Patella and articular capsule removed to allow ligaments and menisci to be seen.

Microscopic Anatomy, Organization, and Classification of Skeletal Muscle, and Body Movements

OBJECTIVES

1. To describe the structure of skeletal muscle from gross to microscopic levels.

2. To define and explain the role of the following:

actin	myofilament	tendon
myosin	perimysium	endomysium
fiber	aponeurosis	epimysium
myofibril		

3. To describe the structure of a neuromuscular junction and to explain its role in muscle function.

4. To define: agonist (prime mover), antagonist, synergist, and fixator.

5. To cite criteria used in naming skeletal muscles.

6. To demonstrate or identify the various body movements.

MATERIALS

Three-dimensional model of skeletal muscle cells (if available)
Forceps
Dissecting needles
Microscope slides and coverslips
0.9% saline solution in dropper bottles
Chicken breast or thigh muscle (freshly obtained from the meat market)
Compound microscope
Histological slides of skeletal muscle (longitudinal and cross-sectional) and skeletal muscle showing neuro-muscular junctions
Three-dimensional model of skeletal muscle showing neuromuscular junction (if available)

The bulk of the body's muscle is called **skeletal muscle** because it is attached to the skeleton (or underlying connective tissue). Skeletal muscle influences body contours and shape, allows you to grin and frown, provides a means of locomotion, and enables you to manipulate the environment. The balance of the body's muscle— smooth and cardiac muscle—is the major component of the walls of hollow organs and the heart, where it is involved with the transport of materials within the body.

Each of the three muscle types has a structure and function uniquely suited to its task in the body. However, because the term *muscular system* applies specifically to skeletal muscle, the primary objective of this unit is to investigate the structure and function of skeletal muscle.

Skeletal muscle is also known as *voluntary muscle* (because it can be consciously controlled) and as *striated muscle* (because it appears to be striped). As you might guess from both of these alternative names, skeletal muscle has some very special characteristics. Thus an investigation of skeletal muscle should begin at the cellular level.

THE CELLS OF SKELETAL MUSCLE

Skeletal muscle is composed of relatively large, long cylindrical cells ranging from 10 to 100 μm in diameter and up to 6 cm in length. However, the cells of large, hard-working muscles like the antigravity muscles of the hip are extremely coarse, ranging up to 25 cm in length, and can be seen with the naked eye.

Skeletal muscle cells (Figure 14.1a) are multinucleate: Multiple oval nuclei can be seen just beneath the plasma membrane (called the *sarcolemma* in these cells). The nuclei are pushed peripherally by the longitudinally arranged **myofibrils,** which nearly fill the sarcoplasm (Figure 14.1b). Alternating light (I) and dark (A) bands along the length of the perfectly aligned myofibrils give the muscle fiber as a whole its striped appearance.

Electron microscope studies have revealed that the myofibrils are made up of even smaller threadlike structures called **myofilaments** (Figure 14.1b and d). The myofilaments are composed largely of two varieties of contractile proteins—**actin** and **myosin**—which slide past each other during muscle activity to bring about shortening or contraction of the muscle cells. It is the highly specific arrangement of the myofilaments within the myofibrils that is responsible for the banding pattern in skeletal muscle. The actual contractile units of muscle, called **sarcomeres,** extend from the middle of one I band (its Z line) to the middle of the next along the length of the myofibrils. (See Figure 14.1c and'd.)

1. Look at the three-dimensional model of skeletal muscle cells, noting the relative shape and size of the cells. Identify the nuclei, myofibrils, and light and dark bands.

2. Obtain forceps, two dissecting needles, slide and coverslip, and a dropper bottle of saline solution. With forceps, remove a very small piece of muscle from the chicken breast (or thigh). Place the tissue on a clean microscope slide, and add a drop of the

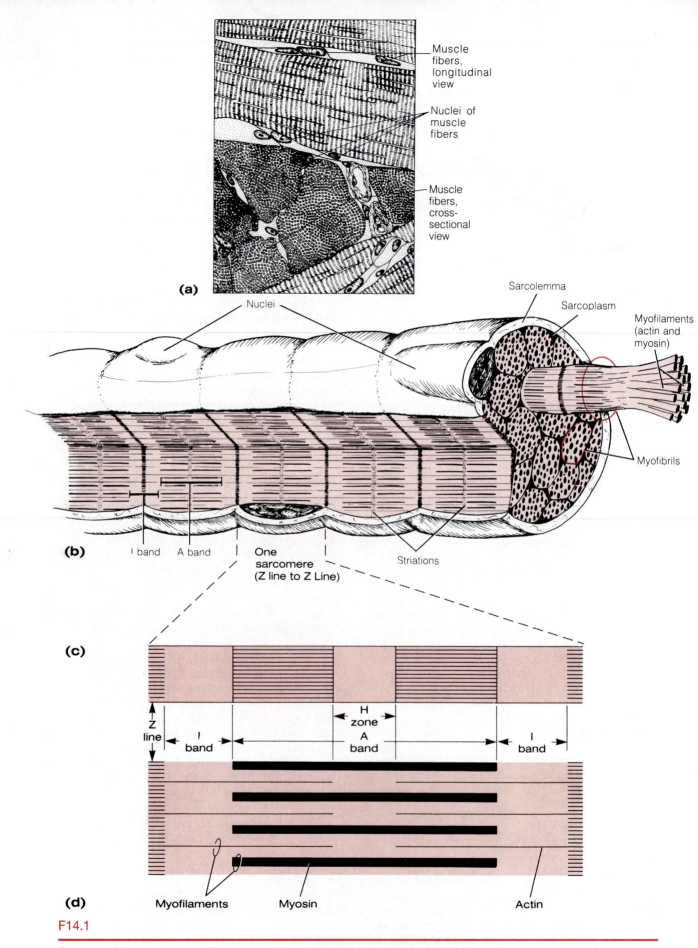

(a)

Muscle fibers, longitudinal view

Nuclei of muscle fibers

Muscle fibers, cross-sectional view

(b)

Nuclei

Sarcolemma

Sarcoplasm

Myofilaments (actin and myosin)

Myofibrils

I band   A band   One sarcomere (Z line to Z Line)   Striations

(c)

Z line

I band

H zone

A band

I band

(d)

Myofilaments   Myosin   Actin

F14.1

Structure of skeletal muscle cells. (a) Muscle fibers, longitudinal and transverse views. (See corresponding photomicrograph in Plate 2 of the Histology Atlas.) (b) A portion of a skeletal muscle cell; one myofibril has been extended and disrupted to indicate its myofilament composition. (c) One sarcomere of the myofibril. (d) Banding pattern in the sarcomere. (From H. E. Huxley, "The Contraction of Muscle." © November 1958 by Scientific American, Inc. All rights reserved.)

saline solution. Pull the muscle fibers apart with the dissecting needles (tease them) until you have a fluffy-looking mass of tissue. Cover the teased tissue with a coverslip, and observe under the high-power lens of a microscope. Look for the banding pattern. Regulate the light carefully to obtain the highest possible contrast.

3.   Now compare your observations with what can be seen with professionally prepared muscle tissue. Obtain a slide of skeletal muscle (longitudinal section), and view it under high power. From your observations, draw a small section of a muscle fiber in the space provided here. Label the nuclei, cell membrane, and A and I bands.

What structural details become apparent with the prepared slide?

_____

_____

ORGANIZATION OF SKELETAL MUSCLE CELLS INTO MUSCLES

Muscle fibers are soft and surprisingly fragile. Thus thousands of muscle fibers are bundled together with connective tissue to form the organs we refer to as skeletal muscles (Figure 14.2). Each muscle fiber is enclosed in a delicate, areolar connective tissue sheath called **endomysium.** Several sheathed muscle fibers are wrapped by a collagenic membrane called **perimysium,** forming a bundle of fibers called a **fascicle,** or **fasciculus.** A large number of fascicles are bound together by a substantially coarser "overcoat" of dense connective tissue called an **epimysium,** which sheathes the entire muscle. These epimysia blend into the **deep fascia,** still coarser sheets of dense connective tissue that bind muscles into functional groups, and into strong cordlike **tendons** or sheetlike **aponeuroses,** which attach muscles to each other or indirectly to bones.

The tendons perform several functions, two of the most important being to provide durability and to conserve space. Because tendons are tough collagenic connective tissue, they can span rough bony prominences that would destroy the more delicate muscle tissues. And because of their relatively small size, more tendons than fleshy muscles can pass over a joint.

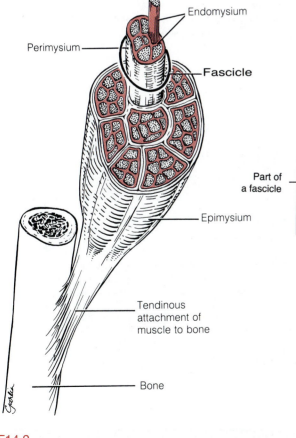

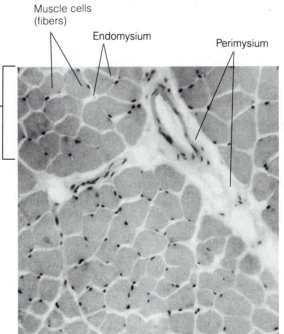

F14.2

Connective tissue coverings of skeletal muscle (64×).

In addition to supporting and binding the muscle fibers, and providing strength to the muscle as a whole, the connective tissue wrappings provide a route for the entry and exit of nerves and blood vessels that serve the muscle fibers. The larger, more powerful muscles have relatively more connective tissue than muscles involved in fine or delicate movements.

As we age, the amount of muscle fiber decreases, and the amount of connective tissue increases; thus the skeletal muscles gradually become more sinewy, or "stringier." ■

 Obtain a slide showing a cross section of skeletal muscle tissue. Using Figure 14.2 as a reference, identify the muscle fibers, endomysium, perimysium, and epimysium (if visible).

Muscle, Skeletal, Sarcomere, Bands	# 44106	‖‖‖‖‖
Muscle, Striated,	# 44115	‖‖‖‖‖
Sarcomere, Muscle, Skeletal	# 48739	‖‖‖‖‖
Muscle, Skeletal, End of Fiber	# 44104	‖‖‖‖‖

THE NEUROMUSCULAR JUNCTION

Voluntary muscle cells are always stimulated by nerve impulses via motor neurons. The junction between a nerve fiber (axon) and a muscle cell is called a **neuromuscular,** or **myoneural, junction** (Figure 14.3).

Each motor axon breaks up into many branches called *axonal terminals* as it approaches the muscle, and each of these branches participates in forming a neuromuscular junction with a single muscle cell. Thus a single neuron may stimulate many muscle fibers. Together, a neuron and all the muscle cells it stimulates make up the functional structure called the **motor unit.** Part of a motor unit is shown in Figure 14.4 and in Plate 3 of the Histology Atlas..

Each axonal terminal has numerous projections called **sole feet.** The neuron and muscle fiber membranes, close as they are, do not actually touch. They are separated by a small fluid-filled gap of 300 to 500 Å, called the **synaptic cleft** (see Figure 14.3).

Within the sole foot are many mitochondria and vesicles containing a neurotransmitter chemical called acetylcholine. When a nerve impulse reaches the end plate, some of these vesicles liberate their contents into the synaptic cleft. The acetylcholine rapidly diffuses

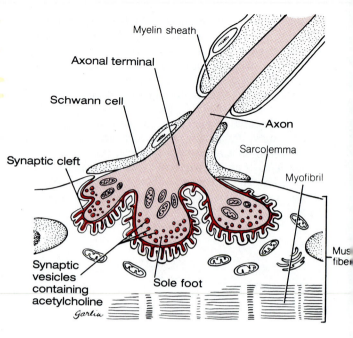

F14.3

The neuromuscular junction.

across the junction and combines with the receptors on the sarcolemma. If sufficient acetylcholine has been released, a transient change in the permeability of the sarcolemma briefly allows more sodium ions to diffuse into the muscle fiber, resulting in the depolarization of the sarcolemma and subsequent contraction of the muscle fiber.

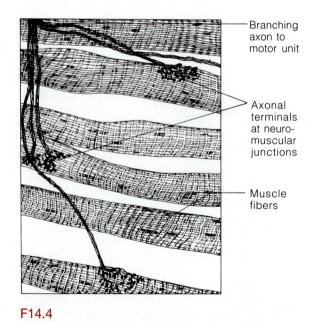

F14.4

A portion of a motor unit. (Corresponding photomicrograph is Plate 3 in the Histology Atlas.)

1. If possible, examine a three-dimensional model of skeletal muscle cells that illustrates the neuromuscular junction. Identify the structures just described.

2. Obtain a slide of skeletal muscle stained to show a portion of a motor unit. Examine the slide under high power to identify the axonal fibers extending leashlike to the muscle cells. Follow one of the axonal fibers to its terminus to identify the oval-shaped motor end plate. Compare your observations to Figure 14.4. Sketch a small section in the space provided, labeling the motor axon, its terminal branches, sole feet, and muscle fibers.

Motor Endplate EM	# 09194	‖‖‖‖‖‖‖‖
Synapse, Neuro-muscular Junction	# 44119	‖‖‖‖‖‖‖‖

CLASSIFICATION OF SKELETAL MUSCLES

Naming Skeletal Muscles

Remembering the names of the skeletal muscles is a monumental task, but certain clues help. Muscles are named on the basis of the following criteria:

- **Direction of muscle fibers:** Some muscles are named in reference to some imaginary line, usually the midline of the body or the longitudinal axis of a limb bone. A muscle with fibers (and fascicles) running parallel to that imaginary line will have the term *rectus* (straight) in its name. For example, the rectus abdominis is the straight muscle of the abdomen. Likewise, the terms *transverse* and *oblique* in-

dicate that the muscle fibers run at right angles and obliquely (respectively) to the imaginary line.
- **Relative size of the muscle:** Terms such as *maximus* (largest), *minimus* (smallest), *longus* (long), and *brevis* (short) are often used in the names of muscles—as in gluteus maximus and gluteus minimus.
- **Location of the muscle:** Some muscles are named according to the bone with which they are associated. For example, the frontalis muscle overlies the frontal bone.
- **Number of origins:** When the term *biceps, triceps,* or *quadriceps* forms part of a muscle name, you can generally assume that the muscle has two, three, or four origins (respectively). For example, the biceps muscle of the arm has two heads, or origins.
- **Location of the muscle's origin and insertion:** For example, the sternocleidomastoid muscle has its origin on the sternum (*sterno*) and clavicle (*cleido*), and inserts on the mastoid process of the temporal bone.
- **Shape of the muscle:** For example, the deltoid muscle is roughly triangular (*deltoid* means "triangle"), and the trapezius muscle resembles a trapezoid.
- **Action of the muscle:** For example, all the adductor muscles of the anterior thigh bring about its adduction, and all the extensor muscles of the wrist extend the wrist.

Types of Muscles

Most often, body movements are not a result of the contraction of a single muscle but instead reflect the coordinated action of several muscles acting together. Muscles that are primarily responsible for producing a particular movement are called **prime movers,** or **agonists.**

Muscles that oppose or reverse a movement are called **antagonists.** When a prime mover is active, the fibers of the antagonist are stretched and in the relaxed state. The antagonist can also regulate the prime mover by providing some resistance, to prevent overshoot or to stop its action.

It should be noted that antagonists can be prime movers in their own right. For example, the biceps muscle of the arm (a prime mover of elbow flexion) is antagonized by the triceps (a prime mover of elbow extension).

Synergists contribute substantially to the action of agonists by reducing undesirable or unnecessary movement. Contraction of a muscle crossing two or more joints would cause movement at all joints spanned if the synergists were not there to stabilize them. For example, you can make a fist without bending your wrist only because synergist muscles stabilize the wrist joint and allow the prime mover to exert its force at the finger joints.

Fixators, or fixation muscles, are specialized synergists. They immobilize the origin of a prime mover so that all the tension is exerted at the insertion. Muscles that help maintain posture are fixators; so too are muscles of the back that stabilize or "fix" the scapula during arm movements.

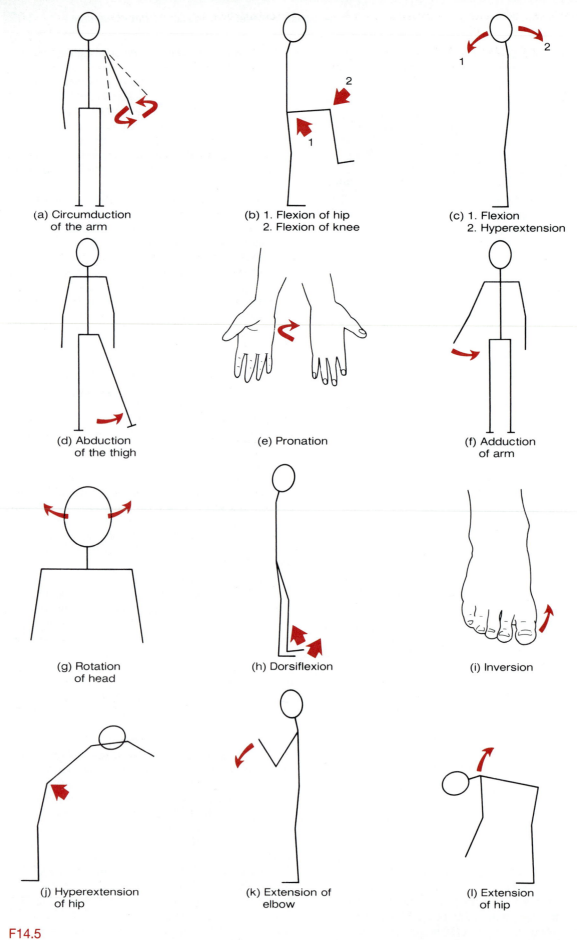

(a) Circumduction of the arm

(b) 1. Flexion of hip
2. Flexion of knee

(c) 1. Flexion
2. Hyperextension

(d) Abduction of the thigh

(e) Pronation

(f) Adduction of arm

(g) Rotation of head

(h) Dorsiflexion

(i) Inversion

(j) Hyperextension of hip

(k) Extension of elbow

(l) Extension of hip

Movements occurring at synovial joints of the body.

BODY MOVEMENTS

Every muscle of the body is attached to bone (or other connective tissue structures) at two points—the **origin** (the stationary, immovable, or less movable attachment) and the **insertion** (the movable attachment). Body movement occurs when muscles contract across diarthrotic or synovial joints. When the muscle contracts and its fibers shorten, the insertion moves toward the origin. The type of movement depends on the construction of the joint (uniaxial, biaxial, or multiaxial) and on the placement of the muscle relative to the joint. The most common types of body movements are described below and illustrated in Figure 14.5.

 Attempt to demonstrate each movement as you read through the following material:

Flexion: a movement, generally in the sagittal plane, that decreases the angle of the joint and lessens the distance between the two bones. Flexion is typical of hinge joints (bending the knee or elbow), but is also common at ball-and-socket joints (bending forward at the hip).

Extension: a movement that increases the angle of a joint and the distance between two bones or parts of the body (straightening the knee or elbow). Extension is the opposite of flexion. If extension is greater than 180 degrees (bending the trunk backward), it is termed *hyperextension.*

Abduction: movement of a limb away from the midline or median plane of the body, generally on the frontal plane, or the fanning movement of fingers or toes when they are spread apart.

Adduction: movement of a limb toward the midline of the body. Adduction is the opposite of abduction.

Rotation: movement of a bone around its longitudinal axis without lateral or medial displacement. Rotation, a common movement of ball-and-socket joints, also describes the movement of the atlas around the odontoid process of the axis.

Circumduction: a combination of flexion, extension, abduction, and adduction commonly observed in ball-and-socket joints like the shoulder. The proximal end of the limb remains stationary, and the distal end moves in a circle. The limb as a whole outlines a cone.

Pronation: movement of the palm of the hand from an anterior or upward-facing position to a posterior or downward-facing position. This action moves the distal end of the radius across the ulna.

Supination: movement of the palm from a posterior position to an anterior position (the anatomical position). Supination is the opposite of pronation. During supination, the radius and ulna are parallel.

The last four terms refer to movements of the foot:

Inversion: a movement that results in the medial turning of the sole of the foot.

Eversion: a movement that results in the lateral turning of the sole of the foot; the opposite of inversion.

Dorsiflexion: a movement of the ankle joint in a dorsal direction (standing on one's heels).

Plantarflexion: a movement of the ankle joint in which the foot is flexed downward (standing on one's toes or pointing the toes).

Know origin + insertion
Know functions

Gross Anatomy of the Muscular System

IDENTIFICATION OF HUMAN MUSCLES

Muscles of the Head and Neck

The muscles of the head serve many specific functions. For instance, the muscles of facial expression differ from most skeletal muscles because they insert into the skin (or other muscles) rather than into bone. As a result, they move the facial skin, allowing a wide range of emotions to be shown on the face. Other muscles of the head are the muscles of mastication, which manipulate the mandible during chewing, and the six extrinsic eye muscles located within the orbit, which aim the eye. (The orbital muscles are studied in conjunction with the anatomy of the eye in Exercise 24.) Neck muscles are primarily concerned with the movement of the head and shoulder girdle. Figures 15.1 and 15.2 are summary figures illustrating the superficial musculature of the body as a whole. The head and neck muscles are discussed in Tables 15.1 and 15.2 and shown in Figures 15.3 and 15.4.

Carefully read the description of each muscle and attempt to visualize what happens when the muscle contracts. Once you have read through the tables and have identified the head and neck muscles in Figures 15.3 and 15.4, use a torso model or an anatomical chart to again identify as many of these muscles as possible. (If a human cadaver is available for observation, specific instructions for muscle examination will be provided by your instructor.) Then carry out the following palpations on yourself:

- To demonstrate how the temporalis works, clench

your teeth. The masseter can also be palpated at this time at the angle of the jaw.

Muscles of the Trunk

The trunk musculature includes muscles that move the vertebral column; anterior thorax muscles that act to move ribs, head, and arms; and muscles of the abdominal wall that play a role in the movement of the vertebral column but more importantly form the "natural girdle," or the major portion of the abdominal body wall.

 The trunk muscles are described in Tables 15.3 and 15.4 and shown in Figures 15.5 and 15.6. As before, identify the muscles in the figure as you read the tabular descriptions and then identify them on the torso or laboratory chart.

When you have completed this study, work with a partner to demonstrate the operation of the following muscles. One of you can demonstrate the movement (the following steps are addressed to this partner); the other can supply the necessary resistance and palpate the muscle being tested.

1. Start by fully abducting the arm and extending the elbow. Now try to adduct the arm against resistance. You are exercising the *latissimus dorsi*.
2. To observe the *deltoid*, attempt to abduct your arm against resistance. Now attempt to elevate your shoulder against resistance; you are contracting the upper portion of the *trapezius*.
3. The *pectoralis major* comes into play when you press your hands together at chest level with your elbows widely abducted.

(Text continues on p. 125)

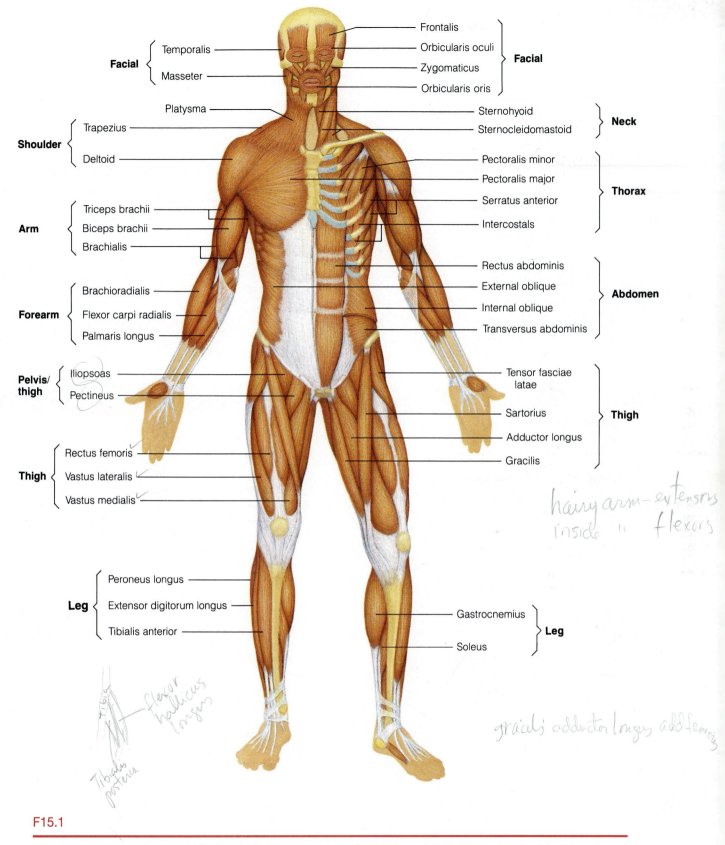

Facial
- Temporalis
- Masseter

Facial
- Frontalis
- Orbicularis oculi
- Zygomaticus
- Orbicularis oris

Platysma

Neck
- Sternohyoid
- Sternocleidomastoid

Shoulder
- Trapezius
- Deltoid

Thorax
- Pectoralis minor
- Pectoralis major
- Serratus anterior
- Intercostals

Arm
- Triceps brachii
- Biceps brachii
- Brachialis

Forearm
- Brachioradialis
- Flexor carpi radialis
- Palmaris longus

Abdomen
- Rectus abdominis
- External oblique
- Internal oblique
- Transversus abdominis

Pelvis/thigh
- Iliopsoas
- Pectineus

Thigh
- Tensor fasciae latae
- Sartorius
- Adductor longus
- Gracilis

Thigh
- Rectus femoris
- Vastus lateralis
- Vastus medialis

Leg
- Peroneus longus
- Extensor digitorum longus
- Tibialis anterior

Leg
- Gastrocnemius
- Soleus

hairy arm-extensors inside " flexors

flexor hallucis longus

Tibialis posterior

Tibia

gracilis adductor longus add femoris

F15.1

Anterior view of superficial muscles of the body. The abdominal surface has been partially dissected on the right side to show somewhat deeper muscles.

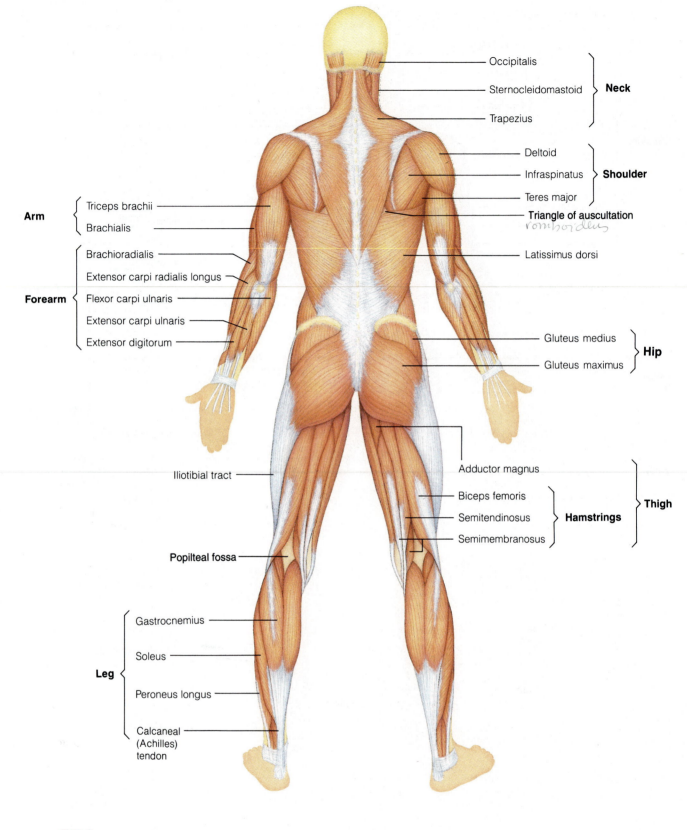

Neck
- Occipitalis
- Sternocleidomastoid
- Trapezius

Shoulder
- Deltoid
- Infraspinatus
- Teres major
- **Triangle of auscultation**

romboidlus

- Latissimus dorsi

Arm
- Triceps brachii
- Brachialis

Forearm
- Brachioradialis
- Extensor carpi radialis longus
- Flexor carpi ulnaris
- Extensor carpi ulnaris
- Extensor digitorum

Hip
- Gluteus medius
- Gluteus maximus

Thigh
- Adductor magnus
- **Hamstrings**
  - Biceps femoris
  - Semitendinosus
  - Semimembranosus

- Iliotibial tract

- **Popilteal fossa**

Leg
- Gastrocnemius
- Soleus
- Peroneus longus
- Calcaneal (Achilles) tendon

F15.2

Posterior view of superficial muscles of the body, diagrammatic view.

TABLE 15.1   Major Muscles of Human Head (see Figure 15.3)

Muscle	Comments	Origin	Insertion	Action
Facial Expression (Figure 15.3a)				
Epicranius—frontalis and occipitalis	Bipartite muscle consisting of frontalis and occipitalis, which covers dome of skull	Frontalis: cranial aponeurosis (galea aponeurotica); occipitalis: occipital bone	Frontalis: skin of eyebrows and root of nose; occipitalis: cranial aponeurosis	With aponeurosis fixed, frontalis raises eyebrows; occipitalis fixes aponeurosis and pulls scalp posteriorly
Orbicularis oculi	Sphincter muscle of eyelids	Frontal and maxillary bones and ligaments around orbit	Encircles orbit and inserts in tissue of eyelid	Various parts can be activated individually; closes eyes, produces blinking, squinting, and draws eyebrows downward
Corrugator supercilii	Small muscle; activity associated with that of orbicularis oculi	Arch of frontal bone above nasal bone	Skin of eyebrow	Draws eyebrows medially; wrinkles skin of forehead vertically
Levator labii superioris	Thin muscle between orbicularis oris and inferior eye margin	Zygomatic bone and infraorbital margin of maxilla	Skin and muscle of upper lip and border of nostril	Raises and furrows upper lip; flares nostril (as in disgust)
Zygomaticus—major and minor	Extends diagonally from corner of mouth to cheekbone	Zygomatic bone	Skin and muscle at corner of mouth	Raises lateral corners of mouth upward (smiling muscle)
Risorius	Slender muscle; runs laterally to zygomaticus	Fascia of masseter muscle	Skin at corner of mouth	Draws corner of lip laterally; tenses lip; zygomaticus synergist
Depressor labii inferioris	Small muscle from lower lip to jawbone	Body of mandible lateral to its midline	Skin and muscle of lower lip	Draws lower lip downward
Depressor anguli oris	Small muscle lateral to depressor labii inferioris	Body of mandible below incisors	Skin and muscle at angle of mouth below insertion of zygomaticus	Zygomaticus antagonist; draws corners of mouth downward and laterally
Orbicularis oris	Multilayered sphincter muscle of lips with fibers that run in many different directions	Arises indirectly from maxilla and mandible; fibers blended with fibers of other muscles associated with lips	Encircles mouth; inserts into muscle and skin at angles of mouth	Closes mouth; purses and protrudes lips (kissing muscle)
Mentalis	One of muscle pair forming V-shaped muscle mass on chin	Mandible below incisors	Skin of chin	Protrudes lower lip; wrinkles chin
Buccinator	Principal muscle of cheek; runs horizontally, deep to the masseter	Molar region of maxilla and mandible	Orbicularis oris	Draws corner of mouth laterally; compresses cheek (as in whistling); holds food between teeth during chewing

(continued)

TABLE 15.3 *(Continued)*

Muscle	Comments	Origin	Insertion	Action
Deltoid	Fleshy triangular muscle forming shoulder muscle mass	Lateral third of clavicle; acromion and spine of scapula	Deltoid tuberosity of humerus	Acting as a whole, prime mover of arm abduction; when only specific fibers are active, can aid in flexion, extension, and rotation of humerus
Pectoralis minor	Flat, thin muscle directly beneath and obscured by pectoralis major	Anterior surface of third, fourth, and fifth ribs, near their costal cartilages	Coracoid process of scapula	With ribs fixed, draws scapula forward and inferiorly; with scapula fixed, draws rib cage superiorly
Intercostals—external	11 pairs lie between ribs; fibers run obliquely downward and forward toward sternum	Inferior border of rib above (not shown in figure)	Superior border of rib below	Pulls ribs toward one another to elevate rib cage; aids in inspiration
Intercostals—internal	11 pairs lie between ribs; fibers run deep and at right angles to those of external intercostals	Superior border of rib below	Inferior border of rib above (not shown in figure)	Draws ribs together to depress rib cage; aids in forced expiration; antagonistic to external intercostals

Abdominal Wall (Figure 15.5b and c)

Muscle	Comments	Origin	Insertion	Action
Rectus abdominis	Medial superficial muscle, extends from pubis to rib cage; ensheathed by aponeuroses of oblique muscles; segmented	Pubic crest and symphysis	Xiphoid process and costal cartilages of fifth through seventh ribs	Flexes vertebral column; increases abdominal pressure; fixes and depresses ribs; stabilizes pelvis during walking
External oblique	Most superficial lateral muscle; fibers run downward and medially; ensheathed by an aponeurosis	Anterior surface of last eight ribs	Linea alba,* pubic tubercles, and iliac crest	See Rectus abdominis, above; also aids muscles of back in trunk rotation and lateral flexion
Internal oblique	Fibers run at right angles to those of external oblique, which it underlies	Lumbodorsal fascia, iliac crest, and inguinal ligament	Linea alba, pubic crest, and costal cartilages of last three ribs	As for External oblique
Transversus abdominis	Deepest muscle of abdominal wall; fibers run horizontally	Inguinal ligament, iliac crest, and cartilages of last five or six ribs	Linea alba and pubic crest	Compresses abdominal contents

*The linea alba ("white line") is a narrow, tendinous sheath that runs along the middle of the abdomen from the sternum to the pubic symphysis. It is formed by the fusion of the aponeurosis of the external oblique and transversus muscles.

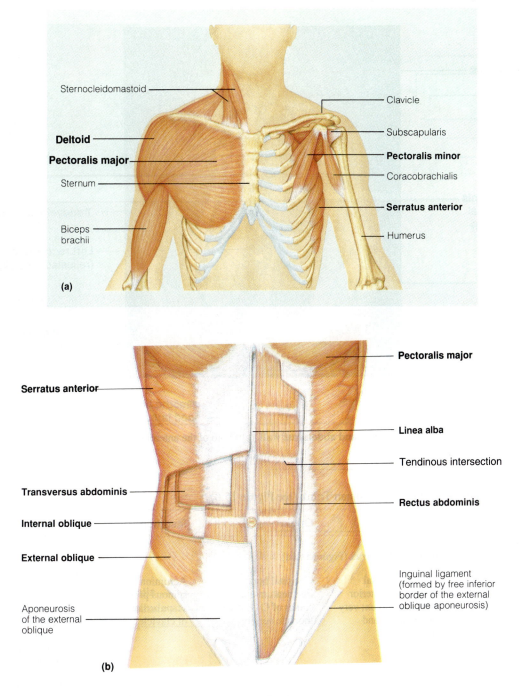

F15.5

Anterior muscles of the thorax, shoulder, and abdominal wall. (a) Anterior thorax. The superficial pectoralis major and deltoid muscles that affect arm movements are illustrated on the left. These muscles have been removed on the right side of the figure to illustrate the pectoralis minor, serratus anterior, and subscapularis muscles. (b) Anterior view of the muscles forming the anterolateral abdominal wall. The superficial muscles have been partially cut away on the left side of the diagram to reveal the deeper internal oblique and transversus abdominis muscles.

(*continued*)

Thorax, Anterior View   # 44935

Thorax, Anterior View   # 44947

TABLE 15.6   *(Continued)*

Muscle	Comments	Origin	Insertion	Action
Flexor digitorum superficialis	Deeper muscle; overlain by muscles named above; visible at distal end of forearm	Medial epicondyle of humerus, medial surface of ulna, and anterior border of radius	Middle phalanges of second through fifth fingers	Flexes wrist and middle phalanges of second through fifth fingers

Deep

Muscle	Comments	Origin	Insertion	Action
Flexor pollicis longus	Deep muscle of anterior forearm; distal to and paralleling lower margin of flexor digitorum superficialis	Anterior surface of radius, and interosseous membrane	Distal phalanx of thumb	Flexes thumb (*pollix* is Latin for "thumb"); weak flexor of wrist
Flexor digitorum profundus	Deep muscle; overlain entirely by flexor digitorum superficialis	Anteromedial surface of ulna and interosseous membrane	Distal phalanges of second through fifth fingers	Sole muscle that flexes distal phalanges; assists in wrist flexion
Pronator quadratus	Deepest muscle of distal forearm	Distal portion of anterior ulnar surface	Anterior surface of radius, distal end	Pronates forearm

Posterior Compartment (Figure 15.8e,f)

Superficial

Muscle	Comments	Origin	Insertion	Action
Extensor carpi radialis longus	Superficial; parallels brachioradialis on lateral forearm	Lateral supracondylar ridge of humerus	Base of second metacarpal	Extends and abducts wrist
Extensor carpi radialis brevis	Posterior to extensor carpi radialis longus	Lateral epicondyle of humerus	Base of third metacarpal	Extends and abducts wrist; steadies wrist during finger flexion
Extensor carpi ulnaris	Superficial; medial posterior forearm	Lateral epicondyle of humerus	Base of fifth metacarpal	Extends and adducts wrist
Extensor digitorum	Superficial; between extensor carpi ulnaris and extensor carpi radialis brevis	Lateral epicondyle of humerus	By four tendons into distal phalanges of second through fifth fingers	Prime mover of finger extension; extends wrist; can flare (abduct) fingers

Deep

Muscle	Comments	Origin	Insertion	Action
Extensor pollicis longus and brevis	Deep muscle pair with a common origin and action; overlain by extensor carpi ulnaris	Dorsal shaft of ulna and radius, interosseous membrane	Base of distal phalanx of thumb (longus) and proximal phalanx of thumb (brevis)	Extends thumb
Abductor pollicis longus	Deep muscle; lateral and parallel to extensor pollicis longus	Posterior surface of radius and ulna; interosseous membrane	First metacarpal	Abducts and extends thumb
Supinator	Deep muscle at posterior aspect of elbow	Lateral epicondyle of humerus	Proximal end of radius	Acts with biceps brachii to supinate forearm; antagonistic to pronator muscles

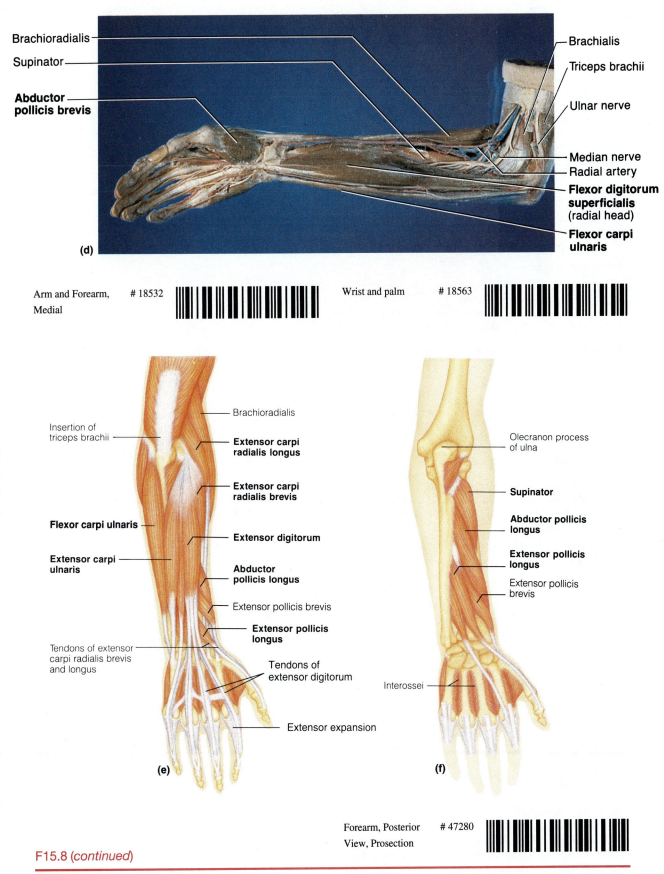

Brachioradialis

Supinator

Abductor pollicis brevis

Brachialis

Triceps brachii

Ulnar nerve

Median nerve

Radial artery

Flexor digitorum superficialis (radial head)

Flexor carpi ulnaris

(d)

Arm and Forearm, Medial   # 18532

Wrist and palm   # 18563

Insertion of triceps brachii

Brachioradialis

Extensor carpi radialis longus

Extensor carpi radialis brevis

Flexor carpi ulnaris

Extensor digitorum

Extensor carpi ulnaris

Abductor pollicis longus

Extensor pollicis brevis

Extensor pollicis longus

Tendons of extensor carpi radialis brevis and longus

Tendons of extensor digitorum

Extensor expansion

(e)

Olecranon process of ulna

Supinator

Abductor pollicis longus

Extensor pollicis longus

Extensor pollicis brevis

Interossei

(f)

Forearm, Posterior View, Prosection   # 47280

F15.8 *(continued)*

Muscles of the forearm and wrist. (d) Photo of muscles of the anteromedial aspect of the forearm. The pronator teres and flexor carpi radialis muscles have been removed. (e) Superficial muscles, posterior view. (f) Deep posterior muscles; superficial muscles have been removed. The interossei, the deepest layer of intrinsic hand muscles, are also illustrated.

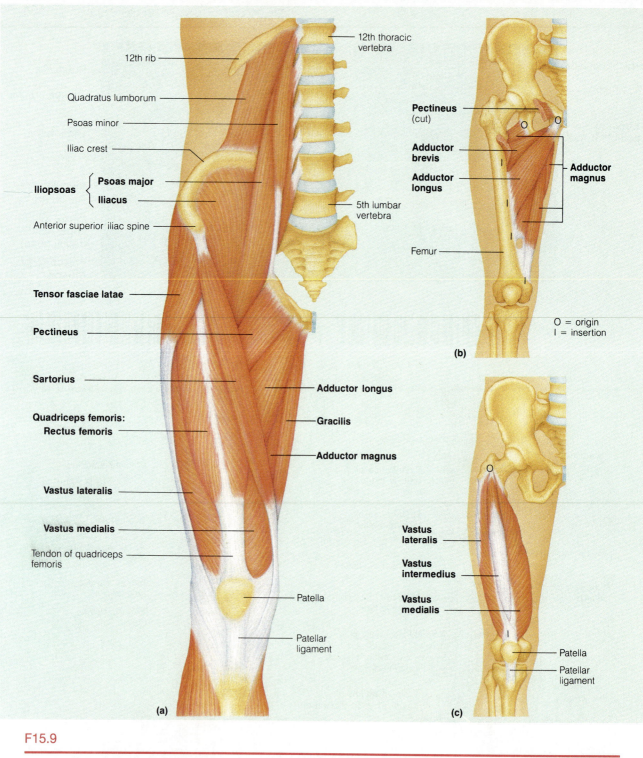

12th thoracic vertebra

12th rib

Quadratus lumborum

Psoas minor

Iliac crest

Iliopsoas { **Psoas major** / **Iliacus** }

5th lumbar vertebra

Anterior superior iliac spine

Tensor fasciae latae

Pectineus

Sartorius

Quadriceps femoris:
Rectus femoris

Vastus lateralis

Vastus medialis

Tendon of quadriceps femoris

Patella

Patellar ligament

Adductor longus

Gracilis

Adductor magnus

(a)

Pectineus (cut)

Adductor brevis

Adductor longus

Adductor magnus

O

O

Femur

O = origin
I = insertion

(b)

Vastus lateralis

Vastus intermedius

Vastus medialis

Patella

Patellar ligament

O

I

(c)

F15.9

Anterior view of the deep muscles of the pelvis and superficial muscles of the right thigh.

Hip, Anterior   # 48779

summarized in Tables 15.7 and 15.8 and illustrated in Figures 15.9 and 15.10.

Muscles acting on the leg form the major musculature of the thigh. (Anatomically the term *leg* refers only to that portion between the knee and the ankle.) The thigh muscles cross the knee to allow its flexion and extension. They include the hamstrings and the quadriceps and, along with the muscles acting on the thigh, are described in Tables 15.7 and 15.8 and illustrated in Figures

15.9 and 15.10. Since some of these muscles also have attachments on the pelvic girdle, they can cause movement at the hip joint.

The muscles originating on the leg and acting on the foot and toes are described in Table 15.9 and shown in Figures 15.11 and 15.12. Identify the muscles as instructed previously.

(*Text continues on p. 138*)

TABLE 15.7 Muscles Acting on Human Thigh and Leg, Anterior and Medial Aspects (see Figure 15.9)

Muscle	Comments	Origin	Insertion	Action
Origin on the Pelvis				
Iliopsoas—iliacus and psoas major	Two closely related muscles; fibers pass under inguinal ligament to insert into femur via a common tendon	Iliacus: iliac fossa; psoas major: transverse processes, bodies, and discs of T_{12} and lumbar vertebrae	Lesser trochanter of femur	Flex trunk on thigh; major flexor of hip (or thigh on pelvis when pelvis is fixed)
Sartorius	Straplike superficial muscle running obliquely across anterior surface of thigh to knee	Anterior superior iliac spine	By an aponeurosis into medial aspect of proximal tibia	Flexes and laterally rotates thigh; flexes knee; known as "tailor's muscle" because it helps bring about cross-legged position in which tailors are often depicted
Medial Compartment				
Adductors—magnus, longus, and brevis	Large muscle mass forming medial aspect of thigh; arise from front of pelvis and insert at various levels on femur	Magnus: ischial and pubic rami; longus: pubis near pubic symphysis; brevis: body and inferior ramus of pubis	Magnus: linea aspera and adductor tubercle of femur; longus and brevis: linea aspera	Adduct and laterally rotate and flex thigh; posterior part of magnus is also a synergist in thigh extension
Pectineus	Overlies adductor brevis on proximal thigh	Pectineal line of pubis	Inferior to lesser trochanter of femur	Adducts, flexes, and laterally rotates thigh
Gracilis	Straplike superficial muscle of medial thigh	Inferior ramus and body of pubis	Medial surface of head of tibia	Adducts thigh; flexes and medially rotates leg, especially during walking
Anterior Compartment				
Quadriceps*				
Rectus femoris	Superficial muscle of thigh; runs straight down thigh; only muscle of group to cross hip joint; arises from two heads	Anterior inferior iliac spine and superior margin of acetabulum	Tibial tuberosity	Extends knee and flexes thigh at hip
Vastus lateralis	Forms lateral aspect of thigh	Greater trochanter and linea aspera	Tibial tuberosity	Extends knee
Vastus medialis	Forms medial aspect of thigh	Linea aspera	Tibial tuberosity	Extends knee
Vastus intermedius	Obscured by rectus femoris; lies between vastus lateralis and vastus medialis on anterior thigh	Anterior and lateral surface of femur (not shown in figure)	Tibial tuberosity	Extends knee
Tensor fasciae latae	Enclosed between fascia layers of thigh	Anterior aspect of iliac crest and anterior superior iliac spine	Iliotibial band of fascia lata	Flexes, abducts, and medially rotates thigh

*The quadriceps form the flesh of the anterior thigh and have a common insertion in the tibial tuberosity via the patellar tendon. They are powerful leg extensors, enabling humans to kick a football, for example.

TABLE 15.8 Muscles Acting on Human Thigh and Leg, Posterior Aspect (see Figure 15.10)

Muscle	Comments	Origin	Insertion	Action
Origin on Pelvis				
Gluteus maximus	Largest and most superficial of gluteal muscles (which form buttock mass)	Dorsal ilium, sacrum, and coccyx	Gluteal tuberosity of femur and iliotibial tract*	Complex, powerful hip extensor (most effective when hip is flexed, as in climbing stairs—but not as in walking); antagonist of iliopsoas; laterally rotates thigh
Gluteus medius	Partially covered by gluteus maximus	Upper lateral surface of ilium	Greater trochanter of femur	Abducts and medially rotates thigh; steadies pelvis during walking
Gluteus minimus	Smallest and deepest gluteal muscle	Inferior surface of ilium (not shown in figure)	Greater trochanter of femur	Abducts and medially rotates thigh
Posterior Compartment				
Hamstrings†				
Biceps femoris	Most lateral muscle of group; arises from two heads	Ischial tuberosity (long head); linea aspera and distal femur (short head)	Tendon passes laterally to insert into head of fibula and lateral condyle of tibia	Extends thigh; laterally rotates leg on thigh; flexes knee
Semitendinosus	Medial to biceps femoris	Ischial tuberosity	Medial aspect of upper tibial shaft	Extends thigh; flexes knee; medially rotates leg
Semimembranosus	Deep to semitendinosus	Ischial tuberosity	Medial condyle of tibia	Extends thigh; flexes knee; medially rotates leg

*The iliotibial tract, a thickened lateral portion of the fascia lata, ensheathes all the muscles of the thigh. It extends as a tendinous band from the iliac crest to the knee.

†The hamstrings are the fleshy muscles of the posterior thigh. The name comes from the butchers' practice of using the tendons of these muscles to hang hams for smoking. As a group, they are strong extensors of the hip; they counteract the powerful quadriceps by stabilizing the knee joint when standing.

TABLE 15.9 Muscles Acting on Human Foot and Ankle (see Figures 15.11 and 15.12)

Muscle	Comments	Origin	Insertion	Action
Posterior Compartment				
Superficial (Figure 15.11a,b)				
Triceps surae	Muscle pair that shapes posterior calf		Via common tendon (calcaneal or Achilles) into heel	Plantar flex foot
Gastrocnemius	Superficial muscle of pair; two prominent bellies	By two heads from medial and lateral condyles of femur	Calcaneus via calcaneal tendon	Crosses knee joint; thus also can flex knee (when foot is dorsiflexed)
Soleus	Deep to gastrocnemius	Proximal portion of tibia and fibula	Calcaneus via calcaneal tendon	Plantar flexion; is an important muscle for locomotion

(continued on p. 134)

Gluteal Region,   # 47151
A=glut. Maximus

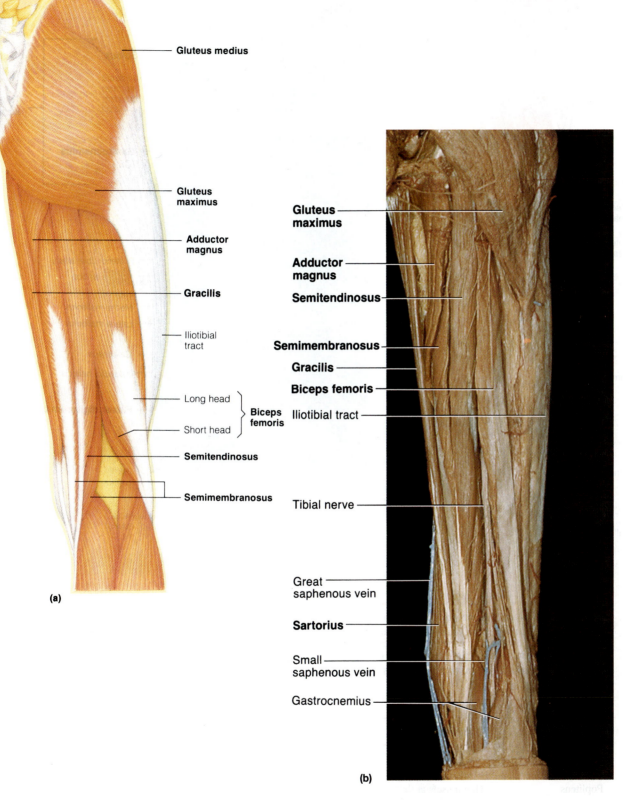

(a)

(b)

F15.10

Muscles of the posterior aspect of the right hip and thigh. (a) Superficial view showing the gluteus muscles of the buttock and hamstring muscles of the thigh. (b) Photo of muscles of the posterior thigh.

TABLE 15.9 (*Continued*)

Muscle	Comments	Origin	Insertion	Action
Flexor hallucis longus (see also Figure 15.12)	Lies lateral to inferior aspect of tibialis posterior	Middle portion of fibula shaft	Tendon runs under foot to insert on distal phalanx of great toe	Flexes great toe; plantar flexes and inverts foot; the "push-off muscle" during walking
Lateral Compartment (Figure 15.11c and Figure 15.12a,b,c)				
Peroneus longus	Superficial lateral muscle; overlies fibula	Head and upper portion of fibula	By long tendon under foot to first metatarsal and medial cuneiform	Plantar flexes and everts foot; helps keep foot flat on ground
Peroneus brevis	Smaller muscle; deep to peroneus longus	Distal portion of fibula shaft	By tendon running behind lateral malleolus to insert on proximal end of fifth metatarsal	Plantar flexes and everts foot, as part of peronei group
Anterior Compartment (Figure 15.12a,b,c)				
Tibialis anterior	Superficial muscle of anterior leg; parallels sharp anterior margin of tibia	Lateral condyle and upper 2/3 of tibia; interosseous membrane	By tendon into inferior surface of first cuneiform and metatarsal 1	Prime mover of dorsiflexion; inverts foot
Extensor digitorum longus	Anterolateral surface of leg; lateral to tibialis anterior	Lateral condyle of tibia; proximal 3/4 of fibula; interosseous membrane	Tendon divides into four parts; insert into middle and distal phalanges of toes 2–5	Prime mover of toe extension; dorsiflexes and everts foot
Peroneus tertius	Small muscle; often fused to distal part of extensor digitorum longus	Distal anterior surface of fibula	Tendon passes anterior to lateral malleolus and inserts on dorsum of fifth metatarsal	Dorsiflexes and everts foot
Extensor hallucis longus	Deep to extensor digitorum longus and tibialis anterior	Anteromedial shaft of fibula and interosseous membrane	Tendon inserts on distal phalanx of great toe	Extends great toe; dorsiflexes foot

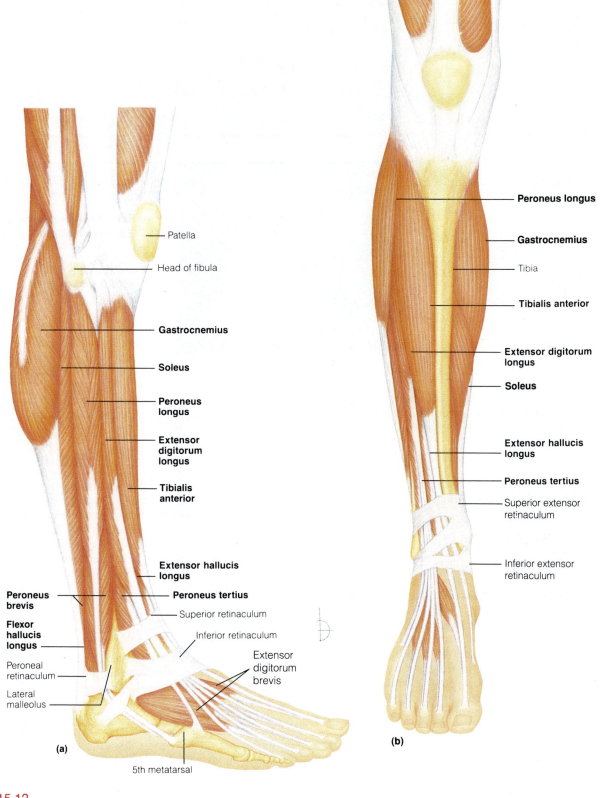

Patella

Head of fibula

Gastrocnemius

Soleus

Peroneus longus

Extensor digitorum longus

Tibialis anterior

Extensor hallucis longus

Peroneus brevis

Flexor hallucis longus

Peroneal retinaculum

Lateral malleolus

Peroneus tertius

Superior retinaculum

Inferior retinaculum

Extensor digitorum brevis

5th metatarsal

(a)

Peroneus longus

Gastrocnemius

Tibia

Tibialis anterior

Extensor digitorum longus

Soleus

Extensor hallucis longus

Peroneus tertius

Superior extensor retinaculum

Inferior extensor retinaculum

(b)

F15.12

Muscles of the anterolateral aspect of the right leg. (a) Superficial view of lateral aspect of the leg, illustrating the positioning of the lateral compartment muscles (peroneus longus and brevis) relative to anterior and posterior leg muscles. (b) Superficial view of anterior leg muscles.

(continued)

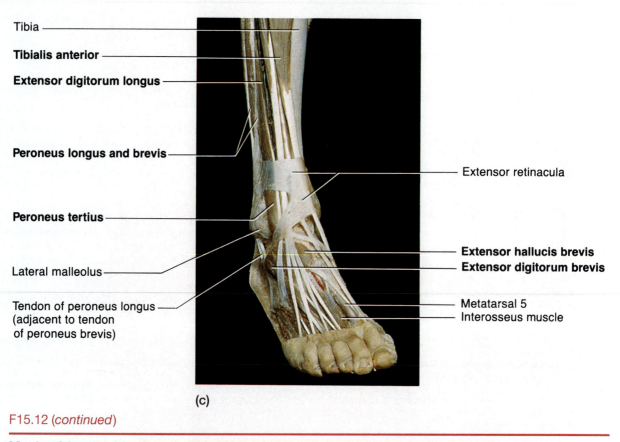

Tibia

Tibialis anterior

Extensor digitorum longus

Peroneus longus and brevis

Peroneus tertius

Lateral malleolus

Tendon of peroneus longus
(adjacent to tendon
of peroneus brevis)

Extensor retinacula

Extensor hallucis brevis
Extensor digitorum brevis

Metatarsal 5
Interosseus muscle

(c)

F15.12 (*continued*)

Muscles of the anterolateral aspect of the right leg. (c) Photo of anteroinferior aspect of right leg and foot, and extensor retinacula, anterolateral view.

Complete this exercise by performing the following palpation demonstrations with your lab partner.

- Go into a deep knee bend and palpate your own *gluteus maximus* muscle as you extend your hip to resume the upright posture.
- Demonstrate the contraction of the *quadriceps femoris* by trying to extend your knee against resistance. Do this while seated and note how the patellar tendon reacts. The *biceps femoris* comes into play when you flex your knee against resistance.
- Now stand on your toes. Have your partner palpate the lateral and medial heads of the *gastrocnemius* and follow it to its insertion in the calcaneal tendon.
- Dorsiflex and invert your foot while palpating your *tibialis anterior* muscle (which parallels the sharp anterior crest of the tibia laterally).

DISSECTION AND IDENTIFICATION OF FETAL PIG MUSCLES

The skeletal muscles of all mammals are named in a similar fashion. However, some muscles that are separate in lower animals are fused in humans, and some muscles present in lower animals are lacking in humans.

This exercise involves dissection of the pig musculature, in conjunction with the study of human muscles, to enhance your knowledge of the human muscular system. Since the aim is to become familiar with the muscles of the human body, you should pay particular attention to the similarities between pig and human muscles. However, pertinent differences will be pointed out as they are encountered.

Surface Anatomy of the Fetal Pig

The preserved laboratory animals purchased for dissection have been embalmed with a solution that prevents deterioration of the tissues. The animals generally are delivered in plastic bags containing a small amount of embalming fluid. Do not dispose of this fluid when removing the pig. It is important to keep the pig's tissues moist, as it will be used for dissection exercises until the end of the course. The embalming fluid may cause your eyes to smart and may dry your skin, but these small irritants are more desirable than working with a dissection specimen that has become hard and odoriferous due to bacterial action. You can alleviate the possibility of skin irritation by using disposable gloves or a protective skin cream before dissection.

1.   Obtain a fetal pig, dissection tray, dissection instruments, and a name tag. Mark the name tag with the names of the members of your group, and set it aside. Attach the name tag to the plastic bag at the end of the laboratory session so that you may identify your animal in subsequent laboratories.

2.   Before actually beginning to dissect the fetal pig, it is worth taking a few minutes to become familiar with the surface anatomy of your dissection animal. Place your specimen on its side on the dissection tray and identify its four major body regions—head, neck, trunk, and tail. Refer to Figure 15.13 as you conduct the following observations.

Head: on the head identify the following.

- **Mouth,** bounded by fleshy lips.
- **External nares (nostrils)** at the end of the rostrum or snout.
- **Auricle (pinna)** of the external ear, which surrounds the external auditory canal that leads to the eardrum.
- **Eyes,** bounded by the eyelids.
- **Nictitating membrane**—pull the upper and lower eyelids apart to view the nictitating membrane (which helps to keep the eyeball clean by sweeping across it) at the medial corner of the eye.

Neck: corresponds to the cervical region of the spine, located between the head and body trunk.

Trunk: accounts for most of the body and includes the appendages (fore- and hindlimbs).

Indentify the following surface anatomy landmarks on the trunk of your specimen.

- **Mammary papillae** (teats), five to seven on each side of the ventral trunk surface. These papillae, which are associated with the mammary glands, allow the mature females to suckle their young.
- **Thorax,** the anterior trunk region encased by the ribcage.
- **Abdomen,** the posterior trunk region from which the **umbilical cord** projects ventrally. (The umbilical cord attaches the developing pig to the placenta.)
- **Anus,** the posterior external opening of the digestive tract.

While examining the posterior abdominal surface, determine the sex of your fetal pig. In females, there is a common opening for the urogenital organs positioned just ventral to the anus in a protrusion called the **genital papilla.** If the animal is a male, the opening of the penis, called the **preputial orifice,** will be seen just posterior to the umbilical cord, and the **scrotal sacs,** the paired skin sacs that contain the testes in the adult animal, will appear as swollen regions between the hind legs.

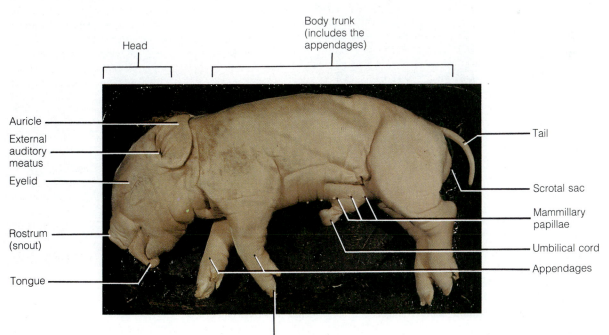

Head

Body trunk (includes the appendages)

Auricle

External auditory meatus

Eyelid

Rostrum (snout)

Tongue

Tail

Scrotal sac

Mammillary papillae

Umbilical cord

Appendages

Hoof of fourth toe

F15.13

External features of a fetal pig, lateral aspect.

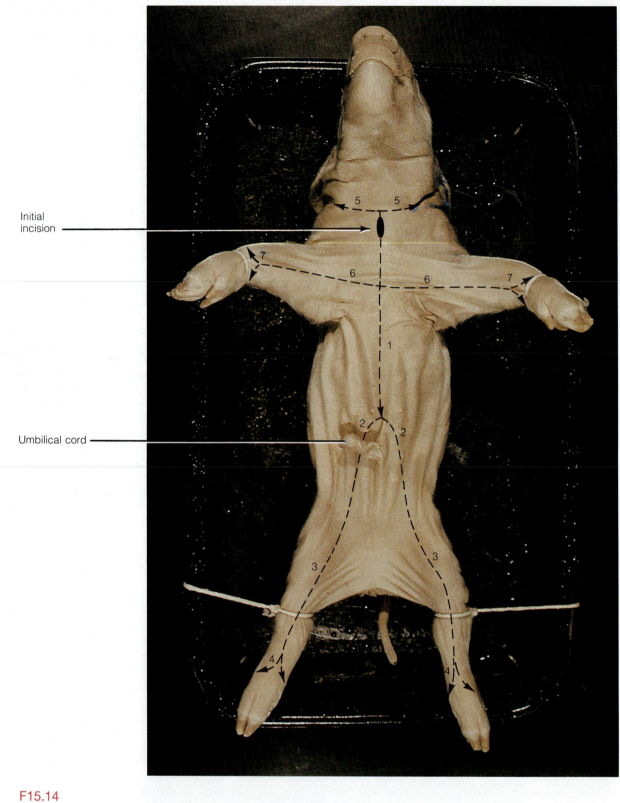

Initial
incision

Umbilical cord

F15.14

Incisions to be made in skinning a pig. Numbers indicate sequence.

● **Appendages**—examine the forelimbs and hind-limbs. Notice that the digits (toes) end in **hooves** and that the first toe is absent. Like other ungulates, pigs walk on their toes; the third and fourth toes bear most of the weight and are the largest digits.

Tail: The posteriormost projection from the body trunk.

3. The normal gestation period, or period of development, is about 115 days for pigs. A fetal pig that is 18 mm long has completed about one-third of its developmental period (about 36 days); one 40 mm long has completed about half (56 days), a 220-mm specimen has gestated for about 100 days, and one that is 300 mm long is full term. Determine the approximate age of your fetal pig specimen by measuring the length of its body. Record below.

_____ mm length

_____ approximate gestation age

Preparing the Fetal Pig for Dissection

1. Now you are ready to begin your dissection. Place the pig dorsal side down on the dissecting tray. To secure the animal to the dissecting tray, make a loop knot with twine around one upper limb, carry the twine under the inferior surface of the tray, and secure the opposing limb. Repeat for the lower extremities.

2. Make a short, *shallow* midventral incision at the base of the throat to just penetrate the skin. From this point on, use scissors. Continue the cut the length of the ventral body surface to the umbilicus. Cut laterally around the umbilicus on each side, and continue with two incisions (flanking the median line to the pelvic region (Figure 15.14)).

3. Continue each incision from the pelvic region down the medial surface of each leg to the hoof, and cut the skin completely around the ankles.

4. Return to the neck. Make an incision completely around the neck. Then cut down each foreleg to the wrist. Completely cut the skin around the wrists.

5. Now free the skin from the loose connective tissue (superficial fascia) that binds it to the underlying structures. With one hand, grasp the skin on one side of the midline ventral incision. Using your fingers, the closed scissor tips, or a blunt probe, break through the "cottony" connective tissue fibers to release the skin from the muscle beneath. Work toward the dorsal surface and then upward toward the neck region. As you pull the skin from the body, you should see small, white, cordlike structures that extend from it to the muscles at fairly regular intervals. These are the cutaneous nerves, which serve the skin. You will also see (particularly on the ventral surface) that a thin layer of muscle fibers adheres to the skin. These are the cutaneous muscles, which enable the pig to move or twitch the skin to get rid of irritants such as insects. Do not remove the skin from the head, since the muscles of the pig are not sufficiently similar to human head muscles to merit study.

6. Complete the skinning process by releasing the skin from the forelimbs, lower torso, and hindlimbs in the same manner.

7. Inspect your skinned pig. It will look much like the view shown in Figure 15.15b, but notice that the cleavage lines between the muscles are indistinct because of the overlying connective tissue. Probably even more important, however, is the fact that a fetal pig's muscles are incompletely developed (remember it's a *fetal* pig) and are easily torn. Consequently, whereas fetal pigs are excellent for other types of anatomy studies, they are less than ideal for a study of the muscular system. Nonetheless, your examination of the fetal pig musculature should help you to understand the structure of human muscles.

8. Note the neck incision where the pig's blood vessels were injected with latex. If time allows, begin on the side opposite the incision, using forceps or fingers, and carefully remove as much gelatinous material, fat, and fascia from the surface of the muscles as possible. Since you will dissect only one side of the animal's musculature, you need to perform this clearing process only on one side. If the muscle dissection exercises are to be done at a later laboratory session, carefully rewrap the pig's skin around its body. Then dampen several paper towels in embalming fluid, and wrap these around the animal. Return the pig to the plastic bag, adding more embalming fluid if necessary, seal the bag, and attach your name tag. <u>Use the same technique for preparing your pig for storage each time the pig is used.</u> Place the pig in the storage container designated by your instructor.

9. Before leaving the laboratory, dispose of any tissue remnants in the "organic debris" container, wash the dissecting tray and instruments with soapy water, rinse and dry, and wash down the laboratory bench.

Dissection of Pig Trunk and Neck Muscles

The proper dissection of muscles involves carefully separating one muscle from another so that they can be identified and transecting the superficial muscles to study the deeper layers. In general, when you want to transect a muscle, you should completely free it from all adhering connective tissue and then cut through about halfway between its origin and insertion attachments.

(*Text continues on p. 144*)

1.   Turn your pig to its lateral surface and begin your dissection. Humans have one large single trapezius muscle, but the pig has three separate muscles: the clavotrapezius, the acromiotrapezius, and the spinotrapezius. The most superior muscle of the group is the **clavotrapezius,** which is homologous to that part of the human trapezius that inserts into the clavicle. Slip a probe under this muscle and follow it to its apparent origin.

Where does it appear to originate?

_____

Is this similar to its origin in humans? _____

The fibers of the clavotrapezius form the superior portion of a much longer muscle called the **brachiocephalic** muscle; the ventral portion is called the **clavobrachialis** muscle. In humans, the portion of the trapezius muscle represented by the clavotrapezius inserts into the clavicle. However, since the clavicle is lacking in the pig, the clavotrapezius is continuous with the clavobrachialis, which inserts into the distal end of the humerus, where it blends with the fibers of the anterior deep pectoral muscle. The two fused portions of this muscle work together to move the forelimb of the pig anteriorly. Release the clavotrapezius muscle from the adjoining muscles.

2.   The **acromiotrapezius** is a short fan-shaped muscle posterior to the clavotrapezius. It originates from the cervical vertebral spines and inserts on the scapular spine by a broad and easily identified aponeurosis. The **spinotrapezius,** the most posterior of the trapezius muscles in the pig, runs from the thoracic vertebrae to the scapula to insert by a thin tendon into the scapula. Pull on the acromiotrapezius and spinotrapezius muscles.

Do they appear to have the same function(s) in the pig as in humans?

_____

3.   The **latissimus dorsi,** a broad muscle covering a sizable portion of the lateral surface of the posterior trunk, is partially covered by the spinotrapezius. Its fibers run downward and anteriorly around the lateral thorax to insert into the humerus (as in humans).

4.   The **deltoid** in the pig is a thin muscle band which adducts the humerus. It extends from the posterior scapula to the proximal end of the humerus. Contrast the deltoid muscle of the pig to the thick fleshy deltoid muscles seen in humans.

DEEP MUSCLES OF THE POSTERIOR TRUNK AND NECK

1.   In preparation, transect the latissimus dorsi, the acromiotrapezius, the spinotrapezius, and the deltoid muscles and reflect them back. Refer to Figure 15.18 as you work. The **supraspinatus** muscle, a portion of which lies deep to the deltoid, can be seen superficially anterior to the caudal border of the deltoid and posterior to the anterior deep pectoral. It originates on the scapular spine and clothes the scapula before inserting on the humerus by dual insertion. Reflect the cut ends of the deltoid muscle to reveal the thicker **infraspinatus** muscle, which lies deep to it. The infraspinatus originates on the lateral-posterior aspect of the scapula, occupies the region beneath the scapular spine, and inserts on the proximal humerus. It abducts and rotates the forelimb laterally. The **serratus ventralis** muscle arises deep to the pectoral muscles and covers the lateral surface of the rib cage. It is easily identified by its fingerlike muscular origins, which arise on the fourth to eighth ribs. It is best seen by raising the forelimb up and away from the body wall.

2.   Reflect the cut ends of the spinotrapezius and acromiotrapezius muscles to expose the **rhomboid** muscles, which originate from several separate muscle slips on the cervical and thoracic vertebrae and extend to the scapula. Note that these muscles insert into the medial border of the scapula rather than into the scapular spine, the insertion site of the trapezius muscles. The cephalic part of this group, which extends downward from the occipital bone to attach to the scapula, is the **rhomboid capitis,** which has no counterpart in the human body. The other muscles in this group are homologous to the rhomboid muscles of humans.

(Text continues on p. 149)

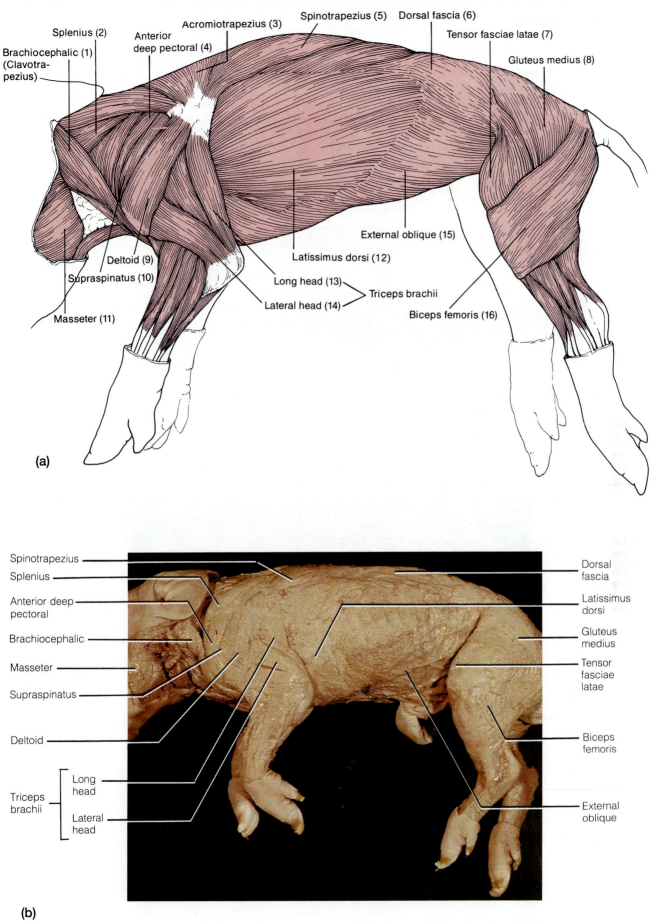

Superficial musculature of the fetal pig, lateral aspect. (a) Diagrammatic view. (b) Photograph.

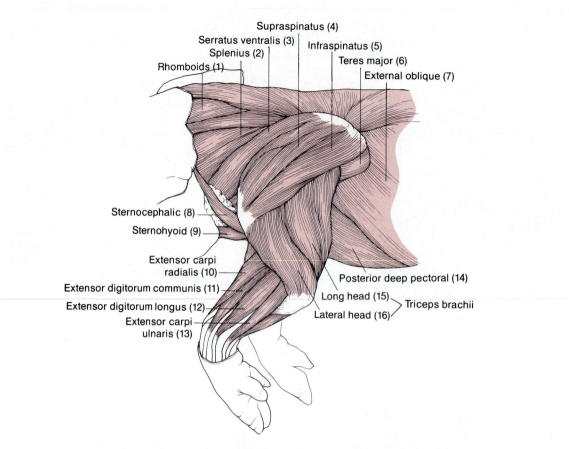

Rhomboids (1)
Splenius (2)
Serratus ventralis (3)
Supraspinatus (4)
Infraspinatus (5)
Teres major (6)
External oblique (7)

Sternocephalic (8)
Sternohyoid (9)
Extensor carpi radialis (10)
Extensor digitorum communis (11)
Extensor digitorum longus (12)
Extensor carpi ulnaris (13)

Posterior deep pectoral (14)
Long head (15)
Lateral head (16)
Triceps brachii

(a)

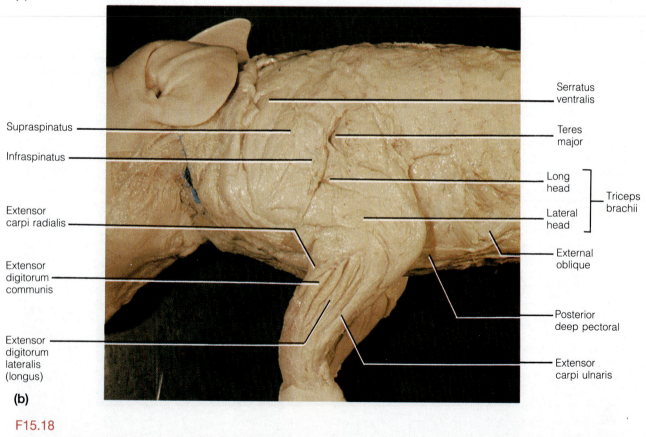

Supraspinatus
Infraspinatus
Extensor carpi radialis
Extensor digitorum communis
Extensor digitorum lateralis (longus)

Serratus ventralis
Teres major
Long head
Lateral head
Triceps brachii
External oblique
Posterior deep pectoral
Extensor carpi ulnaris

(b)

F15.18

Muscles of the left shoulder and forelimb of the fetal pig, with superficial muscles removed. (a) Diagrammatic view. (b) Photograph.

3. The **splenius,** located deep to the rhomboid muscles, is a thick muscle occupying most of the side of the neck close to the vertebrae. It originates on the ligamentum nuchae and inserts into the occipital bones. It functions to raise the head.

Dissection of Pig Forelimb Muscles

Refer to Figures 15.18 and 15.16 as you study these muscles.

UPPER FORELIMB MUSCLES

1. The triceps muscle of the pig **(triceps brachii)** can be easily identified if the pig is placed on its side (Figure 15.18). It is a large fleshy muscle covering the posterior aspect and much of the side of the humerus. As in humans, this muscle arises from three heads, which originate from the humerus and scapula and insert jointly into the olecranon process of the ulna. Remove the fascia from the upper region of the lateral arm surface to identify the lateral and long heads of the triceps. The long head is medial to the lateral head on the posterior surface of the arm. The medial head can be exposed by transecting and reflecting the lateral head.

How does the function of this muscle in the pig compare to its function in humans?

_____

2. The **brachialis** is located anterior to the lateral head of the triceps muscle (Figure 15.16). Identify its origin on the humerus, and trace its course as it crosses the elbow laterally and inserts on the ulna. It flexes the foreleg of the pig.

3. In the pig, the **biceps brachii** muscle is a small, slender, spindle-shaped muscle that is covered almost completely by the clavobrachialis portion of the brachiocephalic muscle. It originates from the scapula in the area anterior to the glenoid fossa and inserts into the proximal radius and ulna. It flexes the forelimb of the pig. Follow this muscle to its origin.

Does the biceps have two heads in the pig? _____

4. The **coracobrachialis** of the pig is rather insignificant and can be seen as a very small muscle crossing the ventral aspect of the shoulder joint. It runs beneath the biceps brachii to insert on the humerus and has the same function as its homologue in humans.

LOWER FORELIMB MUSCLES   Identification of the lower forelimb muscles is difficult because of the tough fascia sheath that encases them.

1. Remove as much of this connective tissue as possible, and cut through the ligaments that secure the tendons at the wrist (transverse carpal ligaments) so that you will be able to follow the various muscles to their insertions. Only selected forelimb muscles will be identified in the pig.

2. Begin your identification of the forearm muscles by examining the lateral surface of the forelimb. The muscles of this region are very much alike in appearance and are difficult to identify unless a definite order is followed. Thus you will begin with the most posterior muscles and proceed to the anterior aspect. Remember to carefully check the tendons of insertion to verify your muscle identification in each case. These muscles are illustrated in Figure 15.18.

3. Follow the **extensor carpi ulnaris** muscle from the lateral epicondyle of the humerus to the ulnar side of the fifth metacarpal. Often this muscle has a shiny insertion tendon that helps in its identification.

4. The **extensor digitorum lateralis,** or **longus**, muscle is similar in appearance to the extensor carpi ulnaris and lies just anterior to it. The extensor digitorum lateralis arises from the distal humerus and inserts by a divided tendon into the digits. This muscle has no human counterpart.

5. You can see the **extensor digitorum communis** for its entire length along the lateral surface of the forelimb just anterior to the extensor digitorum lateralis. Trace it to its four tendons, which insert on the second to the fifth digits. The extensor digitorum communis and the two extensor muscles described above act together to extend the digits.

6. The **extensor carpi radialis** is anterior to the extensor digitorum communis and is sometimes partially covered by it. It originates from the distal end of the humerus and inserts into the distal end of the radius. It rotates the foot of the pig.

7. The ribbonlike muscle seen on the lateral surface of the humerus and passing down the foreleg to insert on the styloid process of the radius is the **brachioradialis.** It acts to rotate the forelimb. (If your removal of the fascia was not very careful, this muscle may have been removed in the clearing process.)

8. Turn the pig so that you can easily observe the ventral forelimb muscles, mostly flexors and pronators. For the following series of muscle identifications refer to Figure 15.16. Your examination of these muscles will be cursory, so you need not attempt to trace out the origins and insertions of these muscles. In the pig, as in humans, most of these muscles arise from the medial epicondyle of the humerus. Identify the following muscles or muscle groups by beginning at the posterior surface of the medial forearm and working anteriorly. The **digital flexor** muscles are two thin muscles seen flanking the flexor carpi ulnaris anteriorly and posteriorly. The **flexor carpi radialis** is located anterior to the **flexor carpi ulnaris** and acts with it to flex the wrist.

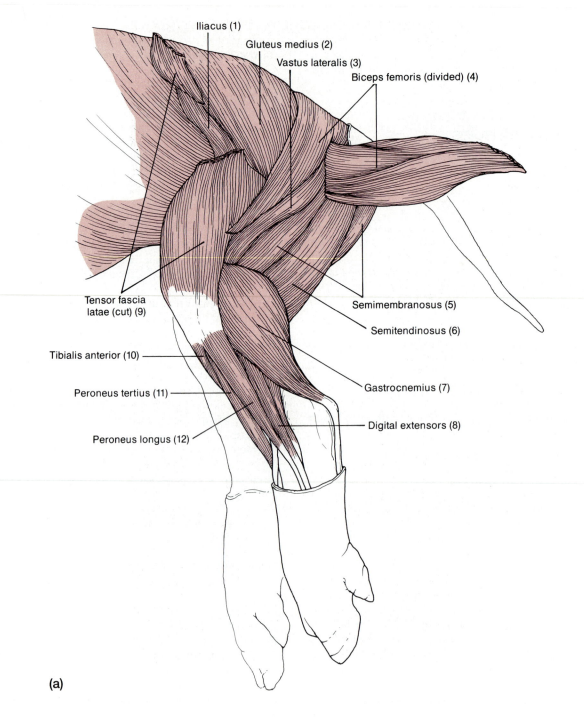

Iliacus (1)
Gluteus medius (2)
Vastus lateralis (3)
Biceps femoris (divided) (4)
Tensor fascia latae (cut) (9)
Semimembranosus (5)
Semitendinosus (6)
Tibialis anterior (10)
Peroneus tertius (11)
Gastrocnemius (7)
Peroneus longus (12)
Digital extensors (8)

(a)

F15.19

Muscles of the left posterolateral thigh and leg of the fetal pig. (a) Diagrammatic view.

Dissection of Pig Hindlimb Muscles

With the pig on its side, remove the fat and fascia from all the thigh surfaces, but do not cut through or remove the **fascia lata,** which is a tough white aponeurosis covering the anterolateral surface of the thigh from the hip to the leg.

MUSCLES OF THE POSTEROLATERAL HIND-LIMB Referring to Figures 15.15, 15.17, and 15.19, identify the following muscles of the hip, thigh, and posterior shank.

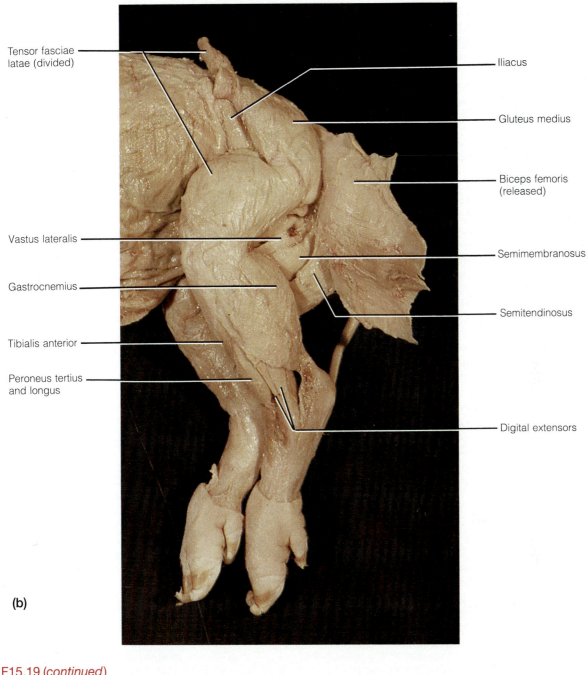

Tensor fasciae latae (divided)

Iliacus

Gluteus medius

Biceps femoris (released)

Vastus lateralis

Semimembranosus

Gastrocnemius

Tibialis anterior

Semitendinosus

Peroneus tertius and longus

Digital extensors

(b)

F15.19 *(continued)*

Muscles of the left posterolateral thigh and leg of the fetal pig. (b) Photograph.

1. The **tensor fasciae latae** is wide and thin at its superior end, where it originates on the iliac crest and narrows to a long tendon that inserts into the fascia lata. Its action is to tighten the fascia lata. Transect this muscle. The **gluteus medius** is a thick muscle lying beneath and posterior to the tensor fasciae latae. It originates from the lumbodorsal and gluteal fascias and inserts into the greater trochanter of the femur. It acts to abduct the thigh.

2. The **gluteus maximus** muscle in the pig is very thin and overlies the anterior portion of the gluteus medius muscle with which it acts synergistically. No attempt will be made to distinguish the limits of the individual gluteal muscles.

3. The **hamstring muscles,** a group in the lower extremity, consist of the biceps femoris, the semitendinosus, and the semimembranosus muscles. The **biceps femoris** is a large triangular muscle of the thigh that covers most of its posterolateral surface. Trace it from its origin on the ischium to its insertion on the distal femur and proximal tibia. It abducts and extends the thigh and flexes the shank. Transect this muscle and reflect its cut ends to identify the following muscles lying deep to it. The **semitendinosus** is a thick narrow muscle band lying deep to the posterior border of the biceps femoris. Contrary to what its name implies ("half-tendon"), this muscle is muscular and fleshy except at its insertion. Trace this muscle from its origin on the pelvic girdle to its insertion on the proximal tibia. It acts to bend the knee. The **semimembranosus,** a large muscle lying medial to the semitendinosus and largely obscured by it, is the most posteriorly placed muscle of the thigh. The distal end of this broad muscle overlies and is closely associated with the adductor magnus muscle. Trace it from its origin on the pelvic girdle to its insertion on the proximal tibia. Before identifying the muscles of the shank, identify the large **vastus lateralis** muscle, which lies anterior to the semimembranosus muscle and is part of the quadriceps muscle group to be dealt with later.

How does the semimembranosus compare with its human homologue?

_____

_____

4. Remove the heavy fascia covering the lateral surface of the shank and proceed from posterior to anterior aspect to identify the following muscles on the posterolateral shank (leg). Reflect the lower portion of the biceps femoris muscle to see the origin of the following muscles. The **triceps surae** is a large composite muscle of the calf, which is homologous to the same-named muscle in humans. The **gastrocnemius** part of the triceps surae is the largest muscle on the shank. As in humans, it has two heads and inserts via the calcaneal (Achilles) tendon into the calcaneus. Run a probe beneath this muscle and then transect it to reveal the **soleus,** which is deep to the gastrocnemius.

5. The **peroneus muscles** are long, thin muscles that arise from the proximal tibia and distal femur and run to tarsal insertions. The **peroneus longus** extends along the lateral surface of the tibia and the **peroneus tertius** runs along the tibia's anterior surface. They flex the ankle.

6. The **extensor digitorum longus** is a thin elongated muscle anterior to the peroneus muscles. It inserts by divided tendon into the digits, and its action is the same as in humans. The **tibialis anterior** is the most anterior muscle of the shank and is in direct contact with the tibia

along its whole length. Its proximal end encases the extensor digitorum longus muscle. Trace it from its origin on the proximal tibia to the second metatarsal, where it inserts by a strong tendon. It acts to flex the ankle.

MUSCLES OF THE ANTEROMEDIAL HINDLIMB

1. Turn the pig on its dorsal surface to identify the following muscles (refer to Figure 15.20). The **sartorius** is seen superficially on the anterior medial thigh as a thin strap of muscle tissue running from the pelvis to the proximal end of the tibia. The femoral artery runs along its posterior edge. This muscle acts to adduct the thigh and flex the hip. Transect this muscle.

2. The **quadriceps** muscles insert in common into the patella and act to extend the shank. The **vastus medialis** is seen just superior to the sartorius muscle on the medial thigh surface. It originates from the head of the femur. The **rectus femoris,** a thick bandlike muscle running along the anterior surface of the femur, is partially overlain by the vastus lateralis (identified earlier), which clothes the anterolateral aspect of the thigh. The rectus femoris takes its origin from the anterior ilium.

What is the origin of the rectus femoris in humans?

_____

_____

3. The **gracilis,** a broad muscle covering the posterior portion of the medial aspect of the thigh, originates on the pubic symphysis and inserts on the medial proximal tibial surface. Its action is to adduct the thigh in the pig. Free and transect this muscle to view the muscles lying deep to it.

How does this compare with the human gracilis?

_____

_____

4. The **adductor magnus** lies deep to the gracilis. Separate and distinguish this muscle from the semimembranosus muscle, which lies inferior to it and with which it is closely associated.

5. Examine the superior margin of the adductor magnus to locate the long slender **pectineus** muscle. It is normally covered by the sartorius muscle distally. It originates on the pubic bone and inserts on the medial aspect of the femur. This muscle is similar in action to its human homologue and acts to adduct the thigh.

6. Just superior to the pectineus muscle, you can see a small portion of the iliopsoas, a composite muscle whose action is similar to that of its counterpart in humans. The dissection of the remaining musculature of the anterior shank in the pig is not included here; however, you might want to examine the general location of the digital flexor muscles shown in Figure 15.20.

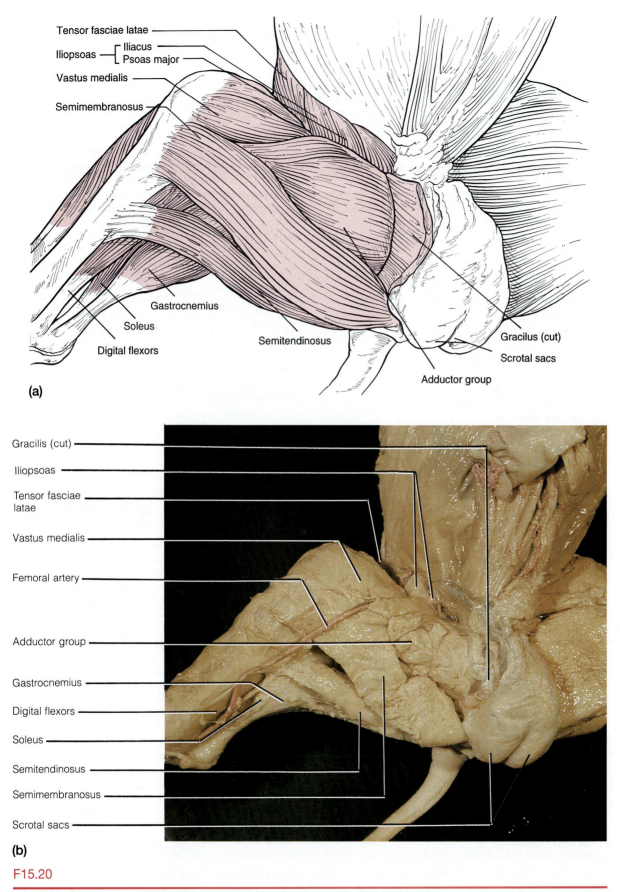

Tensor fasciae latae

Iliopsoas ⎡ Iliacus
         ⎣ Psoas major

Vastus medialis

Semimembranosus

Gastrocnemius

Soleus

Digital flexors

Semitendinosus

Gracilus (cut)

Scrotal sacs

Adductor group

(a)

Gracilis (cut)

Iliopsoas

Tensor fasciae latae

Vastus medialis

Femoral artery

Adductor group

Gastrocnemius

Digital flexors

Soleus

Semitendinosus

Semimembranosus

Scrotal sacs

(b)

F15.20

Muscles of anteromedial aspect of right hindlimb. (a) Diagrammatic view. (b) Photograph.

Muscle Physiology (Frog Experimentation)

OBJECTIVES

1. To observe muscle contraction on the microscopic level and describe the role of ATP and various ions in muscle contraction.

2. To define and explain the physiologic basis of the following:
   action potential
   subthreshold or subliminal stimulus
   threshold or minimal stimulus
   maximal stimulus
   treppe or staircase phenomenon
   wave summation
   multiple motor unit summation
   tetanus
   muscle fatigue
   absolute refractory period
   depolarization
   repolarization

3. To trace the events that result from the electrical stimulation of a muscle.

4. To explain why the "all-or-none" law is demonstrated by the activity of a single muscle cell but not an intact skeletal muscle.

5. To recognize that a graded response of skeletal muscle is a function of the number of muscle fibers stimulated and the frequency of the stimulus.

6. To name and describe the phases of a muscle twitch.

7. To distinguish between a muscle twitch and a sustained (tetanic) contraction and to describe their importance in normal muscle activity.

8. To demonstrate how the kymograph or polygraph can be used to obtain pertinent and representative recordings of various physiologic events of skeletal muscle activity.

9. To explain the significance of muscle tracings obtained during experimentation.

MATERIALS

ATP muscle kits (glycerinated rabbit psoas muscle;* ATP and salt solutions obtainable from Carolina Biological Supply, Item #20-3525)
Petri dishes
Microscope slides
Cover glasses
Millimeter ruler
Compound microscope
Dissecting microscope
Small beaker (50 ml)
Frog Ringer's solution
Scissors
Metal needle probes
Pointed glass probes (teasing needles)
Medicine dropper
Cotton thread
Forceps
Disposable gloves
Glass or porcelain plate
Pithed bullfrog†
Apparatus A or B
A: physiograph (polygraph), polygraph paper and ink, myograph, pin and clip electrodes, stimulator output extension cable, transducer cable, straight pins, frog board, laboratory stand, clamp
B: kymograph, kymograph paper (smoking stand, burner, and glazing fluid if using a smoke-writing apparatus), skeletal muscle lever, signal magnet, laboratory stand, clamp, electronic stimulators

Notes to the Instructor:

* At the beginning of the lab, the muscle bundle should be removed from the test tube and cut into ∼ 2-cm lengths. Both the cut muscle segments and the entubed glycerol should be put into a petri dish. One muscle *segment* is sufficient for each two to four students making observations.

† Bullfrogs to be pithed by lab instructor as needed for student experimentation. (If instructor prefers that students pith their own specimens, an instructional sheet on that procedure suitable for copying for student handouts is provided in the Instructor's Guide.)

Some instructors may prefer to have students study muscle physiology with a computer simulation exercise. Exercise 16B should satisfy this preference.

MUSCLE ACTIVITY

The contraction of skeletal and cardiac muscle can be considered in terms of three events—electrical excitation of the muscle cell, excitation-contraction coupling, and shortening of the muscle cell due to sliding of the myofilaments within it.

At rest, all cells maintain a potential difference, or voltage, across their plasma membrane; the inner face of the membrane is approximately -60 to -90 millivolts (mv) compared with the cell exterior. This potential difference is a result of differences in membrane permeability to cations, most importantly sodium (Na^+) and potassium (K^+) ions. Intracellular potassium concentration is much greater than its extracellular concentration, and intracellular sodium concentration is considerably less than its extracellular concentration. Hence, steep concentration gradients across the membrane exist for both cations. However, because the plasma membrane is slightly more permeable to K^+ than to Na^+, Na^+ influx into the cell is inadequate to balance K^+ outflow. The result of this unequal Na^+–K^+ diffusion across the membrane establishes the cell's **resting membrane potential.** The resting membrane potential is of particular interest in excitable cells, like muscle cells and neurons, because changes in that voltage underlie their ability to do work (to contract or to signal respectively in muscle cells and neurons).

Action Potential

When a muscle cell is stimulated, the sarcolemma becomes temporarily permeable to sodium, which rushes into the cell. This sudden influx of sodium ions alters the membrane potential. That is, the cell interior becomes less negatively charged at that point, an event called **depolarization.** When depolarization reaches a certain level and the sarcolemma momentarily changes its polarity, a depolarization wave travels along the sarcolemma. Even as the influx of sodium ions occurs, the sarcolemma becomes impermeable to sodium and permeable to potassium ions. Consequently, potassium ions leak out of the cell, restoring the resting membrane potential (but not the original ionic conditions), an event called **repolarization.** The repolarization wave follows the depolarization wave across the sarcolemma. This rapid depolarization and repolarization of the membrane that is propagated along the entire membrane from the point of stimulation is called the **action potential**.

Until repolarization of the membrane has been completed, the muscle cell cannot be stimulated to contract again. In this condition it is said to be in the **absolute refractory period.** Repolarization restores the muscle cell's irritability. Temporarily, the sodium-potassium pump, which actively transports K^+ into the cell and Na^+ out of the cell, need not be in operation. But, if the cell is stimulated to contract again and again in rapid-fire order, the loss of potassium and gain of sodium occurring during action potential generation begins to hamper its ability to respond. And so, eventually the sodium-potassium pump must be activated to reestablish the ionic concentrations of the resting state.

Contraction

The propagation of the action potential along the sarcolemma causes the release of calcium ions (Ca^{2+}) from storage depots (tubules of the sarcoplasmic reticulum) within the muscle cell. When the calcium ions reach the myofilaments and bind to regulatory proteins on the actin filaments, they act as an ionic trigger that initiates contraction, and the actin and myosin filaments slide past each other. Once the action potential has ceased, the calcium ions are almost immediately reabsorbed into the tubules of the sarcoplasmic reticulum. Instantly the muscle cell relaxes.

The events of the contraction process can most simply be summarized as follows: muscle cell contraction is initiated by generation and transmission of an action potential along the sarcolemma. This electrical event is coupled with the sliding of the myofilaments—contraction—by the release of Ca^{2+}. Keep in mind this sequence of events as you conduct the experiments.

OBSERVATION OF MUSCLE FIBER CONTRACTION

 In this simple observational experiment, you will have the opportunity to review your understanding of muscle cell anatomy and to watch fibers contracting (or not contracting) in response to the presence of certain chemicals (ATP, and potassium and magnesium ions).

1. Obtain the following materials from the supply area: 2 glass teasing needles, 3 glass microscope slides and cover glasses, millimeter ruler, dropper vials containing the following solutions: (a) 0.25% ATP in triply distilled water; (b) 0.25% ATP plus $0.05M$ KCl plus $0.001M$ MgCl$_2$ in distilled water; and (c) $0.05M$ KCl plus $0.001M$ MgCl$_2$ in distilled water; a petri dish, and a small portion of a previously cut muscle bundle segment. While you are at the supply area, place the muscle fibers in the petri dish and pour a small amount of glycerol (the fluid in the supply petri dish) over your muscle cells. Also obtain both a compound and a dissecting microscope and bring them to your laboratory bench.

2. Using the fine glass needles, tease the muscle segment to separate its fibers. The objective is to isolate *single* muscle cells or fibers for observation. Be patient and work carefully so that the fibers do not get torn during this isolation procedure.

3. Transfer one or more of the fibers (or the thinnest strands you have obtained) onto a clean microscope slide with a glass needle, and cover it with a cover glass. Examine the fiber under low and then high power magnifications to observe the striations and the smoothness of the fibers when they are in the relaxed state.

4. Transfer three or four fibers to a second clean microscope slide with a glass needle. Using the needle as a prod, carefully position the fibers so that they are parallel to one another and as straight as possible. Place this

slide under a dissecting microscope and measure the length of each fiber by holding a millimeter ruler adjacent to it. Alternatively, you can rest the microscope slide *on* the millimeter ruler to make your length determinations. Record the fiber lengths on the chart at the bottom of this page.

5. Flood the fibers (situated under the dissecting microscope) with several drops of the solution containing ATP + potassium ions and magnesium ions. Watch the reaction of the fibers after adding the solution. After 30 seconds (or slightly longer), remeasure each fiber and record the observed lengths on the chart. Also, observe the fibers to see if any width changes have occurred. Calculate the degree (or percentage) of contraction by using the following simple formula, and record this information on the chart also.

$$\begin{array}{ccc} \text{initial} & - & \text{contracted} & = & \text{degree of} \\ \text{length (mm)} & & \text{length (mm)} & & \text{contraction (mm)} \end{array}$$

then:

$$\frac{\text{degree of contraction (mm)}}{\text{initial length (mm)}} \times 100 = \underline{\hspace{1cm}} \% \text{ contraction}$$

6. Carefully transfer one of the contracted fibers to a clean microscope slide, cover with a cover glass, and observe with the compound microscope. Mentally compare your initial observations with the view you are observing now. What differences do you see? (Be specific.)

_____

_____

What zones (or bands) have disappeared?

_____

7. Repeat steps 3 to 6, using clean slides and fresh muscle cells. First use the solution of ATP in distilled water (no salts) and then use the solution containing only salts (no ATP) for the third series.

What degree of contraction was observed when ATP was applied in the absence of potassium and magnesium ions?

_____

What degree of contraction was observed when the muscle fibers were flooded with a K^+- and Mg^{2+}-containing solution that lacked ATP?

_____

What conclusions can you draw about the importance of ATP, and potassium and magnesium ions to the muscle contractile process?

_____

_____

INDUCTION OF CONTRACTION IN THE FROG GASTROCNEMIUS MUSCLE

Physiologists have learned a great deal about the way muscles function by isolating muscles from laboratory animals and then stimulating these muscles to observe their responses. Various stimuli—electrical shock, temperature changes, extremes of pH, certain chemicals—elicit muscle activity, but laboratory experiments of this type typically use electrical shock. This is because it is easier to control the onset and cessation of electrical shock, as well as the strength of the stimulus.

Preparing a Muscle for Experimentation

The preparatory work that precedes the recording of muscle activity tends to be quite time consuming. If you work in teams of two or three, the work can be divided. While one of you is setting up the recording apparatus (kymograph or physiograph), one or two students can dissect the frog leg. Experimentation should begin as soon as the dissection is completed.

Various types of apparatus are used to record muscle contraction. All include a way to mark time intervals, a way to indicate exactly when the stimulus was applied, and a way to measure the magnitude of the contractile response. Instructions are provided here for setting up physiograph (Figure 16A.1) and kymograph (Figure 16A.2) apparatus. Specific instructions for use of recording apparatus during recording will be provided by your instructor.

	Muscle fiber 1	Muscle fiber 2	Muscle fiber 3
Initial length (mm)			
Contracted length (mm)			
% contraction			

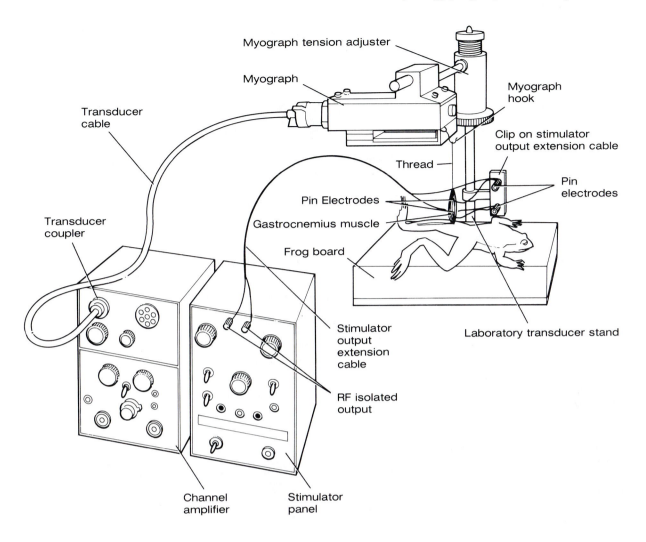

Materials:

Channel amplifier and stimulator transducer cable
Stimulator panel and stimulator output extension cable
Myograph
Myograph tension adjuster
Transducer stand
Two pin electrodes
Frog board and straight pins
Prepared frog (gastrocnemius muscle freed and
 Calcaneal tendon ligated with thread)
Frog Ringer's solution

1. Connect myograph to transducer stand and attach frog board to stand.

2. Attach transducer cable to myograph and to input connection on amplifier channel.

3. Attach stimulator output extension cable to output on stimulator panel (red to red, black to black).

4. Using clip at opposite end of extension cable, attach cable to bottom of transducer stand adjacent to frog board.

5. Attach two pin electrodes securely to electrodes on clip.

6. Place knee of prepared frog in clip on frog board and secure by inserting a straight pin through tissues of frog. Keep frog muscle moistened with Ringer's solution.

7. Attach thread ligating the Calcaneal tendon of frog to myograph leaf-spring hook.

8. Adjust position of myograph on stand to produce a constant tension on thread attached to muscle (taut but not tight). Gastrocnemius muscle should hang vertically directly below myograph hook.

9. Insert free ends of pin electrodes into muscle, one at proximal end and other at distal end.

F16A.1

Physiograph setup for frog gastrocnemius experiments.

the cut completely around the thigh. Grasp the skin with the forceps and strip it from the leg and hindfoot. The skin tends to adhere more at the joints, but a careful, persistent pulling motion—somewhat like pulling off a nylon stocking—will enable you to remove it in one piece. *From this point on, the exposed muscle tissue should be routinely moistened* with the Ringer's solution to prevent spontaneous twitches.

3.   Identify the gastrocnemius muscle (the fleshy muscle of the posterior calf) and the calcaneal (Achilles) tendon that secures it to the heel.

4.   Slip a glass probe under the gastrocnemius muscle and run it along the entire length and under the calcaneal tendon to free them from the underlying tissues.

5.   Cut a piece of thread about 10 in. long and use the glass probe to slide the thread under the calcaneal tendon. Knot the thread firmly around the tendon and then sever the tendon distal to the thread. Alternatively, you can bend a common pin into a Z-shape and insert the pin securely into the tendon. The thread is then attached to the opposite end of the pin. If you are using a physiograph, once the tendon has been tied or pinned, the frog is ready for experimentation (see Figure 16A.1). If you are using a kymograph, the gastrocnemius muscle must be completely isolated, as described in step 6.

6.   Cut away the fibulotibial bone just distal to the knee. Expose the femur of the thigh and cut it completely through at midthigh. Remove as much of the thigh muscle tissue as possible by carefully cutting it away with the scissors. The isolated gastrocnemius muscle can now be mounted on the muscle bar, and the stimulating electrodes of the kymograph can be attached (see Figure 16A.2). About halfway through the laboratory period, dissect the second leg for use.

Recording Muscle Activity

The **"all-or-none" law** of muscle physiology states that a muscle cell will contract maximally when stimulated adequately. Skeletal muscles, however, consisting of thousands of muscle cells, react to stimuli with graded responses. Thus muscle contractions can be slight or vigorous, depending on the requirements of the task. Graded responses (different degrees of shortening) of a skeletal muscle depend on the number of muscle cells being stimulated. In the intact organism, the number of motor units firing at any one time determines how many muscle cells will be stimulated. In this laboratory, the frequency and strength of an electrical current determines the response.

A single contraction of skeletal muscle is called a **muscle twitch.** A tracing of a muscle twitch (Figure 16A.4) shows three distinct phases: latent, contraction, and relaxation. The **latent phase** is the interval from the stimulus application until the muscle begins to shorten. Although no activity is indicated on the tracing during this phase, important electrical and chemical changes are occurring within the muscle. During the **contraction**

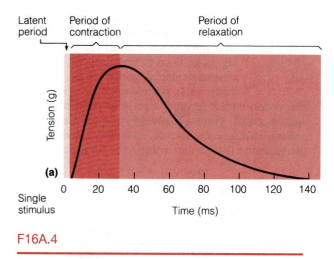

Tracing of a muscle twitch.

phase, the muscle fibers shorten; the tracing shows an increasingly higher needle deflection and the tracing peaks. During the **relaxation phase,** represented by a downward curve of the tracing, the muscle fibers relax and lengthen. On a slowly moving recording surface, the single muscle twitch appears as a spike (rather than a bell-shaped curve, as in Figure 16A.4), but on a rapidly moving recording surface, the three distinct phases just described become recognizable.

DETERMINING THE MINIMAL, OR THRESHOLD, STIMULUS

1.   Assuming that you have already set up the recording apparatus, set the time marker to deliver one pulse per second and set the paper speed at a slow rate, approximately 0.1 cm per second.

2.   Set the duration control on the stimulator between 7 and 15 msec, multiplier × one and the voltage control at zero v, multiplier × one. Turn the sensitivity control knob of the stimulator fully clockwise (lowest value, greatest sensitivity).

3.   Administer single stimuli to the muscle at 1- to 2-sec intervals, beginning with 0.1 v and increasing by 0.1 v between successive stimuli until a contraction is obtained (shown by a spike on the paper).

At what voltage did contraction occur? _____ v

The voltage at which the first perceptible contractile response is obtained is called the **threshold,** or **minimal, stimulus.** All stimuli applied prior to this point are termed **subthreshold,** or **subliminal, stimuli,** because at those voltages no response was elicited.

4. Stop the recording and mark the record to indicate the threshold stimulus, voltage, and time. *Do not remove the record from the recording surface;* continue with the next experiment. *Remember:* keep the muscle preparation moistened with Ringer's solution at all times.

GRADED MUSCLE RESPONSE TO INCREASED STIMULUS INTENSITY

1. Follow the previous setup instructions, but set the voltage control at the threshold voltage (as determined in the first experiment).

2. Deliver single stimuli at 1- or 2-sec intervals. Initially increase the voltage between shocks by 0.5 v; then increase the voltage by 1 to 2 v between shocks as the experiment continues, until contraction height increases no further. Stop the recording apparatus.

What voltage produced the highest spike (thus the maximal strength of contraction)?

_____ v

This voltage, called the **maximal stimulus** (for *your* muscle specimen), is the weakest stimulus at which all muscle cells are being stimulated. As the voltage was increased to this point, more and more muscle cells (motor units) were activated, resulting in a stronger and stronger contraction. Past this point, an increase in the intensity of the stimulus will not produce any greater contractile response. **Multiple motor unit summation** is the process by which the increased contractile strength reflects the relative number of muscle cells stimulated.

3. Mark the record *multiple motor unit summation* and note the maximal stimulus voltage and the time you completed the experiment. Continue on to the next experiment.

TIMING THE MUSCLE TWITCH

1. Follow the previous setup directions, but set the voltage for the maximal stimulus (as determined in the preceding experiment) and set the paper advance or recording speed at maximum. Record the paper speed setting:

_____ mm/sec

2. Determine the time required for the paper to advance 1 mm by using the formula:

$$\frac{1 \text{ mm}}{\text{mm/sec (paper speed)}}$$

(Thus, if your paper speed is 25 mm/sec, each mm on the chart equals 0.04 sec.) Record the computed value:

1 mm = _____ sec

3. Deliver single stimuli at 2- to 3-sec intervals to obtain several "twitch" curves. Stop the recording.

4. Determine the duration of the latent, contraction, and relaxation phases of the twitches and record here:

Duration of latent period: _____ sec

Duration of contraction period: _____ sec

Duration of relaxation period: _____ sec

5. Label the record to indicate the point of stimulus, the beginning of contraction, the end of contraction, and the end of relaxation.

6. Allow the muscle to rest (but keep it moistened) before continuing with the next experiment.

THE TREPPE, OR STAIRCASE, PHENOMENON

As a muscle is stimulated to contract, a curious phenomenon is observed in the tracing pattern of the first few twitches. Even though the stimulus intensity is unchanged, the height of the individual spikes increases in a stepwise manner—producing a sort of staircase pattern (Figure 16A.5). This phenomenon is not well understood, but the following explanation has been offered: in the muscle cell's resting state, there is less Ca^{2+} in the sarcoplasmic reticulum, and the enzyme systems in the muscle cell are less efficient than after it has contracted a few times. As the muscle tissue begins to contract, Ca^{2+} moves into the cells from the extracellular fluid. The heat generated by muscle activity increases the efficiency of the enzyme systems, and the muscle becomes more efficient and contracts more vigorously. This is the physiologic basis of the warm-up period prior to competition in sports events.

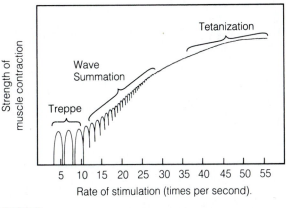

F16A.5

Treppe, wave summation, and tetanization. Progressive summation of successive contractions occurs as the rate of stimulation is increased. Tetanization occurs when the rate of stimulation reaches approximately 35 per second, and maximum contraction force occurs at a stimulation rate of approximately 50 per second.

1.   Set up the apparatus as in the previous experiment, again setting the voltage to the maximal stimulus.

2.   Deliver single stimuli at 1-sec intervals until the strength of contraction does not increase further.

3.   Stop the recording apparatus and mark the record *treppe*. Note also the number of contractions (and seconds) required to reach the constant contraction magnitude. Record the voltage used and the time when you completed this experiment. Continue on to the next experiment.

GRADED MUSCLE RESPONSE TO INCREASED STIMULUS FREQUENCY

Muscles subjected to frequent stimulation, without a chance to relax, exhibit two kinds of responses—wave summation and tetanus—depending on the level of stimulus frequency (Figure 16A.5).

Wave Summation: If a muscle is stimulated with a rapid series of stimuli of the same intensity before it has had a chance to relax completely, the response to the second and subsequent stimuli will be greater than to the first stimulus. This phenomenon, called wave summation, occurs because the muscle is already in a partially contracted state when subsequent stimuli are delivered.

1.   With the recorder running at slow speed and the stimulus intensity set to the maximal stimulus, stimulate the muscle at a rate of 15 to 25 stimuli per second.

2.   Shut off the recorder and label the record as *wave summation*. Note also the time, the voltage, and the frequency.

Tetanus: Stimulation of a muscle at an even higher frequency will produce a "fusion" (tetanization) of the summated twitches. In effect, a single sustained contraction is achieved in which *no* evidence of relaxation can be seen (Figure 16A.5). Tetanus is a feature of normal skeletal muscle functioning; the single muscle twitch is primarily a laboratory phenomenon.

1.   To demonstrate tetanus, maintain the conditions you used for wave summation except for the frequency of stimulation. Set the stimulator to deliver 60 stimuli per second.

2.   As soon as you obtain a single smooth, sustained contraction (with no evidence of relaxation), discontinue stimulation and shut off the recorder.

3.   Label the tracing with the conditions of experimentation, the time, and the area of tetanus.

MUSCLE FATIGUE

Muscle fatigue, the loss of the ability to contract, is believed to be a result of the oxygen debt that occurs in the tissue after prolonged activity (through the accumulation of such waste products as lactic acid as well as the depletion of ATP). True muscle fatigue rarely occurs in the body, because it is most often preceded by a subjective feeling of fatigue. Furthermore, fatigue of the neuromuscular junctions typically precedes fatigue of the muscle.

1.   To demonstrate muscle fatigue, set up an experiment like the tetanus experiment, but deliver the stimulus until the muscle completely relaxes and the contraction curve returns to the base line.

2.   Measure the time interval between the beginning of complete tetanus and the beginning of fatigue (when the tracing begins its downward curve). Mark the record appropriately.

3.   Determine the time required for complete fatigue to occur (the time interval from the beginning of fatigue until the return of the curve to the base line). Mark the record appropriately.

4.   Allow the muscle to rest (keeping it moistened with Ringer's solution) for 10 min, and then repeat the experiment.

What was the effect of the rest period on the fatigued muscle?

_____

_____

What is the physiologic basis for this reaction?

_____

_____

THE EFFECT OF LOAD ON SKELETAL MUSCLE

When the fibers of a skeletal muscle are slightly stretched by a weight or tension, the muscle responds by contracting more forcibly and thus is capable of doing more work. If the load is increased beyond the optimum, the latent period becomes longer, contraction force decreases, and relaxation (fatigue) occurs more quickly. With excessive stretching, the muscle is unable to develop any tension and no contraction occurs. Since the filaments no longer overlap at all with this degree of stretching, the sliding force cannot be generated.

If your equipment allows you to add more weights to the muscle specimen or to increase the tension on the muscle, perform the following experiment to determine the effect of loading on skeletal muscle, and to develop a work curve for the frog's gastrocnemius muscle.

1.   Set the stimulator to deliver the maximal voltage as previously determined.

2.   Stimulate the unweighted muscle with single shocks at 1- to 2-sec intervals to achieve three or four muscle twitches.

3.   Stop the recording apparatus and add 10 g of weight or tension to the muscle. Restart and advance the recording about 1 cm, and then stimulate again to obtain three or four spikes.

4. Repeat the previous step seven more times, increasing the weight by 10 g each time until the total load on the muscle is 80 g or the muscle fails to respond. If the calcaneal tendon tears, the weight will drop, thus ending the trial. In such cases, you will need to prepare another frog's leg to continue the experiments and the maximal stimulus will have to be determined for the new muscle preparation.

5. When these "loading" experiments are completed, discontinue recording and remove the tracing. Mark the curves on the record to indicate the load (in grams).

6. Measure the height of contraction (in millimeters) for each sequence of twitches obtained with each load, and insert this information into the chart below.

7. Compute the work done by the muscle for each twitch (load) sequence.

Weight of load (g) × distance load lifted (mm) = work done

Enter these calculations into the chart in the columns labeled Trial 1.

8. ⚠ Allow the muscle to rest for 5 minutes. Then conduct a second trial in the same manner (i.e., repeat steps 2 through 7). Record this second set of calculations in the columns labeled Trial 2. Be sure to keep the muscle well moistened with Ringer's solution during the resting interval.

9. Using two different colors, plot a line graph of work done against the weight on the accompanying grid for each trial. Label each plot appropriately.

10. Dismantle all apparatus and prepare the equipment for storage. Dispose of the frog remains in the appropriate container. Discard the gloves as instructed and wash and dry your hands.

11. Inspect your records of the experiments and make sure each is fully labeled with the experimental conditions, the date, and the names of those who conducted the experiments. (If you used a smoked-drum kymograph recording system, "fix" the records before leaving the laboratory.) For future reference, attach a tracing (or a photocopy of the tracing) for each experiment to this page.

Load (g)	Distance load lifted (mm)		Work done	
	Trial 1	Trial 2	Trial 1	Trial 2
0				
10				
20				
30				
40				
50				
60				
70				
80				

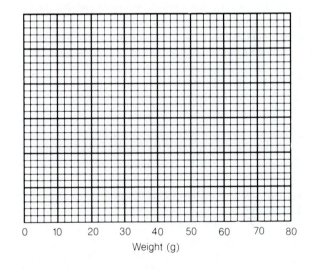

Weight (g)

Muscle Physiology (Computerized Simulations)

OBJECTIVES

1. To define important terms used in describing muscle physiology.
2. To identify the two ways that the mode of stimulation can affect muscle force production.
3. To draw a graph relating stimulus strength and twitch force to illustrate graded muscle response.
4. To explain how slow, smooth, sustained contraction is possible in a skeletal muscle.
5. To graphically understand the relationships between passive, active, and total forces.
6. To identify the conditions under which muscle contraction is isometric or isotonic.
7. To describe in terms of length and force the transitions between isometric and isotonic conditions during a single muscle twitch.
8. To describe the effects of afterload and starting length on the initial velocity of shortening.
9. To explain why muscle force remains constant during isotonic shortening.
10. To explain results obtained in terms of muscle structure.

MATERIALS

Minimum equipment required:
  IBM PC/XT/AT or compatible
  256K RAM—single disk (5.25 in.) drive
  Color graphics adapter (CGA) and compatible graphics monitor
Software:
  Operating system (DOS diskette)
  Mechanical Properties of Active Muscle

Many important physiological concepts of skeletal muscle contraction can be demonstrated using this set of computer simulations, which investigates the mechanical properties of active skeletal muscle. The programs graphically present all the equipment and materials necessary for you, the investigator, to set up experimental conditions and observe the results. In student-conducted laboratory investigations there are many ways to approach a problem and the same is true of these simulations. The instructions provided are intended to guide you in your investigation, but you should also attempt alternate approaches to gain insight into the logical methods employed in scientific experimentation.

Try the following approach: The first time through the programs, follow the instructions closely and answer the questions it poses as you go along. Then try your own ideas, asking "What if . . . ?" questions to test the validity of your theories. Major advantages of these computer simulations are that the muscle cannot be damaged accidentally, lab equipment will not break down at the worst possible time, and you will have ample time to think critically about the processes in question.

Various types of apparatus are used in research settings, and you will find minor differences in the operation of the equipment used in these simulations. This requires that you think about what is happening in each situation because it is important to understand how you are experimentally manipulating the muscle for a complete understanding of the actual results. To aid you in this endeavor, each of the exercises has the following elements:

1. Introduction to the System (explains equipment used);
2. Some Definitions (briefly defines terms); and
3. Experiments (designed to manipulate skeletal muscle).

Work your way through each section in turn so that you are familiar with the simulated equipment you will be using and the terminology involved.

GETTING STARTED

Begin by making sure you have the computer equipment listed in the materials section. If your computer is already running, proceed to step 2.

1. Insert the DOS (operating system) diskette into drive A. Turn the computer on and answer any questions that appear on the screen. When you see "A>" (the A prompt) remove the DOS diskette.
2. Insert the muscle program diskette (Mechanical Properties of Active Muscle) into drive A, type the

word "GO" (but without quotes), and press the ENTER (return) key. You must keep the program diskette in drive A for the entire time you are using the simulation.

The title screen will appear after a few seconds. Press any key to move on to the next information screen and again to advance to the main Index of Programs. This is a list of all the choices available to you. Select Option #1 to see an overview of all programs available. This will display the opening screen of each program in turn and let you examine it in more detail if you wish. Instructions will appear in boxes on the screen. If you get lost, press the ESC key to get back to the Index of Programs.

ELECTRICAL STIMULATION

The contraction of skeletal muscle will produce force and/or shortening when nervous or electrical stimulation is applied. Unlike single cells or motor units, which follow the all-or-none law of muscle physiology, a whole muscle responds to stimuli with a graded response. A *motor unit* consists of a motor neuron and all the muscle cells it innervates. Hence, activation of the neuron innervating a single motor unit will cause all muscle cells in that unit to fire simultaneously in an all-or-none fashion. The graded contractile response of a whole muscle reflects the number of motor units firing at a given time. Strong muscle contraction implies many motor units are activated (and each unit has maximally contracted); weak contraction means few motor units are active (however, the activated units are maximally contracted). By increasing the number of motor units firing, we can produce a slow, steady increase in muscle force, a process called *recruitment* or *motor unit summation.*

Regardless of the number of motor units activated, a single contraction of skeletal muscle is called a *muscle twitch.* A recorded tracing of a twitch is divided into three phases: latent, contraction, and relaxation (Figure 16B.1). The **latent phase** is a short period between the time of stimulation and the beginning of contraction. Although no force is generated during this interval, many chemical changes are taking place intracellularly in preparation for contraction. During **contraction,** the myofilaments are sliding and the muscle shortens. **Relaxation** takes place when contraction has ended and the muscle returns to its normal resting state (and length).

 This selection simulates an **isometric** (fixed-length) **contraction** of an isolated skeletal muscle and allows you to investigate how the strength and frequency of an electrical stimulus affect whole muscle function. Note that these simulations involve *indirect* stimulation by an electrode placed on the surface of the muscle. This differs from the situation *in vivo,* where each fiber in the muscle receives *direct* stimulation via a nerve ending. Now spend a few moments on the introduction to the system and definitions of terms used.

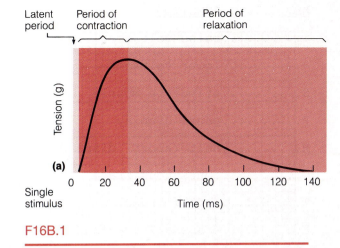

F16B.1

Tracing of a single muscle twitch.

Single Stimulus

Select option 3: *Single Stimulus.* The opening screen will appear in a few seconds (Figure 16B.2).

The oscilloscope display is the most important part of the screen, because it is where all contraction data are graphically presented for analysis. *Time* is displayed on the horizontal axis, where a full sweep is 1 second. It is marked off in 0.1-second intervals. *Force* is displayed on the vertical axis on an arbitrary scale from 0 to 5. Familiarize yourself with the control keys (Figure 16B.3) before proceeding.

1.　Press the "S" key once. Since the VOLTAGE is set to ZERO, no muscle activity will result. However, notice that a yellow line moves across the bottom of the

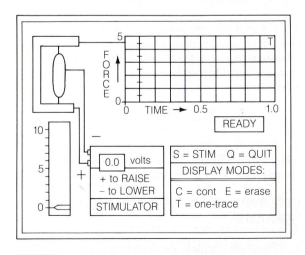

F16B.2

Opening screen of Electrical Stimulation.

```
KEY........FUNCTION

K..........stimulate on/off

R..........selection box to set rate

I..........increase stimulus rate

D..........decrease stimulus rate

V..........return to experiment

C..........continuous trace

T..........single trace

E..........erase all tracings

Q..........quit (return to menu)
```

F16B.4

Summary of Multiple Stimulus control keys.

Stimulus, but you now have the additional ability to select exact stimulus rates. Basic function keys are the same as for Single Stimulus with a few additions (Figure 16B.4). As before, familiarize yourself with all control keys before beginning the experiment.

Press the "R" key and notice that a chart comes up that allows you to select stimulus rate. The "I" key IN-CREASES stimulation rate, the "D" DECREASES it. As before, the "+" and "−" keys increase or decrease VOLTAGE. Pressing the "K" key will start stimulation, pressing it again will stop it, and pressing it once more will stimulate again. Pressing the "C" key puts the oscilloscope in the continuous mode: the tracing will continue running until you stop it or the force is decreased to zero.

FUSION FREQUENCY

1. Set the stimulator at the maximal stimulus.
2. Stimulate at this intensity for all available rates, keeping all tracings on the screen.

At what stimulation rate is tetany produced?

_____ stimuli per second

This rate is the *fusion frequency*. As before, try producing smooth, sustained contraction (tetany) at Force = 2 and Force = 3 by adjusting the stimulus rate. Do these present results support your earlier ideas?

_____

MUSCLE FATIGUE   A prolonged period of sustained contraction will result in **muscle fatigue,** a condition in which the tissue loses its ability to contract. Fatigue is easily demonstrated using the Multiple Stimulus program.

1. Set the voltage control at the maximal stimulus, stimulus rate at 20/sec, and screen on continuous sweep. Stimulate once and observe the results.

   Does the force begin to fall (muscle fatigue)?

   _____

2. Erase the screen. Stimulate as before, but when fatigue has developed, turn off the stimulator (press "K" again) for a second or two, then turn back on.

   Do you see any evidence of recovery? _____

3. When finished with this section, return to the Index of Programs by pressing the ESC key.

ISOMETRIC CONTRACTION

Isometric contraction is the condition in which muscle length does not change regardless of the amount of force generated by the muscle (*iso* = same, *metric* = length). This is accomplished experimentally by holding both ends of the muscle in a fixed position while stimulating it electrically. *Resting length* (length of the muscle before contraction) is an important factor in determining the amount of force that a muscle can develop. *Passive force* is generated by stretching the muscle and is due to the elastic properties of the tissue itself. *Active force* is generated by the physiological contraction of the muscle. *Total force* is the sum of passive and active forces.

This program allows you to set the resting length of the experimental muscle and stimulate it with a single maximal stimulus shock. You can then construct a graph relating the forces generated to length of the muscle. These principles can be applied to human muscles in order to understand how optimum resting length results in maximum force production. In order to understand why muscle tissue behaves as it does, it is necessary to comprehend *how* contraction works at the cellular level. If you have conceptual difficulty with the results of this exercise, review the sliding filament model of muscle contraction.

 Spend a few moments on the "Introduction to the System" and "Some Definitions" sections to gain an understanding of the essential elements of the system.

Select option 3: *Isometric Contraction program.* The opening screen will appear in a few seconds (Figure 16B.5).

The tip of the length-changing device indicates muscle length on the length axis below and is set at approximately 21 units. The Force-Time graph displays the single muscle twitch. Notice a small horizontal line next to the force scale; this will display resting force of the muscle. Familiarize yourself with the control keys (Figure 16B.6) before proceeding.

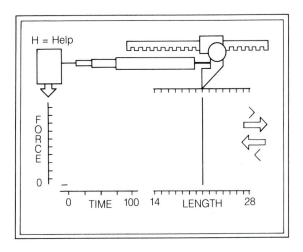

F16B.5

Opening screen of Isometric Contraction.

```
KEY........FUNCTION

>..........lengthen muscle

<..........shorten muscle

S..........stimulate muscle

M..........mark data point

F..........data values

L..........draw line graph

D..........display ideal curves

C..........clear screen

E..........erase tracings only

R..........resume work

H..........help screen

Q..........quit (return to menu)
```

F16B.6

Summary of Isometric Contraction control keys.

1. Shorten the muscle until a length of 14 units is achieved.

2. Press the "M" key once to mark PASSIVE (resting) FORCE (a small dot should appear just above the length axis on the Force-Length graph).

3. Stimulate once by pressing the "S" key. You should see a single force tracing on the Force-Time graph.

4. Press "M" once again to mark PEAK TWITCH (active) FORCE.

5. Increasing the muscle length by 1 unit each time and repeating the MARK-STIMULATE-MARK pattern, complete the tracings for the entire length range.

What is happening to the resting and peak twitch forces as muscle length is increased?

_____

6. When finished with plotting all data, connect points by pressing the "L" key.

Can you explain the dip in the upper curve? (Keep in mind you are measuring total muscle force.)

_____

_____

7. Display the ideal curves by pressing "D." Now is the reason for the dip evident?

8. Press the "X" key to label the graph. Notice that what we have been calling peak force is actually total force and is the sum of the resting and active forces.

9. When you understand these concepts, return to the Index of Programs (ESC).

ISOTONIC CONTRACTION

During **isotonic contraction,** muscle length changes, but the force produced does not (*iso* = same, *tonic* = force). Unlike the isometric exercise, where both ends of the muscle were held in a fixed position, the setup for isotonic contraction requires one end of the muscle to be free. Variable weights can then be attached to the free end, while the other end of the muscle is held fixed. If the weight is not too great, the muscle will be able to lift it with a certain velocity. You can think of lifting an object from the floor as an example: If the object is light, it can be lifted quickly (high velocity), whereas a heavier weight will be lifted more slowly (with a lower velocity). Try to transfer the idea of what is happening in the simulation to the muscles of your arm when you are attempting to lift a weight. The two important variables in this exercise are *starting length* of the muscle and the *afterload* (weight) applied. As before, some background in the sliding filament model of contraction will be helpful.

This program allows you to change muscle length and afterload so that you can investigate the effects of changes in these variables on the speed of skeletal muscle shortening. Both variables can be independently altered and results are graphically presented directly on the screen.

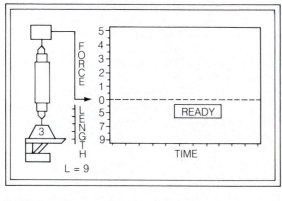

F16B.7

Opening screen of Isotonic Contraction.

```
KEY........FUNCTION

S..........stimulate muscle

V..........view screen

W..........change afterload

L..........change length

G..........graph data

E..........erase screen

H..........help screen

Q..........quit (return to menu)
```

F16B.8

Summary of Isotonic Contraction control keys.

Choose Isotonic Contraction from the Index of Programs and, as before, spend some time on the introductory sections before proceeding. Select option 3: *Contraction and Relaxation.* The opening screen will appear in a few seconds (Figure 16B.7).

The length scale displays 5 to 9 arbitrary units and the force scale indicates a range from 0 to 5 units. Initially, muscle length is set at 9 units and afterload weight at 3 units. Familiarize yourself with the equipment layout and control keys (Figure 16B.8) before proceeding.

Stimulate the muscle once and observe the tracings. Notice the READY box while the tracing is being produced. It will indicate ISOMETRIC conditions (length is constant but force may be changing) and ISOTONIC conditions (force is constant but length is changing). To change weight or length, press the appropriate key ("W" or "L") and select the variable you wish. The upper tracing displays Force as a function of Time.

Does the flat part of the tracings correspond to isotonic conditions or isometric conditions?

_____

_____

The lower tracing indicates Length as a function of Time. Analyze length tracings carefully because they indicate initial velocity of shortening. Think about what the curve means and the following concept should become clear: Using a given weight, a specific change in the length of the muscle will occur in a certain amount of time (heavier afterloads require more time). This means that the *steepness* of the tracing is an indication of initial velocity or speed of shortening; the steeper the tracing, the higher the initial velocity.

THE EFFECT OF LOAD ON SKELETAL MUSCLE

1.   Keeping the resting length constant at 9 units, run through the entire range of afterload weights. After each weight tracing has been completed, press "G" to activate graph, and then press "P" to plot each data point. When the entire set of afterload weights has been plotted, press "D" while in the graph option to draw the plot.

What is the relationship between afterload weight (Fa) and the initial velocity of shortening?

_____

_____

What about afterload and maximum length change?

_____

2.   Now keep afterload weight constant (Wt = #2) and run through the entire range of starting lengths.

What is the relationship between starting length and initial velocity of shortening?

_____

_____

_____

3.   Try the same experiment with a different weight.

Is there a similar pattern? _____

Can you set up a contraction that is entirely isometric?

_____

One that is entirely isotonic? _____

Explain why or why not.

_____

_____

_____

_____

4.   When you are finished with this exercise, press ESC to return to the Index of Programs.

5.   If time allows, try the BIKER selection. This program simulates a bike rider trying to finish a race before exhaustion sets in. You control the gears of the bicycle, and the object of the exercise is to shift effectively so that the biker achieves his or her goal. Bar graphs indicating conditions and a Force-Velocity curve are provided to aid you in your task. Apply what you have learned in this exercise along with a logical interpretation of the Force-Velocity curve and it will be possible to finish the race.

6.   When finished with all exercises, escape to the Index of Programs and select option 8: quit. Remove the simulation program diskette and return the computer to the original starting condition.

Histology of Nervous Tissue

The nervous system is the master integrating and coordinating system, continuously monitoring and processing sensory information both from the external environment and from within the body. Every thought, action, and sensation is a reflection of its activity. Like a computer, it processes and integrates new "inputs" with information previously fed into it ("programmed") to produce an appropriate response ("readout"). However, no computer can possibly compare in complexity and scope to the human nervous system.

Despite its complexity, nervous tissue is made up of just two principal cell populations: the **neurons** and the **neuroglia** (glial cells). The *neuroglia*, literally "nerve glue," include *astrocytes, oligodendrocytes, microglia,* and *ependymal cells* (Figure 17.1). These cells serve the needs of the neurons by acting as supportive and protective cells, myelinating cells, and phagocytes. In addition, they probably serve some nutritive function by acting as a selective barrier between the capillary blood supply and the neurons. Although neuroglia resemble neurons in some ways (they have fibrous cellular extensions), they are not capable of generating and transmitting nerve impulses, a capability that is highly developed in neurons. Our focus in this exercise is the highly irritable neurons.

NEURON ANATOMY

The delicate **neurons** are the structural units of nervous tissue. They are highly specialized to transmit messages (nerve impulses) from one part of the body to another.

Although neurons differ structurally, they have many identifiable features in common (Figure 17.2). All have a **cell body** from which slender processes or fibers extend. Neuron cell bodies, which are found only in the CNS (brain or spinal cord), typically in clusters called **nuclei,** or in **ganglia** (collections of neuron cell bodies outside the CNS), make up the gray matter of the nervous system. Neuron processes running through the CNS form **tracts** of white matter; outside the CNS they form the peripheral **nerves.**

The neuron cell body contains a large round nucleus surrounded by cytoplasm (*neuroplasm*). The cytoplasm is riddled with neurofibrils and with darkly staining structures called Nissl bodies. **Neurofibrils,** the cytoskeletal elements of the neuron, have a support and intracellular transport function. **Nissl bodies,** an elaborate type of rough endoplasmic reticulum, are involved in the metabolic activities of the cell.

Neuron, Multipolar,　# 44438
Nissl Stain

‖‖‖‖‖‖‖‖‖‖‖‖‖‖‖‖

According to the older, traditional scheme, neuron processes that conduct electrical currents *toward* the cell body are called **dendrites;** and those that carry impulses *away from* the nerve cell body are called **axons.** When it was discovered that this anatomical scheme had pitfalls (some axons carry impulses *both* toward and away from the cell body), a newer functional definition of neuron processes was adopted. According to this

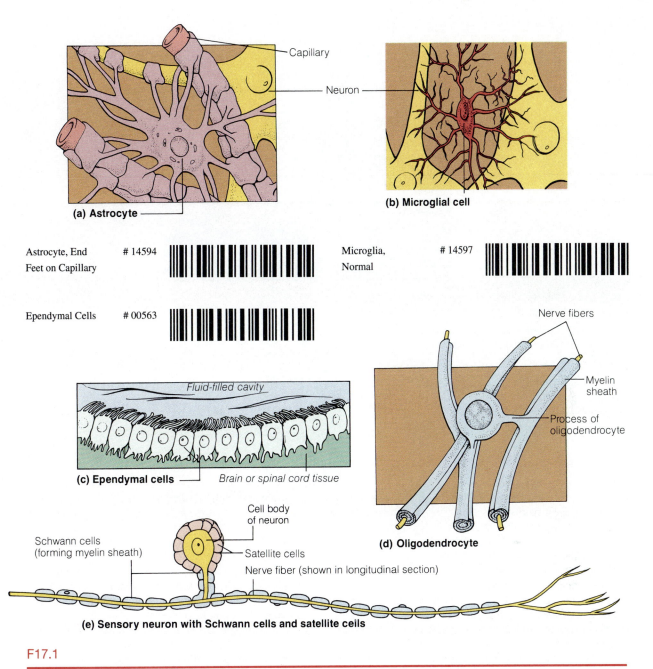

---- Capillary

---- Neuron

(a) Astrocyte

(b) Microglial cell

| Astrocyte, End Feet on Capillary | # 14594 |
| Ependymal Cells | # 00563 |

| Microglia, Normal | # 14597 |

Fluid-filled cavity

(c) Ependymal cells ---- *Brain or spinal cord tissue*

Nerve fibers

Myelin sheath

Process of oligodendrocyte

(d) Oligodendrocyte

Cell body of neuron

Schwann cells (forming myelin sheath)

Satellite cells

Nerve fiber (shown in longitudinal section)

(e) Sensory neuron with Schwann cells and satellite cells

F17.1

Supporting cells of nervous tissue. (a) Astrocyte. (b) Microglial cell. (c) Ependymal cells. (d) Oligodendrocyte. (e) Nerve cell with Schwann cells and satellite cells.

scheme, dendrites are *receptive regions* (they bear receptors for neurotransmitters released by other neurons), whereas axons are *nerve impulse generators* and *transmitters*. Neurons have only one axon (which may branch into **collaterals**) but may have many dendrites, depending on the neuron type. Notice that the term *nerve fiber* is a synonym for axon and is, thus, quite specific.

In general, a neuron is excited by other neurons when their axons release neurotransmitters close to its dendrites or cell body. The electrical current generated travels across the cell body and down the axon. As Fig-

Synapse, Cholinergic EM	# 44130
Node of Ranvier	# 00619
Node of Ranvier	# 32002

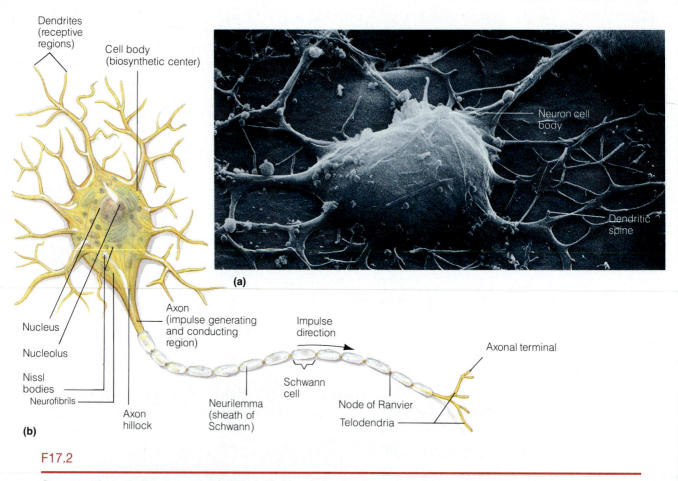

Dendrites (receptive regions)

Cell body (biosynthetic center)

Neuron cell body

Dendritic spine

(a)

Nucleus

Nucleolus

Nissl bodies

Neurofibrils

Axon hillock

(b)

Axon (impulse generating and conducting region)

Neurilemma (sheath of Schwann)

Impulse direction

Schwann cell

Node of Ranvier

Telodendria

Axonal terminal

F17.2

Structure of a typical motor neuron. (a) Photomicrograph showing the neuron cell body and dendrites with obvious dendritic spines, which are synapse sites (5000×). (b) Diagrammatic view.

ure 17.2 shows, the axon (in motor neurons) begins at a slightly enlarged cell body structure called the **axon hillock** and ends in many small structures called **axonal terminals,** or synaptic knobs. These terminals store the neurotransmitter chemical in tiny vesicles. Each axonal terminal is separated from the cell body or dendrites of the next (postsynaptic) neuron by a tiny gap called the **synaptic cleft.** Thus, although they are close, there is no actual physical contact between neurons. When an impulse reaches the axonal terminals, the synaptic vesicles rupture and release the neurotransmitter into the synaptic cleft. The neurotransmitter then diffuses across the synaptic cleft to bind to membrane receptors on the next neuron, initiating the action potential.*

Many drugs can influence the transmission of impulses at synapses. Some, like caffeine, are stimulants which decrease the receptor neuron's threshold and make it more irritable. Others block transmission by

binding competitively with the receptor sites or by interfering with the release of neurotransmitter by the axonal terminals. As might be anticipated, some of these drugs are used as painkillers or tranquilizers. ■

Most long nerve fibers are covered with a fatty material called *myelin,* and such fibers are referred to as **myelinated fibers.** Axons in the peripheral nervous system are typically heavily myelinated by special cells called **Schwann cells,** which wrap themselves tightly around the axon jelly-roll fashion (Figure 17.3). During the wrapping process, the cytoplasm is squeezed from between adjacent layers of the Schwann cell membranes, so that when the process is completed a tight core of plasma membrane material (protein-lipoid material) encompasses the axon. This wrapping is the **myelin sheath.** The Schwann cell nucleus and the bulk of its cytoplasm ends up just beneath the outermost portion of its plasma membrane. This peripheral part of the Schwann cell and its plasma membrane is referred to as the **neurilemma.** Since the myelin sheath is formed by many individual Schwann cells, it is a discontinuous sheath; the gaps or indentations in the sheath are called **nodes of Ranvier** (see Figure 17.2).

* Specialized synapses in skeletal muscle are called neuromuscular junctions. They are discussed in Exercise 14.

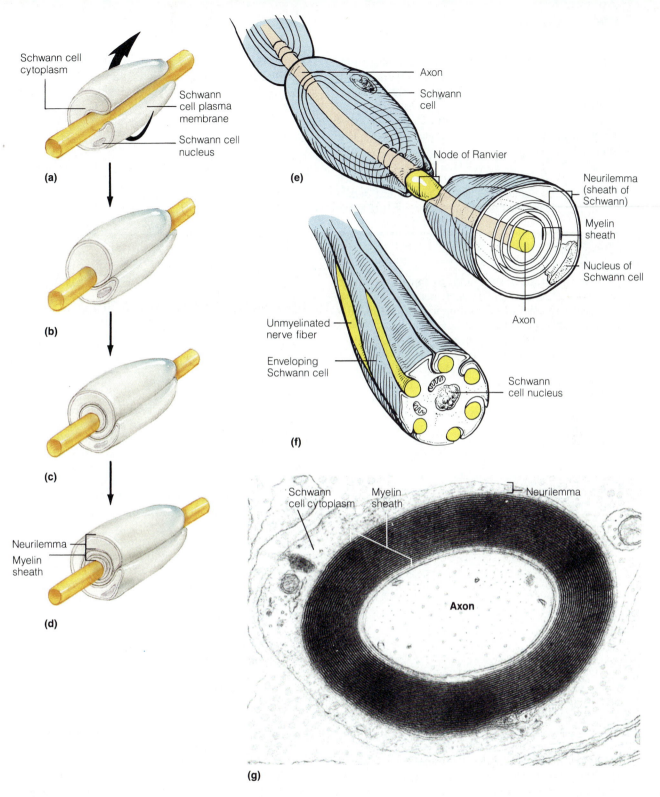

F17.3

Myelination of neuron processes by individual Schwann cells. (a–d) A Schwann cell becomes apposed to an axon and envelops it in a trough. It then begins to rotate around the axon, wrapping it loosely in successive layers of its plasma membrane. Eventually, the Schwann cell cytoplasm is forced from between the membranes and comes to lie peripherally just beneath the exposed portion of the Schwann cell membrane. The tight membrane wrappings surrounding the axon form the myelin sheath. The area of Schwann cell cytoplasm and its exposed membrane are referred to as the neurilemma or sheath of Schwann. (e) Longitudinal view of a myelinated axon showing portions of adjacent Schwann cells and the node of Ranvier between them. (f) Unmyelinated fibers. Schwann cells may associate loosely with several axons, which they partially invest. In such cases, Schwann cell coiling around the axons does not occur. (g) Photomicrograph of a myelinated axon, cross-sectional view.

Within the CNS, myelination is accomplished by glial cells called **oligodendrocytes** (see Figure 17.1d). These CNS sheaths do not exhibit the neurilemma seen in fibers myelinated by Schwann cells. Because of its chemical composition, myelin insulates the fibers and greatly increases the speed of neurotransmission by neuron fibers.

1.   Study the typical motor neuron shown in Figure 17.2, noting the structural details described above, and then identify these structures on a neuron model.

2.   Obtain a prepared slide of the ox spinal cord smear, which has large, easily identifiable neurons. Study one representative neuron under oil immersion and identify the cell body; the nucleus; the large, prominent "owl's eye" nucleolus; and the granular Nissl bodies. If possible, distinguish the axon from the many dendrites. Sketch the cell in the space provided here, and label the important anatomical details you have observed. Compare your sketch to Plate 4 of the Histology Atlas. Also examine plate 5 which differentiates the neuronal processes more clearly.

3.   Obtain a prepared slide of teased myelinated nerve fibers. Using Plate 6 of the Histology Atlas as a guide, identify the following: nodes of Ranvier, neurilemma, axis cylinder (the axon itself), Schwann cell nuclei, and myelin sheath.

Do the nodes seem to occur at consistent intervals, or are they irregularly distributed?

_____

Explain the significance of this finding: _____

_____

_____

_____

_____

Sketch a portion of a myelinated nerve fiber in the space provided here, illustrating two or three nodes of Ranvier. Label the axon, myelin sheath, nodes, and neurilemma.

NEURON CLASSIFICATION

Neurons may be classified on the basis of structure or of function. Figure 17.4 depicts both schemes.

Basis of Structure

Structurally, neurons may be differentiated according to the number of processes attached to the cell body. In **unipolar neurons,** one very short process, which divides into *peripheral* and *central processes,* extends from the cell body. Functionally, only the most distal portions of the peripheral process act as dendrites; the rest acts as an axon along with the central process. Nearly all neurons that conduct impulses toward the CNS are unipolar.

Bipolar neurons have two processes—one axon and one dendrite—attached to the cell body. This neuron type is quite rare, typically found only as part of the receptor apparatus of the eye, ear, and olfactory mucosa.

Many processes issue from the cell body of **multipolar neurons,** all classified as dendrites except for a single axon. Most neurons in the brain and spinal cord (CNS neurons) and those whose axons carry impulses away from the CNS fall into this last category.

Obtain prepared slides of Purkinje cells of the cerebellar cortex, pyramidal cells of the cerebral cortex, and a dorsal root ganglion. As you observe them under the microscope, try to pick out the anatomical details depicted in Figure 17.5. Notice that the neurons of the cerebral and cerebellar tissues (both brain tissues) are extensively branched; in contrast, the neurons of the dorsal root ganglion are more rounded. You may also be able to identify astrocytes (a type of neuroglia) in the brain tissue slides if you examine them closely.

Which of these neuron types would be classified as multipolar neurons?

_____

Which as unipolar? _____

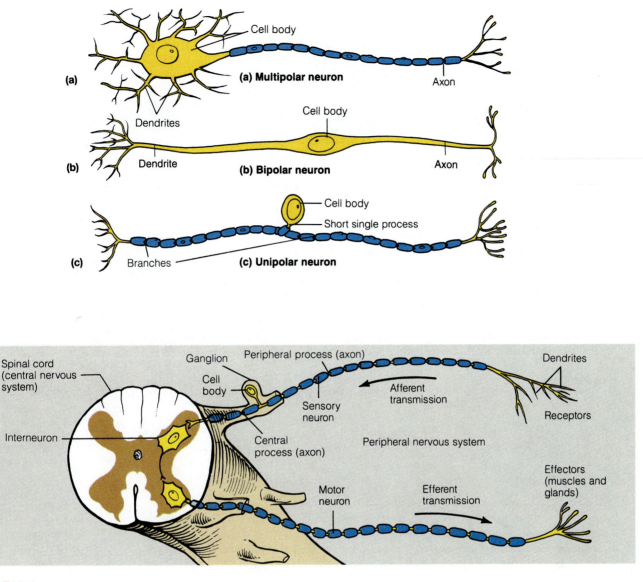

F17.4

Classification of neurons. (a–c) On the basis of structure: (a) multipolar; (b) bipolar; (c) unipolar. (d) On the basis of function, there are sensory, motor, and association neurons. Sensory (afferent) neurons conduct impulses from the body's sensory receptors to the central nervous system; most are unipolar neurons with their nerve cell bodies in ganglia in the PNS. Motor (efferent) neurons transmit impulses from the CNS to effectors such as muscles and glands. Association neurons (interneurons) complete the communication line between sensory and motor neurons. They are typically multipolar and their nerve cell bodies reside in the CNS.

Basis of Function

In general, neurons carrying impulses from the sensory receptors in the internal organs (viscera) or in the skin are termed **sensory,** or **afferent, neurons** (see Figure 17.4d). The dendritic endings of sensory neurons are often equipped with specialized receptors that are stimulated by specific changes in their immediate environment. The structure and function of these receptors is considered separately in Exercise 23 (General Sensation). The cell bodies of sensory neurons are always found in a ganglion outside the CNS, and these neurons are typically unipolar.

Neurons carrying activating impulses from the CNS to the viscera and/or body muscles and glands are termed **motor,** or **efferent, neurons.** Motor neurons are most often multipolar and their cell bodies are almost always located in the CNS.

The third functional category of neurons is the **association neurons,** or **interneurons,** which are situated between and contribute to pathways that connect sensory and motor neurons. Their cell bodies are always

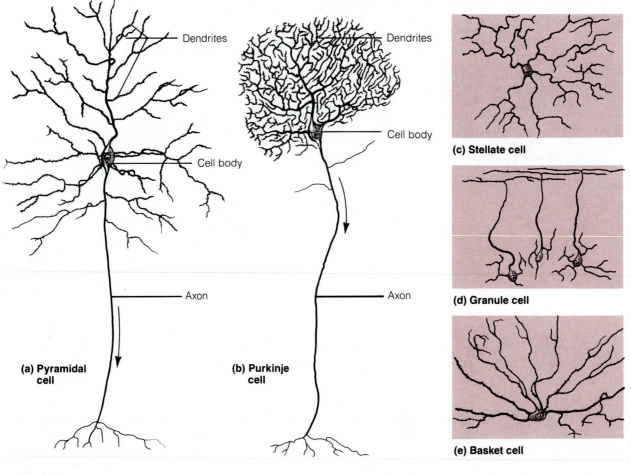

Dendrites

Cell body

Axon

(a) Pyramidal cell

Dendrites

Cell body

Axon

(b) Purkinje cell

(c) Stellate cell

(d) Granule cell

(e) Basket cell

F17.5

Structure of selected neurons. (a) Pyramidal cell of the cerebral cortex and (b) Purkinje cells of the cerebellum have extremely long axons, but they are easily distinguished by their dendrite-branching patterns, whereas cerebellar neurons such as (c) stellate cells, (d) granule cells, and (e) basket cells have short (or even absent) axons and profuse dendrites.

located within the CNS and they are multipolar neurons structurally.

STRUCTURE OF A NERVE

A nerve is a bundle of neuron fibers or processes wrapped in connective tissue coverings that extends to and/or from the CNS and visceral organs or structures of the body periphery (such as skeletal muscles, glands, and skin).

Within a nerve, each fiber is surrounded by a delicate connective tissue sheath called an **endoneurium,** which insulates it from the other neuron processes adjacent to it. (The endoneurium is often mistaken for the myelin sheath; it is instead an additional sheath that surrounds the myelin sheath.) Groups of fibers are bound by a coarser connective tissue, called the **perineurium,** to form bundles of fibers called **fascicles.** Finally, all the fascicles are bound together by a tough, white, fibrous connective tissue sheath called the **epineurium,** forming the cordlike nerve (Figure 17.6). In addition to the connective tissue wrappings, blood vessels and lymphatic vessels serving the fibers also travel within a nerve.

Like neurons, nerves are classified according to the direction in which they transmit impulses. Nerves carrying both sensory (afferent) and motor (efferent) fibers are called **mixed nerves;** all spinal nerves are mixed nerves. Nerves that carry only sensory processes and

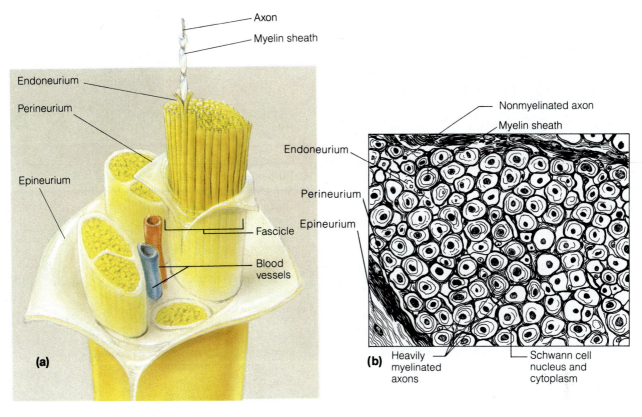

F17.6

Structure of a nerve, showing connective tissue wrappings. (a) Three-dimensional view of a portion of a nerve. (b) Cross-sectional view corresponding to Plate 8 of the Histology Atlas.

conduct impulses only toward the CNS are referred to as **sensory,** or **afferent, nerves.** A few of the cranial nerves are pure sensory nerves, but the majority are mixed nerves. The ventral roots of the spinal cord, which carry only motor fibers, can be considered **motor,** or **efferent, nerves.**

Examine under the compound microscope a prepared cross section of a peripheral nerve. Identify nerve fibers, myelin sheaths, fascicles, and endoneurium, perineurium, and epineurium sheaths. If desired, sketch the nerve in the space to the right.

18 EXERCISE

Neurophysiology of Nerve Impulses

OBJECTIVES

1. To list the two major physiological properties of neurons.
2. To describe the polarized and depolarized states of the nerve cell membrane and to describe the events that lead to generation and conduction of a nerve impulse.
3. To explain how a nerve impulse is transmitted from one neuron to another.
4. To define *action potential, depolarization, repolarization,* and *refractory period.*
5. To list various substances and factors that can stimulate neurons.
6. To recognize that neurotransmitters may be either stimulatory or inhibitory in nature.
7. To state the site of action of the blocking agents ether and curare.

MATERIALS

*Rana pipiens**
Dissecting instruments and tray
Ringer's solution (frog) in dropper bottles, some at room temperature and some in an ice bath
Thread
Glass rods or probes
Glass plates or slides
Ring stand and clamp
Stimulator; platinum electrodes
Oscilloscope
Nerve chamber
Filter paper
0.01% hydrochloric acid (HCl) solution
Sodium chloride (NaCl) crystals
Heat-resistant mitts
Bunsen burner
Absorbent cotton
Ether
Pipettes
1-cc syringe with small-gauge needle
0.5% tubocurarine solution
Frog board
Disposable plastic gloves

*Instructor to provide freshly pithed frogs (*Rana pipiens*) for student experimentation.

THE NERVE IMPULSE

Neurons have two major physiologic properties: **irritability,** or the ability to respond to stimuli and convert them into nerve impulses, and **conductivity,** the ability to transmit the impulse to other neurons, muscles, or glands. In a resting neuron (as in resting muscle cells), the exterior surface of the membrane is slightly more positively charged than the inner surface, as shown in Figure 18.1a. This difference in electrical charge on the two sides of the membrane results in a voltage across the plasma membrane referred to as the **resting membrane potential,** and a neuron in this state is said to be **polarized.** In the resting state, the predominant intracellular ion is potassium (K^+), and sodium ions (Na^+) are found in greater concentration in the extracellular fluids. The resting potential is maintained by a very active sodium-potassium pump, which transports Na^+ out of the cell and K^+ into the cell.

When the neuron is activated by a stimulus of adequate intensity—a **threshold stimulus**—the membrane at its *trigger zone,* typically the axon hillock (or the most peripheral part of a sensory neuron's axon), briefly becomes more permeable to sodium (sodium gates are opened). Sodium ions rush into the cell, increasing the number of positive ions inside the cell and reversing the polarity (Figure 18.1b). Thus the interior of the membrane becomes less negative at that point and the exterior surface becomes less positive—a phenomenon called **depolarization.** When depolarization reaches a certain point such that the local membrane polarity changes (momentarily the external face becomes negative and the internal face becomes positive), it initiates an **action potential*** (Figure 18.1c).

* If the stimulus is of less than threshold intensity, depolarization is limited to a small area of the membrane, and no action potential is generated.

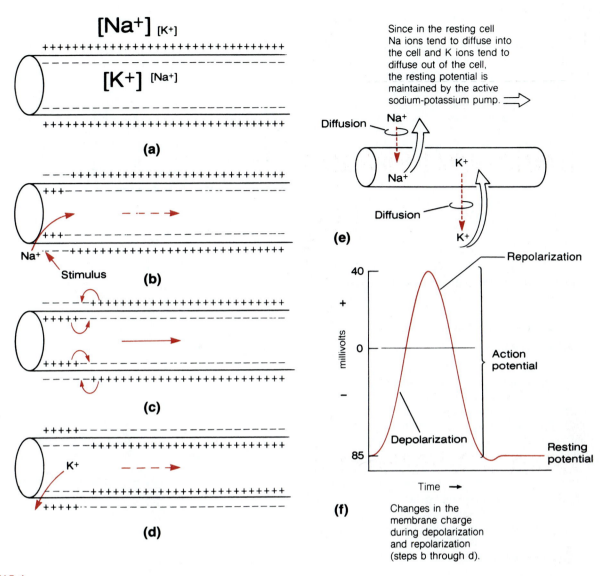

F18.1

The nerve impulse. (a) Resting membrane potential (-85 mv). There is an excess of positive ions outside the cell, with Na$^+$ the predominant extracellular fluid ion and K$^+$ the predominant intracellular ion. The cell membrane has a low permeability to Na$^+$. (b) Depolarization—reversal of the resting potential. Application of a stimulus changes the membrane permeability, and Na$^+$ ions are allowed to diffuse rapidly into the cell. (c) Generation of the action potential or nerve impulse. If the stimulus is of adequate intensity, the depolarization wave spreads rapidly along the entire length of the membrane. (d) Repolarization—reestablishment of the resting potential. The negative charge on the internal cell membrane surface and the positive charge on its external surface are reestablished by diffusion of K$^+$ ions out of the cell, proceeding in the same direction as in depolarization. (e) The original ionic concentrations of the resting state are restored by the sodium-potassium pump. (f) A tracing of an action potential.

Within a millisecond after the inward influx of sodium, the membrane permeability is again altered. As a result, Na$^+$ permeability decreases, K$^+$ permeability increases, and K$^+$ rushes out of the cell. Since K$^+$ ions are positively charged, their movement out of the cell reverses the membrane potential again, so that the external membrane surface is again positive relative to the internal membrane face (Figure 18.1d). This event, called **repolarization,** reestablishes the resting membrane potential. During the time of repolarization, the neuron is insensitive to further stimulation; thus this period is referred to as the **refractory period.**

Once generated, the action potential is a self-propagating phenomenon that spreads rapidly along the entire length of the neuron. It is never partially transmitted; that is, it is an all-or-none response. This propagation of the action potential in neurons is also called the **nerve impulse.** When the nerve impulse reaches the axonal terminals, they release a neurotransmitter that acts either to stimulate or to inhibit the next neuron in the transmission chain. (Note that only stimulatory transmitters are considered here.)

Because only minute amounts of sodium and potassium ions have changed places, once repolarization has been completed, the neuron can quickly respond again to a stimulus. In fact, thousands of impulses can be generated before ionic imbalances prevent the neuron from transmitting impulses. Eventually, however, it is necessary to restore the original ionic concentrations on the two sides of the membrane; this is accomplished by the activity of the Na^+-K^+ pump (Figure 18.1e).

PHYSIOLOGY OF NERVE FIBERS

In this laboratory session, you will investigate the functioning of nerve fibers by subjecting the sciatic nerve of a frog to various types of stimuli and blocking agents. Work in groups of two to four to lighten the work load.

Stimulation of the Nerve Impulse

In the first set of experiments, stimulation of the nerve and generation of the action potential will be indicated by the contraction of the gastrocnemius muscle. Because you will make no mechanical recording (unless your instructor asks you to), you must keep complete and accurate records of all experimental procedures and results.

1. Don gloves to protect yourself from any parasites the frogs might have. Request and obtain a pithed frog from your instructor and bring it to your laboratory bench. Also obtain dissecting instruments and a tray from the supply area.

2. Prepare the sciatic nerve as illustrated in Figure 18.2. Place the pithed frog on the dissecting tray, dorsal side down. Make a cut through the skin around the circumference of the frog approximately halfway down the trunk, and then pull the skin down over the muscles of the legs. Open the abdominal cavity and push the abdominal organs to one side to expose the origin of the glistening white sciatic nerve, which arises from the last three spinal nerves. Once the sciatic nerve has been exposed, it should be kept continually moist with room temperature Ringer's solution.

3. Using a glass probe, slip a piece of thread moistened with Ringer's solution under the sciatic nerve close to its origin at the vertebral column. Make a single ligature (tie it firmly with the thread), and then cut through the nerve roots to free the proximal end of the sciatic nerve from its attachments. Using a glass rod or probe, carefully separate the posterior thigh muscles to locate and then free the sciatic nerve, which runs down the posterior aspect of the thigh.

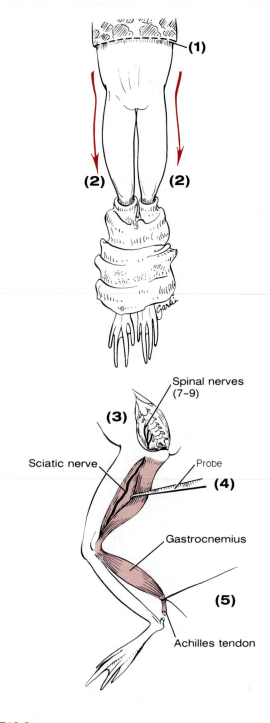

F18.2

Removal of the sciatic nerve and gastrocnemius muscle.
(1) Cut through the frog's skin around the circumference of the trunk. (2) Pull the skin down over the trunk and legs. (3) Make a longitudinal cut through the abdominal musculature and expose the roots of the sciatic nerve (arising from spinal nerves 7–9). Ligate the nerve and cut the roots proximal to the ligature. (4) Use a glass probe to expose the sciatic nerve beneath the posterior thigh muscles. (5) Ligate the calcaneal tendon and cut it free distal to the ligature. (6) Release the gastrocnemius muscle from the connective tissue of the knee region.

4.   Tie a piece of thread around the Achilles tendon of the gastrocnemius muscle, and then cut through the tendon distal to the ligature to free the gastrocnemius muscle from the heel. Using a scalpel, very carefully release the gastrocnemius muscle from the connective tissue in the knee region. At this point you should have completely freed both the gastrocnemius muscle and the sciatic nerve, which innervates it.

5.   With glass rods, transfer the muscle to a glass plate or slide, and then attach the slide to a ring stand with a clamp. Allow the end of the sciatic nerve to hang over the free edge of the glass slide, so that it is easily accessible for stimulation. Remember to keep the nerve moist at all times.

6.   You are now ready to investigate the response of the sciatic nerve to various stimuli, beginning with electrical stimulation. Using the stimulator and platinum electrodes, stimulate the sciatic nerve with single shocks, gradually increasing the intensity of the stimulus until the threshold stimulus is determined.

(The muscle as a whole will just barely contract at the threshold stimulus.) Record the voltage of this stimulus:

———————— v

Continue to increase the voltage until you find the point beyond which no further increase occurs in the strength of muscle contraction—that is, the point at which the maximal contraction of the muscle is obtained. Record this voltage below.

———————— v

Delivering multiple or repeated shocks to the sciatic nerve causes volleys of impulses in the nerve. Shock the nerve with multiple stimuli. Observe the response of the muscle. How does this response compare with the response to the single electrical shocks?

————————————————————

————————————————————

————————————————————

7.   To investigate mechanical stimulation, pinch the free end of the nerve by firmly pressing it between two glass rods or by pinching it with forceps. What is the result?

————————————————————

8.   Chemical stimulation can be tested by applying a small piece of filter paper saturated with 0.01% hydrochloric acid (HCl) solution to the free end of the nerve. What is the result?

————————————————————

Drop a few grains of salt (NaCl) on the free end of the nerve. What is the result?

————————————————————

9.   Now test thermal stimulation. Wearing the heat-resistant mitts, heat a glass rod for a few moments over a Bunsen burner. Then touch the rod to the free end of the nerve. What is the result?

————————————————————

What do these muscle reactions say about the irritability and conductivity of neurons?

————————————————————

————————————————————

————————————————————

Although most neurons within the body are stimulated to the greatest degree by a particular stimulus (in many cases, a chemical neurotransmitter), a variety of other stimuli may trigger nerve impulses, as illustrated by the experimental series just conducted. Generally, no matter what type of stimulus is present, if the affected part responds by becoming activated, it will always react in the same way. Familiar examples are the well-known phenomenon of "seeing stars" when you receive a blow to the head or press on your eyeball (try it), both of which trigger impulses in your optic nerves.

Inhibition of the Nerve Impulse

Numerous physical factors and chemical agents can impair the ability of nerve fibers to function. For example, deep pressure and cold temperature both block nerve impulse transmission by preventing the local blood supply from reaching the nerve fibers. Local anesthetics, alcohol, and numerous other chemicals are also very effective at blocking nerve transmission. Ether, one such chemical blocking agent, will be investigated first.

⚠ Since ether is extremely volatile and explosive, be sure that laboratory fans are on and that *all Bunsen burners are off* during this procedure.

1.   Clamp a second glass slide to the ring stand slightly below the first slide of the apparatus setup for the previous experiment. With glass rods, gently position the sciatic nerve on this second slide, allowing a small portion of the nerve's distal end to extend over the edge. Place a piece of absorbent cotton soaked with ether under the midsection of the nerve on the slide, prodding it into position with a glass rod. Using a voltage slightly above the threshold stimulus, stimulate the distal end of the nerve at 2-min intervals until the muscle fails to respond. (If the cotton dries be-

fore this, rewet it with ether using a pipette.) How long did it take for anesthesia to occur?

_____ sec

2. Once anesthesia has occurred, stimulate the nerve beyond the anesthetized area, between the ether-soaked pad and the muscle. What is the result?

_____

3. Remove the ether-soaked pad and flush the nerve fibers with saline. Again stimulate the nerve at its distal end at 2-min intervals. How long does it take for recovery?

_____

Does ether exert its blocking effect on the nerve fibers or on the muscle cells?

_____ Explain your reasoning.

_____

_____

If sufficient frogs are available and time allows, you may do the following classic experiment. In the 1800s Claude Bernard described an investigation into the effect of curare on nerve-muscle interaction. _Curare_ was commonly used by some South American Indian tribes to tip their arrows. Victims struck with these arrows were paralyzed, but the paralysis was not accompanied by loss of sensation.

1. Prepare another frog as described in steps 1 through 3 of Stimulation of the Nerve Impulse. However, in this case position the frog ventral side down on a frog board. In exposing the sciatic nerve, take care not to damage the blood vessels in the thigh region, as the success of the experiment depends on maintaining the blood supply to the muscles of the leg.

2. Expose and gently tie the left sciatic nerve so that it can be lifted away from the muscles of the leg for stimulation. Slip another length of thread under the nerve, and then tie the thread tightly around the thigh muscles to cut off circulation to the leg. The sciatic nerve should be above the thread and _not in_ the ligatured tissue. Expose and ligature the sciatic nerve of the _right_ leg in the same manner, but this time do _not_ ligate the thigh muscles.

⚠ 3. Using a syringe and needle, slowly and carefully inject 1 cc of 0.5% tubocurarine into the dorsal lymph sac of the frog.* The dorsal lymph sacs are located dorsally at the level of the scapulae, so introduce the needle of the syringe just beneath the skin between the scapulae and toward one side of the spinal column. _Handle the tubocurarine very carefully, because it is extremely poisonous._ Do not get any on your skin.

4. Wait 15 min after injection of the tubocurarine to allow it to be distributed throughout the body in the blood and lymphatic stream. Then stimulate electrically the left sciatic nerve. Be careful not to touch any of the other tissues with the electrode. Gradually increasing the voltage, deliver single shocks until the threshold stimulus has been determined for this specimen.

Threshold stimulus: _____ v

Now stimulate the right sciatic nerve with the same voltage intensity. Is there any difference in the reaction of the two muscles?

_____ If so, explain. _____

_____

_____

If you did not find any difference, wait an additional 10 to 15 min and restimulate both sciatic nerves.

What is the result? _____

5. To determine the site at which tubocurarine acts, directly stimulate each gastrocnemius muscle. What is the result?

_____

_____

_____

Explain the difference between the responses of the right and left sciatic nerves.

_____

_____

_____

Explain the results when the muscles were stimulated directly.

_____

_____

_____

At what site does tubocurarine (or curare) act?

_____

---

* To obtain 1 cc of the tubocurarine, inject 1 cc of air into the vial through the rubber membrane, and then draw up 1 cc of the chemical into the syringe.

Visualization of the Action Potential with an Oscilloscope

The *oscilloscope* is an instrument that visually displays the rapid but extremely minute changes in voltage that occur during an action potential. The oscilloscope is similar to a TV set in that the screen display is produced by a stream of electrons generated by an electron gun (cathode) at the rear of a tube. The electrons pass through the tube and between two sets of plates that lie alongside the beam pathway. When the electrons reach the fluorescent screen, they create a tiny glowing spot. The plates determine the placement of the glowing spot by controlling the vertical or horizontal sweep of the beam. Vertical movement represents the voltage of the input signal, and horizontal movement indicates the time base. When there is no electrical output signal to the oscilloscope, the electron beam sweeps horizontally (left to right) across the screen, but when the plates are electrically stimulated, the path of electrons is deflected vertically.

In this exercise, a frog's sciatic nerve will be electrically stimulated, and the action potentials generated will be observed on the oscilloscope. The dissected nerve will be placed in contact with two pairs of electrodes—stimulating and recording. The stimulating electrodes will be used to deliver a pulse of electricity to a point on the sciatic nerve. At another point on the nerve, a pair of recording electrodes connected to the oscilloscope will deliver the current to the plates inside the tube, and the electrical pulse will be recorded on the screen as a vertical deflection, or a *stimulus artifact* (Figure 18.3a). As the nerve is stimulated with increasingly higher voltage, the stimulus artifact increases in amplitude as well. When the stimulus voltage reaches a high enough level (threshold), an action potential will be generated by the nerve, and a *second* vertical deflection will appear on the screen, approximately 2 milliseconds after the stimulus artifact (Figure 18.3b–d). This second deflection reports the potential difference between the two recording electrodes—that is, between the first recording electrode which has already depolarized (and is in the process of repolarizing as the action potential travels along the nerve) and the second recording electrode.

1. Obtain a nerve chamber, an oscilloscope, a stimulator, frog Ringer's solution (room temperature), a dissecting needle, and glass probes. Set up the experimental apparatus as illustrated in Figure 18.4. Connect the two stimulating electrodes to the output terminals of the stimulator and the two recording electrodes to the preamplifier of the oscilloscope.

2. Obtain another pithed frog, and prepare one of its sciatic nerves for experimentation as indicated on page 182 in steps 1 through 3 under Stimulation of the Nerve Impulse. While working, be careful not to touch the nerve with your fingers, and do not allow the nerve to touch the frog's skin.

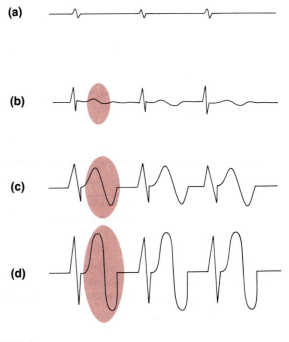

(a)

(b)

(c)

(d)

F18.3

Oscilloscope scans of nerve stimulation using stimuli with increasing intensities. The first action potential in each scan is circled. (a) Stimulus artifacts only; no action potential produced. Subthreshold stimulation. (b) Threshold stimulation. (c) Submaximal stimulation. (d) Maximal stimulus.

3. When you have freed the sciatic nerve to the knee region with the glass probe, slip another thread length beneath that end of the nerve and make a ligature. Cut the nerve distal to this tied thread and then carefully lift the cut nerve away from the thigh of the frog by holding the threads at the nerve's proximal and distal ends. Place the nerve in the nerve chamber so that it rests across all four electrodes (the two stimulating and two recording electrodes) as shown in Figure 18.4. Flush the nerve with room temperature frog Ringer's solution.

4. Adjust the horizontal sweep according to the instructions given in the manual or by your instructor, and set the stimulator duration, frequency, and amplitude to their lowest settings.

5. Begin to stimulate the nerve with single stimuli, slowly increasing the voltage until a threshold stimulus is achieved. The action potential will appear as a small rounded "hump" immediately following the stimulus artifact. Record the voltage of the threshold stimulus:

_____ v

6. Flush the nerve with the Ringer's solution and continue to increase the voltage, watching as the vertical deflections produced by the action potentials become diphasic (show both upward and downward vertical de-

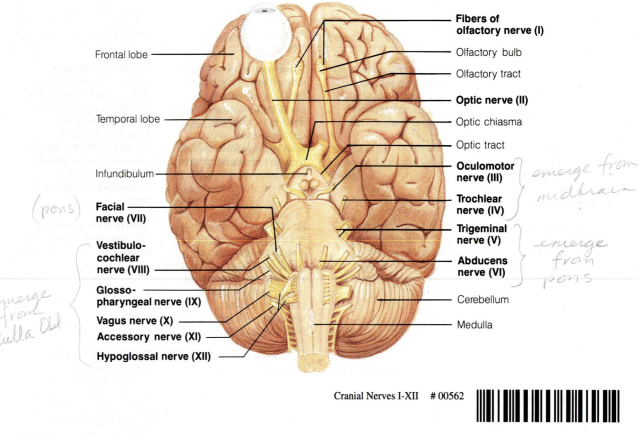

Fibers of
olfactory nerve (I)

Olfactory bulb

Olfactory tract

Optic nerve (II)

Optic chiasma

Optic tract

Oculomotor
nerve (III)   ⎱ emerge from
Trochlear   ⎰ midbrain
nerve (IV)

Trigeminal
nerve (V)   ⎱
              ⎰ emerge
Abducens   from
nerve (VI)   pons

Cerebellum

Medulla

Frontal lobe

Temporal lobe

Infundibulum

(pons)

Facial
nerve (VII)

Vestibulo-
cochlear
nerve (VIII)

Glosso-
pharyngeal nerve (IX)

Vagus nerve (X)

Accessory nerve (XI)

Hypoglossal nerve (XII)

emerge
from
medulla Obl

Cranial Nerves I-XII   # 00562

F19.8

Ventral aspect of the human brain, showing the cranial nerves.

1. Observe the anterior surface of the brain model to identify the cranial nerves. Figure 19.8 may also aid you in this study. Note that the first (olfactory) cranial nerves are not visible on the model because they consist only of those short axons that run from the nasal mucosa through the cribriform plate of the ethmoid bone. (However, the synapse points of the first cranial nerves, the *olfactory bulbs,* are visible on the model.)

2. The last column of Table 19.1 describes techniques for testing cranial nerves, which is an important part of any neurologic examination. This information may help you understand cranial nerve function, especially as it pertains to some aspects of brain function. Conduct tests of cranial nerve function following directions given in the "testing" column of the table.

3. Several cranial nerve ganglia are named here. *Using your textbook or an appropriate reference,* name the cranial nerve the ganglion is associated with and state its location.

Cranial nerve ganglion	Cranial nerve	Site of ganglion
gasserian		
geniculate		
inferior		
superior		
spiral		
vestibular		

DISSECTION OF THE SHEEP BRAIN

The brain of any mammal is enough like the human brain to warrant comparison. Obtain a sheep brain, protective skin cream or disposable gloves, dissecting pan, and instruments, and bring them to your laboratory bench.

 1.   Place the intact sheep brain ventral surface down on the dissecting pan and observe the dura mater. Feel its consistency and note its toughness. Cut through the dura mater along the line of the longitudinal fissure (which separates the cerebral hemispheres) to enter the superior sagittal sinus. Gently force the cerebral hemispheres apart laterally to expose the corpus callosum deep to the longitudinal fissure.

2.   Carefully remove the dura mater and examine the superior surface of the brain. Note that its surface is thrown into convolutions (fissures and gyri), just as the human brain is. Locate the arachnoid meninx, which appears on the brain surface as a delicate "cottony" material spanning the fissures. In contrast, the innermost meninx, the pia mater, closely follows the cerebral contours.

Dorsal Structures

1.   Refer to Figures 19.9a and c as a guide in identifying the following structures. The cerebral hemispheres should be easy to locate. How do the size of the sheep's cerebral hemispheres and the depth of the fissures compare to those in the human brain?

_____

_____

_____

2.   Carefully examine the cerebellum. Notice that it is not divided longitudinally, in contrast to the human cerebellum, and that its fissures are oriented differently. What dural falx is missing that is present in humans?

_____

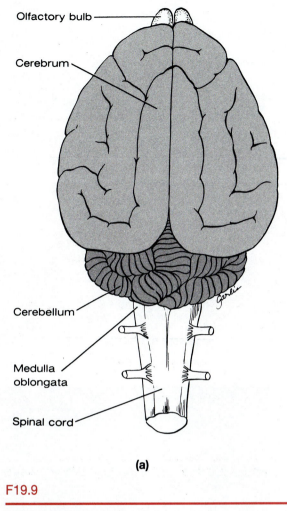

(a)

F19.9

Intact sheep brain. (a) Dorsal view.

3.   Locate the three pairs of cerebellar peduncles, fiber tracts that connect the cerebellum to other brain structures, by lifting the cerebellum dorsally away from the brain stem. The most posterior pair, the inferior cerebellar peduncles, connect the cerebellum to the medulla. The middle cerebellar peduncles attach the cerebellum to the pons, and the superior cerebellar peduncles run from the cerebellum to the midbrain.

(*Text continues on p. 203*)

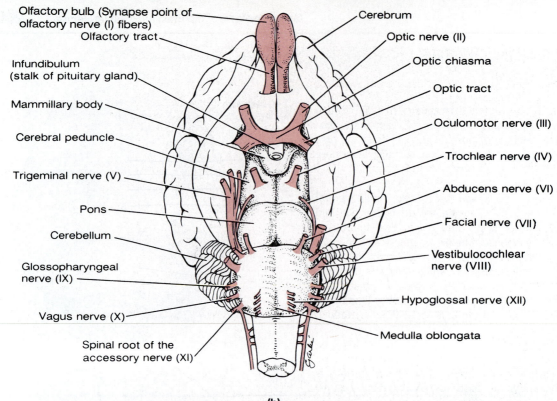

Olfactory bulb (Synapse point of olfactory nerve (I) fibers)

Olfactory tract

Infundibulum (stalk of pituitary gland)

Mammillary body

Cerebral peduncle

Trigeminal nerve (V)

Pons

Cerebellum

Glossopharyngeal nerve (IX)

Vagus nerve (X)

Spinal root of the accessory nerve (XI)

Cerebrum

Optic nerve (II)

Optic chiasma

Optic tract

Oculomotor nerve (III)

Trochlear nerve (IV)

Abducens nerve (VI)

Facial nerve (VII)

Vestibulocochlear nerve (VIII)

Hypoglossal nerve (XII)

Medulla oblongata

(b)

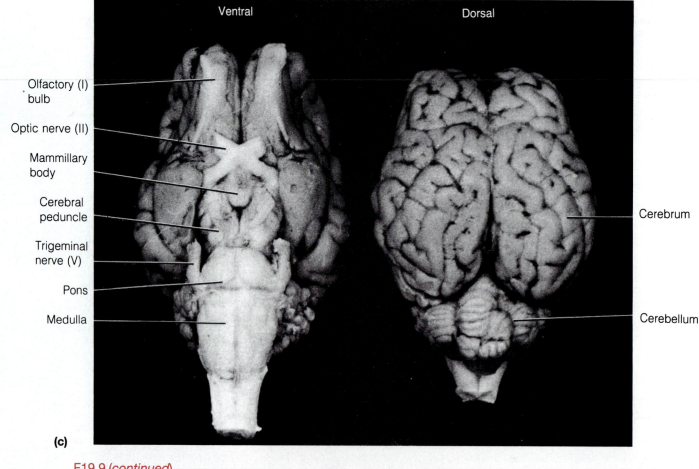

Ventral

Dorsal

Olfactory (I) bulb

Optic nerve (II)

Mammillary body

Cerebral peduncle

Trigeminal nerve (V)

Pons

Medulla

Cerebrum

Cerebellum

(c)

F19.9 (continued)

Intact sheep brain. (b) Ventral view. (c) Photograph showing ventral and dorsal views.

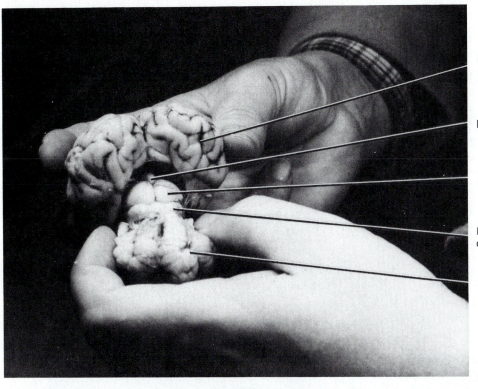

Occipital lobe of
cerebral hemisphere

Pineal body

Superior colliculi
of corpora quadrigemina

Inferior colliculi
of corpora quadrigemina

Cerebellum

F19.10

Means of exposing the dorsal midbrain structures of the sheep brain.

4.   To expose the dorsal surface of the midbrain, gently spread the cerebrum and cerebellum apart, as shown in Figure 19.10. Identify the corpora quadrigemina, which appear as four rounded prominences on the dorsal midbrain surface. What is the function of the corpora quadrigemina?

_____

_____

_____

Also locate the pineal body, which appears as a small oval protrusion in the midline just anterior to the corpora quadrigemina.

Ventral Structures

Figures 19.9b and c show the important features of the ventral surface of the brain.

1.   Look for the clublike olfactory bulbs anteriorly, on the inferior surface of the frontal lobes of the cerebral hemispheres. Axons of olfactory neurons run from the nasal mucosa through the perforated cribriform plate of the ethmoid bone to synapse with the olfactory bulbs.

How does the size of these olfactory bulbs compare with those of humans?

_____

Is the sense of smell more important as a protective and a food-getting sense in sheep *or* in humans?

_____

2.   The optic nerve (II) carries sensory impulses from the retina of the eye. Thus this cranial nerve is involved in the sense of vision. Identify the optic nerves, optic chiasma, and optic tracts.

3.   Posterior to the optic chiasma, two structures protrude from the ventral aspect of the hypothalamus—the infundibulum (stalk of the pituitary gland) immediately posterior to the optic chiasma and the mammillary body. Notice that the sheep's mammillary body is a single rounded eminence; in humans it is a double structure.

4.   Identify the cerebral peduncles on the ventral aspect of the midbrain, just posterior to the mammillary body of the hypothalamus. The cerebral peduncles are fiber tracts connecting the cerebrum and medulla. Identify the large oculomotor nerves (III), which arise from the ventral midbrain surface, and the tiny trochlear nerves (IV), which can be seen at the junction of the midbrain and pons. Both of these cranial nerves provide motor fibers to extrinsic muscles of the eyeball.

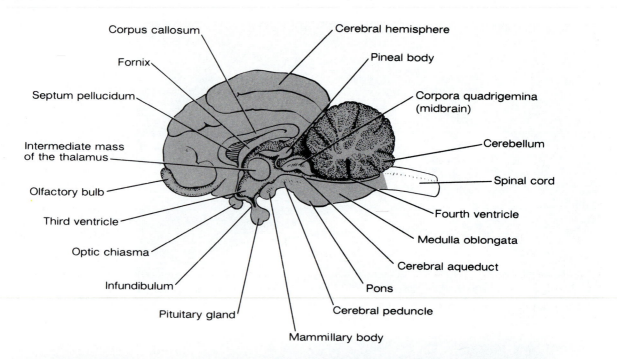

Corpus callosum
Fornix
Septum pellucidum
Intermediate mass of the thalamus
Olfactory bulb
Third ventricle
Optic chiasma
Infundibulum
Pituitary gland
Mammillary body
Cerebral hemisphere
Pineal body
Corpora quadrigemina (midbrain)
Cerebellum
Spinal cord
Fourth ventricle
Medulla oblongata
Cerebral aqueduct
Pons
Cerebral peduncle

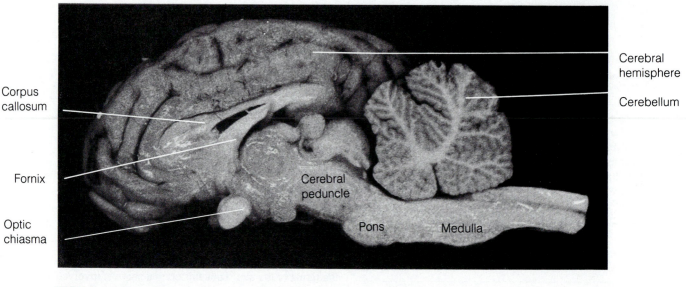

Corpus callosum
Fornix
Optic chiasma
Cerebral peduncle
Pons
Medulla
Cerebral hemisphere
Cerebellum

F19.11

Sagittal section of the sheep brain showing internal structures. (a) Diagrammatic view. (b) Photograph.

5.   Move posteriorly from the midbrain to identify first the pons and then the medulla oblongata, both hindbrain structures composed primarily of ascending and descending fiber tracts.

6.   Return to the junction of the pons and midbrain and proceed posteriorly to identify the following cranial nerves, all arising from the pons: the trigeminal nerves (V), which are involved in chewing and sensations of the head and face; the abducens nerves (VI), which abduct the eye (and thus work in conjunction with cranial nerves III and IV); and the large facial nerves (VII), which are involved in taste sensation, gland function (salivary and lacrimal glands), and facial expression.

7.   Continue posteriorly to identify the purely sensory vestibulocochlear nerves (VIII), which are involved with hearing and equilibrium; the glossopharyngeal nerves (IX), which contain motor fibers innervating throat structures and sensory fibers transmitting taste stimuli (in conjunction with cranial nerve VII); the vagus nerves (X), often called "wanderers," which serve many organs of the head, thorax, and abdominal cavity; the accessory nerves (XI), which serve muscles of the neck, larynx, and shoulder; and the hypoglossal nerves (XII), which stimulate tongue and neck muscles. Note that the accessory nerves arise from both the medulla and the spinal cord.

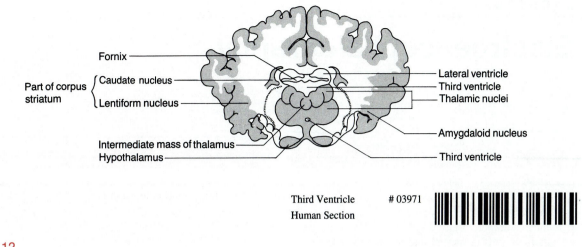

Fornix

Part of corpus striatum

Caudate nucleus

Lentiform nucleus

Intermediate mass of thalamus

Hypothalamus

Lateral ventricle

Third ventricle

Thalamic nuclei

Amygdaloid nucleus

Third ventricle

Third Ventricle   # 03971
Human Section

F19.12

Frontal section of a sheep brain. Major structures revealed are the location of major basal nuclei deep in the interior, the thalamus, hypothalamus, and lateral and third ventricles.

Internal Structures

1. The internal structure of the brain can only be examined after further dissection. Place the brain ventral side down on the dissecting pan and make a cut completely through it in a superior to inferior direction. Cut through the longitudinal fissure, corpus callosum, and midline of the cerebellum. Refer to Figure 19.11 as you work.

2. The thin nervous tissue membrane immediately ventral to the corpus callosum that separates the lateral ventricles is the septum pellucidum. Pierce this membrane and probe the lateral ventricle cavity. The fiber tract ventral to the septum pellucidum and anterior to the third ventricle is the fornix.

How does the size of the fornix in this brain compare with the human fornix?

_____

_____

Why do you suppose this is so? (Hint: What is the function of this band of fibers?)

_____

_____

_____

3. Identify the thalamus, which forms the walls of the third ventricle and is located posterior and ventral to the fornix. The intermediate mass spanning the ventricular cavity appears as an oval protrusion of the thalamic wall. Anterior to the intermediate mass, locate the interventricular foramen, a canal connecting the lateral ventricle on the same side with the third ventricle.

4. The hypothalamus forms the floor of the third ventricle. Identify the optic chiasma, infundibulum, and mammillary body on its exterior surface. You can see the pineal body at the superoposterior end of the third ventricle, just beneath the junction of the corpus callosum and fornix.

5. Locate the midbrain by identifying the corpora quadrigemina that form its dorsal roof. Follow the cerebral aqueduct (the narrow canal connecting the third and fourth ventricles) through the midbrain tissue to the fourth ventricle. Identify the cerebral peduncles, which form its anterior walls.

6. Identify the pons and medulla, which lie anterior to the fourth ventricle. The medulla continues into the spinal cord without any obvious anatomical change, but the point at which the fourth ventricle narrows to a small canal is generally accepted as the beginning of the spinal cord.

7. The cerebellum can be seen posterior to the fourth ventricle. Note its internal treelike arrangement of white matter, the arbor vitae.

8. If time allows, obtain another sheep brain and section it along the frontal plane so that the cut passes through the infundibulum. Compare your specimen to the diagrammatic view in Figure 19.12, and attempt to identify all the structures shown in the figure.

9. Check with your instructor to determine if cow spinal cord sections (preserved) are available for the spinal cord studies in Exercise 21. If not, save the small portion of the spinal cord from your brain specimen. Otherwise, dispose of all the organic debris in the appropriate laboratory containers and clean the dissecting instruments and tray before leaving the laboratory.

Electroencephalography

BRAIN WAVE PATTERNS AND THE ELECTROENCEPHALOGRAM

Any physiologic investigation of the brain can emphasize and expose only a very minute portion of its function. Higher brain functions, such as consciousness and logical reasoning, are extremely difficult to investigate. It is obviously much easier to do experiments on the brain's input-output functions, some of which can be detected with appropriate recording equipment. Still, the ability to record brain activity does not necessarily guarantee an understanding of the brain.

The **electroencephalogram** (**EEG**), a record of the electrical activity of the brain, can be obtained through electrodes placed at various points on the skin or scalp of the head. This electrical activity, which is recorded as waves (Figure 20.1), is not completely understood at present but may be regarded as action potentials generated by brain neurons.

Certain characteristics of brain waves are known. They have a frequency of 1 to 30 cycles per second (cps), a dominant rhythm of 10 cps, and an average amplitude (voltage) of 20 to 100 microvolts. They vary in frequency in different brain areas, occipital waves having a lower frequency than those associated with the frontal and parietal lobes. In addition, brain waves are known to change with age, sensory stimuli, brain pathology or disease, and the physiochemical state of the body. (Glucose deprivation, oxygen poisoning, and sedatives all interfere with the rhythmic activity of brain output by disturbing the metabolism of the neurons.)

The first of the brain waves to be described by scientists were the **alpha waves** (or alpha rhythm). Alpha waves have an average frequency range of 8 to 13 cps and are produced when the individual is in a relaxed state with the eyes closed. **Alpha block,** suppression of the alpha rhythm, occurs if the eyes are opened or if the individual begins to concentrate on some mental problem or visual stimulus. Under these conditions, the waves decrease in amplitude but increase in frequency. Under conditions of fright or excitement, the frequency increases still more.

Beta waves, closely related to alpha waves, are faster (14 to 25 cps) and have a lower amplitude. They are typical of the attentive or alert state.

Very large (high-amplitude) waves with a frequency of 4 cps or less that are seen in deep sleep are **delta waves. Theta waves** are large, abnormally contoured waves with a frequency of 4 to 7 cps. Although theta waves are normal in children, they represent emotional problems or some sort of neural imbalance in adults.

Sleeping individuals and patients in a stupor have EEGs that are slower (or lower frequency) than the alpha rhythm of normal adults. Fright, epileptic seizures, and various types of drug intoxication are associated with comparatively faster cortical activity. Thus impairment of cortical function is indicated by neuronal activity that is either too fast or too slow; unconsciousness occurs at both extremes of the frequency range. In young infants, the frequency of the fundamental wave pattern is quite slow (0.5 to 2 cps), but the frequency of the major waves increases with age, and at about age 12 the EEG recording is similar to that of an adult.

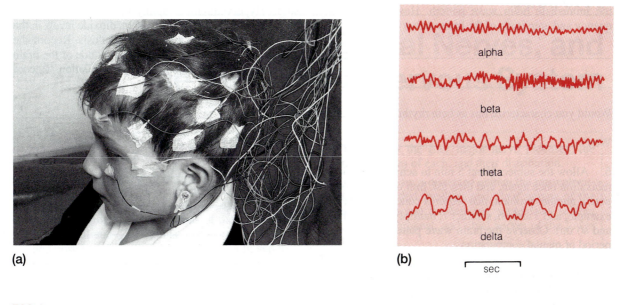

(a)

(b)

sec

Electroencephalography and brain waves. (a) To obtain a recording of brain wave activity (an EEG), electrodes are positioned on the patient's scalp and attached to a recording device called an electroencephalograph. (b) Typical EEGs. Alpha waves are typical of the awake but relaxed state; beta waves occur in the awake, alert state; theta waves are common in children but not in normal adults; and delta waves occur during deep sleep.

Since spontaneous waves are always present, even during unconsciousness, the absence of brain waves (a "flat" EEG) is taken as evidence of clinical death. The EEG is used clinically to aid in the diagnosis and localization of a number of brain lesions, including epileptic lesions, infections, abscesses, and brain tumors. ■

OBSERVING BRAIN WAVE PATTERNS

If one electrode (the *active electrode*) is placed over a particular cortical area and another (the *indifferent electrode*) is placed over an inactive part of the head, such as the earlobe, all of the activity of the cortex underlying the active electrode will, theoretically, be recorded. The inactive area provides a zero reference point or a base line, and the EEG represents the difference between "activities" occurring under the two electrodes.

 1.   Connect the EEG selector box to the oscilloscope preamplifier, or connect the high-gain preamplifier to the polygraph channel amplifier. Adjust the horizontal sweep and sensitivity according to the directions given in the manual or by your instructor.

2.   Prepare the subject. The subject should lie undisturbed with eyes closed in a quiet, dimly lit area. (Some-

one who is able to relax easily makes a good subject.) Apply a small amount of electrode gel to the subject's forehead above the left eye and on the left earlobe. Press an electrode to each prepared area and secure them by (1) applying a film of collodion gel to the electrode surface and the adjacent skin, or (2) with a long elastic EEG strap (knot tied at the back of the head). If the collodion gel is used, allow it to dry before continuing.

3.   Connect the active frontal lead (forehead) to EEG selector box outlet marked "L Frontal" and the lead from the indifferent electrode (earlobe) to the ground outlet (or to the appropriate input terminal on the high-gain preamplifier).

4.   Turn the oscilloscope or polygraph on, and observe the EEG pattern of the relaxed subject for a period of 5 min. If the subject is truly relaxed, you should see a typical alpha-wave pattern. (If the subject is unable to relax and the alpha-wave pattern does not appear in this time interval, test another subject.) Discourage all muscle movement during the monitoring period.*

5.   Abruptly and loudly clap your hands. The subject's eyes should open and alpha block should occur. Observe

---

* Note that 60-cycle "noise" (appearing as fast, regular, low amplitude waves superimposed on the more irregular brain waves) may interfere with the tracings being made, particularly if the laboratory has a lot of electrical equipment.

nerve cell bodies of motor neurons of the autonomic nervous system (sympathetic division). Their axons also leave the cord via the ventral roots, along with those of the motor neurons of the anterior horns.

Dorsal Root   # 28306

Motor Neuron   # 14581
Spinal Cord

Dorsal Root Ganglion # 20771
Sensory Cell Body

White Matter

The **white matter** of the spinal cord is nearly bisected by fissures (see Figure 21.2). The more open anterior fissure is the **anterior median fissure,** and the posterior one is the **posterior median sulcus.** The white matter is composed of myelinated fibers—some running to higher centers, some traveling from the brain to the cord, and some conducting impulses from one side of the cord to the other.

Because of the irregular shape of the gray matter, the white matter on each side of the cord can be divided into three primary regions or *white columns:* the **posterior, lateral,** and **anterior funiculi.** Each funiculus contains a number of fiber **tracts** composed of axons with the same origin, terminus, and function. Tracts conducting sensory impulses to the brain are called ascending, or sensory, tracts; those carrying impulses from the brain to the skeletal muscles are descending, or motor, tracts.

Because it serves as the transmission pathway between the brain and the body periphery, the spinal cord is an extremely important functional area. Even though it is protected by meninges and cerebrospinal fluid in the vertebral canal, it is highly vulnerable to traumatic injuries, such as might occur in an automobile accident.

When the cord is transected (or severely traumatized), both motor and sensory functions are lost in body areas normally served by that (and lower) regions of the spinal cord. Injury to certain spinal cord areas may even result in a permanent flaccid paralysis of both legs (paraplegia) or of all four limbs (quadraplegia). ■

 With the help of your textbook or a laboratory chart showing the tracts of the spinal cord, label Figure 21.3 with the tract names that follow. Since each tract is represented on both sides of the cord, for clarity you can label the motor tracts on the right side of the diagram and the sensory tracts on the left side of the diagram. *Color ascending tracts red and descending tracts blue.* Then fill in the functional importance of each tract beside its name below. As you work, try to be aware of how the naming of the tracts is related to their anatomical distribution.

① Fasciculus gracilis _____

② Fasciculus cuneatus _____

③ Dorsal spinocerebellar _____

④ Ventral spinocerebellar _____

⑤ Lateral spinothalamic _____

⑥ Ventral spinothalamic _____

⑦ Lateral corticospinal _____

Spinal Cord Section, # 47339
Spinal Nerve, Drg

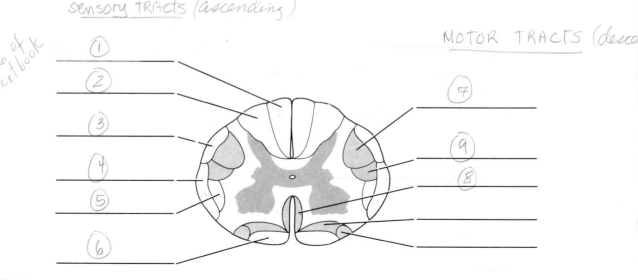

F21.3

Cross section of the spinal cord showing the relative positioning of its major tracts.

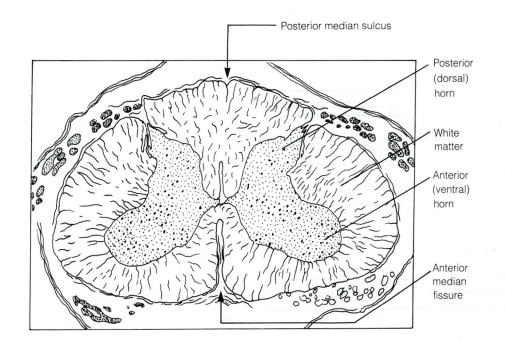

Posterior median sulcus

Posterior (dorsal) horn

White matter

Anterior (ventral) horn

Anterior median fissure

F21.4

Cross section of the spinal cord. See corresponding Plate 7 in the Histology Atlas.

(8) Ventral corticospinal _____

(9) Rubrospinal _____

(10) Tectospinal _____

(11) Vestibulospinal _____

Spinal Cord Dissection

1. Obtain a dissecting tray and instruments and a segment of preserved spinal cord (from a cow or saved from the brain specimen used in Exercise 19). Identify the tough outer meninx (dura mater) and the weblike arachnoid membrane.

What name is given to the third meninx, and where is it found?

_____ *pia mater* _____

_____

Peel back the dura mater and observe the fibers making up the dorsal and ventral roots. If possible, identify a dorsal root ganglion.

2. Cut a thin cross section of the cord and identify the anterior and posterior horns of the gray matter with the naked eye or with the aid of a dissecting microscope.

How can you be certain that you are correctly identifying the anterior and posterior horns?

_____

_____

Also identify the central canal, white matter, anterior median fissure, posterior median sulcus, and posterior, anterior, and lateral funiculi.

3. Obtain a prepared slide of the spinal cord (cross section) and a compound microscope. Refer to Figure 21.4 as you examine the slide carefully under low power. Observe the shape of the central canal.

Is it basically circular or oval? _____

Name the glial cell type that lines this canal. _____

What would you expect to find in this canal in the living animal?

_____

Can any neuron cell bodies be seen? _____

Where? _____

_____

What type of neurons would these most likely be—motor, association, or sensory?

_____

_____

SPINAL NERVES AND NERVE PLEXUSES

The 31 pairs of human spinal nerves arise from the fusions of the ventral and dorsal roots of the spinal cord. Figure 21.5 shows how the nerves are named according to their point of issue. Because the ventral roots contain myelinated axons of motor neurons located in the cord and the dorsal roots carry sensory fibers entering the cord, all spinal nerves are **mixed nerves.** The first pair of spinal nerves leaves the vertebral canal between the base of the occiput and the atlas, but all the rest exit via the intervertebral foramina. The second through seventh pairs of cervical nerves emerge *above* the vertebra for which they are named. C_8 emerges between C_7 and T_1. (Notice that there are 7 cervical vertebrae, but 8 pairs of cervical nerves.) The remaining spinal nerve pairs emerge from the spinal cord below the same-numbered vertebra.

Almost immediately after emerging, each nerve divides into **dorsal** and **ventral rami.** (Thus each spinal nerve is only about 1 or 2 cm long.) The rami, like the spinal nerves, contain both motor and sensory fibers. The smaller dorsal rami serve the skin and musculature of the posterior body trunk at their approximate level of emergence. The ventral rami of spinal nerves $T_2–T_{12}$ pass anteriorly as the **intercostal nerves** to supply the muscles of intercostal spaces, and the skin and muscles of the anterior and lateral trunk. The ventral rami of all other spinal nerves form complex networks of nerves called **plexuses.** These plexuses serve the motor and sensory needs of the muscles and skin of the limbs. The fibers of the ventral rami unite in the plexuses (with a few rami supplying fibers to more than one plexus). From the plexuses the fibers diverge again to form peripheral nerves, each of which contains fibers from more than one spinal nerve. The four major nerve plexuses and their chief peripheral nerves are illustrated in Figures 21.5 and 21.6 and are described below. Their names and site of origin should be committed to memory.

The **cervical plexus** arises from the ventral rami of C_1 through C_5 to supply muscles of the shoulder and neck. The major motor branch of this plexus is the **phrenic nerve,** which arises from $C_3–C_5$ and passes into the thoracic cavity in front of the first rib to innervate the diaphragm. The primary danger of a broken neck is that the phrenic nerve may be severed, leading to paralysis of the diaphragm and cessation of breathing. A jingle to help you remember the rami (roots) forming the phrenic nerves is "C_3, C_4, C_5 keep the diaphragm alive."

The **brachial plexus** is large and complex, arising from the ventral rami of C_5 through C_8 and T_1. The plexus, after being rearranged consecutively into trunks, divisions, and then cords, finally becomes subdivided into five major peripheral nerves.

The **axillary nerve,** which serves the muscles and skin of the shoulder, has the most limited distribution. The large **radial nerve** passes down the posterolateral surface of the arm and forearm, supplying all the extensor muscles of the arm, forearm, and hand and the skin along its course. The radial nerve is often injured in the axillary region by the pressure of a crutch or by hanging one's arm over the back of a chair. The **median nerve** passes down the anteromedial surface of the arm to supply most of the flexor muscles in the forearm and several muscles in the hand (plus the skin of the lateral surface of the palm of the hand).

- Hyperextend your wrist to identify the long, obvious tendon of your palmaris longus muscle, which crosses the exact midline of the anterior wrist. Your median nerve lies immediately deep to that tendon, and the radial nerve lies just *lateral* to it.

The **musculocutaneous nerve** supplies the arm muscles that flex the forearm and the skin of the lateral surface of the forearm. The **ulnar nerve** travels down the posteromedial surface of the arm. It courses around the medial epicondyle of the humerus to supply the flexor carpi ulnaris, the ulnar head of the flexor digitorum profundus of the forearm, and all intrinsic muscles of the hand not served by the median nerve. It supplies the skin of the medial third of the hand, both the anterior and posterior surfaces. Trauma to the ulnar nerve, which often occurs when the elbow is hit, produces a smarting sensation commonly referred to as "hitting the funny bone."

The **lumbosacral plexus,** which serves the pelvic region of the trunk and the lower limbs, is actually a complex of two plexuses, the lumbar plexus and the sacral plexus (see Figure 21.6). The **lumbar plexus** arises from ventral rami of L_1 through L_4 (and sometimes T_{12}). Its nerves serve the lower abdominopelvic region and the anterior thighs. The largest nerve of this plexus is the **femoral nerve,** which passes beneath the inguinal ligament to innervate the anterior thigh muscles. The cutaneous branches of the femoral nerve (median and anterior femoral cutaneous and the saphenous nerves) supply the skin of the anteromedial surface of the entire lower limb.

Arising from L_4 through L_5 and S_1 through S_4, the nerves of the **sacral plexus** supply the buttock, the posterior surface of the thigh, and virtually all sensory and motor fibers of the leg and foot. The major peripheral nerve of this plexus is the **sciatic nerve,** which is the largest nerve in the body. The sciatic nerve leaves the pelvis through the greater sciatic notch and travels down the posterior thigh, serving its flexor muscles and skin. In the popliteal region, the sciatic nerve divides into the **common peroneal nerve** and the **tibial nerve,** which together supply the balance of the leg muscles and skin, both directly and via several branches.

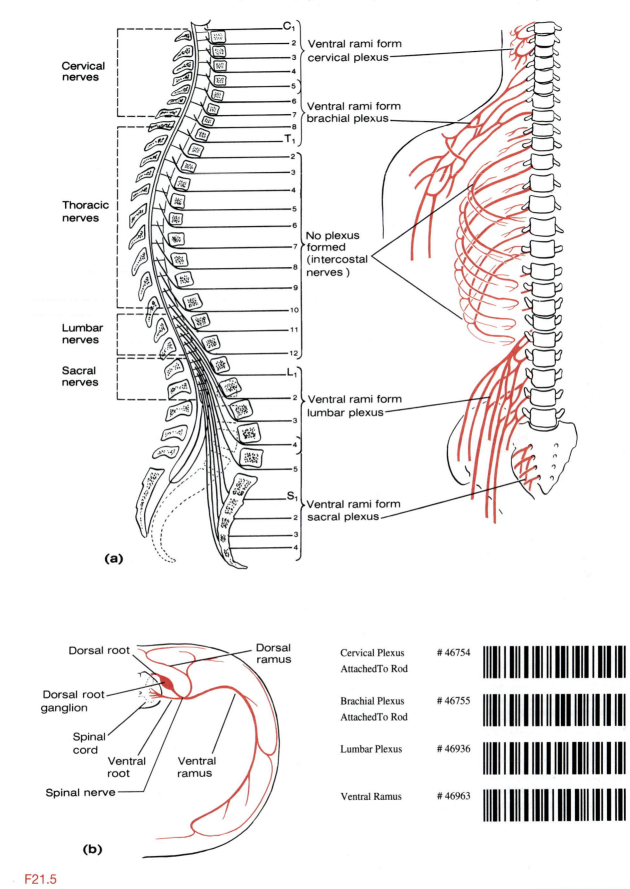

(a)

Cervical nerves

Thoracic nerves

Lumbar nerves

Sacral nerves

C_1
2 — Ventral rami form cervical plexus
3
4
5
6
7 — Ventral rami form brachial plexus
8
T_1
2
3
4
5
6 — No plexus formed (intercostal nerves)
7
8
9
10
11
12
L_1
2 — Ventral rami form lumbar plexus
3
4
5
S_1
2 — Ventral rami form sacral plexus
3
4

F21.7

The autor... fibers.

system is...
system.
Ther...
motor pa...
system,...
those of t...
division,...
the CNS (...
in spinal...
cles they s...
consists o...
neuron of...
sides in th...
synapse...
neuron),...
side the C...
then exter...

Dorsal root
Dorsal ramus
Dorsal root ganglion
Spinal cord
Ventral root
Ventral ramus
Spinal nerve

(b)

Cervical Plexus AttachedTo Rod	# 46754	
Brachial Plexus AttachedTo Rod	# 46755	
Lumbar Plexus	# 46936	
Ventral Ramus	# 46963	

F21.5

Human spinal nerves. (a) Relationship of spinal nerves to vertebrae (areas of plexuses formed by the ventral rami are indicated). (b) Relative distribution of the ventral and dorsal rami of a spinal nerve (cross section of left trunk).

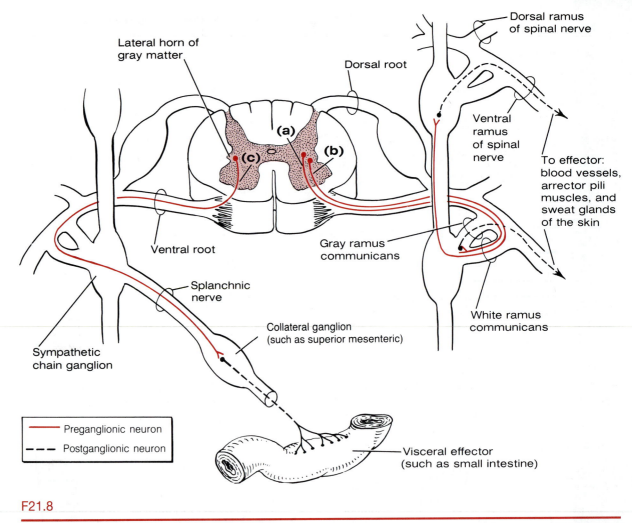

Lateral horn of gray matter

Dorsal ramus of spinal nerve

Dorsal root

(a)

(b)

(c)

Ventral ramus of spinal nerve

To effector: blood vessels, arrector pili muscles, and sweat glands of the skin

Ventral root

Gray ramus communicans

Splanchnic nerve

White ramus communicans

Collateral ganglion (such as superior mesenteric)

Sympathetic chain ganglion

——— Preganglionic neuron

- - - - - Postganglionic neuron

Visceral effector (such as small intestine)

F21.8

Sympathetic pathways. (a) Synapse in a sympathetic chain (paravertebral) ganglion at the same level. (b) Synapse in a sympathetic chain ganglion at a different level. (c) Synapse in a collateral (prevertebral) ganglion.

Sympathetic Chain, Lumbar   # 46965

alongside the vertebral column (the literal meaning of *paravertebral*).

Having reached the ganglion, an axon may take one of three main courses (see Figure 21.8). First, it may synapse with a postganglionic neuron in the sympathetic chain at that level. Second, the axon may travel upward or downward through the sympathetic chain to synapse with a postganglionic neuron in a paravertebral ganglion at another level. In either of these two instances, the postganglionic axons then reenter the ventral or dorsal ramus of a spinal nerve via a **gray ramus communicans** and travel in the ramus to innervate skin structures (sweat glands, arrector pili muscles attached to hair follicles, and the smooth muscles of blood vessel walls). Third, the axon may pass through the ganglion without synapsing and form part of the **splanchnic nerves,** which travel to the viscera to synapse with a postganglionic neuron in a **prevertebral** or **collateral ganglion.** The major prevertebral ganglia—the celiac, superior mesenteric, and inferior mesenteric ganglia—supply the abdominal and pelvic visceral organs. The postganglionic axon then leaves the ganglion and travels to a nearby visceral organ which it innervates.

Parasympathetic Division

The preganglionic neurons of the **parasympathetic,** or **craniosacral,** division are located in brain nuclei of cranial nerves III, VII, IX, X and in the S_2 through S_4 level of the spinal cord. The axons of the preganglionic neurons of the cranial region travel in their respective cranial nerves to the *immediate area* of the head and neck organs to be stimulated. There they synapse with the postganglionic neuron in a **terminal,** or **intramural** (literally, "within the walls"), **ganglion.** The postganglionic neuron then sends out a very short axon to the organ it serves. In the sacral region, the preganglionic axons leave the ventral roots of the spinal cord and collectively form the **pelvic nerves,** which travel to the pelvic cavity. In the pelvic cavity, the preganglionic axons synapse with the postganglionic neurons in ganglia located on or close to the organs served.

Locate the sympathetic chain on the spinal nerve chart.

218

Autonomic Functioning

As noted earlier, most body organs served by the autonomic nervous system receive fibers from both the sympathetic and parasympathetic divisions. The only exceptions are the structures of the skin (sweat glands and arrector pili muscles attached to the hair follicles), the pancreas and liver, the adrenal medulla, and essentially all blood vessels except those of the external genitalia, all of which receive sympathetic innervation only. When both divisions serve an organ, they have antagonistic effects. This is because their postganglionic axons release different neurotransmitters. The parasympathetic fibers, called **cholinergic fibers,** release acetylcholine; the sympathetic postganglionic fibers, called **adrenergic fibers,** release norepinephrine. (However, there are isolated examples of postganglionic sympathetic fibers, such as those serving blood vessels in the skeletal muscles, that release acetylcholine.) The preganglionic fibers of both divisions release acetylcholine.

The parasympathetic division is often referred to as the housekeeping, or "resting and digesting," system because it maintains the visceral organs in a state most suitable for normal functions and internal homeostasis; that is, it promotes normal digestion and elimination. In contrast, activation of the sympathetic division is referred to as the "fight or flight" response because it readies the body to cope with situations that threaten homeostasis. Under such emergency conditions, the sympathetic nervous system induces an increase in heart rate and blood pressure, dilates the bronchioles of the lungs, increases blood sugar levels, and promotes many other effects that help the individual cope with a stressor.

As we grow older, our sympathetic nervous system gradually becomes less and less efficient, particularly in causing vasoconstriction of blood vessels. When elderly people stand up quickly after sitting or lying down, they often become light-headed or faint. This is because the sympathetic nervous system is not able to react quickly enough to counteract the pull of gravity by activating the vasoconstrictor fibers; and so blood pools in the feet. This condition, **orthostatic hypotension,** is a type of low blood pressure resulting from changes in body position as described. Orthostatic hypotension can be prevented to some degree if *slow* changes in position are made. This gives the sympathetic nervous system a little more time to react and adjust. ■

Several body organs are listed in the chart below. *Using your textbook as a reference,* list the effect of the sympathetic and parasympathetic divisions on each.

DISSECTION OF PIG SPINAL CORD AND SPINAL NERVES

As in humans, the spinal cord of the fetal pig is a basically cylindrical mass of nervous tissue lying within the vertebral canal of the spinal column. It is enlarged in the cervical and lumbar regions where the spinal nerves serving the limbs arise. The pig has 33 pairs of spinal nerves (as compared to 31 in humans). Of these, 8 are cervical, 14 thoracic, 7 lumbar, and 4 sacral.

A complete dissection of the spinal cord and spinal nerves of the pig would be extraordinarily time-consuming and exacting, and is not warranted in a basic anatomy and physiology course. However, it is desirable to have some dissection work to complement your study of the anatomical charts. Thus you will carry out a partial dissection of the cord and of the brachial and lumbar plexuses, and identify some of the major nerves to provide some "hands-on" experience.

Organ or function	Parasympathetic effect	Sympathetic effect
Heart		
Bronchioles of lungs		
Digestive tract activity		
Urinary bladder		
Iris of the eye		
Blood vessels (most)		
Penis/clitoris		
Sweat glands		
Adrenal medulla		
Pancreas		

The Spinal Cord

Though the photograph in Figure 21.9 shows the dorsal aspect of nearly the entire spinal cord of the fetal pig, only a section of the cord need be exposed and studied during this laboratory session.

1.   Obtain dissection tools and tray, your animal specimen, and protective hand cream or gloves and bring them to your bench.

2.   Place your pig on the dissecting tray ventral side down and carefully remove the epiaxial muscles overlying approximately 10 cm (4 inches) of the vertebral column. Although this muscle clearing can be done anywhere along the length of the spinal cord, it is most easily done in the thoracic region.

3.   Using bone cutters, cut across the pedicles of the exposed vertebrae and remove the vertebral arches to reveal the spinal cord lying snugly in the vertebral canal. Continue to chip away carefully at the bone, and remove the epidural fat until you have exposed several spinal nerves at the lateral aspects of the cord.

4.   Observe the tough glistening dura mater covering the cord and spinal roots. Notice that it is not fused with the periosteum lining the vertebral canal (as is the dura mater covering the brain in the cranial cavity).

5.   Slit open the dura mater and observe that each spinal nerve arises from two roots—the dorsal (sensory) and ventral (motor) roots—which, in turn, originate from several rootlets issuing from the cord.

6.   Identify the dorsal root ganglia, small round enlargements on the dorsal roots that are the "residences" of the cell bodies of sensory neurons serving the body periphery.

7.   Trace a spinal nerve laterally to see it divide into dorsal and ventral rami. The dorsal rami supply structures of the dorsal body wall, whereas ventral rami distribute to the anterior and lateral body trunk and (via plexuses) to the limbs.

8.   If you have exposed a region of the cord other than the thoracic region, you may be able to identify other anatomical features of the spinal cord, such as the cervical or lumbar enlargements, or the conus medullaris and cauda equina at the caudal end of the cord.

Nerves of the Brachial Plexus

1.   Place your pig dorsal side down on the dissecting tray to make these initial observations on the nerves of the brachial plexus. Reflect the cut ends of the left pectoralis muscles to expose the large brachial plexus in the axillary region. Carefully clean the exposed nerves as far back toward their points of origin as possible. The brachial plexus, which consists of tough interconnected nerves emerging from the last three cervical and first thoracic vertebrae, should now be visible. Refer to Figure 21.10 on page 222 as you work.

2.   The *median nerve* is closely associated with the brachial artery and vein, which course through the arm. It supplies most of the ventral muscles of the forearm. The *radial nerve* is a large nerve seen just superior to the median nerve. Follow it into the triceps brachii muscle of the arm. The *ulnar nerve* is the most posterior of the large brachial plexus nerves and supplies forearm and hand muscles that are not innervated by the median nerve.

3.   Although not actually part of the brachial plexus, the **sympathetic trunk** (chain of sympathetic nervous system ganglia) may be easily identified in the thoracic region. Pull the heart and lungs ventrally to expose the descending aorta. Carefully examine the dorsolateral surface of the aorta as it travels through the thorax. The sympathetic trunk appears as a slender white cord with segmental enlargements (the ganglia) in it lying alongside the aorta.

Nerves of the Lumbosacral Plexus

1.   To locate the *femoral nerve* (see Figure 21.10) as it emerges from the pelvic cavity to enter the ventromedial aspect of the thigh, first identify the femoral artery and vein, with which it is closely associated. Follow it into the muscles and skin of the anterior thigh, which it supplies.

2.   Turn the pig ventral side down so that you can see the posterior aspect of the lower limb. Reflect the ends of the transected biceps femoris muscle to view the large, cordlike *sciatic nerve.* The sciatic nerve arises from the sacral plexus and serves the dorsal thigh muscles and all of the muscles of the leg and foot via its various branches. Follow the nerve as it travels down the posterior thigh lateral to the semimembranosus muscle. Notice that it divides into its two major branches just superior to the gastrocnemius muscle of the calf. These branches, the *internal* and *external popliteal nerves,* innervate the leg.

3.   When you have finished making your observations, wrap the pig in paper towels soaked in embalming solution, place it in the plastic bag, and return it to the storage area. Clean all dissecting tools and equipment used before you leave the laboratory.

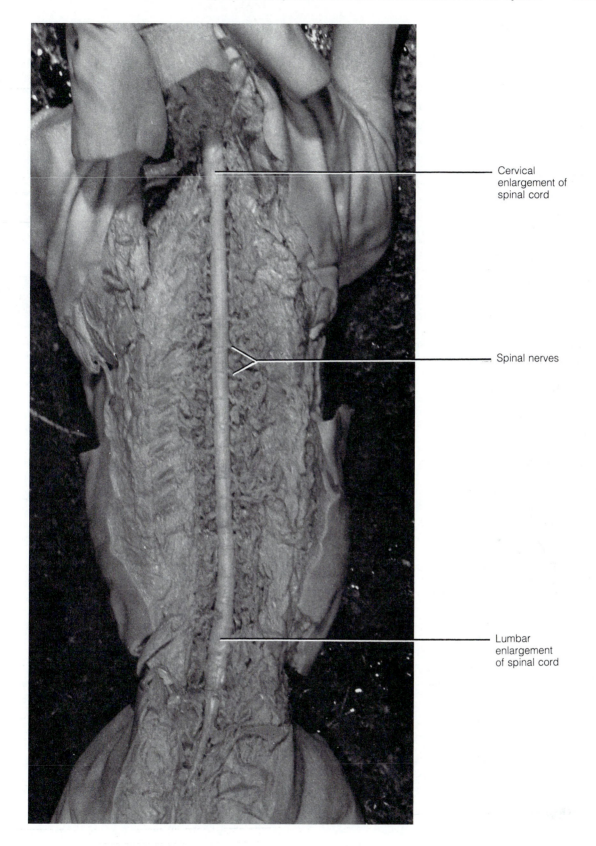

Cervical enlargement of spinal cord

Spinal nerves

Lumbar enlargement of spinal cord

F21.9

Spinal cord of the fetal pig, dorsal aspect. The spinal nerves and cervical and lumbar enlargements of the spinal cord are obvious in this view.

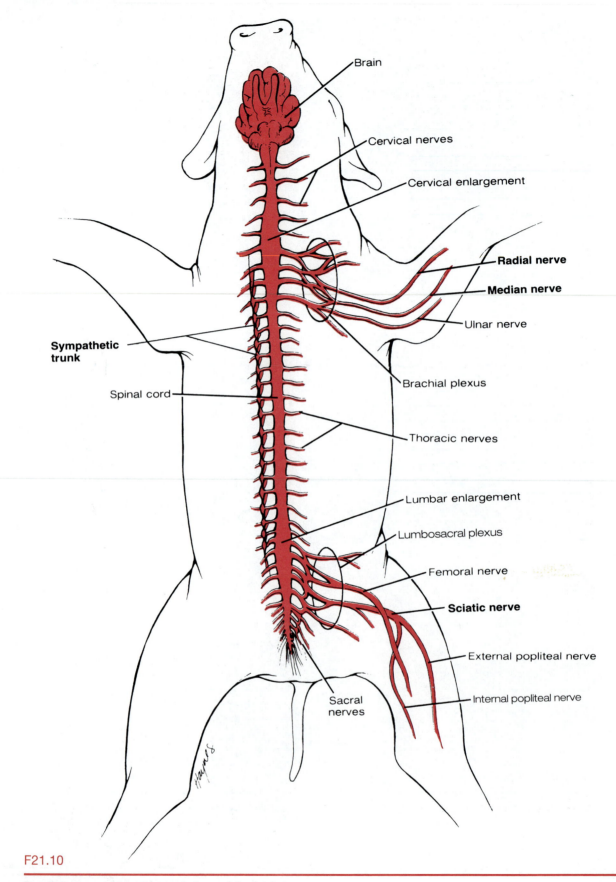

Brain

Cervical nerves

Cervical enlargement

Radial nerve

Median nerve

Ulnar nerve

Sympathetic trunk

Brachial plexus

Spinal cord

Thoracic nerves

Lumbar enlargement

Lumbosacral plexus

Femoral nerve

Sciatic nerve

External popliteal nerve

Internal popliteal nerve

Sacral nerves

F21.10

Brachial plexus and lumbosacral plexus of the fetal pig.

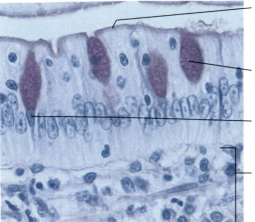

PLATE 1 Simple columnar epithelium. Mucus in goblet cells stains pink in this view (543X)

Labels: Microvilli of columnar epithelial cells; Mucus in goblet cell; Nucleus of goblet cell; Underlying connective tissue

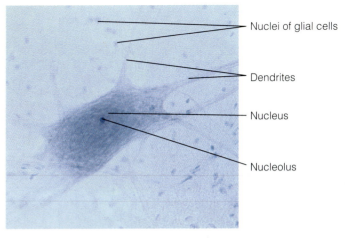

PLATE 4 Multipolar neuron in spinal cord smear (212X)

Labels: Nuclei of glial cells; Dendrites; Nucleus; Nucleolus

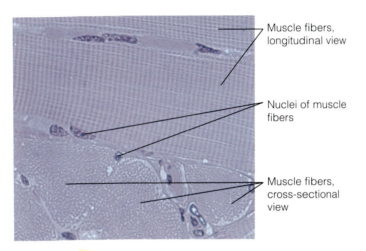

PLATE 2 Skeletal muscle, transverse and longitudinal views shown (543X)

Labels: Muscle fibers, longitudinal view; Nuclei of muscle fibers; Muscle fibers, cross-sectional view

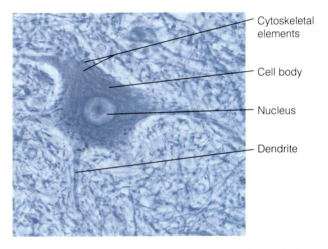

PLATE 5 Neuron stained to allow cytoskeletal elements in their processes to be seen (265X)

Labels: Cytoskeletal elements; Cell body; Nucleus; Dendrite

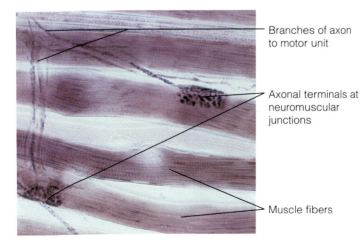

PLATE 3 Part of a motor unit (265X)

Labels: Branches of axon to motor unit; Axonal terminals at neuromuscular junctions; Muscle fibers

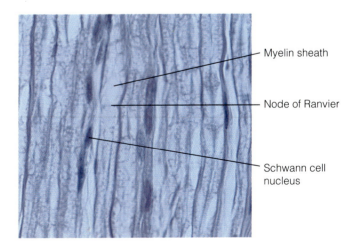

PLATE 6 Teased myelinated axons (543X). Myelin sheaths appear "bubbly" because most of the fatty myelin is dissolved during slide preparation

Labels: Myelin sheath; Node of Ranvier; Schwann cell nucleus

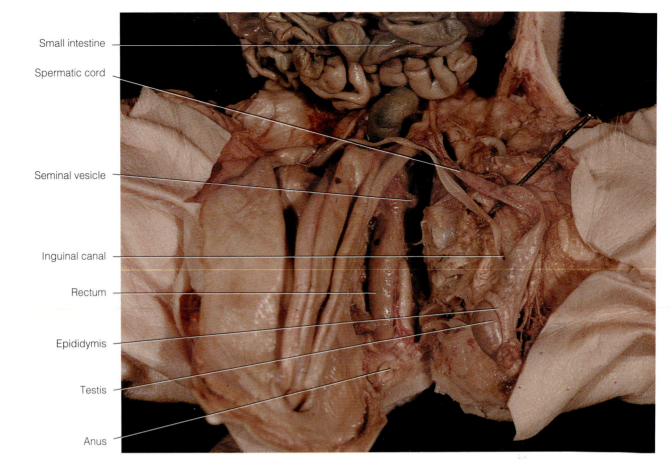

Small intestine

Spermatic cord

Seminal vesicle

Inguinal canal

Rectum

Epididymis

Testis

Anus

PLATE I Reproductive system organs of the male fetal pig. See pages 430–433.

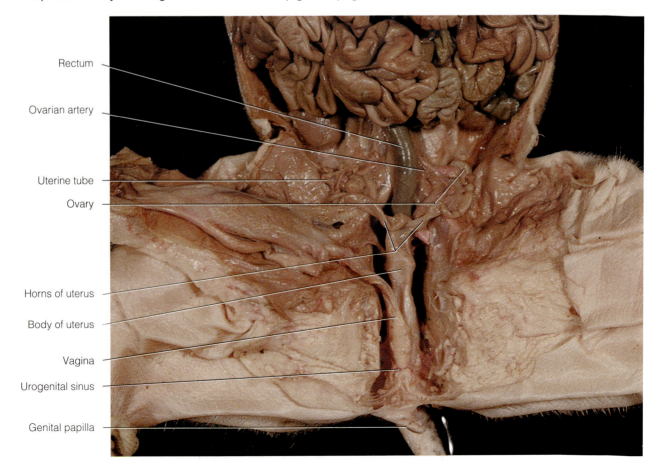

Rectum

Ovarian artery

Uterine tube

Ovary

Horns of uterus

Body of uterus

Vagina

Urogenital sinus

Genital papilla

PLATE J Reproductive system organs of the female fetal pig. See pages 432–433.

Human Reflex Physiology

OBJECTIVES	MATERIALS
1. To define *reflex*.	Reflex hammer
2. To name, identify, and describe the function of each element of a reflex arc.	Sharp pencils
	Cot (if available)
3. To state why reflex testing is an important part of every physical examination.	Absorbent cotton (sterile)
	Tongue depressor
4. To describe and discuss several types of reflex activities as observed in the laboratory; to indicate the functional or clinical importance of each; and to categorize each as a somatic or autonomic reflex action.	Metric and 12-in. ruler
	Flashlight
	100- or 250-ml beaker
	10- or 25-ml graduated cylinder
	Lemon juice
	Wide-range pH paper
5. To explain why cord-mediated reflexes are generally much faster than those involving input from the higher brain centers.	Large laboratory bucket containing freshly prepared 10% household bleach solution (for saliva-soiled glassware)
6. To investigate differences in reaction time of reflexes and unlearned responses.	Disposable autoclave bag
	Wash bottle containing 10% bleach solution

THE REFLEX ARC

Reflexes are rapid, predictable, and involuntary motor responses to stimuli; they are mediated over neural pathways called **reflex arcs.**

There are five essential components of all reflex arcs (Figure 22.1a):

1. The *receptor,* which reacts to a stimulus.
2. The *sensory neuron,* which conducts the afferent impulses to the CNS.
3. The *integration center,* consisting of one to several synapses in the CNS.
4. The *motor neuron,* which conducts the efferent impulses from the integration center to an effector.
5. The *effector,* the muscle fibers or glands that respond to the efferent impulses by contracting or secreting a product, respectively.

The simple patellar or knee-jerk reflex shown in Figure 22.1b is an example of a simple, two-neuron, monosynaptic reflex arc, and it will be demonstrated in the laboratory. However, most reflexes are more complex, involving the participation of one or more association neurons in the reflex arc pathway. A three-neuron reflex arc (flexor reflex) is diagramed in Figure 22.1c. Since delay or inhibition of the reflex may occur at the synapses, the larger the number of synapses encountered in a reflex pathway, the greater the time required to effect the reflex.

Reflexes of many types may be considered programed into the neural anatomy. For example, many *spinal reflexes* (reflexes that are initiated and completed at the spinal cord level such as the flexor reflex) occur without the involvement of higher brain centers. These reflexes work equally well in decerebrate animals (those in which the brain has been destroyed), as long as the spinal cord is functional. Conversely, other reflexes require the involvement of functional brain tissue, since many different inputs must be evaluated before the appropriate reflex is determined. The superficial cord reflexes and pupillary responses to light are in this category. In addition, although many spinal reflexes do not require the involvement of higher centers, the brain is frequently "advised" of spinal cord reflex activity and may alter it by facilitating or inhibiting the reflexes.

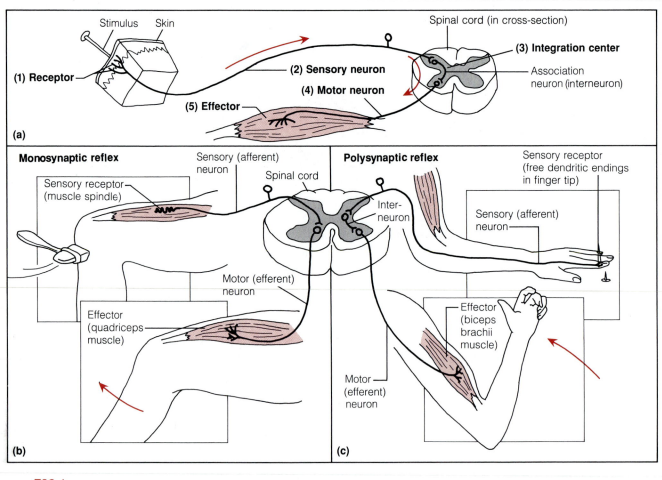

Simple reflex arcs. (a) Components of all human reflex arcs: receptor, sensory neuron, integration center (one or more synapses in the CNS), motor neuron, and effector. (b) Monosynaptic reflex arc. (c) Polysynaptic reflex arc. The integration center is the spinal cord, and in each example the receptor and effector are in the same limb.

Reflex testing is an important diagnostic tool to the doctor in assessing the condition of the nervous system. Distorted, exaggerated, or absent reflex responses may indicate degeneration or pathology of portions of the nervous system, often before other signs are apparent.

If the spinal cord is damaged, the easily performed reflex tests can help pinpoint the area (level) of spinal cord injury. Motor nerves above the injured area may be unaffected, whereas those at or below the lesion site may be unable to participate in normal reflex activity. ■

Reflexes can be categorized into one of two large groups: the somatic reflexes and the autonomic reflexes. **Autonomic** (or visceral) **reflexes** are mediated through the autonomic nervous system and are not subject to

conscious control. These reflexes result in the activation of smooth muscles, cardiac muscle, and the glands of the body; they involve the regulation of such body functions as digestion, elimination, blood pressure, salivation, and sweating. **Somatic reflexes** include all those reflexes that involve stimulation of skeletal muscles by the somatic division of the nervous system. An example of such a reflex is the rapid withdrawal of a hand from a hot object.

SOMATIC REFLEXES

There are several types of somatic reflexes, including the stretch, crossed extensor, superficial cord, corneal, and gag reflexes. Some require only spinal cord activity; others require brain involvement as well.

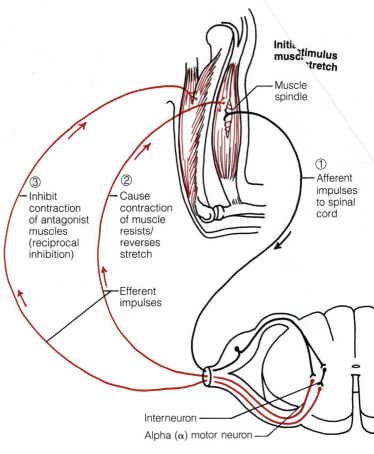

Initial stimulus
muscle stretch

Muscle
spindle

① Afferent
impulses
to spinal
cord

③ Inhibit
contraction
of antagonist
muscles
(reciprocal
inhibition)

② Cause
contraction
of muscle
resists/
reverses
stretch

Efferent
impulses

Interneuron

Alpha (α) motor neuron

F22.2

Events of the stretch reflex by which muscle stretch is damped. The events are shown in circular fashion.
(1) Stretching of the muscle activates a muscle spindle. (2) Impulses transmitted by afferent fibers from muscle spindle to α motor neurons in the spinal cord result in activation of the stretched muscle causing it to contract. (3) Impulses transmitted by afferent fibers from muscle spindle to interneurons in the spinal cord result in reciprocal inhibition of the antagonist muscle.

Spinal Reflexes

STRETCH REFLEXES   **Stretch reflexes** are important postural reflexes, normally acting to maintain posture, balance, and locomotion. Stretch reflexes are initiated by tapping a tendon, which stretches the muscle the tendon is attached to. This stimulates the muscle spindles and results in reflex contraction of the stretched muscle or muscles, which resists further stretching. Even as the primary stretch reflex is occurring, impulses are being sent to other destinations as well. For example, branches of the afferent fibers (from the muscle spindles) also synapse with interneurons (association neurons) controlling the antagonist muscles (Figure 22.2). The inhibition of the antagonist muscles that follows, called *reciprocal inhibition,* causes them to relax and prevents them from resisting (or reversing) the contraction of the stretched muscle caused by the main reflex arc. Additionally, impulses are relayed to higher brain centers (largely via the dorsal white columns) to advise of muscle length, speed of shortening, and the like—information needed to maintain muscle tone and posture. Stretch reflexes tend to be hypoactive or absent in cases of peripheral nerve damage or ventral horn disease, and hyperactive in corticospinal tract lesions. They are absent in deep sedation and coma.

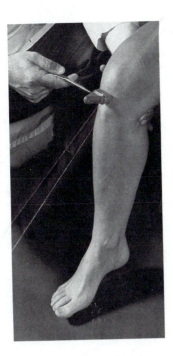

F22.3

Testing the patellar reflex. The examiner supports the subject's knee so that the subject's muscles are relaxed. The reflex hammer then strikes the patellar ligament (straight arrow). The proper location may be ascertained by palpation of the patella (curved arrow).

1. Test the **patellar,** or knee-jerk, **reflex** by seating a subject on the laboratory bench with legs hanging free (or with knees crossed). Tap the patellar ligament sharply with the reflex hammer just below the knee to elicit the knee-jerk response (Figure 22.3). Test both knees and record your observations.

_____

_____

_____

Which muscles contracted? _rectus femoris, vastus_
lateralis, intermedius, medialis and tensor fasciae
latae

Quadriceps {

What nerve is carrying the afferent and efferent impulses?
sciatic — both

2. Test the effect of mental distraction on the patellar reflex by having the subject add a column of three-digit numbers while you test the reflex again. Is the response greater than or less than the first response?

response is greater

What are your conclusions about the effect of mental distraction on reflex activity?

When your not expecting
they react more like a reflex

3. Now test the effect of muscular activity occurring simultaneously in other areas of the body. Have the subject clasp the edge of the laboratory bench and vigorously attempt to pull it upward with both hands. At the same time, test the patellar reflex again. Is the response more or less vigorous than the first response?

greater

4. Fatigue also influences the reflex response. The subject should jog in position until she or he is very fatigued (**really fatigued**—no slackers). Test the patellar reflex again and record whether it is more or less vigorous.

_____

_____

Would you say that nervous system activity _or_ muscle function is responsible for the changes you have just observed?

_____

_____

Explain your reasoning. _____

_____

_____

_____

5. To demonstrate the **Achilles,** or ankle-jerk, **reflex,** kneel on a chair with the feet dangling (relaxed) over the seat edge. Dorsiflex the foot slightly to increase the tension on the gastrocnemius muscle. Have your partner sharply tap the Achilles (calcaneal) tendon with the reflex hammer.

What is the result? _causes foot to jerk down_
causes plantarflexion
movement

Does the contraction of the gastrocnemius normally result in the activity you have observed?

yes (plantarflexion)

CROSSED EXTENSOR REFLEX

The **crossed extensor reflex** is more complex than the stretch reflex, consisting of a flexor, or withdrawal, reflex followed by extension of the opposite limb.

This reflex is quite obvious when, for example, a stranger suddenly and strongly grips one's arm. The immediate response is to withdraw the clutched arm and push the intruder away with the other arm. The reflex is more difficult to demonstrate in a laboratory because it is anticipated, and under these conditions the extensor part of the reflex may be inhibited.

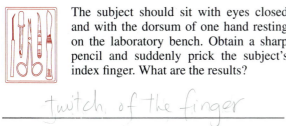 The subject should sit with eyes closed and with the dorsum of one hand resting on the laboratory bench. Obtain a sharp pencil and suddenly prick the subject's index finger. What are the results?

twitch of the finger

Did the extensor part of this reflex seem to be slow compared to the other reflexes you have observed?

yes is slower

What are the reasons for this? _hands + fingers are more used to touching rough surfaces + are used to that_

The reflexes that have been demonstrated so far—the stretch and crossed extensor reflexes—are examples of reflexes in which the reflex pathway is initiated and completed at the spinal cord level.

SUPERFICIAL CORD REFLEXES

The **superficial cord reflexes** (abdominal, cremaster, and plantar reflexes) result from pain and temperature changes. They are initiated by stimulation of receptors in the skin and mucosae. The superficial cord reflexes depend *both* on functional upper-motor pathways and on the cord-level reflex arc. Since only the plantar reflex can be tested conveniently in a laboratory setting, we will use this as our example.

The **plantar** reflex, an important neurological test, is elicited by stimulating the cutaneous receptors in the sole of the foot. In adults, stimulation of these receptors causes the toes to flex and move closer together. Damage to the pyramidal (or corticospinal) tract, however, produces *Babinski's sign,* an abnormal response in which the toes flare and the great toe moves in an upward direction. (In newborn infants, Babinski's sign is seen due to incomplete myelination of the nervous system.)

 Have the subject remove a shoe and lie on the cot or laboratory bench with knees slightly bent and thighs rotated so that the lateral side of the foot rests on the cot. Alternatively, the subject may sit up and rest the lateral surface of the foot on a chair. Draw the handle of the reflex hammer firmly down the lateral side of the exposed sole from the heel to the base of the toes.

What is the response? _all her toes move_

Is this a normal plantar reflex or Babinski's sign?

Cranial Nerve Reflex Tests

In these experiments, you will be working with your lab partner to illustrate two somatic reflexes mediated by cranial nerves.

CORNEAL REFLEX

The **corneal reflex** is mediated through the trigeminal nerve (cranial nerve V). The absence of this reflex is an ominous sign, because it often indicates damage to the brain stem, resulting from compression of the brain or other trauma.

Stand to one side of the subject; the subject should look away from you toward the opposite wall. Wait a few seconds and then quickly, *but gently,* touch the subject's cornea (on the side toward you) with a wisp of absorbent cotton. What is the reaction?

What is the function of this reflex?

Was the sensation that of touch *or* of pain?

Why?

GAG REFLEX

The **gag reflex** tests the somatic motor responses of cranial nerves IX and X. When the oral mucosa on the side of the uvula is stroked, each side of the mucosa should rise, and the amount of elevation should be equal.*

* The uvula is the fleshy tab hanging from the roof of the mouth just above the root of the tongue.

For this experiment, select a subject who does not have a queasy stomach, because regurgitation is a possibility. Stroke the subject's oral mucosa on each side of the uvula with a tongue depressor. What are the results?

_____

_____

Discard the used tongue depressor in the disposable autoclave bag before continuing. Do *not* lay it on the laboratory bench at any time.

AUTONOMIC REFLEXES

The autonomic reflexes include the pupillary, ciliospinal, and salivary reflexes, as well as a multitude of other reflexes. Work with your partner to demonstrate the four autonomic reflexes described next.

Pupillary Reflexes

There are several types of pupillary reflexes. The **pupillary light reflex** and the **consensual reflex** will be examined here. In both of these pupillary reflexes, the retina of the eye is the receptor, the optic nerve (cranial nerve II) contains the afferent fibers, the oculomotor nerve (cranial nerve III) is responsible for conducting efferent impulses to the eye, and the smooth muscle of the iris is the effector. Many central nervous system centers are involved in the integration of these responses. Absence of the normal pupillary reflexes is generally a late indication of severe trauma or deterioration of the vital brain stem tissue due to metabolic imbalance.

1. Conduct the reflex testing in an area where the lighting is relatively dim. Before beginning, obtain a metric ruler to measure and record the size of the subject's pupils.

Right pupil: _____ mm

Left pupil: _____ mm

2. Stand to the left of the subject to conduct the testing. The subject should shield her right eye by holding her hand vertically between the eye and the right side of the nose.

3. Shine a flashlight into the subject's left eye. What is the pupillary response?

_____

Measure the size of the left pupil: _____ mm

4. Observe the right pupil. Has the same type of change (called a *consensual response*) occurred in the right eye?

_____

Measure the size of the right pupil: _____ mm

The consensual response, or any reflex observed on one side of the body when the other side has been stimulated, is called a **contralateral response.** The pupillary light response, or any reflex occurring on the same side stimulated, is referred to as an **ipsilateral response.**

When a contralateral response occurs, what does this indicate about the pathways involved?

_____

_____

_____

Was the sympathetic *or* the parasympathetic division of the autonomic nervous system active during the testing of these reflexes?

_____

What is the function of these pupillary responses?

_____

_____

_____

Ciliospinal Reflex

The **ciliospinal reflex** is another example of reflex activity in which pupillary responses can be observed. This response may initially seem a little bizarre, especially in view of the consensual reflex just demonstrated. While observing the subject's eyes, gently stroke the skin (or just the hairs) on the left side of the back of the subject's neck, close to the hairline.

What is the reaction of the left pupil? _smaller than right_

The reaction of the right pupil? _larger_

If you see no reaction, repeat the test using a gentle pinch in the same area.

The response you should have noted—pupillary dilation—is consistent with the pupillary changes occurring when the sympathetic nervous system is stimulated. Such a response may also be elicited in a single pupil when more impulses from the sympathetic nervous system reach it for any reason. For example, when the left side of the subject's neck was stimulated, sympathetic impulses to the left iris increased, resulting in the ipsilateral reaction of the left pupil.

On the basis of your observations, would you say that the sympathetic innervation of the two irises is closely integrated?

_____ Why or why not? _____

_____

_____

Salivary Reflex

Unlike the other reflexes, in which the effectors were smooth or skeletal muscles, the effectors of the **salivary reflex** are glands. The salivary glands secrete varying amounts of saliva in response to reflex activation.

1. Obtain a small beaker, a graduated cylinder, lemon juice, and wide-range pH paper. After refraining from swallowing for 2 minutes, the subject is to expectorate (spit) the accumulated saliva into a small beaker. Using the graduated cylinder, measure the volume of the expectorated saliva and determine its pH.

Volume: _____ cc; pH: _____

2. Now place 2 or 3 drops of lemon juice on the subject's tongue. Allow the lemon juice to mix with the saliva for 5 to 10 seconds, and then determine the pH of the subject's saliva by touching a piece of pH paper to the tip of his tongue.

pH: _____

As before, the subject is to refrain from swallowing for 2 minutes. After the 2 minutes is up, again collect and measure the volume of the saliva and determine its pH.

Volume: _____ cc; pH: _____

3. How does the volume of saliva collected after the application of the lemon juice compare with the volume of the first saliva sample?

_____

How does the final saliva pH reading compare to the initial reading?

_____

To that obtained 10 seconds after the application of lemon juice?

_____

What division of the autonomic nervous system mediates the reflex release of saliva?

_____

Dispose of the saliva-containing beakers and the graduated cylinders in the laboratory bucket that contains bleach and put the used pH paper into the disposable autoclave bags. Wash the bench down with 10% bleach solution before continuing.

Other Autonomic Reflexes

Very few autonomic reflexes were investigated in this exercise because most are difficult to illustrate in a laboratory situation. To rectify this omission, several autonomic reflexes are listed below. Name the organ involved, receptors stimulated, and resulting action involved in each case. (Use an appropriate reference as necessary.)

Micturition (urination):

Organ/receptors: _____

Result: _____

_____

Hering-Breuer:

Organ/receptors: _____

Result: _____

_____

Defecation:

Organ/receptors: _____

Result: _____

_____

Carotid sinus:

Organ/receptors: _____

Result: _____

_____

REACTION TIME OF UNLEARNED RESPONSES

The time required for reaction to a stimulus depends on many factors—the sensitivity of the receptors, the velocity of nerve conduction, the number of neurons and synapses involved, and the speed of effector activation, to name just a few. The type of response to be elicited is also important. If the response involves a reflex arc, the synapses are facilitated and response time will be short. If, on the other hand, the response can be categorized as an unlearned response, then a far larger number of neural pathways and many types of higher intellectual activities—including choice and decision making—will be involved, and the time for response will be considerably lengthened.

There are various ways of testing the reaction time of unlearned responses. The tests range in difficulty from simple to ultrasophisticated. Since the objective here is to demonstrate the major time difference between reflexes and unlearned responses, the simple approach will suffice.

 1.   Using a reflex hammer, elicit the patellar reflex in your partner. Note the relative reaction time needed for this reflex to occur.

2.   Now test the reaction time for unlearned responses. The subject should hold his hand out, with the thumb and index finger extended. Hold a 12-in. ruler so that its end is exactly 1 in. above the subject's outstretched hand. The ruler should be in the vertical position with the numbers reading from the bottom up. When the ruler is dropped, the subject should be able to grasp it between thumb and index finger as it passes, without having to change position. Have the subject catch the ruler five times, varying the time between each trial. The relative speed of reaction can be determined by reading the number on the ruler at the point of the subject's fingertips. (Thus if the number at the fingertips is 6 in., the subject was unable to catch the ruler until 7 in. of length had passed through his fingers; 6 in. of ruler length plus 1 in. to account for the distance of the ruler above the hand.) Record the number of inches that pass through the subject's fingertips for each trial:

Trial 1: _____ in.   Trial 2: _____ in.

Trial 3: _____ in.   Trial 4: _____ in.

Trial 5: _____ in.

3.   Perform the test again, but this time say a simple word each time you release the ruler. Designate a specific word as a signal for the subject to catch the ruler. On all other words, the subject is to allow the ruler to pass through his fingers. Trials in which the subject erroneously catches the ruler are to be disregarded. Record the distance the ruler travels for five *successful* trials:

Trial 1: _____ in.   Trial 2: _____ in.

Trial 3: _____ in.   Trial 4: _____ in.

Trial 5: _____ in.

Did the addition of a specific word to the stimulus increase or decrease the reaction time?

_____

4.   Perform the testing once again to investigate the subject's reaction to word association. As you drop the ruler, say a word—for example, *hot*. The subject is to respond with a word he associates with the stimulus word—for example, *cold*—catching the ruler as he responds. If he is unable to make a word association, he must allow the ruler to pass through his fingers. Record the distance the ruler travels for five successful trials, as well as the number of times the ruler is not caught by the subject.

Trial 1: _____ in.   Trial 2: _____ in.

Trial 3: _____ in.   Trial 4: _____ in.

Trial 5: _____ in.

The number of times the subject was unable to catch the ruler:

_____

You should have noticed quite a large variation in reaction time in this series of trials. Why is this so?

_____

_____

_____

_____

General Sensation

It can be said without reservation that people are irritable creatures. Hold a sizzling steak before them and their mouths water. Flash your high beams in their eyes on the highway and they cuss. Tickle them and they giggle. These "irritants" (the steak, the light, and the tickle) and many others are stimuli that continually assault us.

The body's *sense organs,* which include its sensory receptors, react to stimuli or changes within the body and in the external environment. The tiny sensory receptors of the general senses react to touch, pressure, pain, heat, cold, and changes in position and are distributed throughout the body. In contrast to the widely distributed *general receptors,* the receptors of the special senses are large, complex sensory organs or small, localized groups of receptors. The special senses include sight, hearing, equilibrium, smell, and taste.

Sensory receptors may be classified according to the source of their stimulus. **Exteroceptors** react to stimuli in the external environment, and typically they are found close to the body surface. Exteroceptors include the cutaneous receptors in the skin and the highly specialized receptor structures of the special senses (the vision apparatus of the eye, and the hearing and equilibrium receptors of the ear, for example). **Interoceptors** respond to stimuli arising within the body. Interoceptors are found in the internal visceral organs, and include stretch receptors (in walls of hollow organs), chemo-

receptors, and others. A subdivision of the interoceptors, the **proprioceptors,** are located in joint capsules and in skeletal muscles and their tendons. They provide information on the position and degree of stretch of those structures. The receptors of the special sense organs are complex and deserve considerable study. Thus the special senses (vision, hearing, equilibrium, taste, and smell) are covered separately in Exercises 24 through 26. Only the anatomically simpler cutaneous sensory receptors and proprioceptors will be studied in this exercise.

STRUCTURE OF SENSORY RECEPTORS

You cannot become aware of changes in the environment unless your sensory neurons and their receptors are operating properly. Sensory receptors are modified dendritic endings (or specialized cells associated with the dendrites) that are sensitive to certain environmental stimuli. They react to such stimuli by initiating a nerve impulse. Several histologically distinct types of receptors in the skin have been identified; their structures are depicted in Figure 23.1.

Many references link each type of receptor to specific stimuli, but there is still considerable controversy

231

Meissner's Corpuscle   # 14801

Pacinian Corpuscle   # 00692

Free dendritic
nerve endings
(pain, temperature)

Meissner's corpuscle
(touch, light pressure)

Merkel discs
(light touch)

Epidermis

Dermis

Krause's end-bulb
(touch, light
pressure)

Pacinian
corpuscle
(deep pressure)

Root hair plexus
(hair movement-
light touch)

Ruffini's corpuscle
(pressure, stretch)

F23.1

Cutaneous receptors. Free dendritic nerve endings, Merkel discs, root hair plexus, Meissner's corpuscle, Pacinian corpuscle, Krause's end bulb, and Ruffini's corpuscle. See also Plates 9, 10, and 11 of the Histology Atlas.

about the precise qualitative function of each receptor. It may be that the responses of all these receptors overlap considerably. Certainly, intense stimulation of any of them is always interpreted as pain.

The least specialized of the cutaneous receptors are the **free dendritic endings** of sensory neurons (Figure 23.1 and Plate 10 of the Histology Atlas), which respond chiefly to pain and temperature. (The pain receptors are widespread in the skin and make up a sizable portion of the visceral interoceptors.) Certain free dendritic endings associate with specific epidermal cells to form **Merkel discs,** or entwine in hair follicles to form **root hair plexuses.** Both Merkel discs and root hair plexuses function as light touch receptors.

The other cutaneous receptors are more complex, with the dendritic endings *encapsulated* by connective tissue cells. **Meissner's corpuscles,** commonly referred to as *tactile receptors* because they respond to light touch, are located in the dermal papillae of the skin. Al-

though **Krause's end bulbs** and **Ruffini's corpuscles** were presumed to be thermoreceptors, now most authorities classify Krause's end bulbs with Meissner's corpuscles as a special kind of touch, or light pressure, receptor. Ruffini's corpuscles appear to respond to pressure and stretch stimuli. As you inspect Figure 23.1, note that all of the encapsulated receptors are quite similar, with the possible exception of the **Pacinian corpuscles** (deep pressure receptors), which are anatomically more distinctive and lie deepest in the dermis.

1.   Obtain histologic slides of Pacinian and Meissner's corpuscles. Locate, under low power, a Meissner's corpuscle in the dermal layer of the skin. As mentioned above, these are usually found in the dermal papillae. Then, switch to the oil immersion lens for a detailed study. Notice that the naked dendritic fibers within the capsule are aligned parallel to the skin surface. Compare your observations to Figure 23.1 and Plate 9 of the Histology Atlas.

2.   Next observe a Pacinian corpuscle located much deeper in the dermis. Try to identify the slender naked dendrite ending in the center of the receptor and the heavy capsule of connective tissue surrounding it (which looks rather like an onion cut lengthwise). Also, note how much larger the Pacinian corpuscles are than the Meissner's corpuscles. Compare your observations to the views shown in Figure 23.1 and Plate 11 of the Histology Atlas.

3.   Obtain slides of muscle spindles and Golgi tendon organs, the two major types of proprioceptors (see Figure 23.2). In the slide of **muscle spindles,** note that minute extensions of the dendrites of the sensory neurons coil around specialized slender skeletal muscle cells called **intrafusal cells,** or **fibers.** The **Golgi tendon organs** are composed of dendrites that ramify through the tendon tissue close to the muscle tendon attachment. Stretching of the muscle or tendon excites both types of receptors, which then transmit impulses that ultimately reach the cerebellum for interpretation. Compare your observations to Figure 23.2.

RECEPTOR PHYSIOLOGY

Sensory receptors act as *transducers,* changing environmental stimuli into afferent nerve impulses. Since the action potential generated in all nerves is essentially identical, the stimulus is identified entirely by the area of the brain's sensory cortex that is stimulated (which, of course, differs for the various afferent nerves).

Four qualities of cutaneous sensations have traditionally been recognized: tactile (touch), heat, cold, and pain. Mapping these sensations on the skin has revealed that the sensory receptors for these qualities have discrete locations and are characterized by clustering at certain points—**punctate distribution**—rather than by uniform distribution.

The simple pain receptors, extremely important in protecting the body, are the most numerous. Touch receptors tend to be clustered where greater sensitivity is desirable, as on the hands and face. It is surprising to learn that rather large areas of the skin are quite insensitive to touch because of a relative lack of touch receptors.

There are several simple experiments you can conduct to investigate the location and physiology of cutaneous receptors. In each of the following activities, work in pairs with one person as the subject and the other as the experimenter. After you have completed an experiment, switch roles and go through the procedures again so that all class members obtain individual results. Keep an accurate account of each test that you perform.

Density and Location of Temperature and Touch Receptors

1. Obtain 2 Mall probes (or temperature rods), Von Frey hairs (or a sharp pencil), and black, red, and blue felt-tipped markers and bring them to your laboratory bench.

2. Place one Mall probe (or temperature rod) in a beaker of ice water and the other in a water bath controlled at 45°C. With a felt marker, draw a square (2 cm on each side) on the ventral surface of the subject's forearm. During the following tests, the subject's eyes are to remain closed; the subject should tell the examiner when a stimulus is detected.

3. Working in a systematic manner from one side of the marked square to the other, gently touch the Von Frey's hairs or a sharp pencil tip to different points within the square. The *hairs* should be applied with a pressure that just causes them to bend; use the same pressure for each contact. Do not apply deep pressure; the goal is to stimulate only the more superficially located Meissner's corpuscles (as opposed to the Pacinian corpuscles located in the subcutaneous tissue). Mark with a *black dot* all points at which the touch is perceived.

4. Remove the Mall probe (or temperature rod) from the ice water and quickly wipe it dry. Repeat the procedure outlined above, noting all points of cold perception with a *blue dot.** Perception should be for temperature, not simply touch.

5. Remove the second Mall probe from the 45°C water bath and repeat the procedure once again, marking all points of heat perception with a *red dot.**

---

* The Mall probes will have to be returned to the water baths approximately every 2 minutes to maintain the desired testing temperatures.

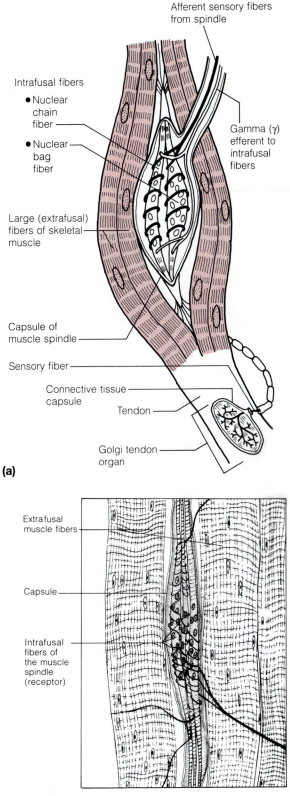

(a)

(b)

F23.2

Proprioceptors. (a) Diagrammatic view of a muscle spindle and Golgi tendon organ. (b) Drawing of a photomicrograph of a muscle spindle. See corresponding Plate 12 in the Histology Atlas.

GolgiTendon Organ   # 01956
Nerve Ending

6.   After each student has acted as the subject, produce a "map" of your own receptor areas in the squares provided here.

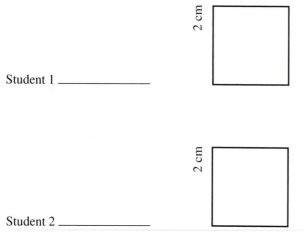

Student 1 _____

Student 2 _____

How does the density of the heat receptors correspond to that of the touch receptors?

_____

To that of the cold receptors? _____

_____

On the basis of your observations, which type of receptor appears to be most abundant (at least in the area tested)?

_____

Two-Point Discrimination Test

The density of the touch receptors varies significantly in different areas of the body. In general, areas that have the greatest density of tactile receptors have a heightened ability to "feel." These areas correspond to areas that receive the greatest motor innervation; thus they are also typically areas of fine motor control.

On the basis of this information, which areas of the body do you *predict* will have the greatest density of touch receptors?

_____

_____

 Using a caliper or esthesiometer and a metric ruler, test the ability of the subject to differentiate two distinct sensations when the skin is touched simultaneously at two points. Beginning with the face, start with the caliper arms completely together. Gradually increase the distance between the arms, testing the subject's skin after each adjustment. Continue with this testing procedure until the subject reports that

two points of contact can be felt. This measurement, the smallest distance at which two points of contact can be felt, is the **two-point threshold.** Repeat this procedure on the back and palm of the hand, fingertips, lips, back of the neck, and back of the calf. Record your results in the accompanying chart.

Body area tested	Two-point threshold (millimeters)
Face	
Back of hand	
Palm of hand	
Fingertips	
Lips	
Back of neck	
Back of calf	

Tactile Localization

Tactile localization is the ability to determine which portion of the skin has been touched. The tactile receptor field of the body periphery has a corresponding "touch" field in the brain's somatosensory association area. Some body areas are well represented with touch receptors, allowing tactile stimuli to be localized with great accuracy, but the density of the touch receptors in other body areas allows only a crude discrimination.

1.   The subject's eyes should be closed during the testing. The experimenter touches the palm of the subject's hand with a pointed black felt-tipped marker. The subject should then try to touch the exact point with his or her own marker, which should be of a different color. Measure the error of localization in millimeters. Repeat the test in the same spot twice more, recording the error of localization for each test. Average the results of the three determinations and record it in the chart below.

Body area tested	Average error of localization (millimeters)
Palm of hand	
Fingertip	
Ventral forearm	
Ventral surface of arm	
Upper back	

Does the ability to localize the stimulus improve the second time?

_____ The third time? _____ Explain. ____

_____

_____

2.   Repeat the above procedure on a fingertip, the ventral forearm, the ventral surface of the upper arm, and the upper back between the shoulder blades. Record the averaged results in the chart.

Adaptation of Touch Receptors

The number of impulses transmitted by sensory receptors often changes both with the intensity of the stimulus and with the length of time the stimulus is applied. In many cases, when a stimulus is applied for a prolonged period, the rate of receptor discharge slows and conscious awareness of the stimulus declines or is lost until some type of stimulus change occurs. This phenomenon is referred to as **adaptation.** The touch receptors adapt particularly rapidly, which is highly desirable. Who, for instance, would want to be continually aware of the pressure of clothing on their skin? The simple experiments to be conducted next allow you to investigate this phenomenon of adaptation.

1.   The subject's eyes should be closed. Place a coin on the anterior surface of the subject's forearm, and determine how long the sensation persists for the subject. Duration of the sensation:

_____ sec

2.   Repeat the test, placing the coin at a different forearm location. How long does the sensation persist at the second location?

_____ sec

After awareness of the sensation has been lost at the second site, stack three more coins atop the first one.

Does the pressure sensation return? _____

If so, for how long is the subject aware of the pressure in this instance?

_____ sec.

Are the same receptors being stimulated when the four coins, rather than the one coin, are used?

_____ Explain. _____

_____

3.   To further illustrate the adaptation of touch receptors—in this case, the root hair plexuses of the hair fol-

licles—gently and slowly bend one hair shaft with a pen or pencil until it springs back (away from the pencil) to its original position. Is the tactile sensation greater when the hair is being slowly bent or when it springs back?

_____

Why is the adaptation of the touch receptors in the hair follicles particularly important to a woman who wears her hair in a ponytail? If the answer is not immediately apparent, consider the opposite phenomenon: what would happen, in terms of sensory input from her hair follicles, if these receptors did not exhibit adaptation?

_____

_____

Adaptation of Temperature Receptors

Adaptation of the temperature receptors can be tested using some very unsophisticated methods.

1.   Obtain three large finger bowls or 1000-ml beakers and fill the first with 45°C water. Have the subject immerse her or his left hand in the water and report the sensation. Keep the left hand immersed for 1 min and then also immerse the right hand in the same bowl.

What is the sensation of the left hand when it is first immersed?

_____

What is the sensation of the left hand after 1 min as compared to the sensation in the right hand just immersed?

_____

Had adaptation occurred in the left hand? _____

2.   Rinse both hands in tap water, dry them, and wait 5 min before conducting the next test. Just before beginning the test, refill the finger bowl with fresh 45°C water, fill a second with ice water, and fill a third with water at room temperature.

3.   Place the *left* hand in the ice water and the *right* hand in the 45°C water. What is the sensation in each hand after 2 min as compared to the sensation perceived when the hands were first immersed?

_____

_____

Which hand seemed to adapt more quickly?

_____

4. After reporting these observations, the subject should then place both hands simultaneously into the finger bowl containing the water at room temperature. Record the sensation in the left hand:

_____

The right hand: _____

The sensations that the subject experiences when both hands were put into room-temperature water are called **negative afterimages.** They are explained by the fact that sensations of heat and cold depend on the rapidity of heat loss or gain by the skin and differences in the temperature gradient.

Referred Pain

Experiments on pain receptor localization and adaptation are commonly conducted in the laboratory. However, there are certain problems with such experiments. Pain receptors are densely distributed in the skin, and they adapt very little, if at all. (This lack of adaptability is due to the protective function of the receptors. The sensation of pain often indicates tissue damage or trauma to body structures.) Thus no attempt will be made in this exercise to localize the pain receptors or to prove their nonadaptability, since both would cause needless discomfort to those of you acting as subjects and would not add any additional insight.

However, the phenomenon of referred pain is easily demonstrated in the laboratory, and such experiments provide information that may be useful in explaining common examples of this phenomenon. **Referred pain** is a sensory experience in which pain is perceived as arising in one area of the body when in fact another, often quite remote area is receiving the painful stimulus. Thus the pain is said to be "referred" to a different area.

The phenomenon of **projection,** the process by which the brain refers sensations to their *usual* point of stimulation, provides the most simple explanation of such experiences. Many of us have experienced referred pain as a radiating pain in the forehead after quickly swallowing an ice-cold drink. Referred pain is important in many types of clinical diagnosis, since damage to many visceral organs results in this phenomenon. For example, inadequate oxygenation of the heart muscle often results in pain being referred to the chest wall and left shoulder (*angina pectoris*), and the reflux of gastric juice into the esophagus causes a sensation of intense discomfort in the thorax referred to as *heartburn*. In addition, amputees often report *phantom limb pain*—feelings of pain that appear to be coming from a part of the body that is no longer there.

 Immerse the subject's elbow in a finger bowl containing ice water. Record the quality (such as discomfort, tingling, or pain) and the quality progression of the sensations he or she reports for 2 min. Also record the location of the perceived sensations. The ulnar nerve, which serves the medial third of the hand, is involved in the phenomenon of referred pain experienced during this test. How does the localization of this referred pain correspond to the areas served by the ulnar nerve?

_____

_____

_____

_____

Time of observation	Quality of sensation	Localization of sensation
On immersion		
After 1 min		
After 2 min		

Special Senses: Vision

ANATOMY OF THE EYE

External Anatomy and Accessory Structures

The adult human eye is a sphere measuring about 2.5 cm (1 inch) in diameter. Only about one-sixth of the eye's anterior surface is observable; the remainder is enclosed and protected by a cushion of fat and the walls of the bony orbit.

Six **external, or extrinsic, eye muscles** attached to the exterior surface of each eyeball control eye movement and make it possible for the eye to follow a moving object. The names and positioning of these extrinsic muscles are noted in Figure 24.1. Their actions are given in the chart accompanying that figure.

The anterior surface of each eye is protected by the **eyelids,** or **palpebrae.** (See Figure 24.2.) The medial and lateral junctions of the upper and lower eyelids are referred to as the **medial and lateral canthus** (respectively). A mucous membrane, the **conjunctiva,** lines the internal surface of the eyelids (as the *palpebral conjunctiva*) and continues over the anterior surface of the eyeball to its junction with the corneal epithelium (as the *ocular,* or *bulbar, conjunctiva*). The conjunctiva secretes mucus, which aids in lubricating the eyeball. Inflammation of the conjunctiva, often accompanied by redness of the eye, is called **conjunctivitis.**

Projecting from the border of each eyelid is a row of short hairs, the **eyelashes.** The **ciliary glands,** a type of sweat gland, lie between the eyelash hair follicles and help lubricate the eyeball. An inflammation of one of

Name	Innervation (cranial nerve)	Action
Lateral rectus	VI	Moves eye horizontally (laterally)
Medial rectus	III	Moves eye horizontally (medially)
Superior rectus	III	Elevates eye
Inferior oblique	III	Elevates eye and turns it laterally
Inferior rectus	III	Depresses eye
Superior oblique	IV	Depresses eye and turns it laterally

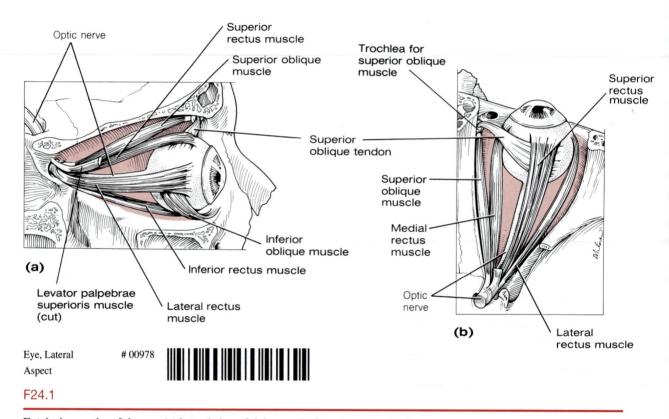

(a)

Optic nerve

Superior rectus muscle

Superior oblique muscle

Levator palpebrae superioris muscle (cut)

Lateral rectus muscle

Inferior rectus muscle

Inferior oblique muscle

Superior oblique tendon

(b)

Trochlea for superior oblique muscle

Superior rectus muscle

Superior oblique muscle

Medial rectus muscle

Optic nerve

Lateral rectus muscle

Eye, Lateral Aspect   # 00978

F24.1

Extrinsic muscles of the eye. (a) Lateral view of right eye. (b) Superior view of right eye.

these glands is called a **sty.** Small sebaceous glands associated with the hair follicles and the larger **meibomian glands,** located posterior to the eyelashes, secrete an oily substance.

The **lacrimal apparatus** consists of the **lacrimal gland, lacrimal canals, lacrimal sac,** and the **nasolacrimal duct.** The lacrimal glands are situated superior to the lateral aspect of each eye. They continually liberate a dilute salt solution (tears) that flows onto the anterior surface of the eyeball through several small ducts. The tears flush across the eyeball into the lacrimal canals medially, then into the lacrimal sac, and finally into the nasolacrimal duct, which empties into the nasal cavity. The lacrimal secretion also contains **lysozyme,** an antibacterial enzyme. Because it constantly flushes the eyeball, the lacrimal fluid cleanses and protects the eye surface as it moistens and lubricates it. As we age, our eyes tend to become dry due to decreased lacrimation, and thus are more vulnerable to bacterial invasion and irritation.

Observe the eyes of another student and identify as many of the accessory structures as possible. Ask the student to look to the left. What extrinsic eye muscles are responsible for this action?

Right eye ___medial rectus___

Left eye ___lateral r'___

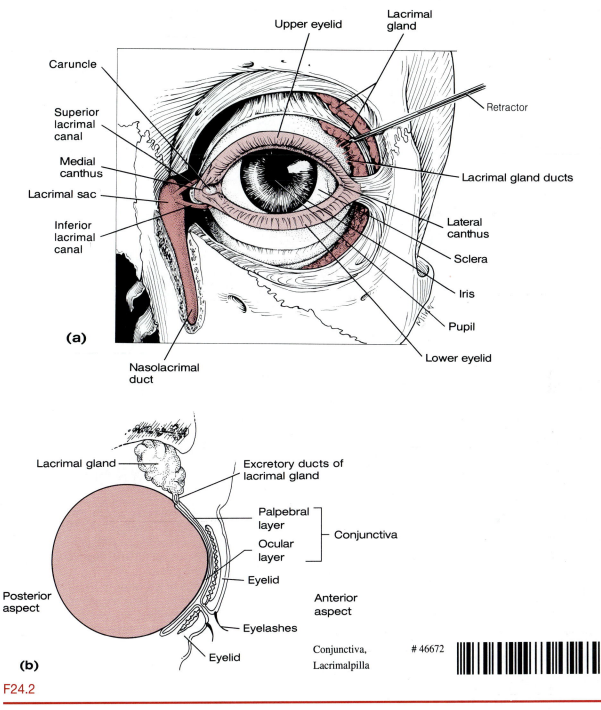

(a)

Caruncle

Superior lacrimal canal

Medial canthus

Lacrimal sac

Inferior lacrimal canal

Nasolacrimal duct

Upper eyelid

Lacrimal gland

Retractor

Lacrimal gland ducts

Lateral canthus

Sclera

Iris

Pupil

Lower eyelid

(b)

Lacrimal gland

Posterior aspect

Excretory ducts of lacrimal gland

Palpebral layer

Ocular layer

Conjunctiva

Eyelid

Anterior aspect

Eyelashes

Eyelid

Conjunctiva, Lacrimalpilla   # 46672

F24.2

External anatomy of the eye and accessory structures. (a) Anterior view. (b) Sagittal section.

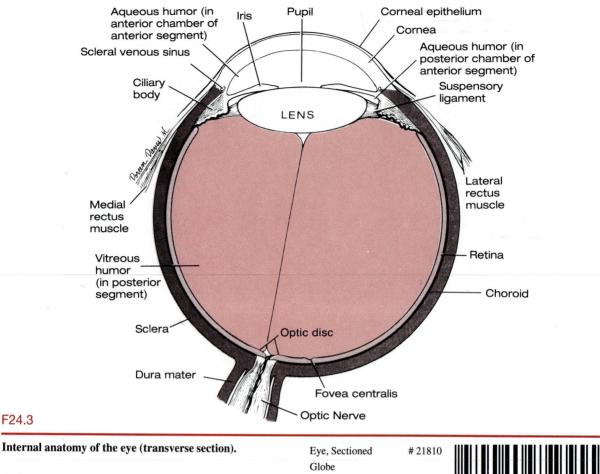

F24.3

Internal anatomy of the eye (transverse section).

Eye, Sectioned   # 21810
Globe

Internal Anatomy of the Eye

Obtain a dissectible eye model and identify its internal structures as they are described below. As you work, also refer to Figure 24.3.

Anatomically, the wall of the eye is constructed of three tunics, or coats. The outermost **fibrous tunic** is a protective layer composed of dense avascular connective tissue. It has two obviously different regions: The opaque white **sclera** forms the bulk of the fibrous tunic and is observable anteriorly as the "white of the eye." Its anteriormost portion is modified structurally to form the transparent **cornea,** through which light enters the eye.

The middle tunic, called the **uvea,** is the **vascular tunic.** Its posteriormost part, the **choroid,** is a richly vascular nutritive layer that contains a dark pigment that prevents light scattering within the eye. Anteriorly, the choroid is modified to form the **ciliary body,** to which the lens is attached, and then the pigmented **iris.** The iris is incomplete, resulting in a rounded opening, the **pupil,** through which light passes.

The iris is composed of circularly and radially arranged smooth muscle fibers and acts as a reflexively activated diaphragm in regulating the amount of light entering the eye. In close vision and bright light, the circular muscles of the iris contract, and the pupil constricts. In distant vision and in dim light, the radial fibers contract, enlarging (dilating) the pupil and allowing more light to enter the eye.

The innermost **sensory tunic** of the eye is the delicate, two-layered **retina.** The outer **pigmented epithelial layer** abuts and lines the entire uvea. The transparent inner **neural (nervous) layer** extends anteriorly only to the ciliary body. It contains the photoreceptor cells, the **rods** and **cones,** which begin the chain of electrical events that ultimately result in the transduction of light energy into nerve impulses that are transmitted to the optic cortex of the brain. Vision is the result. The photoreceptor cells are distributed over the entire neural retina, except where the optic nerve leaves the eyeball. This site is called the **optic disc,** or blind spot. Lateral to each blind spot, and directly posterior to the lens, is an area called the **macula lutea** (yellow spot), an area of high cone density. In its center is the **fovea centralis,** a minute pit about ½ mm in diameter, which contains only cones and is the area of greatest visual acuity. Focusing for discriminative vision occurs in the fovea centralis.

Light entering the eye is focused on the retina by the **lens,** a flexible crystalline structure held vertically in the eye's interior by the **suspensory ligament** attached to the ciliary body. Activity of the ciliary muscle, which

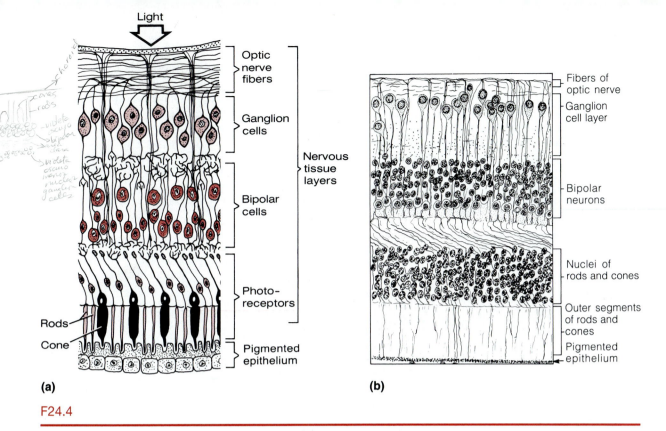

(a)

Light

Optic nerve fibers

Ganglion cells

Nervous tissue layers

Bipolar cells

Photo-receptors

Rods

Cone

Pigmented epithelium

(b)

Fibers of optic nerve

Ganglion cell layer

Bipolar neurons

Nuclei of rods and cones

Outer segments of rods and cones

Pigmented epithelium

F24.4

Microscopic anatomy of the cellular layers of the retina. (a) Diagrammatic view. (b) Line drawing of the photomicrograph provided in Plate 13 of the Histology Atlas.

accounts for the bulk of ciliary body tissue, changes lens thickness to allow light to be properly focused on the retina.

In the elderly the lens becomes increasingly hard and opaque. **Cataracts,** which are often the result of this process, cause vision to become hazy or entirely obstructed. ■

Cataract   # 12428

The lens divides the eye into two segments: the **anterior segment** anterior to the lens, which contains a clear watery fluid called the **aqueous humor,** and the **posterior segment** behind the lens, filled with a gel-like substance, the **vitreous humor,** or **vitreous body.** The anterior segment is further divided into **anterior** and **posterior chambers,** located before and after the iris, respectively. The aqueous humor is continually formed by the capillaries of the **ciliary processes** of the ciliary body. It helps to maintain the intraocular pressure of the eye and provides nutrients for the avascular lens and cornea. The aqueous humor is reabsorbed into the **scleral venous sinus (canal of Schlemm).** The vitreous humor provides the major internal reinforcement of the posterior part of the eyeball, and helps to keep the neural layer of the retina pressed firmly against the wall of the eyeball. It is formed *only* before birth.

Any interference with aqueous fluid drainage increases intraocular pressure. When the intraocular pressure reaches dangerously high levels, the retina and

optic nerve are compressed, resulting in pain and possible blindness, a condition called **glaucoma.** ■

Glaucoma,   # 21990
Optic Nerve Changes

MICROSCOPIC ANATOMY OF THE RETINA

As described above, the retina consists of two main types of cells: a pigmented *epithelial* layer, which abuts the choroid, and an inner cell layer composed of *neurons,* which is in contact with the vitreous humor (Figure 24.4). The inner nervous layer is composed of three major neuronal populations. These are, from outer to inner aspect, the **photoreceptors** (rods and cones), the **bipolar cells,** and the **ganglion cells.**

The **rods** are the specialized receptors for dim light. Visual interpretation of their activity is in gray tones. The **cones** are color receptors that permit high levels of visual acuity, but they function only under conditions of high light intensity; thus, for example, no color vision is possible in moonlight. Only cones are found in the fovea centralis, and their number decreases as the retinal periphery is approached. Conversely, the rods are most numerous in the periphery, and their density decreases as the macula is approached.

Light must pass through the ganglion cell layer and the bipolar neuron layer to reach and excite the rods and cones, which then undergo changes in their membrane potential that ultimately influence the bipolar neurons.

241

These in turn stimulate the ganglion cells, whose axons leave the retina in the tight bundle of fibers known as the optic nerve. The retinal layer is thickest (approximately 4 μm) where the optic nerve attaches to the eyeball because an increasing number of ganglion cell axons converge at this point. It thins as it approaches the ciliary body.

Obtain a histologic slide of a longitudinal section of the eye. Identify the retinal layers by comparing it to Figure 24.4.

| Fovea, Retina | # 01033 | |
| Ganglion Cells, Human Retina | # 29075 | |

VISUAL PATHWAYS TO THE BRAIN

The axons of the ganglion cells of the retina converge at the posterior aspect of the eyeball and exit from the eye as the optic nerve. At the **optic chiasma,** the fibers from the medial side of each eye cross over to the opposite side. The fiber tracts thus formed are called the **optic tracts.** Each optic tract contains fibers from the lateral side of the eye on the same side and from the medial side of the opposite eye.

The optic tract fibers synapse with neurons in the **lateral geniculate nucleus** of the thalamus, whose axons form the **optic radiation,** terminating in the **optic,** or **visual, cortex** in the occipital lobe of the brain. Here they synapse with the cortical cells, and visual interpretation occurs.

After examining Figure 24.5, determine what effects lesions in the following areas would have on vision:

In the right optic nerve *cause blindness on right eye*

Through the optic chiasma _____

In the left optic tract *partial blindness on right eye*

In the right cerebral cortex (visual area) *partial blindness in both eyes*

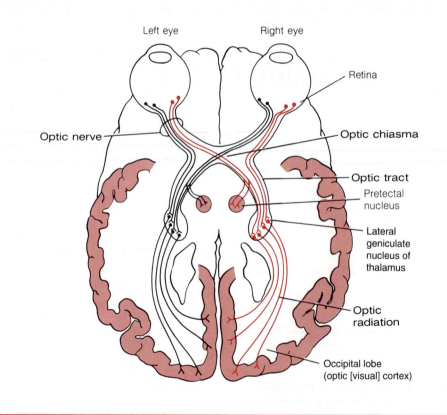

Left eye   Right eye

Retina

Optic nerve

Optic chiasma

Optic tract

Pretectal nucleus

Lateral geniculate nucleus of thalamus

Optic radiation

Occipital lobe (optic [visual] cortex)

F24.5

Visual pathway to the brain. (Note that fibers from the lateral portion of each retinal field do not cross at the optic chiasma.)

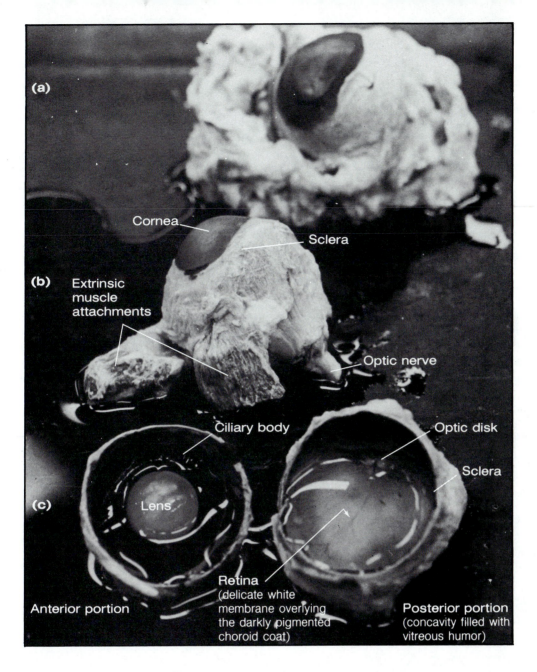

(a)

Cornea

Sclera

(b) Extrinsic
muscle
attachments

Optic nerve

Ciliary body

Optic disk

Sclera

(c)

Lens

Anterior portion

Retina
(delicate white
membrane overlying
the darkly pigmented
choroid coat)

Posterior portion
(concavity filled with
vitreous humor)

F24.6

Anatomy of the cow eye. (a) Cow eye (entire) removed from orbit (note the large amount of fat cushioning the eyeball). (b) Cow eye (entire) with fat removed to show the extrinsic muscle attachments and optic nerve. (c) Cow eye cut along the coronal plane to reveal internal structures.

DISSECTION OF THE COW (SHEEP) EYE

1.   Obtain a preserved cow or sheep eye, dissecting instruments, and a dissecting pan. Apply protective skin cream or don disposable gloves if desired.

2.   Examine the external surface of the eye, noting the thick cushion of adipose tissue. Identify the optic nerve (cranial nerve II) as it leaves the eyeball, the remnants of the extrinsic eye muscles, the conjunctiva, the sclera, and the cornea. The normally transpar-ent cornea is opalescent or opaque if the eye has been preserved. Refer to Figure 24.6 as you work.

3.   Trim away most of the fat and connective tissue, but leave the optic nerve intact. Holding the eye with the cornea facing downward, make an incision with a sharp scalpel into the sclera about ¼ inch above the cornea. Complete the incision around the circumference of the eyeball paralleling the corneal edge.

4.   Carefully lift the anterior part of the eyeball away from the posterior portion. Conditions being proper, the vitreous body should remain with the posterior part of the eyeball.

243

5.   Examine the anterior part of the eye and identify the following structures:

Ciliary body: black pigmented body that appears to be a halo encircling the lens.
Lens: biconvex structure that appears opaque in preserved specimens.
Suspensory ligament: a halo of delicate fibers attaching the lens to the ciliary body.

Carefully remove the lens and identify the adjacent structures:

Iris: anterior continuation of the ciliary body penetrated by the pupil.
Cornea: more convex anteriormost portion of the sclera; normally transparent but cloudy in preserved specimens.

6.   Examine the posterior portion of the eyeball. Remove the vitreous humor, and identify the following structures:

Retina: the neural layer of the retina appears as a delicate white, probably crumpled membrane that separates easily from the pigmented choroid.

Note its point of attachment. What is this point called?

_____

Pigmented choroid coat: appears iridescent in the cow or sheep eye owing to a special reflecting surface called the **tapetum lucidum.** This specialized surface reflects the light within the eye and is found in the eyes of animals that live under conditions of low-intensity light. It is not found in humans.

VISUAL TESTS AND EXPERIMENTS

Demonstration of the Blind Spot

1.   Hold Figure 24.7 about 18 inches from your eyes. Close your left eye, and focus your right eye on the X, which should be positioned so that it is directly in line with your right eye. Move the figure slowly toward your face, keeping your right eye focused on the X. When the dot focuses on the blind spot, which lacks photoreceptors, it will disappear.

X   ●

F24.7

_____

Blind spot test figure.

2.   Have your laboratory partner record in metric units the distance at which this occurs. The dot will reappear as the figure is moved closer. Distance at which the dot disappears:

Right eye _____ 10 inches _____

Repeat the test for the left eye, this time closing the right eye and focusing the left eye on the dot. Record the distance at which the X disappears:

Left eye _____ 10.5 inches _____

Afterimages

When light from an object strikes **rhodopsin,** the purple pigment contained in the rods of the retina, it triggers a photochemical reaction that causes the rhodopsin to be split into its colorless precursor molecules (vitamin A and a protein called opsin). This event, called *bleaching of the pigment,* initiates a chain of events leading to impulse transmission along fibers of the optic nerve. Once bleaching has occurred in a rod, the photoreceptor pigment must be resynthesized before the rod can be restimulated. This takes a certain period of time. Both phenomena—that is, the stimulation of the photoreceptor cells and their subsequent inactive period—can be demonstrated indirectly in terms of positive and negative afterimages.

1.   Stare at a bright light bulb for a few seconds, and then gently close your eyes for approximately one minute.

2.   Record, in sequence of occurrence, what you "saw" after closing your eyes:

_____

_____

_____

The bright image of the light bulb initially seen was a **positive afterimage** caused by the continued firing of the rods. The dark image of the light bulb that subsequently appeared against a lighter background was the **negative afterimage,** an indication that the rhodopsin in the affected photoreceptor cells had been bleached.

Refraction, Tests for Visual Acuity, and Astigmatism

When light rays pass from one medium to another, their velocity, or speed of transmission, changes, and the rays are bent or refracted. Thus the light rays in the visual field are refracted as they encounter the cornea, lens, and vitreous body of the eye.

The refractive index (bending power) of the cornea and vitreous humor are constant. But the lens's refractive index, or strength, can be varied by changing the

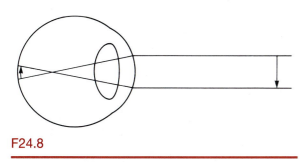

Refraction of light in the eye, resulting in the production of a real image on the retina.

lens's shape—that is, by making it more or less convex so that the light is properly converged and focused on the retina. The greater the lens convexity, or bulge, the more the light will be bent and the stronger the lens. Conversely, the less the lens convexity (the flatter it is), the less it bends the light.

In general, light from a distant source (over 20 feet) approaches the eye as parallel rays, and no change in lens convexity is necessary for it to focus properly on the retina. However, light from a close source tends to diverge, and the convexity of the lens must increase to make close vision possible. To achieve this, the ciliary muscle contracts, decreasing the tension on the suspensory ligament attached to the lens and allowing the elastic lens to "round up." Thus, a lens capable of bringing a *close* object into sharp focus is stronger (more convex) than a lens focusing on a more distant object. The ability of the eye to focus differentially for objects of near vision (less than 20 feet) is called **accommodation.** It should be noted that the image formed on the retina as a result of the refractory activity of the lens (see Figure 24.8) is a **real image** (reversed from left to right, inverted, and smaller than the object).

The normal or **emmetropic eye** is able to accommodate properly. However, visual problems may result from lenses that are too strong or too "lazy" (overconverging and underconverging, respectively) or from structural problems such as an eyeball that is too long or too short to provide for proper focusing by the lens, or a cornea or lens with improper curvatures.

Individuals in whom the image normally focuses in front of the retina are said to have **myopia,** or "nearsightedness" (Figure 24.9a); they can see close objects without difficulty, but distant objects are blurred or seen indistinctly. Correction requires a concave lens, which causes the light reaching the eye to diverge (Figure 24.9b).

If the image focuses behind the retina, the individual is said to have **hyperopia** or farsightedness. Such persons have no problems with distant vision but need glasses with convex lenses to augment the converging power of the lens for close vision (Figure 24.9c and d).

Irregularities in the curvatures of the lens and/or the cornea lead to a blurred vision problem called **astigmatism.** Cylindrically ground lenses, which compensate for inequalities in the curvatures of the refracting surfaces, are prescribed to correct the condition. ■

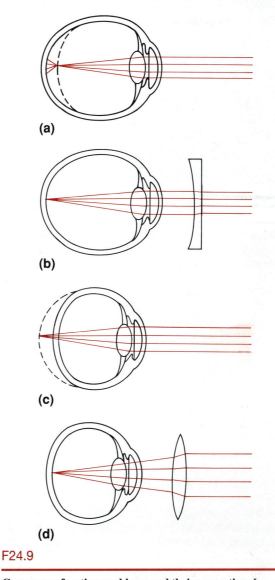

(a)

(b)

(c)

(d)

Common refraction problems and their correction. In myopia: (a) light from a distant object focuses in front of the retina, and (b) correction involves the use of a concave lens that diverges the light before it enters the eye. In hyperopia: (c) light from a distant object focuses behind the retina, and (d) correction requires a convex lens that converges the light rays as they enter the eye.

TEST FOR NEAR-POINT ACCOMMODATION

The elasticity of the lens decreases dramatically with age, resulting in difficulty in focusing for near or close vision. This condition is called **presbyopia**—literally, old vision. Lens elasticity can be tested by measuring the **near point of accommodation.** The near point of vision is about 7.5 cm (or 3 inches) at age 10, 20–25 cm (or 8–10 inches) in young adults, and 83 cm (or 33 inches) at the age of 60.

To determine your near point of accommodation, hold a common straight pin at arm's length in front of one eye. Slowly move the pin toward that eye until the pin image becomes distorted. Have your lab partner measure the distance from your eye to the pin at this point, and record the distance below. Repeat the procedure for the other eye.

Near point for right eye _____

Near point for left eye _____

TEST FOR VISUAL ACUITY **Visual acuity,** or sharpness of vision, is generally tested with a Snellen eye chart, which consists of letters of various sizes printed on a white card. This test is based on the fact that letters of a certain size can be seen clearly by eyes with normal vision at a specific distance. The distance at which the normal, or emmetropic, eye can read a line of letters is printed at the end of that line.

1. Have your partner stand 20 feet from the posted Snellen eye chart and cover one eye with a card or hand. As your partner reads each consecutive line aloud, check for accuracy. If this individual wears glasses, give the test twice—first with glasses off and then with glasses on.

2. Record the number of the line with the smallest-sized letters read. If it is 20/20, the person's vision for that eye is normal. If it is 20/40, or any ratio with a value less than one, he or she has less than the normal visual acuity. (Such an individual is myopic.) If the visual acuity is 20/15, vision is better than normal, because this person can stand at 20 feet from the chart and read letters that are only discernible by the normal eye at 15 feet. Give your partner the number of the line corresponding to the smallest letters read, to record in step 4.

3. Repeat the process for the other eye.

4. Have your partner test and record your visual acuity. If you wear glasses, the test results *without* glasses should be recorded first.

Visual acuity, right eye _____

Visual acuity, left eye _____

TEST FOR ASTIGMATISM The astigmatism chart (Figure 24.10) is designed to test for defects in the refracting surface of the lens and/or cornea.

View the chart first with one eye and then with the other, focusing on the center of the chart. If all the radiating lines appear equally dark and distinct, there is no distortion of your refracting surfaces. If some of the lines are blurred or appear less dark than others, at least some degree of astigmatism is present.

Is astigmatism present in your left eye? _____

Right eye? _____

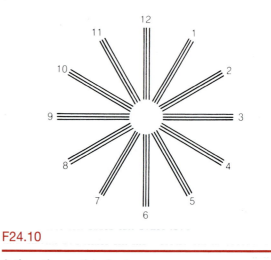

F24.10
_____

Astigmatism testing chart.

Test for Color Blindness

Ishihara's color plates are designed to test for deficiencies in the cones or color photoreceptor cells. Studies suggest that there are three cone types, each containing a different light-absorbing pigment. One type primarily absorbs the red wavelengths of the visible light spectrum, another the blue wavelengths, and a third the green wavelengths. Nerve impulses reaching the brain from these different photoreceptor types are then interpreted (seen) as red, blue, and green, respectively.

The interpretation of the intermediate colors of the visible light spectrum is a result of overlapping input from more than one cone type.

1. View the various color plates in bright light or sunlight while holding them about 30 inches away and at right angles to your line of vision. Report to your laboratory partner what you see in each plate. (Take no more than 3 seconds for each decision.)

2. Your partner is to write down your responses and then check their accuracy with the correct answers given at the front of the color plate book. Is there any indication that you have some degree of color blindness?

_____ If so, what type? _____

_____

Repeat the procedure to test your partner's color vision.

Relative Positioning of Rods and Cones on the Retina

The test subject for this demonstration should have shown no color vision problems during the test for color blindness. Students may work in pairs, or two students may perform the test for the entire class. White, red, blue, and green paper discs and chalk will be needed for this demonstration.

1. Position the subject about 1 foot away from the blackboard.

2. Make a small white chalk circle on the board immediately in front of the subject's right eye. Have her close her left eye and stare fixedly at the circle with the right eye throughout the test.

3. To map the extent of the rod field, begin to move a white paper disc into the field of vision from various sides of the visual field (beginning at least 2 feet away from the white chalk circle) and plot with white chalk dots the points at which the disc first becomes visible to the test subject.

4. Repeat the procedure, using red, green, and blue paper discs and like-colored chalk to map the cone fields. Color (not object) identification is required.

5. After the test has been completed for all four discs, connect all dots of the same color. It should become apparent that each of the color fields has a different radius and that the rod and cone distribution on the retina is not uniform. (Normal fields have white outermost, followed by blue, red, and green as the fovea is approached.)

6. Record the rod and cone color field distribution observed in the laboratory review section using appropriately colored pencils.

Tests for Binocular Vision

Humans, cats, predatory birds, and most primates are endowed with **binocular,** or two-eyed, **vision.** Although both eyes look in approximately the same direction, they see slightly different views. Their visual fields, each about 170 degrees, overlap to a considerable extent; thus there is two-eyed vision at the overlap area (Figure 24.11).

In contrast, the eyes of many animals (rabbits, pigeons, and others) are more on the sides of their head. Such animals see in two different directions and thus have a panoramic field of view and **panoramic vision**.

Although both types of vision have their good points, we now know that binocular vision provides three-dimensional vision and an accurate means of locating objects in space. The slight differences between the views seen by the two eyes are fused by the higher centers of the visual cortex to give us *depth perception.* Because of the manner in which the visual cortex re-

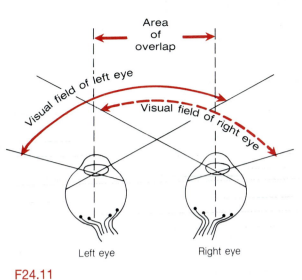

F24.11

Overlapping of the visual fields.

solves these two different views into a single image, it is sometimes referred to as the "cyclopean eye of the binocular animal."

1. To demonstrate that a slightly different view is seen by each eye, perform the following simple experiment.

Close your left eye. Hold a pencil at arm's length directly in front of your right eye. Position another pencil directly beneath it and then move the lower pencil about half the distance toward you. As you move the lower pencil, make sure it remains in the *same plane* as the stationary pencil, so that the two pencils continually form a straight line. Then, without moving the pencils, close your right eye and open your left eye. Notice that with only the right eye open, the moving pencil stays in the same plane as the fixed pencil, but that when viewed with the left eye, the moving pencil is displaced laterally away from the plane of the fixed pencil.

2. To demonstrate the importance of two-eyed binocular vision for depth perception, perform this second simple experiment.

Have your laboratory partner hold a test tube erect about arm's length in front of you. With both eyes open, quickly insert a pencil into the test tube. Remove the pencil, bring it back close to your body, close one eye, and quickly and without hesitation insert the pencil into the test tube. (Do not feel for the test tube with the pencil!) Repeat with the other eye closed.

Was it as easy to dunk the pencil with one eye closed as with both eyes open?

Tests of Eye Reflexes

Both intrinsic (internal) and extrinsic (external) muscles are necessary for proper eye functioning. The *intrinsic muscles,* controlled by the autonomic nervous system, are those of the ciliary body (which alters the lens curvature in focusing) and the radial and circular muscles of the iris (which control pupillary size and thus regulate the amount of light entering the eye). The *extrinsic muscles* are the rectus and oblique muscles, which are attached to the eyeball exterior. These muscles control eye movement and make it possible to keep moving objects focused on the fovea centralis. They are also responsible for **convergence,** or medial eye movements, which is essential for near vision. When convergence occurs, both eyes are directed toward the near object viewed. The extrinsic eye muscles are controlled by the somatic nervous system.

Involuntary activity of both of these muscle types is brought about by reflex actions that can be observed in the following experiments.

PHOTOPUPILLARY REFLEX   Sudden illumination of the retina by a bright light causes the pupil to contract reflexively in direct proportion to the light intensity. This protective response prevents damage to the delicate photoreceptor cells.

Obtain a laboratory lamp or penlight. Have your laboratory partner sit with eyes closed and hands over his or her eyes. Turn on the light and position it so that it shines on the subject's right hand. After 1 minute, ask your partner to open his right eye. Quickly observe the pupil of that eye. What happens to the pupil?

_____

Shut off the light and ask your partner to open the opposite eye. What are your observations?

_____

_____

ACCOMMODATION PUPILLARY REFLEX   Have your partner gaze for approximately 1 minute at a distant object in the lab—*not* toward the windows or another light source. Observe your partner's pupils, then hold some printed material 6 to 10 inches from his or her face.

How does pupil size change as your partner focuses on the printed material?

pupils shrunk

Explain the value of this reflex. _____

_____

_____

_____

CONVERGENCE REFLEX   Repeat the previous experiment, this time using a pen or pencil as the close object to be focused on. Note the position of your partner's eyeballs both while he or she is gazing at the distant and at the close object. Do they change position as the object of focus is changed?

_____ In what way? _____

_____

_____

_____

Explain the importance of the convergence reflex.

_____

_____

_____

Ophthalmoscopic Examination of the Eye (Optional)

The opthalmoscope is an instrument used to examine the *fundus,* or eyeball interior, to determine visually the condition of the retina, optic disc, and internal blood vessels. Certain pathologic conditions such as diabetes mellitus, arteriosclerosis, and degenerative changes of the optic nerve and retina can be detected by such an examination. The ophthalmoscope consists of a set of lenses mounted on a rotating disc (the **lens selection disc**), a light source regulated by a **rheostat control,** and a mirror that reflects the light so that the eye interior can be illuminated (Figure 24.12).

The lens selection disc is positioned in a small slit in the mirror, and the examiner views the eye interior through this slit, appropriately called the **viewing window.** The focal length of each lens is indicated in diopters preceded by a + sign if the lens is convex and by a − sign if the lens is concave. When the zero (0) is seen in the **diopter window,** there is no lens in position in the slit. The depth of focus for viewing the eye interior is changed by changing the lens.

The light is turned on by depressing the red **rheostat lock** button and then rotating the rheostat control in the clockwise direction. The aperture selection disc on the front of the instrument allows the nature of the light beam to be altered. Generally, green light allows for clearest viewing of the blood vessels in the eye interior and is most comfortable for the subject. Now that you are familiar with the ophthalmoscope, you are ready to conduct an eye examination.

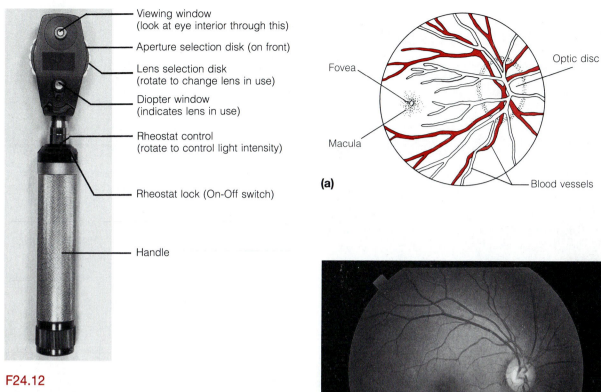

Viewing window
(look at eye interior through this)

Aperture selection disk (on front)

Lens selection disk
(rotate to change lens in use)

Diopter window
(indicates lens in use)

Rheostat control
(rotate to control light intensity)

Rheostat lock (On-Off switch)

Handle

F24.12

Structure of an opthalmoscope.

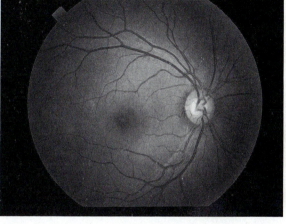

Fovea

Macula

Optic disc

Blood vessels

(a)

(b)

F24.13

Posterior portion of right retina. (a) Diagram.
(b) Photograph taken with slit-lamp camera.

1.   Conduct the examination in a dimly lit or darkened room with the subject comfortably seated and gazing straight ahead. To examine the right eye, sit face-to-face with the subject, and hold the instrument in your right hand. Use your right eye to view the eye interior. To view the left eye, use your left eye, and hold the instrument in your left hand. When the opthalmoscope is correctly set, the fundus of the right eye should appear as shown in Figure 24.13.

2.   Begin the examination with the 0 (no lens) in position. Hold the instrument so that the lens disc may be rotated with the index finger. Hold the ophthalmoscope about 6 inches from the subject's eye, and direct the light into the pupil at a slight angle—through the pupil edge rather than directly through its center. You will see a red circular area that is the illuminated eye interior.

3.   Move in as close as possible to the subject's cornea as you continue to observe the area. Steady your instrument-holding hand on the subject's cheek if necessary. If both your eye and that of the subject are normal, the fundus can be viewed clearly without further adjustment of the ophthalmoscope. If the fundus cannot be focused, slowly rotate the lens disc counterclockwise until the fundus can be clearly seen. (Note: If a positive (convex) lens is required and your eyes are normal, the subject has hyperopia. If a negative (concave) lens is necessary

to view the fundus and your eyes are normal, the subject is myopic.)

When the examination is proceeding correctly, the subject can often see images of retinal vessels in his own eye that appear rather like cracked glass. If you are unable to achieve a sharp focus or to see the optic disc, move medially or laterally and begin again.

4.   Examine the optic disc for color, elevation, and sharpness of outline, and observe the blood vessels radiating from near its center. Locate the macula, which is lateral to the optic disc. It is a darker area in which blood vessels are absent, and the fovea appears to be a slightly lighter area in its center. The macula is most easily seen when the subject looks directly into the light of the ophthalmoscope.

Special Senses: Hearing and Equilibrium

ANATOMY OF THE EAR

Gross Anatomy

The ear is a complex structure containing sensory receptors for hearing and equilibrium. The ear is divided into three major areas: the **outer** or **external ear,** the **middle ear,** and the **inner ear** (Figure 25.1). The outer and middle ear structures serve the needs of the sense of hearing *only,* while inner ear structures function both in equilibrium and hearing reception.

Obtain a dissectible ear model and identify the structures described below. Refer to Figure 25.1 as you work.

The outer ear is composed primarily of the **pinna,** or **auricle,** and the **external auditory canal.** The pinna is the skin-covered cartilaginous structure encircling the auditory canal opening. In many animals, it collects and directs sound waves into the auditory canal. In humans this function of the pinna is largely lost.

The external auditory canal is a short, narrow (about 1 inch long by ¼ inch wide) chamber carved into the temporal bone. In its skin-lined walls are wax-secreting glands called **ceruminous glands.** The sound waves that enter the external auditory canal eventually encounter the **tympanic membrane,** or **eardrum,** which vibrates at exactly the same frequency as the sound wave(s) hitting it. The membranous eardrum separates the outer from the middle ear.

The middle ear is essentially a small chamber—the **tympanic cavity**—found within the temporal bone. The cavity is spanned by three small bones, collectively called the **ossicles** (hammer, anvil, and stirrup),* which articulate to form a lever system that transmits the vibratory motion of the eardrum to the fluids of the inner ear via the **oval window.**

Connecting the middle ear chamber with the nasopharynx is the **auditory,** or **eustachian, tube.** Normally

---

* The ossicles are often referred to by their Latin names, that is, **malleus, incus,** and **stapes,** respectively.

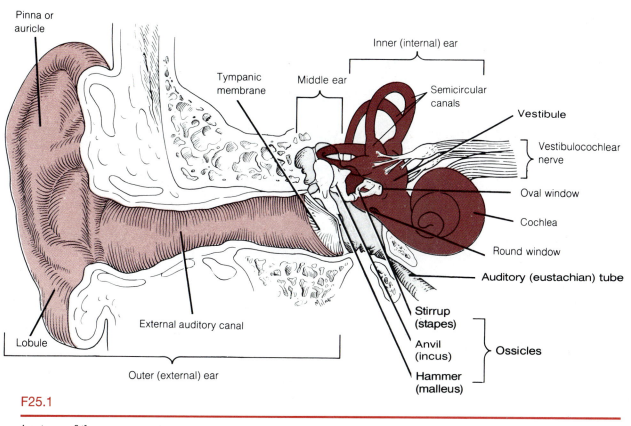

F25.1

Anatomy of the ear.

this tube is flattened and closed, but swallowing or yawning can cause it to open temporarily to equalize the pressure of the middle ear cavity with external air pressure. This is an important function, since the eardrum does not vibrate properly unless the pressure on both of its surfaces is the same.

Because the mucosal membranes of the middle ear cavity and the nasopharynx are continuous through the eustachian tube, **otitis media,** or inflammation of the middle ear, is a fairly common condition, especially among youngsters prone to sore throats. In cases where large amounts of fluid or pus accumulate in the middle ear cavity, an emergency myringotomy (lancing of the eardrum) may be necessary to relieve the pressure. Frequently, tiny ventilating tubes are put in during the procedure. ■

EustachianTube   # 44765

TympanostomyTube   # 13170

The inner ear consists of a system of bony and rather tortuous chambers called the **osseous,** or **bony, labyrinth,** which is filled with an aqueous fluid called perilymph (Figure 25.2). Suspended in the perilymph is the **membranous labyrinth,** a system that mostly follows the contours of the osseous labyrinth. The interior of the membranous labyrinth is filled with a more viscous fluid called **endolymph.** The three subdivisions of the bony labyrinth are the **cochlea,** the **vestibule,** and the **semicircular canals,** with the vestibule situated between the cochlea and semicircular canals.

The snail-like cochlea (see Figures 25.2 and 25.3) contains the sensory receptors for hearing. The cochlear membranous labyrinth, the **cochlear duct,** is a soft wormlike tube about 1½ inches long. It winds through the full two and three-quarter turns of the cochlea and separates the perilymph-containing cochlear cavity into upper and lower chambers, the **scala vestibuli** and **scala tympani,** respectively. The scala vestibuli terminates at the oval window, which "seats" the foot plate of the stirrup located laterally in the tympanic cavity. The scala tympani is bounded by a membranous area called the **round window.** The cochlear duct, itself filled with endolymph, supports the **organ of Corti,** which contains the receptors for hearing—the sensory hair cells and nerve endings of the cochlear division of the vestibulocochlear nerve (VIII).

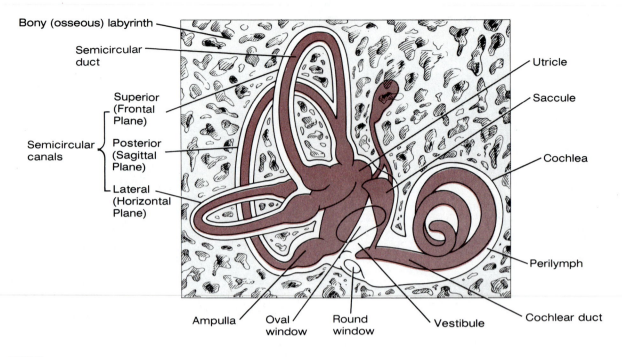

Bony (osseous) labyrinth

Semicircular duct

Superior (Frontal Plane)

Semicircular canals

Posterior (Sagittal Plane)

Lateral (Horizontal Plane)

Utricle

Saccule

Cochlea

Perilymph

Ampulla   Oval window   Round window   Vestibule   Cochlear duct

F25.2

Inner ear. Right membranous labyrinth shown within the bony labyrinth.

Otoscopic Examination of the Ear (Optional)

1. Obtain an otoscope and two alcohol swabs. Inspect your partner's ear canal and then select the largest-*diameter* (not length!) speculum that will fit comfortably into his or her ear to permit full visibility. Clean the speculum thoroughly with an alcohol swab, and then attach it to the battery-containing otoscope handle. Before beginning, check that the otoscope light beam is strong. (If not, obtain another otoscope or new batteries.)

2. Hold the lighted otoscope securely between your thumb and forefinger (like a pencil), and rest the little finger of the otoscope-holding hand against your partner's head when you are ready to begin the examination. This maneuver forms a brace that allows the speculum to move as your partner moves and prevents the speculum from penetrating too deeply into the ear canal during unexpected movements.

3. Grasp the ear pinna firmly and pull it up, back, and slightly laterally. If your partner experiences pain or discomfort when the pinna is manipulated, an inflammation or infection of the external ear may be present. If this occurs, do not attempt to examine the ear canal.

4. Carefully insert the speculum of the otoscope into the external auditory canal in a downward and forward direction only far enough to permit examination of the tympanic membrane or eardrum. Note its shape, color, and vascular network. The healthy tympanic membrane is pearly white. During the examination, note if there is any discharge or redness in the canal and identify earwax.

5. After the examination, thoroughly clean the speculum with the second alcohol swab before returning it to the supply area.

Tympanic Membrane   # 44819

Tympanic Membrane,   # 44863
Otoscopic View

Microscopic Anatomy of the Receptors

ORGAN OF CORTI AND THE MECHANISM OF HEARING   The anatomical details of the organ of Corti are shown in Figure 25.3. The hair (auditory receptor) cells rest on the **basilar membrane,** which forms the floor of the cochlear duct, and their "hairs" (stereocilia) project into a gelatinous membrane, the **tectorial membrane,** that overlies them. The roof of the cochlear duct is called the **vestibular membrane.** The endolymph-filled chamber of the cochlear duct is the **scala media.**

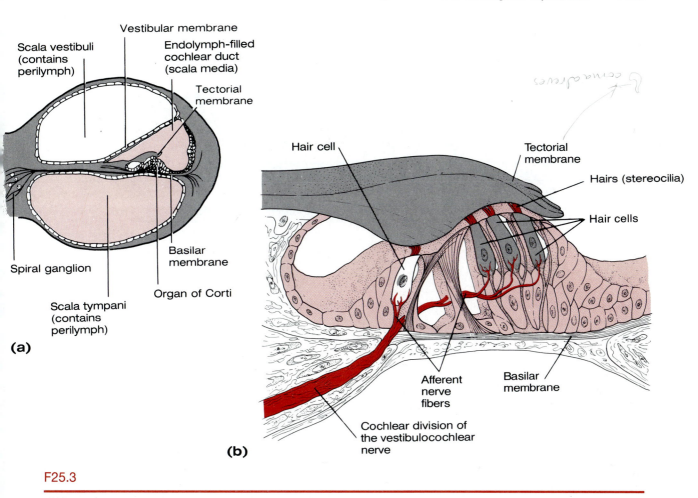

(a)

(b)

F25.3

Organ of Corti. (a) Cross section through one turn of the cochlea showing the position of the organ of Corti. (b) Enlarged view of the organ of Corti. Corresponding photomicrographs are Plates 14 and 15 respectively in the Histology Atlas.

Organ of Corti	# 01376
Cochlear Nerve Within Cochlea	# 01346

Obtain a compound microscope and a prepared microscope slide of the cochlea and identify the areas shown in Figure 25.3a and b.

The mechanism of hearing begins as sound waves pass through the external auditory canal and through the middle ear into the inner ear, where the vibration eventually reaches the organ of Corti, which contains the receptors for hearing. Many theories have attempted to explain how the organ of Corti actually responds to sound.

The popular "traveling wave" hypothesis of Von Békésy suggests that vibration of the stirrup at the oval window initiates traveling waves that cause maximal

displacements of the basilar membrane where they peak and stimulate the hair cells of the organ of Corti in that region. Since the area at which the traveling waves peak is a high-pressure area, the vestibular membrane is compressed at this point and, in turn, compresses the endolymph and the basilar membrane of the cochlear duct. The resulting pressure on the perilymph in the scala tympani causes the membrane of the round window to bulge outward into the middle ear chamber, thus acting as a relief valve for the compressional wave (Figure 25.4). Von Békésy found that high-frequency waves (high-pitched sounds) peaked close to the oval window and that low-frequency waves (low-pitched sounds) peaked farther up the basilar membrane near the apex of the cochlea. Although the mechanism of sound reception by the organ of Corti is not completely understood, we do know that hair cells on the basilar membrane are uniquely stimulated by sounds of various frequencies and amplitude and that once stimulated they depolarize and begin the chain of nervous impulses to the auditory centers of the temporal lobe cortex. This series of events results in the phenomenon we call hearing.

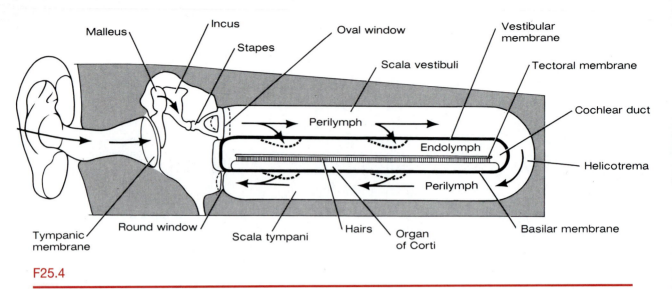

Fluid movement in the cochlea following stirrup thrust on the oval window. Compressional wave created causes the round window to bulge into the middle ear.

Middle Ear Transformer   # 44883

SoundTransmission, Inner Ear   # 44909

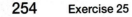

By the time most people are in their 60s, a gradual deterioration and atrophy of the organ of Corti begins, and leads to a loss in the ability to hear high tones and speech sounds. This condition, **presbycusis,** is a type of sensorineural deafness. Because many elderly people refuse to accept their hearing loss and resist using hearing aids, they begin to rely more and more on their vision for clues as to what is going on around them, and may be accused of ignoring people.

Although presbycusis is considered to be a disability of old age, it is becoming much more common in younger people as our world grows noisier. The damage (breakage of the ''hairs'' of the hair cells) caused by excessively loud sounds is progressive and cumulative. Each assault causes a bit more damage. Rock music played and listened to at deafening levels is definitely a contributing factor to the deterioration of hearing receptors. ■

EQUILIBRIUM APPARATUS AND MECHANISMS OF EQUILIBRIUM

The equilibrium apparatus of the inner ear is in the vestibular and semicircular canal portions of the bony labyrinth. Their chambers are filled with perilymph, in which membranous labyrinth structures are suspended. The vestibule contains the saclike **utricle** and **saccule,** and the semicircular chambers contain **membranous semicircular ducts.** Like the cochlear duct, these membranes are filled with endolymph and contain receptor cells that are activated by the disturbance of their cilia.

The semicircular canals are centrally involved in the **mechanism of dynamic equilibrium.** They are about ½ inch in circumference and are oriented in three planes—horizontal, frontal, and sagittal. At the base of each semicircular duct is an enlarged region, the **ampulla,** which communicates with the utricle of the vestibule. Within each ampulla is a receptor region called a **crista ampullaris,** which consists of a tuft of hair cells covered with a gelatinous cap, or **cupula** (Figure 25.5). When your head position changes in an angular direction, as when twirling on the dance floor or when taking a rough boat ride, the endolymph in the canal lags behind, pushing the cupula—like a swinging door—in a direction opposite to that of the angular motion. This movement initiates an action potential in the hair cells. These impulses are then transmitted up the vestibular division of the eighth cranial nerve to the brain. Likewise, when the angular motion stops suddenly, the inertia of the endolymph causes it to continue to move, pushing the cupula in the same direction as the previous motion. This movement again initiates electrical changes in the hair cells. (This phenomenon accounts for the reversed motion sensation you feel when you stop suddenly after twirling.) If you begin to move at a constant rate of motion, the cupula gradually returns to its original position. The hair cells, no longer bent, send no new signals, and you lose the sensation of spinning. Thus the response of these dynamic equilibrium receptors is a reaction to *changes* in angular motion rather than to motion itself.

Crista Ampullaris, Deflected   # 44920

Vestibular Nerve Endings   # 44923

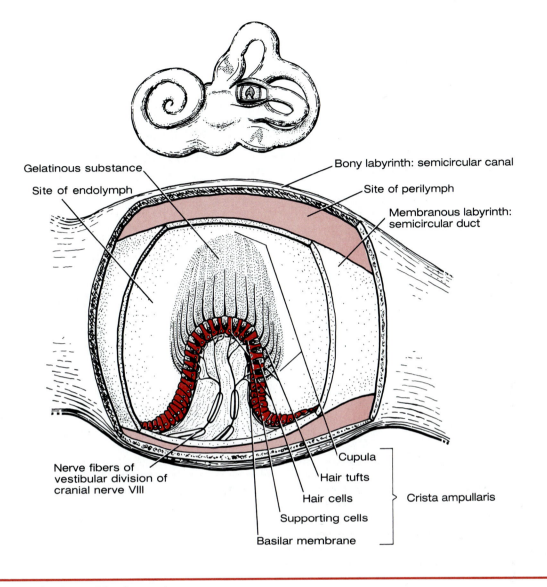

F25.5

Crista ampullaris in the semicircular canal.

Go to the demonstration area and examine the slide of a crista ampullaris. Identify the areas depicted in Figure 25.5.

The vestibule contains **maculae,** receptors that are essential to the **mechanism of static equilibrium.** The maculae respond to gravitational pull, thus providing information on which way is up or down, and to linear or straightforward changes in speed. They are located on the walls of the saccule and utricle. The **otolithic membrane,** a gelatinous material containing small grains of calcium carbonate (**otoliths**), overrides the hair cells in each macula. As the head moves, the otoliths move in response to variations in gravitational pull (Figure 25.6). As they deflect different hair cells, they trigger nerve impulses along the vestibular nerve.

Although the receptors of the semicircular canals and the vestibule are responsible for dynamic and static equilibrium, respectively, they rarely act independently. Complex interaction of many of the receptors is the rule. Also, the information these equilibrium, or balance, senses provide is significantly augmented by the proprioceptors and sight, as some of the following laboratory experiments demonstrate.

Hair Cell Deflection,   # 44922
Vestibular Apparatus

☯ LABORATORY TESTS

Hearing Tests

Perform the following hearing tests in a quiet area.

ACUITY TEST   Have your lab partner pack one ear with cotton and sit quietly with eyes closed. Obtain a

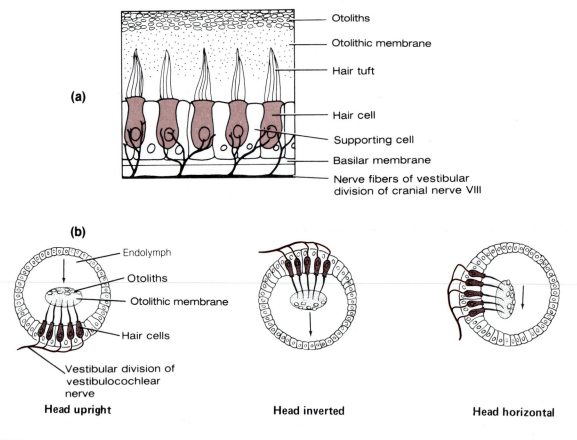

(a)

Otoliths
Otolithic membrane
Hair tuft
Hair cell
Supporting cell
Basilar membrane
Nerve fibers of vestibular division of cranial nerve VIII

(b)

Endolymph
Otoliths
Otolithic membrane
Hair cells
Vestibular division of vestibulocochlear nerve

Head upright   **Head inverted**   **Head horizontal**

F25.6

Structure and function of static equilibrium receptors (maculae). (a) Diagrammatic view of a portion of a macula. (b) Stimulation of the maculae by movement of otoliths in the gelatinous otolithic membrane that creates a pull on the hair cells. Arrows indicate direction of gravitational pull.

ticking clock or pocket watch and hold it very close to his or her unpacked ear. Then slowly move it away from the ear until your partner signals that the ticking is no longer audible. Record the distance in inches at which ticking is inaudible.

Right ear _____ Left ear _____

Is the threshold of audibility sharp or indefinite?

_____

SOUND LOCALIZATION   Ask your partner to close both eyes. Hold the pocket watch at an audible distance (about 6 inches) from his or her ear, and move it to various locations (front, back, sides, and above his or her head). Have your partner locate the position by pointing in each instance. Can the sound be localized equally well at all positions?

_____ If not, at what position(s) was the sound less easily located?

_____

_____

The ability to localize the source of a sound depends on two factors—the difference in the loudness of the sound reaching each ear and the time of arrival of the sound at each ear. How does this information help to explain your findings?

_____

_____

_____

FREQUENCY RANGE OF HEARING   Obtain three tuning forks: one with a low frequency (75 to 100 cps), one with a frequency of approximately 1000 cps, and one with a frequency of 4000 to 5000 cps. Strike the lowest-frequency fork on the heel of your hand or with a rubber mallet, and hold it close to your partner's ear. Repeat with the other two forks.

Which fork was heard most clearly and comfortably?

_____ cps

Which was heard least well? _____ cps

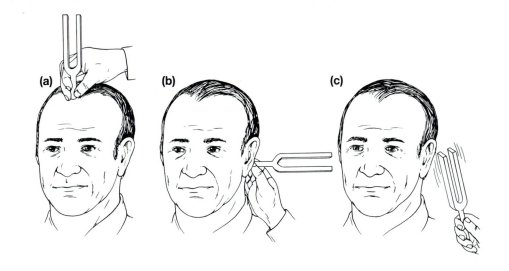

F25.7

The Weber and Rinne tuning fork tests. (a) The Weber test to evaluate whether the sound remains centralized (normal) or lateralizes to one side or the other (indicative of some degree of conductive or sensorineural deafness). (b and c) The Rinne test to compare bone conduction and air conduction.

WEBER TEST TO DETERMINE CONDUCTIVE AND PERCEPTIVE DEAFNESS
Strike a tuning fork and place the handle of the tuning fork medially on your forehead (see Figure 25.7a). Is the tone equally loud in both ears, or is it louder in one ear?

_____

If it is equally loud in both ears, you have equal hearing or equal loss of hearing in both ears. If perceptive (sensorineural) deafness is present in one ear, the tone will be heard in the unaffected ear, but not in the ear with sensorineural deafness. If conduction deafness is present, the sound will be heard more strongly in the ear in which there is a hearing loss. Conduction deafness can be simulated by plugging one ear with cotton to interfere with the conduction of sound to the inner ear.

RINNE TEST FOR COMPARING BONE- AND AIR-CONDUCTION HEARING

1. Strike the tuning fork, and place its handle on your partner's mastoid process (Figure 25.7b).
2. When your partner indicates that the sound is no longer audible, hold the still-vibrating prongs close to his auditory canal (Figure 25.7c). If your partner hears the fork again (by air conduction) when it is moved to that position, hearing is not impaired and the test result is to be recorded as positive (+). (Record below.)
3. Repeat the test, but this time test air conduction hearing first.
4. After the tone is no longer heard by air conduction, hold the handle of the tuning fork on the bony mastoid process. If the subject hears the tone again by bone conduction after hearing by air conduction is lost, there is some conductive deafness and the result is recorded as negative (−).
5. Repeat the sequence for the opposite ear.

Right ear _____ Left ear _____

Does the subject hear better by bone or by air conduction?

_____

Audiometry

When the simple tuning fork tests reveal a problem in hearing, audiometer testing is usually prescribed to determine the precise nature of the hearing deficit. An *audiometer* is an instrument (specifically, an electronic oscillator with earphones) used to determine hearing acuity by exposing each ear to sound stimuli of differing *frequencies* and *intensities*. The hearing range of human beings during youth is from 30 to 22,000 cps, but hearing acuity declines with age, with reception for the high frequency sounds lost first. Though this loss represents a major problem for some people, such as musicians, most of us tend to be fairly unconcerned until we begin to have problems hearing sounds in the range of 125 to 8000 cps, the normal frequency range of speech.

The basic procedure of audiometry is to initially deliver tones of different frequencies to one ear of the subject at an intensity of 0 decibels (db). (Zero decibels is not the complete absence of sound, but rather the softest sound intensity that can be heard by a person of normal hearing at each frequency.) If the subject cannot hear a particular frequency stimulus of 0 db, the hearing threshold level control is adjusted until the subject reports that he or she can hear the tone. The number of decibels of intensity required above 0 db is recorded as the hearing loss. For example, if the subject cannot hear a particular frequency tone until it is delivered at 30 db intensity, then he or she has a hearing loss of 30 db for that frequency.

 1. Before beginning the tests, examine the audiometer to identify the two tone controls: one to regulate frequency and a second to regulate the intensity (loudness) of the sound stimulus. Also identify the two output control switches that regulate the delivery of sound to one ear or the other (*red* to the

257

right ear, *blue* to the left ear). Also find the *hearing threshold level control,* which is calibrated to deliver a basal tone of 0 db to the subject's ears.

2.   Place the earphones on the subject's head so that the red cord or ear-cushion is over the right ear and the blue cord or ear-cushion is over the left ear. Instruct the subject to raise one hand when he or she hears a tone.

3.   Set the frequency control at 125 cps and the intensity control at 0 db. Press the red output switch to deliver a tone to the subject's right ear. If the subject does not respond, raise the sound intensity slowly by rotating the hearing level control counterclockwise until the subject reports (by raising a hand) that a tone is heard. Repeat this procedure for frequencies of 250, 500, 1000, 2000, 4000, and 8000.

4.   Record the results in the chart below by marking a small red circle on the chart at each frequency-db junction indicated. Then connect the circles with a red line to produce a hearing acuity graph for the right ear.

5.   Repeat steps 3 and 4 for the left (blue) ear and record the results with blue circles and connecting lines on the chart.

Equilibrium Experiments

The function of the semicircular canals and vestibule are not routinely tested in the laboratory, but the following simple tests should serve to illustrate normal equilibrium apparatus functioning.

BALANCE TEST   Have your partner walk a straight line, placing one foot directly in front of the other.

Is he or she able to walk without undue wobbling from side to side?

_____

Did he or she experience any dizziness? _____

The ability to walk with balance and without dizziness, unless subject to rotational forces, indicates normal function of the equilibrium apparatus.

Was nystagmus* present? _____

BARANY TEST (INDUCTION OF NYSTAGMUS AND VERTIGO†)   This experiment evaluates the semicircular canals and should be conducted as a group effort to protect test subject(s) from possible injury.

⚠ The following precautionary notes should be read before beginning:

● The subject(s) chosen should not be easily inclined to dizziness during rotational or turning movements.
● Rotation should be stopped immediately if the subject complains of feeling nauseous.
● Because the subject(s) will experience vertigo and loss of balance as a result of the rotation, several classmates should be prepared to catch, hold, or support the subject(s) as necessary until the symptoms pass.

1.   Instruct the subject to sit on a rotating chair or stool, and to hold on to the arms or seat of the chair, feet on stool rungs. The subject's head should be tilted forward approximately 30 degrees (almost touching the chest).

---

* **Nystagmus** is the involuntary rolling of the eyes in any direction or the trailing of the eyes slowly in one direction, followed by their rapid movement in the opposite direction. It is normal after rotation; abnormal otherwise. The direction of nystagmus is that of its quick phase on acceleration.

† **Vertigo** is a sensation of dizziness and rotational movement when such movement is not occurring or has ceased.

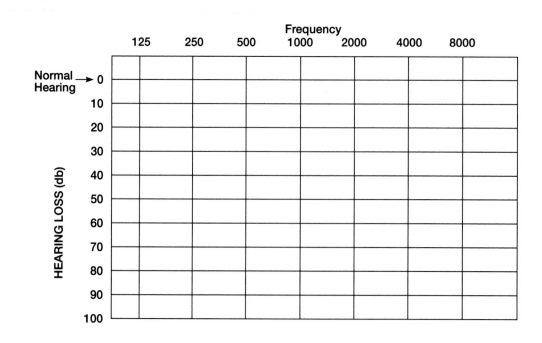

The horizontal (lateral) semicircular canal will be stimulated when the head is in this position. The subject's eyes are to remain *open* during the test.

2.   Four classmates should position themselves so that the subject is surrounded on all sides. The classmate posterior to the subject will rotate the chair.

3.   Rotate the chair to the subject's right approximately 10 revolutions in 10 seconds, and then suddenly stop the rotation.

4.   Immediately note the direction of the subject's resultant nystagmus; and ask him or her to describe the feelings of movement, indicating speed and direction sensation. Record below.

_____

_____

_____

_____

If the semicircular canals are operating normally, the subject will experience a sensation that the stool is still rotating immediately after it has stopped and *will* demonstrate nystagmus.

When the subject is rotated to the right, the cupula will be bent to the left, causing nystagmus during rotation in which the eyes initially move slowly to the left and then quickly to the right. Nystagmus will continue until the cupula has returned to its initial position. Then, when rotation is stopped abruptly, the cupula will be bent to the right, producing nystagmus with its slow phase to the right and its rapid phase to the left. In many subjects, this will be accompanied by a feeling of vertigo and a tendency to fall to the right.

ROMBERG TEST   The Romberg test determines the integrity of the dorsal white column of the spinal cord, which transmits impulses to the brain from the proprioceptors involved with posture.

1.   Have your partner stand with his or her back to the blackboard.

2.   Draw one line parallel to each side of your partner's body. He or she should stand erect, with eyes open and staring straight ahead for 2 minutes while you observe any movements. Did you see any gross swaying movements?

_____

3.   Repeat the test. This time the subject's eyes should be closed. Note and record the degree of side-to-side movement.

_____

4.   Repeat the test with the subject's eyes first open and then closed. This time, however, the subject should be positioned with his or her left shoulder toward, but not touching, the board so that you may observe and record the degree of front-to-back swaying.

_____

Do you think the equilibrium apparatus of the inner ear was operating equally well in all these tests?

_____

The proprioceptors? _____

Why was the observed degree of swaying greater when the eyes were closed?

_____

_____

_____

What conclusions can you draw regarding the factors necessary for maintaining body equilibrium and balance?

_____

_____

_____

_____

ROLE OF VISION IN MAINTAINING EQUILIBRIUM   To further demonstrate the role of vision in maintaining equilibrium, perform the following experiment. (Ask your lab partner to record observations and act as a "spotter.") Stand erect, with your eyes open. Raise your left foot approximately 1 foot off the floor, and hold it there for 1 minute.

Record the observations: _____

_____

_____

Rest for 1 or 2 minutes; and then repeat the experiment with the same foot raised, but with your eyes closed. Record the observations:

_____

_____

_____

Special Senses: Taste and Olfaction

The receptors for taste and olfaction are classified as **chemoreceptors** because they respond to chemicals or volatile substances in solution. Although four relatively specific types of taste receptors have been identified, the olfactory receptors are considered sensitive to a much wider range of chemical sensations. The sense of smell is the least understood of the special senses.

LOCALIZATION AND ANATOMY OF TASTE BUDS

The **taste buds,** specific receptors for the sense of taste, are widely but not uniformly distributed in the oral cavity. Most are located on the dorsal surface of the tongue (as described next). A few are found on the soft palate, epiglottis, and inner surface of the cheeks.

The dorsal tongue surface is covered with small projections, or **papillae,** of three major types: sharp *filiform papillae* and the rounded *fungiform* and *circumvallate papillae.* The taste buds are located primarily on the sides of the circumvallate papillae (arranged in a V-for-

mation on the posterior surface of the tongue) and on the more numerous fungiform papillae. The latter look rather like minute mushrooms and are widely distributed on the tongue. (See Figure 26.1.)

● Use a mirror to examine your tongue. Can you pick out the various papillae types?

_____ If so, which? _____

_____

Each taste bud consists largely of a globular arrangement of two types of modified epithelial cells: the **gustatory,** or **taste cells,** which are the actual receptor cells, and **supporting cells.** Several nerve fibers enter each taste bud and supply sensory nerve endings to each of the taste cells. The long microvilli of the receptor cells penetrate the epithelial surface through an opening called the **taste pore.** When these microvilli (called *gustatory hairs*) contact specific chemicals in the solution, the taste cells depolarize. The afferent fibers from the taste buds to the sensory cortex in the postcentral gyrus

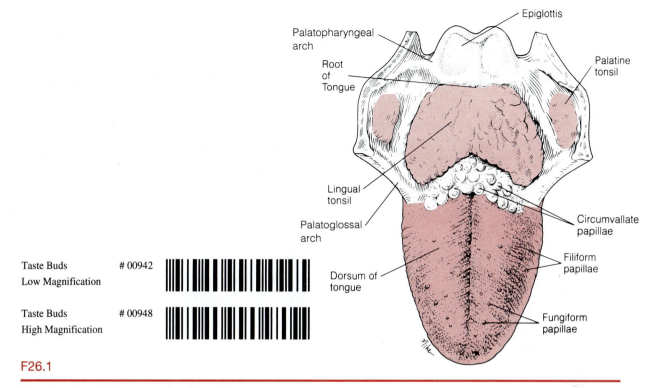

F26.1

Dorsal surface of the tongue, showing major structures.

of the brain are carried in three cranial nerves: the *facial nerve* (*VII*) serves the anterior two-thirds of the tongue; the *glossopharyngeal nerve* (*IX*) serves the posterior third of the tongue; and the *vagus nerve* (*X*) carries a few fibers from the pharyngeal region.

Obtain a microscope and a prepared slide of a tongue cross section. Use Figure 26.2 as a guide to aid you in locating the taste buds on the tongue papillae. Make a detailed study of one taste bud. Identify the taste pore and gustatory hairs if observed.

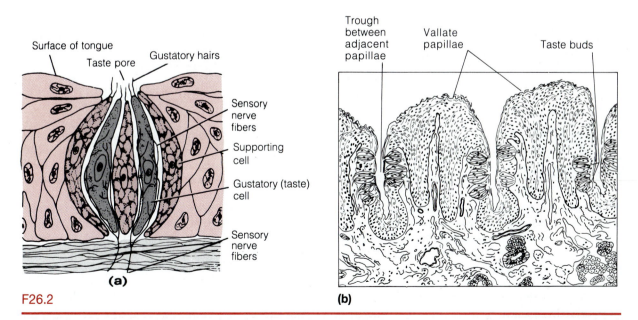

F26.2

Taste bud anatomy and localization. (a) Diagrammatic view of taste bud; (b) View of tongue papillae, showing position of taste buds. See Plate 16 in the Histology Atlas for corresponding photomicrograph.

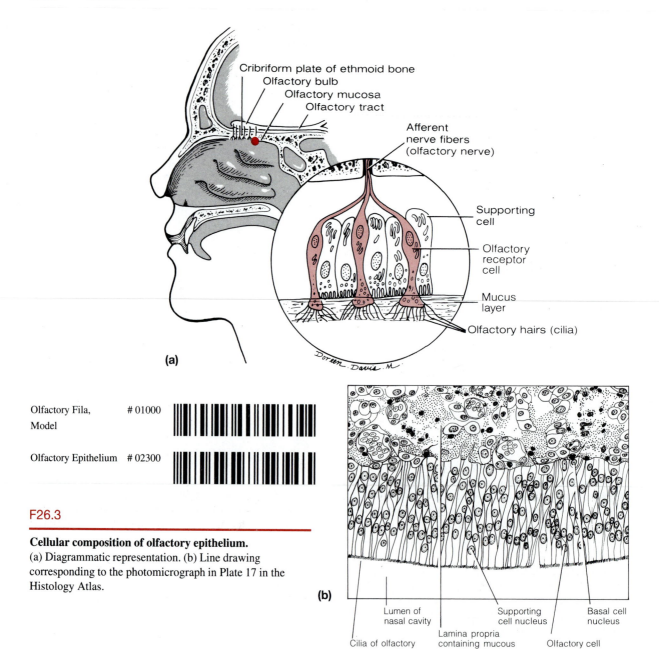

Olfactory Fila,   # 01000
Model

Olfactory Epithelium   # 02300

F26.3

Cellular composition of olfactory epithelium.
(a) Diagrammatic representation. (b) Line drawing
corresponding to the photomicrograph in Plate 17 in the
Histology Atlas.

(b)

Cilia of olfactory
receptor cells

Lumen of
nasal cavity

Lamina propria
containing mucous
secreting glands

Supporting
cell nucleus

Olfactory cell
nucleus

Basal cell
nucleus

LOCALIZATION AND ANATOMY OF THE OLFACTORY RECEPTORS

The **olfactory epithelium** (organ of smell) occupies an area of about 2.5 cm in the roof of each nasal cavity. Since the air entering the human nasal cavity must make a hairpin turn to enter the respiratory passages below, the nasal epithelium is in a rather poor position for performing its function. This is why sniffing, which brings a greater airflow into contact with the receptors, intensifies the sense of smell.

The specialized receptor cells in the olfactory epithelium are surrounded by **supporting cells,** nonsensory epithelial cells. The **olfactory receptor cells** are bipolar neurons whose *olfactory hairs* (actually cilia) extend outward from the epithelium. Emerging from their basal ends are axonal nerve fibers that penetrate the cribriform plate of the ethmoid bone and proceed as the olfactory nerves to synapse in the olfactory bulbs lying on either side of the crista galli of the ethmoid bone. Impulses from neurons of the olfactory bulbs are then conveyed to the olfactory portion of the cortex (uncus).

Obtain a longitudinal section of olfactory epithelium. Examine it closely, comparing it to Figure 26.3.

LABORATORY EXPERIMENTS

Stimulation of Taste Buds

1. Obtain several paper towels and a disposable autoclave bag and bring them to your bench.

2. With a paper towel, dry the dorsal surface of your tongue.

Immediately dispose of the paper towel in the autoclave bag.

3. Place a few sugar crystals on your dried tongue. Do *not* close your mouth. Time how long it takes to taste the sugar.

_____90_____ sec

Why couldn't you taste the sugar immediately?

_____

_____

Plotting Taste Bud Distribution

There are four basic taste sensations, which correspond to the stimulation of four major types of taste buds. Although all taste buds are believed to respond in some degree to all four classes of chemical stimuli, each type responds optimally to only one. This characteristic makes it possible to map the tongue to show the relative density of each type of taste bud.

The *sweet receptors* respond to a number of seemingly unrelated compounds such as sugars (fructose, sucrose, glucose), saccharine, and some amino acids. Some believe the common factor is the hydroxyl (OH^-) group. *Sour receptors* respond to hydrogen ions (H^+) or the acidity of the solution, *bitter receptors* to alkaloids, and *salty receptors* to metallic ions in solution.

1. Prepare to make a taste sensation map of your lab partner's tongue by obtaining the following: cotton-tipped swabs, one vial each of NaCl, quinine or Epsom salt solution, sucrose solution, acetic acid, paper cups, and a flask of distilled or tap water.

2. Before each test, the subject should rinse his or her mouth thoroughly with water and lightly dry his or her tongue with a paper towel.

Dispose of used paper towels in the autoclave bag.

3. Moisten a swab with 5% sucrose solution and touch it to the center, back, tip, and sides of the dorsal surface of the subject's tongue.

4. Map, with an O on the tongue outline below, the location of the sweet receptors.

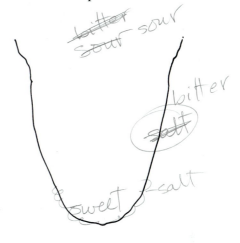

Put the used swab in the autoclave bag.

5. Repeat the procedure with quinine (or Epsom salt solution) to map the location of the bitter receptors (use the symbol B), with NaCl to map the salt receptors (symbol +), and with acetic acid to map the sour receptors (symbol −).

Use a fresh swab for each test, and properly dispose of the swabs immediately after use.

What area of the dorsum of the tongue seems to lack taste receptors?

_____

How closely does your localization of the different taste receptors coincide with the information in your textbook?

_____

_____

Combined Effects of Smell, Texture, and Temperature on Taste

1. Ask the subject to sit with eyes closed and to pinch his or her nostrils shut.

2. Using a paper plate, obtain samples of the food items listed in the chart below. At no time should the subject be allowed to see the foods being tested.

3. Use an out-of-sequence order of food testing. For each test, place a cube of food in the subject's mouth and ask him or her to identify the food by using the following sequence of activities:

- First, by manipulating the food with the tongue
- Second, by chewing the food
- Third, if a positive identification is not made with the first two techniques and the taste sense, ask the subject to release the pinched nostrils and to continue chewing with the nostrils open to determine if a positive identification can be made.

Record the results on the chart by checking the appropriate column.

Was the sense of smell equally important in all cases?

_____

Where did it seem to be important and why?

_____

_____

Effect of Olfactory Stimulation on Taste

There is no question that what is commonly referred to as the sense of taste depends heavily on stimulation of the olfactory receptors, particularly in the case of strongly odoriferous substances. The following experiment should illustrate this fact.

1. Obtain vials of oil of wintergreen, peppermint, and cloves and some fresh cotton-tipped swabs. Ask the subject to sit so that he cannot see which vial is being used, and to dry his tongue and close his nostrils.
2. Apply a drop of one of the oils to his tongue. Can he distinguish the flavor?

    yes   peppermint

3. Have the subject open his nostrils and record the change in sensation he reports.

    _____

4. Have the subject rinse his mouth well and dry his tongue.
5. Prepare two swabs, each with one of the two remaining oils.
6. Hold one swab under the subject's open nostrils, _vanil_ while touching the second swab to his tongue. _— maple_

    Record the reported sensations. _____

    did not taste the maple

    smell — maple

    _____

Method of Identification

Food	Texture only	Chewing with nostrils pinched	Chewing with nostrils open	Identification not made
Cheese	_____	_____	_____	_____
Apple	_____	_____	_____	_____
Raw potato	_____	_____	_____	_____
Banana	_____	_____	_____	_____
Dried prunes	_____	_____	_____	_____
Raw carrot	_____	_____	_____	_____
Hard-cooked egg white	_____	_____	_____	_____

7. Dispose of the used swabs in the autoclave bag before continuing.

Which sense, taste or smell, appears to be more important in the proper identification of a strongly flavored volatile substance?

_____

● In addition to the effect that olfaction and textural factors play in determining our taste sensations, the temperature of foods also helps determine if the food is appreciated or even tasted. To illustrate this, have your partner hold some chipped ice on the tongue for approximately a minute and then close his or her eyes. Immediately place any of the foods previously identified in his or her mouth and ask for an identification.

Results? _____

Olfactory Adaptation

Obtain some absorbent cotton and two of the following oils (oil of wintergreen, peppermint, or cloves). Press one nostril shut. Hold the bottle of oil under the open nostril and exhale through the mouth. Record the time required for the odor to disappear (for olfactory adaptation to occur).

_____15_____ sec   peppermint

Repeat the procedure with the other nostril.

_____15_____ sec

Immediately test another oil with the nostril that has just experienced olfactory adaptation. What are the results?

10sec (vanilla)

_____

What conclusions can you draw? _____

_____

_____

GROSS ANATOMY AND BASIC FUNCTION OF THE ENDOCRINE GLANDS

As the endocrine organs are described, *locate and identify them by name* on Figure 27.2. When you have completed the descriptive material, also locate the organs on the anatomical charts or torso.

Pituitary Gland (Hypophysis)

The pituitary gland, or hypophysis, is located in the concavity of the sella turcica of the sphenoid bone. It consists largely of two functional areas, the **adenohypophysis,** or **anterior pituitary,** and the **neurohypophysis,** or **posterior pituitary,** and is attached to the hypothalamus by a stalk called the **infundibulum.**

ADENOHYPOPHYSEAL HORMONES The adenohypophyseal hormones include the following tropic hormones or hormone groups: The **gonadotropins**—

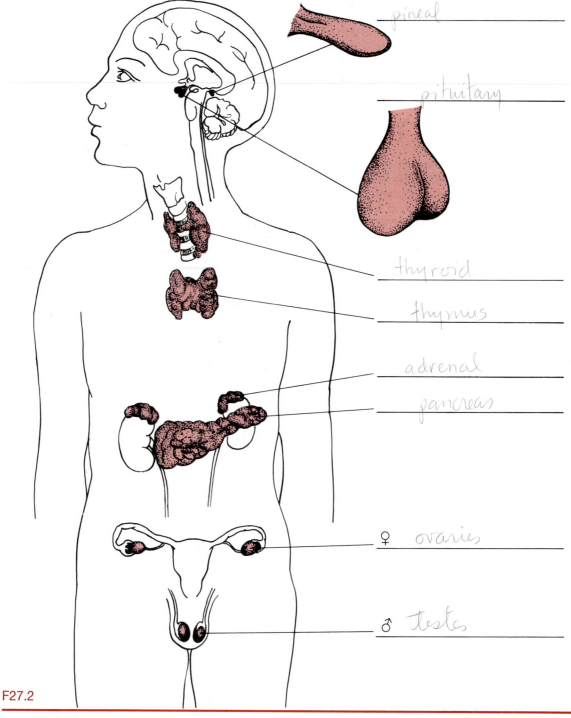

pineal

pituitary

thyroid

thymus

adrenal

pancreas

♀ ovaries

♂ testes

F27.2

Human endocrine organs.

follicle-stimulating hormone (FSH) and luteinizing hormone (LH)—regulate gamete production and hormonal activity of the gonads (ovaries and testes). The precise roles of the gonadotropins are described in Exercise 43 along with other considerations of reproductive system physiology. Adrenocorticotropic hormone (ACTH) regulates the endocrine activity of the cortex portion of the adrenal gland. Thyrotropic hormone (TSH) influences the growth and activity of the thyroid gland. These adenohypophyseal hormones are all tropic hormones. In each case, a tropic hormone released by the anterior pituitary stimulates its target organ, which is also an endocrine gland, to secrete its hormones. Target organ hormones then exert their effects on other body organs and tissues.

Three other major hormones produced by the anterior pituitary are not directly involved in the regulation of other endocrine glands of the body. Growth hormone (GH) is a general metabolic hormone that plays an important role in determining body size. It is essential for normal retention of body protein and affects many tissues of the body. Its major effects, however, are exerted on the growth of muscle and the long bones of the body. Prolactin (PRL), acting synergistically with the female sex hormones (estrogens and progesterone), stimulates breast development and promotes and maintains lactation by the mammary glands after childbirth. Its function in males is unknown. Melanocyte-stimulating hormone (MSH) does not appear to be of major significance in humans, but it darkens the skin of reptiles and amphibians and may similarly affect the melanocytes that produce pigment in human skin.

The anterior pituitary controls the activity of so many other endocrine glands that it has often been called the *master endocrine gland.* Its removal dramatically interferes with body metabolism: the gonads and adrenal and thyroid glands atrophy, and changes resulting from subsequent inadequate hormone production become obvious. However, the anterior pituitary is not autonomous in its control because the release of the anterior pituitary hormones is controlled by neurosecretions, *releasing* or *inhibiting hormones,* produced by the hypothalamus. These hypothalamic hormones are liberated into the hypophyseal portal system, which serves the circulatory needs of the anterior pituitary (Figure 27.3).

NEUROHYPOPHYSEAL HORMONES   The neurohypophysis, or posterior pituitary, is not an endocrine gland in a strict sense, because it does not synthesize the hormones it releases. (This relationship is also indicated in Figure 27.3.) Instead, it acts as a storage area for two hormones transported to it from the paraventricular and supraoptic nuclei of the hypothalamus. The first of these hormones is oxytocin, which stimulates powerful uterine contractions during birth and coitus and also causes milk ejection in the lactating mother. The second, antidiuretic hormone (ADH), causes the distal and collecting tubules of the kidneys to reabsorb water from the urinary filtrate, thereby reducing urine production and conserving body water. It also plays a minor role in increasing blood pressure because of its vasoconstrictor effect on the arterioles.

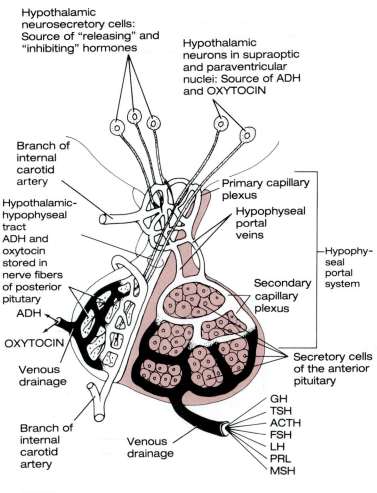

F27.3

Neural and vascular relationships between the hypothalamus and the anterior and posterior lobes of the pituitary. (Note: PRL = prolactin.)

Hyposecretion of ADH results in dehydration from excessive urine output, a condition called diabetes insipidus. Individuals with this condition experience an insatiable thirst. ■

Thyroid Gland

The thyroid gland is composed of two lobes joined by a central mass, or isthmus. It is located in the throat, just inferior to the larynx. It produces two major hormones, thyroid hormone and calcitonin.

Thyroid hormone (TH) is actually two physiologically active hormones known as T_4 (thyroxine) and T_3 (triiodothyronine). Because its primary function is to control the rate of body metabolism and cellular oxidation, TH affects virtually every cell in the body. In addition, it is an important regulator of tissue growth and development, especially in the reproductive and nervous systems.

Hyposecretion of thyroxine leads to a condition of mental and physical sluggishness, which is called myxedema in the adult. ■

Calcitonin (also called **thyrocalcitonin**) decreases blood calcium levels by causing calcium to be deposited in the bones. It acts antagonistically to parathyroid hormone, the hormonal product of the parathyroid glands.

- Try to palpate your thyroid gland by placing your fingers against your windpipe. As you swallow, the thyroid gland will move up and down on the sides and front of the windpipe.

Parathyroid Glands

The parathyroid glands are found embedded in the posterior surface of the thyroid gland. Typically, there are two small oval glands on each lobe. They secrete **parathyroid hormone (PTH),** the most important regulator of calcium-phosphate ion homeostasis of the blood. When blood calcium levels decrease below a certain critical level, the parathyroids release PTH, which causes bone to release calcium from the matrix and causes the kidney to increase calcium reabsorption and decrease reabsorption of phosphate from the filtrate. If blood calcium levels fall too low, **tetany** results and may be fatal.

state of equilibrium

Adrenal Glands

The two bean-shaped adrenal, or suprarenal, glands are located atop or close to the kidneys. Anatomically, the adrenal medulla, develops from neural crest tissue, and the **adrenal medulla** is directly controlled by sympathetic nervous system neurons. The cells of the medulla respond to this stimulation by releasing **epinephrine** (80%) or **norepinephrine** (20%), which act in conjunction with the sympathetic nervous system to elicit the "flight or fight" response to stressors.

The **adrenal cortex** produces three major groups of steroid hormones, collectively called the **corticosteroids**—the mineralocorticoids, the glucocorticoids, and the gonadocorticoids. The **mineralocorticoids,** chiefly **aldosterone,** regulate water and electrolyte balance in the extracellular fluids, mainly by regulating sodium ion reabsorption by kidney tubules. The **glucocorticoids** (cortisone, hydrocortisone, and corticosterone) enable the body to resist long-term stressors, primarily by increasing blood glucose levels. Because of their antiinflammatory properties at pharmacologic levels, they are often administered to decrease tissue edema and counteract vascular dilation. The **gonadocorticoids,** or **sex hormones,** produced by the adrenal cortex are chiefly androgens (male sex hormones), but some estrogens (female sex hormones) are also formed. The gonadocorticoids are produced throughout life in relatively insignificant amounts; however, hypersecretion of these hormones produces abnormal hairiness (**hirsutism),** and masculinization occurs.

Pancreas

The pancreas, which functions as both an endocrine and exocrine gland, produces digestive enzymes as well as insulin and glucagon, important hormones concerned with the regulation of blood sugar levels. The pancreas is found close to the stomach.

Elevated blood glucose levels stimulate release of **insulin,** which decreases blood sugar levels, primarily by accelerating the transport of glucose into the body cells, where it is oxidized for energy or converted to glycogen or fat for storage.

Hyposecretion of insulin or some deficiency in the insulin receptors leads to **diabetes mellitus,** which is characterized by the inability of body cells to utilize glucose and the subsequent loss of glucose in the urine. Alterations of protein and fat metabolism also occur, but these are probably secondary to derangements in carbohydrate metabolism. ■

Glucagon acts antagonistically to insulin. Its release is stimulated by low blood glucose levels, and its action is basically hyperglycemic. Its primary target organ is the liver. It stimulates the liver to break down its glycogen stores to glucose and subsequently to release the glucose to the blood.

The Gonads

The female gonads, or ovaries, are paired, almond-sized organs located in the pelvic cavity. In addition to producing the female sex cells (ova), the ovaries produce two steroid hormone groups, the estrogens and progesterone. The endocrine and exocrine functions of the ovaries do not begin until the onset of puberty, when the anterior pituitary gonadotropic hormones prod the ovary into action that produces rhythmic ovarian cycles in which ova develop and hormonal levels rise and fall. The **estrogens** are responsible for the development of the secondary sex characteristics of the female at puberty (primarily maturation of the reproductive organs and development of the breasts) and act with progesterone to bring about cyclic changes of the uterine lining that occur during the menstrual cycle. The estrogens also help prepare the mammary glands for lactation.

Progesterone, as already noted, acts with estrogen to bring about the menstrual cycle. During pregnancy it maintains the uterine musculature in a quiescent state and helps to prepare the breast tissue for lactation.

The paired oval testes of the male are suspended in a pouchlike sac, the scrotum, outside the pelvic cavity. In addition to the male sex cells, sperm, the testes also produce the male sex hormone, **testosterone.** Testosterone promotes the maturation of the reproductive system accessory structures, brings about the development of the secondary sex characteristics, and is responsible for the male sexual drive, or libido. Both the endocrine and exocrine functions of the testes begin at puberty under the influence of the anterior pituitary gonadotropins.

Two glands not mentioned earlier as major endocrine glands should also be briefly considered here, the thymus and the pineal gland.

Thymus

The thymus is a bilobed gland situated in the superior thorax, posterior to the sternum and overlying the heart and lungs. Conspicuous in the infant, it begins to atrophy at puberty, and by old age it is relatively inconspicuous. Researchers now believe that the thymus produces a hormone called **thymosin** and that during early life the thymus acts as an incubator for the maturation and specialization of a unique population of white blood cells called T-lymphocytes or T cells. The T-lymphocytes are responsible for the cellular immunity aspect of body defense; that is, rejection of foreign grafts, tumors, or virus-infected cells.

Pineal Body

The pineal body, or **epiphysis cerebri,** is a small cone-shaped gland located in the roof of the third ventricle of the brain. Its major endocrine product is **melatonin.**

The endocrine role of the pineal body in humans is still controversial (early philosophers regarded it as the seat of the soul), but it is known to play a role in the biological rhythms (particularly mating and migratory behavior) of other animals. In humans, melatonin appears to exert some inhibitory effect on the reproductive system (especially on the ovaries) that prevents precocious sexual maturation. Serotonin, a neurotransmitter produced by many regions of brain tissue, is known to be a chemical precursor of melatonin in the pineal body.

Pineal Gland,   # 20713
Brain Sand

Once you are satisfied that you can name and locate the endocrine organs and you have labeled Figure 27.2, use an appropriate reference to define the following pathologic conditions (which have not been described here) resulting from hypersecretion or hyposecretion of the various hormones.

acromegaly _____

_____

_____

_____

Addison's disease _____

_____

_____

_____

cretinism _____

_____

_____

_____

_____

Cushing's syndrome _____

_____

_____

_____

diabetes insipidus _____

_____

_____

_____

pituitary dwarfism _____

_____

_____

_____

eunuchism _____

_____

_____

_____

exophthalmic goiter _____

_____

_____

_____

gigantism _____

_____

_____

_____

hypercalcemia _____

_____

_____

Simmonds' disease _____

_____

_____

_____

MICROSCOPIC ANATOMY OF SELECTED ENDOCRINE GLANDS (OPTIONAL)

To prepare for the histologic study of the endocrine glands, obtain a microscope, one each of the slides listed in the list of materials, and colored pencils. We will study only organs in which it is possible to identify the endocrine-producing cells. Compare your observations with the line drawings in Figure 27.4a–f of the endocrine tissue photomicrographs.

Thyroid Gland

1.   Scan the thyroid under low power, noting the *follicles*, spherical sacs containing a pink-stained material (*colloid*). Stored T_3 and T_4 are attached to the protein colloidal material in the follicles as **thyroglobulin** and are released gradually to the blood. Compare the tissue viewed to Figure 27.4a and Plate 18 in the Histology Atlas.

2.   Observe the tissue under high power. Note that the walls of the follicles are formed by simple cuboidal epithelial cells that synthesize the follicular products. The **parafollicular, or C, cells** you see between the follicles are responsible for calcitonin production.

3.   Color appropriately two or three follicles in Figure 27.4a. Label the colloid, cuboidal epithelial cells (follicular cells), and parafollicular cells.

When the thyroid gland is actively secreting, the follicles appear small, and the colloidal material has a ruffled border. When the thyroid is hypoactive or inactive, the follicles are large and plump and the follicular epithelium appears to be squamouslike. What is the physiologic state of the tissue you have been viewing?

_____

_____

Thyroid   # 00135

Thyroid,   # 11803
Unfixed

Parathyroid Glands

1.   Observe the parathyroid tissue under low power to view its two major cell types, the **chief cells** and the **oxyphil cells.** Compare your observations to the view in Plate 19 of the Histology Atlas. The chief cells, which are thought to bear the major responsibility for the synthesis of PTH, are small and abundant, and arranged in thick branching cords. The function of the scattered, much larger oxyphil cells is unknown.

2.   Color a small portion of the parathyroid tissue in Figure 27.4b. Label the chief cells, oxyphil cells, and the connective tissue matrix.

Parathyroid Gland,   # 15060
Oxyphil & Chief

Pancreas

1.   Observe pancreas tissue under low power to identify the roughly circular **islets of Langerhans,** the endocrine portions of the pancreas. The islets are scattered amid the more numerous acinar cells and stain differently (usually lighter), which makes their identification possible (Figure 38.15 (p. 392) and Plate 40 in the Histology Atlas).

2.   Focus on an islet and examine its cells under high power. Notice that the islet cells are densely packed and have no definite arrangement. In contrast, the cuboidal acinar cells are arranged around secretory ducts. Unless special stains are used, it will not be possible to distinguish the **alpha cells,** which tend to cluster at the periphery of the islets and produce glucagon, from the **beta cells,** which synthesize insulin. With these specific stains, the beta cells are larger and stain gray-blue; and the alpha cells are smaller and appear bright pink, as hinted at in Figure 27.4c and shown in Plate 20 in the Histology Atlas. What is the product of the acinar cells?

_____

_____

3.   Draw a section of the pancreas in the space below. Label the islets and the acinar cells. If possible, differentiate the alpha and beta cells of the islets by color.

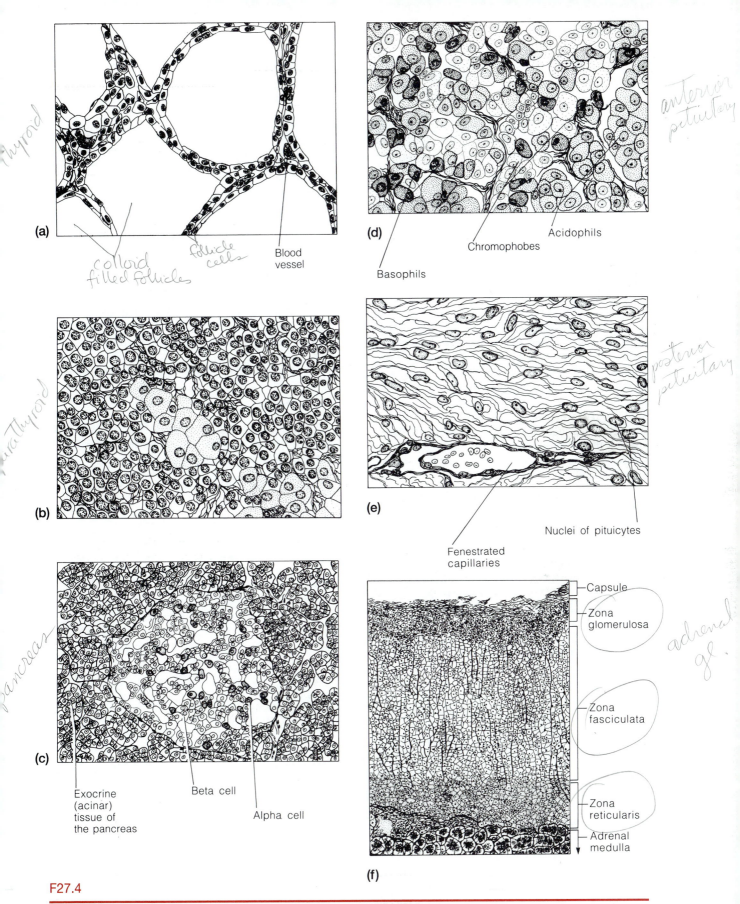

(a) colloid filled follicles · follicle cells · Blood vessel

Thyrosid

(d) Basophils · Chromophobes · Acidophils

anterior pituitary

Parathyroid

posterior pituitary

(e) Fenestrated capillaries · Nuclei of pituicytes

pancreas

(c) Exocrine (acinar) tissue of the pancreas · Beta cell · Alpha cell

(f) Capsule · Zona glomerulosa · Zona fasciculata · Zona reticularis · Adrenal medulla

adrenal gl.

F27.4

Line drawings of Histology Atlas photomicrographs of selected endocrine organs. (a) Thyroid (see corresponding Plate 18 in the Histology Atlas); (b) parathyroid (see Plate 19); (c) pancreas showing an islet of Langerhans (see Plate 20); (d) anterior pituitary (see Plate 21); (e) posterior pituitary (see Plate 22); (f) adrenal gland (ZG = zona glomerulosa, ZF = zona fasciculata, ZR = zona reticularis) (see Plate 23).

Pancreas,   # 25019
Unfixed

Islets of Langerhans   # 12463

Pituitary Gland

anterior 4

1.   Observe the general structure of the pituitary gland under low power to differentiate between the glandular anterior pituitary and the neural posterior pituitary. Figure 27.4d and e should help you get started.

2.   Using the high-power lens, focus on the nests of cells of the anterior pituitary. It is possible to identify the specialized cell types that secrete the specific hormones when differential stains are used. Using Plate 21 in the Histology Atlas as a guide, locate the reddish-brown stained **acidophil cells,** which produce growth hormone and prolactin, and the **basophil cells,** whose deep-blue granules are responsible for the production of the other four anterior pituitary hormones (TSH, ACTH, FSH, and LH). **Chromophobes,** the third cellular population, do not take up the stain and appear rather dull and colorless. The role of the chromophobes is controversial, but they apparently are not directly involved in hormone production.

3.   Use appropriately colored pencils to identify acidophils, basophils, and chromophobes in Figure 27.4d.

posterior

4.   Switch your focus to the posterior pituitary. Observe the nerve fibers (axons of hypophyseal neurons) that compose most of this portion of the pituitary. Also note the **pituicytes,** glial cells which are randomly distributed among the nerve fibers. Refer to Plate 22 in the Histology Atlas as you scan the slide.

What two hormones are stored here?

_____

What is their source? _the hypothalamus_____

_____

Pituitary, Anterior   # 34358
Lobe

Pituitary, Posterior   # 34361
Lobe

Adrenal Gland

5

1.   Hold the slide of the adrenal gland up to the light to distinguish the outer cortex and inner medulla areas. Then scan the cortex under low power to distinguish the differences in cell appearance and arrangement in the three cortical areas. Refer to Figure 27.4f, Plate 23 in the Histology Atlas, and the descriptions below to identify the following cortical areas:

- Connective tissue capsule of the adrenal gland.
- The outermost **zona glomerulosa,** where most mineralocorticoid production occurs and where the tightly packed cells are arranged in spherical clusters.
- The deeper intermediate **zona fasciculata,** which produces glucocorticoids. This is the thickest part of the cortex. Its cells are arranged in parallel cords.
- The innermost cortical zone, the **zona reticularis** abutting the medulla, which produces sex hormones and some glucocorticoids. The cells here stain intensely and form a branching network.

2.   Switch focus to view the lightly stained cells of the adrenal medulla under high power. Note their clumped arrangement and that they are relatively large oval cells.

What hormones are produced by the medulla?

_____ and _____

3.   Draw a representative area of each of the adrenal regions, indicating in your sketch the differences in relative cell size and arrangement.

Zona glomerulosa   Zona fasciculata

Zona reticularis   Adrenal medulla

Adrenal Gland Unfixed	# 25025	‖‖‖ ‖ ‖ ‖‖ ‖ ‖‖ ‖‖ ‖ ‖‖
Adrenal Gland (Cortex)	# 15040	‖‖‖ ‖ ‖ ‖ ‖‖ ‖ ‖‖ ‖ ‖‖
Adrenal Gland (Medulla)	# 15044	‖‖‖ ‖ ‖ ‖‖ ‖ ‖‖ ‖‖ ‖ ‖‖

Ovary

Because you will consider the ovary in greater histologic detail when you study the reproductive system, the objective in this laboratory exercise is just to identify the endocrine-producing parts of the ovary.

1. Scan an ovary slide under low power, and look for a **vesicular (Graafian) follicle,** a circular arrangement of cells enclosing a central cavity. See Figure 43.4 (p. 440) and Plate 24 in the Histology Atlas. This structure synthesizes estrogens.
2. Examine the vesicular follicle under high power, identifying the follicular cells that produce estrogens, the antrum (fluid-filled cavity), and developing ovum (if present). The ovum will be the largest cell in the follicle.
3. Draw and color a vesicular follicle below, labeling the antrum, follicle cells, and developing ovum.

4. Switch to low power, and scan the slide to find a **corpus luteum,** a large amorphous-looking area that produces progesterone (and some estrogens). A corpus luteum is shown in Plate 25 in the Histology Atlas.

Secondary Follicle	# 14972	‖‖ ‖‖ ‖ ‖‖ ‖ ‖ ‖‖ ‖ ‖
Graafian Follicle, Ovary	# 24696	‖‖ ‖ ‖‖ ‖ ‖‖ ‖ ‖ ‖‖ ‖
Interstitial Cells, Leydig	# 15010	‖‖ ‖ ‖‖ ‖ ‖ ‖‖ ‖ ‖‖ ‖

Testis

1. Examine a section of a testis under low power. Identify the seminiferous tubules, which produce sperm, and the **interstitial cells,** which produce testosterone. The interstitial cells are scattered between the seminiferous tubules in the connective tissue matrix. The photomicrograph of seminiferous tubules, Plate 49 in the Histology Atlas, will be helpful here.
2. Draw a representative area of the testis in the space provided. Label the seminiferous tubules and area of the interstitial cells.

Blood

1. To name the two major components of blood and state their average percentages in whole blood.

2. To cite the composition and functional importance of plasma.

3. To define *formed elements* and list the cell types composing them, cite their relative percentages, and describe their major functions.

4. To identify red blood cells, basophils, eosinophils, monocytes, lymphocytes, and neutrophils when provided with a microscopic preparation or appropriate diagram.

5. To conduct the following blood test determinations in the laboratory, and to state their norms and the importance of each.

   hematocrit
   hemoglobin determination
   clotting time
   sedimentation rate
   differential white blood cell count
   total white blood cell count
   total red blood cell count
   ABO and Rh blood typing

6. To discuss the reason for transfusion reactions resulting from the administration of mismatched blood.

7. To define *anemia, polycythemia, leukopenia,* and *leukocytosis* and to cite a possible reason for each condition.

MATERIALS

Compound microscope
Immersion oil
Models and charts of blood cells

General supply area:
Plasma (obtained from an animal hospital or prepared by centrifuging animal (e.g., cattle) blood
Wide-range pH paper

Stained smears of human blood or, if desired by the instructor, heparinized blood obtained from an animal hospital (e.g., dog blood)
Clean microscope slides
Sterile lancets
Glass stirring rods
Alcohol swabs (wipes)

Absorbent cotton balls
Wright's stain in dropper bottle
Distilled water in dropper bottle
Test tubes
Test tube racks
Disposable gloves
Pipette cleaning solutions — (1) 10% household bleach solution, (2) distilled water, (3) 70% ethyl alcohol, (4) acetone
Bucket or large beaker containing 10% household bleach solution for slide and glassware disposal
Disposable autoclave bag
Spray bottles containing 10% bleach solution

Because many blood tests are to be conducted in this exercise, it seems advisable to set up a number of appropriately labeled supply areas for the various tests. These are designated below.

Blood cell count supply area:
Hemacytometer
Unopette reservoir system apparatus for conducting blood counts (available from Becton-Dickinson (Test #5851 for RBCs and #5855 for WBCs))
Mechanical hand counters

Hematocrit supply area:
Heparinized capillary tubes
Microhematocrit centrifuge and reading gauge (if the reading gauge is not available, millimeter ruler may be used)
Seal-ease (Clay Adams Co.) or modeling clay

Hemoglobin determination supply area:
Tallquist hemoglobin scales and test paper or a hemoglobinometer and hemolysis applicator

Sedimentation rate supply area:
Landau Sed-rate pipettes with tubing and rack
Wide-mouthed bottle of 5% sodium citrate
Mechanical suction device
Millimeter ruler

Coagulation time supply area:
Capillary tubes (nonheparinized)
Triangular file

(Materials list continues on p. 283)

In this exercise you will study plasma and formed elements of blood and conduct various hematological tests. These tests are extremely useful diagnostic tools for the physician because blood composition (number and types of blood cells, and chemical composition) reflects the status of many body functions and malfunctions.

ALERT: The decision to use animal blood for testing or to have students test their own blood will be made by the instructor in accordance with the educational purpose of the student group. For example, for students in the nursing or laboratory technician curricula, learning how to safely handle human blood or other human wastes is essential. If blood samples are provided and they are *human* blood samples, gloves should be worn while conducting the blood tests. If human blood is being tested, yours or that obtained from a clinical agency, precautions provided in the text for disposal of human waste **must be observed.** All soiled glassware is to be immersed in household bleach solution immediately after use, and disposable items (lancets, cotton balls, alcohol swabs, etc.) are to be placed in a disposable autoclave bag so that they can be sterilized before disposal.

COMPOSITION OF BLOOD

The blood circulating to and from the body cells within the vessels of the vascular system is a rather viscous substance that varies from bright scarlet to a dull brick red, depending on the amount of oxygen it is carrying. The circulatory system of the average adult contains about 5.5 liters of blood.

Blood is classified as a type of connective tissue, because it is composed of a nonliving fluid matrix (the **plasma**) in which living cells (**formed elements**) are suspended. The fibers typical of a connective tissue matrix become visible in blood only when clotting occurs. They then appear as fibrin threads, which form the structural basis for clot formation.

Over 100 different substances are dissolved or suspended in plasma (Figure 29.1), which is over 90% water. These include nutrients, gases, hormones, various wastes and metabolites, many types of functional proteins, and mineral salts. The composition of plasma varies continuously as cells remove or add substances to the blood.

Three types of formed elements are present in blood. The most numerous are the **erythrocytes, or red blood cells (RBCs),** which are literally sacs of hemoglobin molecules that transport the bulk of the oxygen carried in the blood (and a small percentage of the carbon dioxide). **Leukocytes,** or **white blood cells (WBCs),** are part of the body's nonspecific defenses and the immune system, and **platelets** function in hemostasis (blood clot formation). Formed elements normally constitute 45% of whole blood and plasma the remaining 55%.

Physical Characteristics of Plasma

 Go to the general supply area and carefully pour a few milliliters of plasma into a test tube. Also obtain some wide-range pH paper and then return to your laboratory bench to make the following simple observations.

pH OF PLASMA Test the pH of the plasma with wide-range pH paper. Record the pH observed.

_____

COLOR AND CLARITY OF PLASMA Hold the test tube up to a source of natural light. Note and record its color and degree of transparency. Is it clear, translucent, or opaque?

Color _____

Degree of transparency _____

CONSISTENCY Dip your finger and thumb into the plasma and then press them firmly together for a few seconds. Gently pull them apart. How would you describe the consistency of plasma? Slippery, watery, sticky, or granular? Record your observations.

_____

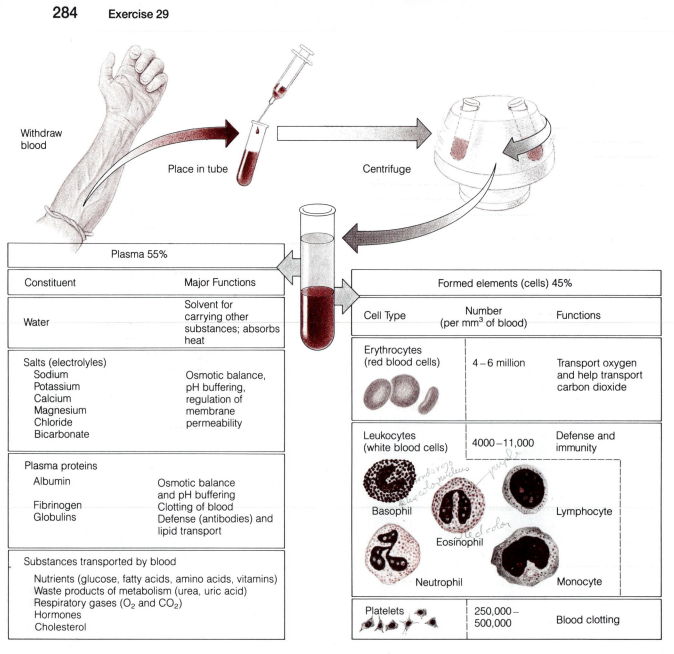

Withdraw
blood

Place in tube

Centrifuge

Plasma 55%	
Constituent	Major Functions
Water	Solvent for carrying other substances; absorbs heat

Salts (electrolytes)
  Sodium
  Potassium
  Calcium
  Magnesium
  Chloride
  Bicarbonate
	Osmotic balance, pH buffering, regulation of membrane permeability

Plasma proteins
  Albumin
 	
  Fibrinogen
  Globulins
	Osmotic balance and pH buffering
	Clotting of blood
	Defense (antibodies) and lipid transport

Substances transported by blood
 	
  Nutrients (glucose, fatty acids, amino acids, vitamins)
  Waste products of metabolism (urea, uric acid)
  Respiratory gases (O_2 and CO_2)
  Hormones
  Cholesterol	

Formed elements (cells) 45%		
Cell Type	Number (per mm^3 of blood)	Functions
Erythrocytes (red blood cells)	4 – 6 million	Transport oxygen and help transport carbon dioxide
Leukocytes (white blood cells)	4000 – 11,000	Defense and immunity
Basophil		Lymphocyte
	Eosinophil	
Neutrophil		Monocyte
Platelets	250,000 – 500,000	Blood clotting

F29.1

The composition of blood.

Formed Elements of Blood

In this section, you will conduct your observations of blood cells on an already prepared (purchased) blood slide, or on a slide prepared from your own blood or blood provided by your instructor. Those using the purchased blood slide are to obtain a slide and begin their observations at step 6. Those testing blood provided by a clinical agency are to obtain a tube of the supplied blood, disposable gloves, and the supplies listed in step 1, except for the lancets and alcohol swabs. After donning gloves, those students will jump to step 3b to begin their observations. If you are examining your own blood, you will perform all the steps described below *except* step 3b.

1. Obtain two glass slides, a glass stirring rod, dropper bottles of Wright's stain and distilled water, two or three lancets, cotton balls, and alcohol swabs. Bring this equipment to the laboratory bench. Clean the slides thoroughly and dry them.

2. Open the alcohol swab packet and scrub your third or fourth finger with the swab. (Because the pricked finger may be a little sore later, it is better to prepare a finger on the hand used less often.) Circumduct your hand (swing it in a cone-shaped path) for 10 to 15 sec-

onds. This will dry the alcohol and cause your fingers to become engorged with blood. Then, open the lancet packet and grasp the lancet by its blunt end. Quickly jab the pointed end into the prepared finger to produce a free flow of blood. It is *not* a good idea to squeeze or "milk" the finger, as this forces out tissue fluid as well as blood. If the blood is not flowing freely, another puncture should be made.

Under no circumstances is a lancet to be used for more than one puncture. Dispose of the lancets in the disposable autoclave bag *immediately* after use.

3a.   With a cotton ball, wipe away the first drop of blood; then allow another large drop of blood to form. Touch the blood to one of the cleaned slides approximately ½ inch from the end. Then quickly (to prevent clotting) use the second slide to form a blood smear as shown in Figure 29.2. When properly prepared, the blood smear is uniformly thin. If it appears streaked, the blood probably began to clot or coagulate before the smear was made, and another slide should be prepared. Continue at step 4.

3b.   Dip a glass rod in the blood provided, and transfer a generous drop of blood to the end of a cleaned microscope slide. Then, as described just above, use the second slide to make your blood smear.

4.   Dry the slide by waving it in the air. When it is completely dry, it will look dull. Place it on a paper towel, and flood it with Wright's stain. Count the number of drops of stain used. Allow the stain to remain on the slide for 3 to 4 minutes and then flood the slide with an equal number of drops of distilled water. Allow the water and Wright's stain mixture to remain on the slide for 4 or 5 minutes or until a metallic green film or scum is apparent on the fluid surface. Blow on the slide gently every minute or so to keep the water and stain mixed during this interval.

5.   Rinse the slide with a stream of distilled water. Then flood it with distilled water, and allow it to lie flat until the slide becomes translucent and takes on a pink cast. Then stand the slide on its long edge on the paper towel, and allow it to dry completely. Once the slide is dry, you can begin your observations.

6.   Obtain a microscope and scan the slide under low power to find the area where the blood smear is the thinnest. After scanning the slide in low power to find the areas with the largest numbers of nucleated WBCs, read the following descriptions of cell types, and find each one on Figure 29.1 (The formed elements are also shown in Plates 55 through 60 in the Histology Atlas.) Then, switch to the oil immersion lens and observe the slide carefully to identify each cell type.

ERYTHROCYTES   Erythrocytes, or red blood cells, which range in size from 5 to 10 μm in diameter (averaging 7.5 μm), are cells whose color varies from a salmon red color to pale pink, depending on the effec-

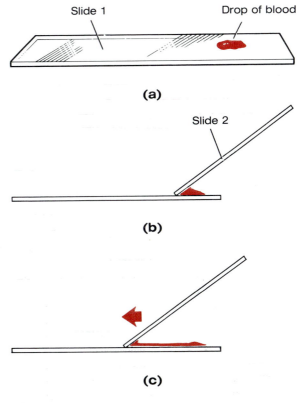

(a)

(b)

(c)

F29.2

Procedure for making a blood smear. (a) Place drop of blood on slide 1 approximately ½ inch from one end. (b) Hold slide 2 at a 30° to 40° angle to slide 1 (it should touch the drop of blood); allow blood to spread along entire bottom edge of angled slide. (c) Smoothly advance slide 2 to end of slide 1 (blood should run out before reaching the end of slide 1).

tiveness of the stain. They have a distinctive biconcave disk shape and appear paler in the center than at the edge.

As you observe the slide, note that the red blood cells are by far the most numerous blood cells seen in the field. Their number averages 4.5 million to 5.0 million cells per cubic millimeter of blood (for women and men, respectively).

Red blood cells differ from the other blood cells because they are anucleate when mature and circulating in the blood. As a result, they are unable to reproduce and have a limited life span of 100 to 120 days, after which they begin to fragment and are destroyed in the spleen and other reticuloendothelial tissues of the body.

Red Cell   # 46538

In various anemias, the red blood cells may appear pale (an indication of decreased hemoglobin content) or may be nucleated (an indication that the bone marrow is turning out cells prematurely). ■

Anemia,   # 12269
Iron Deficient

Basophil, Blood   # 16185

LEUKOCYTES

LEUKOCYTES   Leukocytes, or white blood cells, are nucleated cells that are formed in the bone marrow from the same stem cell (*hemocytoblast*) as red blood cells. They are much less numerous than the red blood cells, averaging from 4000 to 11,000 cells per cubic millimeter. Basically, white blood cells are protective, pathogen-destroying cells that are transported to all parts of the body in the blood or lymph. Important to their protective function is their ability to move in and out of blood vessels, a process called **diapedesis,** and to wander through body tissues by **ameboid motion** to reach sites of inflammation or tissue destruction. They are classified into two major groups, depending on whether or not they contain conspicuous granules in their cytoplasm.

Granulocytes comprise the first group. The granules in their cytoplasm stain differentially with Wright's stain, and they have peculiarly lobed nuclei, which often consist of expanded nuclear regions connected by thin strands of nucleoplasm. Additional information about the three types of granulocytes follows:

Neutrophil: The most abundant of the white blood cells (40% to 70% of the leukocyte population); nucleus consists of 3 to 7 lobes and the pale lilac cytoplasm contains fine cytoplasmic granules, which are generally indistinguishable and take up both the acidic (red) and basic (blue) dyes (*neutrophil* = acid loving); functions as an active phagocyte. The number of neutrophils increases exponentially during acute infections.

Neutrophil   # 13655

Eosinophil: Represents 1% to 4% of the leukocyte population; nucleus is generally figure 8 or bilobed in shape; contains large cytoplasmic granules (elaborate lysosomes) that stain red-orange with the acid dyes in Wright's stain. Precise function is unknown, but they increase in number during allergies and parasite infections and may selectively phagocytize antigen-antibody complexes.

Eosinophil   # 14709

Basophil: Least abundant leukocyte type representing less than 1% of the population; large U- or S-shaped nucleus with two or more indentations. Cytoplasm contains coarse, sparse granules (stained deep purple by the basic dyes in Wright's stain). The granules contain histamine, a vasodilator which is discharged on exposure to antigens and helps mediate the inflammatory response.

The second group, **agranulocytes,** or **agranular leukocytes,** contains no observable cytoplasmic granules. Although found in the bloodstream, they are much more abundant in lymphoid tissues and lymph. Their nuclei tend to be closer to the norm, that is, spherical, oval, or kidney-shaped. Specific characteristics of the two types of agranulocytes are listed below.

Lymphocyte: The smallest of the leukocytes, approximately the size of a red blood cell. The dark blue-purple staining nucleus is generally spherical or slightly indented and accounts for most of the cell mass. Sparse cytoplasm appears as a thin blue rim around the nucleus. Concerned with immunologic responses in body; one population, the B lymphocytes, oversees the production of antibodies that are released to blood. The second population, T lymphocytes, plays a regulatory role and destroys grafts, tumors, and virus-infected cells and activates B lymphocytes. Represents 20% to 45% of the WBC population.

Lymphocyte,   # 13715
Normal, Blood

Monocyte: The largest of the leukocytes; approximately twice the size of red blood cells. Represents 3% to 8% of the leukocyte population. Dark blue nucleus is generally kidney-shaped; abundant cytoplasm stains grey-blue. Functions as an active phagocyte (the "long-term cleanup team"), increasing dramatically in number during chronic infections such as tuberculosis.

Monocyte   # 14714

Students are often asked to list the leukocytes in order from the most abundant to the least abundant. The following silly phrase may help you with this task: **N**ever **l**et **m**onkeys **e**at **b**ananas (neutrophils, lymphocytes, monocytes, eosinophils, basophils).

PLATELETS

PLATELETS   Platelets are cell fragments of large multinucleate cells (**megakaryocytes**) formed in the bone marrow. They appear as darkly staining, irregularly shaped bodies interspersed among the blood cells. The normal platelet count in blood ranges from 250,000 to 500,000 per cubic millimeter. Platelets are instrumental in the clotting process that occurs in plasma when blood vessels are ruptured.

Platelets   # 14726
and Neutrophil

After you have identified these cell types on your slide, observe three-dimensional models of blood cells if these are available. *Do not dispose of your slide,* as it will be used later for the differential white blood cell count.

HEMATOLOGIC TESTS

When one enters a hospital as a patient, several hematologic tests are routinely done to determine general level of health as well as the presence of pathologic conditions. You will be conducting the most common of these tests in this exercise.

Materials such as cotton balls, lancets, and alcohol swabs are used in nearly all of the following diagnostic tests. These supplies are at the general supply area and should be properly disposed of (glassware to the "bleach bucket" and disposable items to the autoclave bag) immediately after use.

Other necessary supplies and equipment are at specific supply areas marked according to the test with which they are used. Since nearly all of the tests require a finger stab to obtain blood, it might be wise to quickly read through the various tests to determine in which instances more than one preparation can be done from the same finger stab. For example, the hematocrit capillary tubes and sedimentation rate samples might be prepared at the same time the chamber is being prepared for the total blood cell counts. A little preplanning will save you the discomfort of a multiply punctured finger.

An alternative to using blood obtained from the finger stab technique is using heparinized blood samples supplied by your instructor. The purpose of using heparinized tubes is to prevent the blood from clotting. Thus blood collected and stored in such tubes will be suitable for all tests except coagulation time testing.

Differential White Blood Cell Count

To make a differential white blood cell count, 100 WBCs are counted and classified according to type. Such a count is routine in a physical examination and in diagnosing illness, since any abnormality or significant elevation in percentages of WBC types may indicate the source of pathology. Use the slide prepared for the identification of the blood cells (pp. 284–285) for the count.

1. Begin at the edge of the smear and move the slide in a systematic manner on the microscope stage—either up and down or from side to side as indicated in Figure 29.3.

2. Record each type of white blood cell you observe by making a count on the chart to the right (for example, ⵜⵜ II = 7 cells) until you have observed and recorded a total of 100 WBCs. Using the equation below, compute the percentage of each WBC type counted, and record

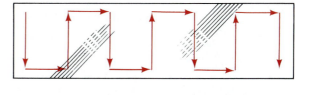

or

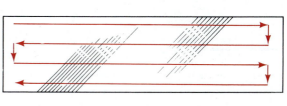

F29.3

Alternative methods of moving the slide for a differential WBC count.

the percentages on the data sheet at the end of this exercise.

$$\text{Percent } (\%) = \frac{\# \text{ observed}}{\text{Total } \# \text{ counted } (100)} \times 100$$

Cell type	Number observed
Neutrophils	
Eosinophils	
Basophils	
Lymphocytes	
Monocytes	

How does your differential white blood cell count correlate with the percentages given for each type on p. 286?

Total White and Red Blood Cell Counts

To conduct a total or direct WBC or RBC count, you will dilute a known volume of blood with a fluid that prevents blood coagulation and place the mixture into a counting chamber of known volume—a **hemacytometer.** The cells are then counted by microscopic inspection, and corrections for dilution and chamber volume are made to obtain the result in cells per cubic millimeter. The white and red blood cell diluents differ. They are isotonic for the cell type to be counted and cause dissolution of the cell types not being counted. In other words, if the WBC diluent is used, the RBCs are hemolyzed and thus do not interfere with the WBC counting process. The Unopette apparatus for conducting blood

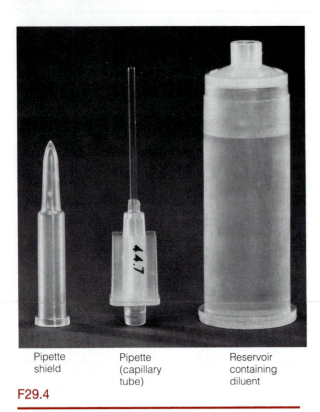

Pipette shield   Pipette (capillary tube)   Reservoir containing diluent

F29.4

The Unopette reservoir system for blood counts. The system consists of a reservoir containing a premeasured amount of RBC or WBC diluent and a plastic capillary tube pipette with a shield that is used for puncturing the reservoir top.

counts is shown in Figure 29.4. The reservoir contains the required amount of the appropriate diluting fluid (acetic acid for WBC counts and Hayem's solution for RBC counts). Note that this hand counting technique is rather outdated, since most clinical agencies now have computerized equipment for performing blood counts.

TOTAL WHITE BLOOD CELL COUNT   Since white blood cells are an important part of the body's defense system, it is essential to note any abnormalities in them. **Leukocytosis,** an abnormally high WBC count, may indicate bacterial or viral infection, metabolic disease, hemorrhage, or poisoning by drugs or chemicals. A decrease in the white cell number below 4000/mm³ (**leukopenia**) may indicate typhoid fever, measles, infectious hepatitis or cirrhosis, tuberculosis, or excessive antibiotic or X-ray therapy. A person with leukopenia lacks the usual protective mechanisms.

1.   Obtain a hemacytometer and cover glass, cotton balls, lancets, alcohol swabs, and a hand counter. Also obtain the Unopette system for conducting WBC counts (the reservoir has a *white* bottom).

2.   Puncture the top (diaphragm) of the reservoir container with the pointed end of the protective pipette shield. Then cleanse your finger thoroughly, and obtain a second drop of blood as described on p. 285.

3.   Now you are ready to charge the Unopette pipette with blood. Twist off the protective shield and, holding the pipette horizontally, touch the tip of the capillary tube pipette to the blood drop. When the pipette has filled by capillary action, wipe its tip with a cotton ball.
 Squeeze the reservoir slightly to expel some air. While the reservoir is still compressed, insert the blood-charged pipette into the reservoir and then release the pressure on the reservoir. As you do so, the blood will be drawn into the diluent in the reservoir.

4.   Squeeze the reservoir and invert it gently several times to thoroughly mix the contents. Remove the pipette from the reservoir, and then reverse it and insert its opposite end into the reservoir to convert the capillary tube to a dropper.

5.   Place a cover slip on the hemacytometer, and prepare to charge it. Discard the first 2 to 3 drops—which is only diluent—from the Unopette onto a paper towel. Squeeze the reservoir to apply one drop of the diluted blood at each end of the cover slip at the junction of the hemacytometer and cover slip (Figure 29.5a), and then immediately lift the pipette away from the hemacytometer surface. *Do this quickly;* otherwise the hemacytometer will overfill, and the mixture will flow under the cover slip by capillary action. You now have two charged chambers. If the chambers are properly charged, no fluid will appear in the moat.

6.   Place the hemacytometer on the microscope stage and allow it to remain undisturbed for 2 to 3 minutes to allow the cells to become evenly distributed.

7.   Bring the grid lines into focus under low power (10× objective lens) and check for uniformity of white blood cell distribution. If it is uneven, switch to the other chamber for observation.

8.   Move the slide into position so that one of the W areas can be seen (see Figure 29.5b), and proceed to count all WBCs observed in the four corner W areas. Use a hand counter to facilitate the counting process. *To prevent overcounts of cells at boundary lines, count only those that touch the left and upper boundary lines of the W area but not those touching the right and lower boundaries.* Record the number of WBCs counted and multiply this number by 50 to obtain the number of WBCs per cubic millimeter.[*]

---

[*] The factor of 50 is obtained by multiplying the volume dilution factor (20) by the volume correction factor (2.5): $20 \times 2.5 = 50$. The 2.5 volume correction factor is obtained in the following manner: Each W area on the grid is exactly 1 mm² × 0.1 mm deep; therefore, the volume of each W section is 0.1 mm³. Since WBCs in four W areas are counted (a total of 0.4 mm³), this volume must be multiplied by 2.5 (correction factor) to obtain the number of cells in 1 mm³.

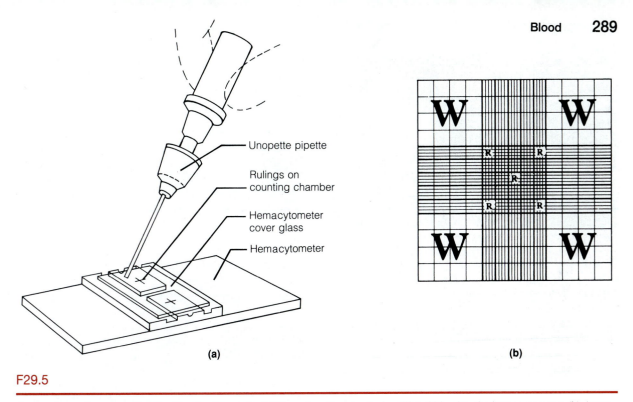

F29.5

Apparatus and preparation for blood cell counts. (a) Procedure for introducing diluted blood to the hemacytometer. (b) Areas of the hemacytometer used for red and white blood cell counts.

No. WBCs: _____ WBC/mm³: _____

Record this information on the data sheet on p. 296. How does your result compare with the norms for a white blood cell count?

_____

9.   Discard the used Unopette equipment in the disposable autoclave bag. Clean the hemacytometer and coverslip in preparation for the red blood cell count.

TOTAL RED BLOOD CELL COUNT   The red blood cell count, like the white blood cell count, determines the total number of this cell type per unit volume of blood. Since RBCs are absolutely necessary for oxygen transport, the doctor should investigate any excessive change in their number immediately.

▶ An increase in the number of RBCs (**polycythemia**) may result from bone marrow cancer or from living at high altitudes where less oxygen is available. A decrease in the number of RBCs results in anemia. (The term **anemia** simply indicates a decreased oxygen-carrying capacity of blood that may result from a decrease in RBC number or size or a decreased hemoglobin content of the RBCs.) A decrease in RBCs may result suddenly from hemorrhage or more gradually from conditions that increase RBC destruction or decrease RBC production. ■

1.   Obtain a Unopette apparatus for performing a RBC count (*red* bottom on the reservoir). Also obtain other supplies as required for the WBC count. Follow the same procedure for obtaining blood and charging the chamber as for the WBC count, except be very careful when reinserting the pipette into the reservoir (step 4) and when mixing the blood with the diluent (Hayem's solution, in this case).

⚠ Do not squeeze the reservoir hard because this might force Hayem's solution out the overflow opening in the reservoir. Hayem's solution contains sodium azide, an antibacterial agent that is very toxic. Hence, it is best to prevent it from splashing on your skin.

2.   Allow the hemacytometer to rest on the microscope stage as before. Using the high-power lens, count all RBCs in the R-marked areas (see Figure 29.5b). Again, at the boundary lines, count only those cells touching the left and upper lines.

3.   Record the number of cells counted, and multiply that number by 10,000 to compute the RBC/mm³. (Note: the dilution factor (200) × volume correction factor (50) = 10,000.)

No. RBCs: _____ RBCs/mm³: _____

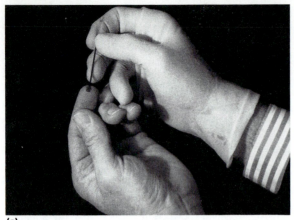

(a)

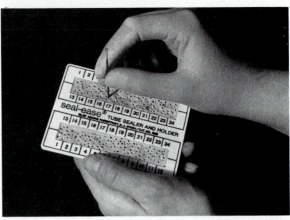

(b)

Steps in a hematocrit determination. (a) Load a heparinized capillary tube with blood. (b) Plug the blood-containing end of the tube with clay. (c) Place the tube in a microhematocrit centrifuge. (Centrifuge must be balanced.)

How does your result compare with normal RBC values?

(c)

4. Place all used glassware (including the hema-cytometer) in the beaker containing bleach. Put disposable items, including the Unopette apparatus, in the disposable autoclave bag.

Hematocrit

The *hematocrit,* or *packed cell volume (PCV),* is routinely determined when anemia is suspected. Centrifuging whole blood causes the formed elements to spin to the bottom of the tube, with plasma forming the top layer (see Figure 29.1). Since the blood cell population is primarily RBCs, the PCV is generally considered equivalent to the RBC volume, and this is the only value reported. However, the relative percentage of WBCs can be differentiated, and both WBC and plasma volume will be reported here. Normal PCV values for the male and female, respectively, are 47.0 ± 7 and 42.0 ± 5.

The PCV is determined by the micromethod, so only a drop of blood is needed. If possible, all members of the class should prepare their capillary tubes at the same time so the centrifuge can be properly balanced and run only once.

1. Obtain two heparinized capillary tubes, Seal-ease or modeling clay, a lancet, alcohol swabs, and some cotton balls.

2. Cleanse the finger, and allow the blood to flow freely. Wipe away the first few drops and, holding the red-line-marked end of the capillary tube to the blood drop, allow the tube to fill at least three-fourths full by capillary action (Figure 29.6a). If the blood is not flowing freely, the end of the capillary tube will not be completely submerged in the blood during filling, air will enter, and you will have to prepare another sample.

3. Plug the blood-containing end by pressing it into the Seal-ease or clay (Figure 29.6b). Prepare a second tube in the same manner.

4. Place the prepared tubes opposite one another in the radial grooves of the microhematocrit centrifuge with the sealed ends abutting the rubber gasket at the centrifuge periphery (Figure 29.6c). This loading procedure balances the centrifuge and prevents blood from spraying everywhere by centrifugal force. Make a note of the numbers of the grooves your tubes are in. When all the tubes have been loaded, make sure the centrifuge is properly balanced, and secure the centrifuge cover. Turn the centrifuge on, and set the timer for 4 or 5 minutes.

5. Determine the percentage of RBCs, WBCs, and plasma by using the microhematocrit reader. The RBCs are the bottom layer, the plasma is the top layer, and the WBCs are the buff-colored layer between the two. If the

<handwriting>plasma – 1.8 mm
clens   3.6 mm
$\overline{5.4}$

3

$\frac{3.6}{5.4} \times 100$

SKIP</handwriting>

reader is not available, use a millimeter ruler to measure the length of the filled capillary tube occupied by each element, and compute its percentage by using the following formula:

$$\frac{\text{Height of the column composed of the element (mm)}}{\text{Height of the original column of whole blood (mm)}} \times 100$$

Record your calculations below and on the data sheet.

% RBC _____ % WBC _____ % plasma _____

Usually WBCs constitute 1% of the total blood volume. How do your blood values compare to this figure and to the normal percentages for RBCs and plasma? (See p. 286.)

_____

As a rule, the PCV is considered a more accurate test for determining the RBC composition of the blood than the total RBC count. A hematocrit within the normal range generally indicates a normal RBC number, whereas an abnormally high or low PCV is cause for concern.

Hemoglobin Concentration Determination

As noted earlier, a person can be anemic even with a normal RBC count. Since hemoglobin is the RBC protein responsible for oxygen transport, perhaps the most accurate way of measuring the oxygen-carrying capacity of the blood is to determine its hemoglobin content. Oxygen, which combines reversibly with the heme (iron-containing portion) of the hemoglobin molecule, is picked up by the blood cells in the lungs and unloaded in the tissues. Thus, the more hemoglobin molecules the RBCs contain, the more oxygen they will be able to transport. Normal blood contains 12 to 16 g hemoglobin per 100 ml blood. Hemoglobin content in men is slightly higher (14 to 18 g) than in women (12 to 16 g).

Several techniques have been developed to estimate the hemoglobin content of blood, ranging from the old, rather inaccurate Tallquist method to expensive colorimeters, which are precisely calibrated and yield highly accurate results. Directions for both the Tallquist method and a hemoglobinometer are provided here.

TALLQUIST METHOD

1. Obtain a Tallquist hemoglobin scale, lancets, alcohol swabs, and cotton balls.

2. Use instructor-provided blood or prepare the finger as previously described. (For best results, make sure the alcohol evaporates before puncturing your finger.) Place one good-sized drop of blood on the special absorbent paper provided with the color chart. The blood stain should be larger than the holes on the color chart.

3. As soon as the blood has dried and loses its glossy appearance, match its color, under natural light, with the color standards by moving the specimen under the comparison chart so that the blood stain appears at all the various apertures. (The blood should not be allowed to dry to a brown color, as this will result in an inaccurate reading.) Because the colors on the chart represent 1% variations in hemoglobin content, it may be necessary to estimate the percentage if the color of your blood sample is intermediate between two color standards.

4. On the data sheet, record your results as the percentage of hemoglobin concentration and as grams per 100 ml of blood.

HEMOGLOBINOMETER DETERMINATION

1. Obtain a hemoglobinometer, hemolysis applicator stick, alcohol swab, and lens paper and bring them to your bench. Test the hemoglobinometer light source to make sure it is working; if not, request new batteries before proceeding and test it again.

2. Remove the blood chamber from the slot in the side of the hemoglobinometer and disassemble the blood chamber by separating the glass plates from the metal clip. Notice as you do this that the larger glass plate has an H-shaped depression cut into it that acts as a moat to hold the blood, whereas the smaller glass piece is flat and serves as a coverslip.

3. Clean the glass plates with an alcohol swab and then wipe dry with lens paper. Hold the plates by their sides to prevent smearing during the wiping process.

4. Reassemble the blood chamber (remember: larger glass piece on the bottom with the moat up), but leave the moat plate about halfway out to provide adequate exposed surface to charge it with blood.

5. Obtain a drop of blood (from the provided sample or from your fingertip as before), and place it on the depressed area of the moat plate that is closest to you (Figure 29.7a).

6. Using the wood hemolysis applicator, stir or agitate the blood to rupture (lyse) the RBCs (Figure 29.7b). This usually takes 35 to 45 seconds; hemolysis is complete when the blood appears transparent rather than cloudy.

7. Push the blood-containing glass plate all the way into the metal clip and then firmly insert the charged blood chamber back into the slot on the side of the instrument (Figure 29.7c).

8. Hold the hemoglobinometer in your left hand with your left thumb resting on the light switch located on the underside of the instrument. Look into the eyepiece and notice that there is a green area divided into two halves (a split field).

9. With the index finger of your right hand, slowly move the slide on the right side of the hemoglobinome-

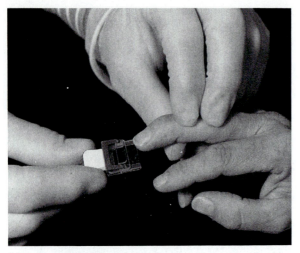

(a) A drop of blood is added to the moat plate of the blood chamber. The blood must flow freely.

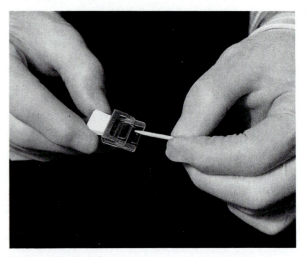

(b) The blood sample is hemolyzed with a wooden hemolysis applicator. Thirty-five to forty-five seconds are required for complete hemolysis.

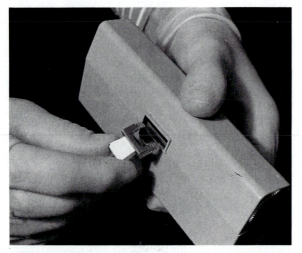

(c) The charged blood chamber is inserted into the slot on the side of the hemoglobinometer.

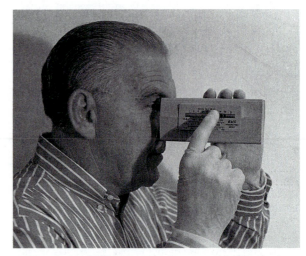

(d) The colors of the green split screen are matched by moving the slide with right index finger. When the two colors match in density, the grams/100 ml and %Hb are read on the scale.

F29.7

Hemoglobin determination using a hemoglobinometer.

ter back and forth until the two halves of the green field match (Figure 29.7d).

10.   Note and record on the data sheet on p. 296 the grams Hb (hemoglobin)/100 ml blood indicated on the uppermost scale by the index mark on the slide. Also record % Hb, indicated by one of the lower scales.

11.   Disassemble the blood chamber once again, and carefully place its parts (glass plates and clip) into a bleach-containing beaker.

Generally speaking, the relationship between the PCV and grams of hemoglobin per 100 ml blood is 3:1.

How do your values compare?

_____

Record, on the data sheet, the value obtained from your data.

Sedimentation Rate

The speed at which red blood cells settle to the bottom of a vertical tube when allowed to stand is called the *sedimentation rate*. The normal rate for adults is 0 to 6 mm/hr (averaging 3 mm/hr) and for children 0 to 8 mm/hr (averaging 4 mm/hr). Sedimentation of RBCs apparently proceeds in three stages: rouleaux formation, rapid settling, and final packing. *Rouleaux formation* (alignment of RBCs like a stack of pennies) does not occur with abnormally shaped red blood cells (as in sickle cell anemia); therefore, the sedimentation rate is decreased. The size and number of RBCs affect the packing phase. In anemia the sedimentation rate increases; in polycythemia the rate decreases. The sedimentation rate is greater than normal during menses and pregnancy, and very high sedimentation rates may indicate infectious conditions or tissue destruction occurring somewhere in the body. Although this test is nonspecific, it alerts the diagnostician to the need for further tests to pinpoint the site of pathology. The Landau micromethod, which uses just one drop of blood, is used here.

1. Obtain lancets, cotton balls, alcohol swabs, and Landau Sed-rate pipette and tubing, the Landau rack, a wide-mouthed bottle of 5% sodium citrate, a mechanical suction device, and a millimeter ruler.

2. Use the mechanical suction device to draw up the sodium citrate to the first (most distal) marking encircling the pipette. Prepare the finger for puncture, and produce a free flow of blood.

3. Wipe off the first drop, and then draw the blood into the pipette until the mixture reaches the second encircling line. Keep the pipette tip immersed in the blood to avoid air bubbles.

4. Thoroughly mix the blood with the citrate (an anticoagulant) by drawing the mixture into the bulb and then forcing it back down into the lumen. Repeat this mixing procedure six times, and then adjust the top level of the mixture as close to the zero marking as possible. *If any air bubbles are introduced during the mixing process, discard the sample and begin again.*

5. Seal the tip of the pipette by holding it tightly against the tip of your index finger, and then carefully remove the suction device from the upper end of the pipette.

6. Stand the pipette in an exactly vertical position on the Sed-rack with its lower end resting on the base of the rack. Record the time, and allow it to stand for exactly 1 hour.

time _____

7. After 1 hour, measure the number of millimeters of visible clear plasma (which indicates the amount of settling of the RBCs), and record this figure here and on the data sheet.

sedimentation rate _____ mm/hr

8. Clean the pipette by using the mechanical suction device to draw up each of the cleaning solutions (available at the general supply area) in succession—bleach, distilled water, alcohol, and acetone

Discharge the contents each time, before drawing up the next solution. Place the cleaned pipette in the bleach-containing beaker at the general supply area, after first drawing bleach up into the pipette.

Coagulation Time

Blood clotting, or *coagulation,* is a protective device that minimizes blood loss when blood vessels are ruptured. This process requires the interaction of many substances normally present in the plasma (clotting factors, or procoagulants) as well as some released by platelets and injured tissues. Basically hemostasis proceeds as follows: The injured tissues and platelets release **thromboplastin** and **PF$_3$**, respectively, which trigger the clotting mechanism, or cascade. Thromboplastin and PF$_3$ interact with other blood protein clotting factors and calcium ions to convert **prothrombin** (present in plasma) to **thrombin.** Thrombin then acts enzymatically to polymerize the soluble **fibrinogen** proteins (present in plasma) into insoluble **fibrin,** which forms a meshwork of strands that traps the RBCs and forms the basis of the clot (Figure 29.8). Normally, blood removed from the body clots within 2 to 6 minutes.

1. Obtain a *nonheparinized* capillary tube, a lancet, cotton balls, a triangular file, and alcohol swabs.

2. Use instructor-supplied blood or clean and prick the finger to produce a free flow of blood.

3. Place one end of the capillary tube in the blood drop, and hold the opposite end at a lower level to collect the sample.

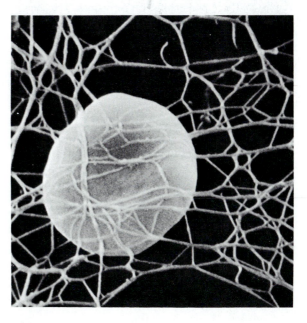

F29.8

Photomicrograph of a RBC trapped in a fibrin mesh.

4.   Lay the capillary tube on a paper towel.

Record the time. _____

5.   At 30-sec intervals, make a small nick on the tube close to one end with the triangular file, and then carefully break the tube. Slowly separate the ends to see if a gel-like thread of fibrin spans the gap. When this occurs, record below and on the data sheet the time for coagulation to occur. Are your results within the normal time range?

_____

6.   Dispose of the capillary tube and used supplies in the disposable autoclave bag.

Blood Typing

Blood typing is a system of blood classification based on the presence of specific proteins (combined with polysaccharides) on the outer surface of the RBC plasma membrane. Such proteins are called **antigens,** or **agglutinogens,** and are genetically determined. In many cases, these antigens are accompanied by other plasma proteins, **antibodies** or **agglutinins,** which react with RBCs bearing different antigens, and cause them to become clumped, agglutinated, and eventually hemolyzed. It is because of this phenomenon that a person's blood must be carefully typed before a whole blood or packed cell transfusion.

Several blood typing systems exist, based on the various possible antigens, but the factors typically typed for are the antigens of the ABO and Rh blood groups which are most commonly involved in transfusion reactions. Other blood factors, such as Kell, Lewis, M, and N, are not routinely typed for unless the individual is expected to require multiple transfusions. The basis of the ABO typing is shown in the chart below.

Individuals whose red blood cells carry the Rh antigen are considered to be Rh positive (approximately 85% of the U.S. population); those lacking the antigen are Rh negative. Unlike ABO blood groups neither the blood of the Rh-positive (Rh^+) nor Rh-negative (Rh^-) individuals carries preformed anti-Rh antibodies. This is understandable in the case of the Rh-positive individual. However, Rh-negative persons who receive transfusions of Rh-positive blood become sensitized by the Rh antigens of the donor RBCs and their systems begin to produce anti-Rh antibodies. On subsequent exposures to Rh-positive blood, typical transfusion reactions occur, resulting in the clumping and hemolysis of the donor blood cells.

1.   Obtain two clean microscope slides, a wax marking pencil, anti-A, anti-B, and anti-Rh typing sera, toothpicks, lancets, alcohol swabs, and the Rh typing box.

2.   Divide slide 1 into two equal halves with the wax marking pencil. Label the lower left-hand corner "anti-A" and the lower right-hand corner "anti-B." Mark the bottom of slide 2 "anti-Rh."

3.   Place one drop of anti-A serum on the *left* side of slide 1. Place one drop of anti-B serum on the *right* side of slide 1. Place one drop of anti-Rh serum in the center of slide 2.

4.   Cleanse your finger with an alcohol swab, pierce the finger with a lancet, and wipe away the first drop of blood. Obtain 3 drops of freely flowing blood, placing one drop on each side of slide 1 and a drop on slide 2.

5.   Quickly mix each blood–antiserum sample with a *fresh* toothpick. Then dispose of the toothpicks, lancet, and used alcohol swab in the autoclave bag.

6.   Place slide 2 on the Rh typing box and rock gently back and forth. (A slightly higher temperature is required for precise Rh typing than for ABO typing.)

7.   After 2 minutes, observe all three blood samples for evidence of clumping. The agglutination that occurs in the positive test for the Rh factor is very fine and difficult to perceive; thus if there is any question, observe the slide under the microscope. Record your observations below:

	Observed (+)	Not observed (−)
Presence of clumping with anti-A		
Presence of clumping with anti-B		
Presence of clumping with anti-Rh		

ABO blood type	Antigens present on RBC membranes	Antibodies present in plasma	% of U.S. Population White	Black	Asian
A	A	Anti-B	41	27	28
B	B	Anti-A	9	20	27
AB	A and B	None	3	4	5
O	Neither	Anti-A and anti-B	47	49	40

8. Interpret your results in light of the following information: Slide 1: If clumping occurs on both sides, your ABO blood group is AB. If clumping occurs only in the blood sample mixed with anti-A serum, you are ABO type A. If clumping occurs only in the blood sample mixed with anti-B serum, you are type B. If clumping was not observed with either serum, you are type O. Slide 2: If clumping was observed, you are Rh positive. If not, you are Rh negative.

9. Record your blood type on the data sheet.

10. Put the used slides in the bleach-containing bucket at the general supply area; put disposable supplies in the autoclave bag.

Measurement of Cholesterol Concentration in Plasma

Atherosclerosis is the disease process in which the body's blood vessels (particularly the coronary and cerebral arteries, and the aorta and its major branch points) become increasingly occluded by plaques. Because the plaques narrow the arteries, they can contribute to hypertensive heart disease. They also serve as focal points for the formation of blood clots (thrombi) which may break away and block smaller vessels farther downstream in the circulatory pathway, causing heart attacks or strokes (myocardial or cerebral infarcts respectively).

Since medical clinicians discovered that cholesterol is a major component of the smooth muscle plaques formed during atherosclerosis, it has had a bad press. Today, virtually no physical examination of an adult is considered complete until data on cholesterol levels are assessed along with other life-style risk factors. A normal value for plasma cholesterol in adults ranges from 130 to 200 mg/100 ml plasma; you will be making such a determination on the animal plasma provided by the instructor.

Although the total plasma cholesterol concentration is valuable information, it may be misleading, particularly if a person's high-density lipoprotein (HDL) level is high and low-density lipoprotein (LDL) level is relatively low. (Cholesterol, being water insoluble, is transported in the blood complexed to lipoproteins. In general, cholesterol bound into HDLs is destined to be degraded by the liver and then eliminated from the body, whereas that forming part of the LDLs is "traveling" to the body's tissue cells. When LDL levels are excessive, cholesterol is deposited in the blood vessel walls; hence, LDLs are considered to carry the "bad" cholesterol.)

1. Go to the appropriate supply area, put three test tubes in a test tube rack, and add 5 ml of cholesterol reagent into each of the three test tubes. Mark the test tubes 1–3 with a wax marker.

2. Using the mechanical pipettor and a fresh 0.1-ml pipette each time, add 0.1 ml of the following to each of the numbered test tubes:

- 1: Add 0.1 ml of cholesterol standard (200 mg/100 ml).
- 2: Add 0.1 ml of plasma (available at the general supply area).
- 3: Add 0.1 ml of distilled water.

3. Mix each tube by shaking it gently from side to side and then place the tubes (in the rack) into the water bath set at 37°C. (Note: if there is any question about your ability to identify your test tubes, put your initials on them with the wax marker *before* placing them into the water bath.)

Record the time: _____

4. Obtain three spectrophotometer cuvettes (containers for the solutions to be "read" by the spectrophotometer). Clean them thoroughly with cuvette brushes and laboratory detergent, rinsing several times with distilled water. Invert them on a paper towel to drain.

5. After the test tubes have been in the water bath for 10 minutes, remove them and transfer their contents to similarly numbered cuvettes. Standardize the spectrophotometer at 625 nm using sample 3 (distilled water) as the *blank*.

6. Determine and record the absorbance of samples 1 and 2.

Absorbance of 1: _____ Absorbance of 2: _____

7. Calculate the cholesterol concentration (C) in sample 2 (the "unknown" plasma sample) using the following equation:

$$C_{plasma} = \frac{absorbance_{plasma}}{absorbance_{standard}} \times C_{standard}$$

Record the computed cholesterol concentration here and on the data sheet.

Cholesterol concentration: _____ mg/100 ml plasma

8. Clean the pipettes using the mechanical pipettor to draw up each of the pipette cleaning solutions (bleach, distilled water, ethyl alcohol, and acetone) in turn, and then return them to the general supply area.

9. Before leaving the laboratory, use a paper towel saturated with bleach solution to wash down your laboratory bench.

Hematologic Test Data Sheet

Differential WBC count:

_____% granulocytes   _____% agranulocytes

_____% neutrophils   _____% lymphocytes

_____% eosinophils   _____% monocytes

_____% basophils

Total WBC count _____ WBCs/mm^3

Total RBC count _____ RBCs/mm^3

Hematocrit (PCV):

RBC _____% of blood volume

WBC _____% of blood volume   } not
generally
Plasma _____% of blood volume   reported

Hemoglobin content:

Tallquist method:

_____ **g/100 ml blood;** _____ %

Hemoglobinometer (type: _____)

_____ **g/100 ml blood;** _____ %

Ratio (PCV/grams Hb per 100 ml blood: _____

Sedimentation rate _____ mm/hr

Coagulation time _____

Blood typing:

ABO group _____ Rh factor _____

Cholesterol concentration _____ mg/100 ml plasma

Anatomy of the Heart

The major function of the **cardiovascular system** is transportation. Using blood as the transport vehicle, the system carries oxygen, digested foods, cell wastes, electrolytes, and many other substances vital to the body's homeostasis to and from the body cells. The system's propulsive force is the contracting heart, which can be compared to a muscular pump equipped with one-way valves. As the heart contracts, it forces blood into a closed system of large and small plumbing tubes (blood vessels) within which the blood is confined and circulated. This exercise deals with the structure of the heart or circulatory pump. The anatomy of the blood vessels is considered separately in Exercise 32.

GROSS ANATOMY OF THE HUMAN HEART

The heart is a cone-shaped organ approximately the size of a fist and is located within the mediastinum, or medial cavity, of the thorax. It is flanked laterally by the lungs, posteriorly by the vertebral column, and anteriorly by the sternum. Its more pointed **apex** extends slightly to the left and rests on the diaphragm, approximately at the level of the fifth intercostal space. Its broader **base,** from which the great vessels emerge, lies beneath the second rib and points toward the right shoulder. *In situ,* the right ventricle of the heart forms most of its anterior surface.

If an X-ray of a human thorax is available, verify the relationships described above.

Figure 30.1 shows two views of the heart—an external anterior view and a frontal section. As its anatomical areas are described in the text, consult the figure. When you have pinpointed all the structures, observe the human heart model, and reidentify the same structures without reference to the figure.

The heart is enclosed within a double-walled fibroserous sac called the pericardium. The thin **visceral pericardium,** or **epicardium,** which is closely applied to the heart muscle, reflects downward at the base of the heart to form its companion serous membrane, the outer, loosely applied **parietal pericardium,** which is attached at the heart apex to the diaphragm. Serous fluid produced by these membranes allows the heart to beat in a relatively frictionless environment. The serous parietal pericardium, in turn, lines the loosely fitting superficial **fibrous pericardium** composed of dense connective tissue.

Inflammation of the pericardium, **pericarditis,** causes painful adhesions between the serous pericardial layers. These adhesions interfere with heart movements. ∎

The walls of the heart are composed primarily of cardiac muscle—the **myocardium**—which is rein-

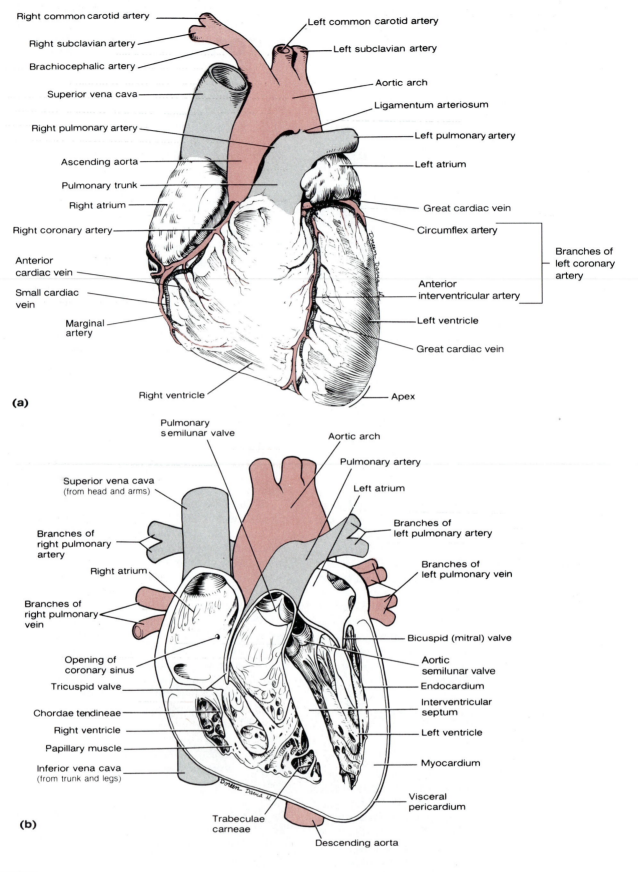

Right common carotid artery

Right subclavian artery

Brachiocephalic artery

Superior vena cava

Right pulmonary artery

Ascending aorta

Pulmonary trunk

Right atrium

Right coronary artery

Anterior cardiac vein

Small cardiac vein

Marginal artery

Right ventricle

Left common carotid artery

Left subclavian artery

Aortic arch

Ligamentum arteriosum

Left pulmonary artery

Left atrium

Great cardiac vein

Circumflex artery

Anterior interventricular artery

Branches of left coronary artery

Left ventricle

Great cardiac vein

Apex

(a)

Pulmonary semilunar valve

Superior vena cava (from head and arms)

Branches of right pulmonary artery

Right atrium

Branches of right pulmonary vein

Opening of coronary sinus

Tricuspid valve

Chordae tendineae

Right ventricle

Papillary muscle

Inferior vena cava (from trunk and legs)

Aortic arch

Pulmonary artery

Left atrium

Branches of left pulmonary artery

Branches of left pulmonary vein

Bicuspid (mitral) valve

Aortic semilunar valve

Endocardium

Interventricular septum

Left ventricle

Myocardium

Visceral pericardium

Trabeculae carneae

Descending aorta

(b)

F30.1

Anatomy of the human heart. (a) External anterior view. (b) Frontal section.

forced internally by a dense fibrous connective tissue network. This network—the *fibrous skeleton of the heart*—is more elaborate and thicker in certain areas, for example, around the valves and at the base of the great vessels leaving the heart (see Figure 30.2).

Heart Anterior	# 03719	‖‖‖‖‖‖‖‖‖
Frontal Section	# 03605	‖‖‖‖‖‖‖‖
Pericardium, Composite of Gross	# 03395	‖‖‖‖‖‖‖‖
Pericarditis, Fibrinous, Heart	# 18719	‖‖‖‖‖‖‖

Heart Chambers

The heart is divided into four chambers: two superior **atria** and two inferior **ventricles,** each lined with a thin serous lining called the **endocardium.** The septum that divides the heart longitudinally is referred to as the **interatrial** or **interventricular septum,** depending on which chambers it partitions. Functionally, the atria are receiving chambers and are relatively ineffective as pumps. Blood flows into the atria under low pressure from the veins of the body. The right atrium receives relatively oxygen-poor blood from the body via the **superior** and **inferior venae cavae.** Four **pulmonary veins** deliver oxygen-rich blood from the lungs to the left atrium.

The inferior thick-walled ventricles, which form the bulk of the heart, are the discharging chambers. They force blood out of the heart into the large arteries that emerge from its base. The right ventricle pumps blood into the **pulmonary trunk,** which routes blood to the lungs to be oxygenated. The left ventricle discharges blood into the **aorta,** from which all systemic arteries of the body diverge to supply the body tissues. Discussions of the heart's pumping action usually refer to ventricular activity.

Pulmonary and Systemic Circulations

The heart functions as a double pump. The right side serves as the **pulmonary circulation** pump, shunting the carbon dioxide–rich blood entering its chambers to the lungs to unload carbon dioxide and pick up oxygen, and then back to the left side of the heart. The function of this circuit is strictly to provide for gas exchange. The second circuit, which carries oxygen-rich blood from the left heart through the body tissues and back to the right heart is called the **systemic circulation.** It supplies the functional blood supply to all body tissues.

Trace the pathway of blood through the heart by adding arrows to the frontal section diagram (see Figure 30.1b). Use red arrows for the oxygen-rich blood and blue arrows for the less oxygen-rich blood.

Heart Valves	# 03587	‖‖‖‖‖‖‖‖‖

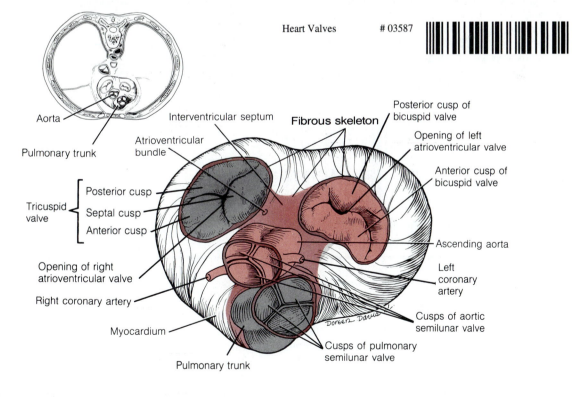

Heart valves (superior view).

Heart Valves

Four valves enforce a one-way blood flow through the heart chambers. The **atrioventricular (AV) valves,** located between the atrial and ventricular chambers on each side, prevent backflow into the atria when the ventricles are contracting. The left atrioventricular valve, also called the **mitral** or **bicuspid valve,** consists of two cusps, or flaps, of endocardium. The right atrioventricular valve, the **tricuspid valve,** has three cusps (see Figure 30.2). Tiny white collagenic cords called the **chordae tendineae** (literally, heart strings) anchor the cusps to the ventricular walls. The chordae tendineae originate from small bundles of cardiac muscle, called **papillary muscles,** that project from the myocardial wall.

When blood is flowing passively into the atria and then into the ventricles during **diastole** (the period of ventricular relaxation), the atrioventricular valve flaps hang limply into the ventricular chambers and then are carried passively toward the atria by the accumulating blood. When the ventricles contract (**systole**) and compress the blood in their chambers, the intraventricular blood pressure rises causing the valve flaps to be reflected superiorly, which closes the AV valves. The chordae tendineae, pulled taut by the contracting papillary muscles, anchor the flaps in a closed position preventing backflow into the atria during ventricular contraction. If unanchored, the flaps would blow upward into the atria rather like an umbrella being turned inside out by a strong wind.

The second set of valves, the **pulmonary** and **aortic semilunar valves,** each composed of three pocket-like cusps, guards the bases of the two large arteries leaving the ventricular chambers. The valve cusps are forced open and flatten against the walls of the artery as the ventricles discharge their blood into the large arteries during systole. However, when the ventricles relax, blood flows backward toward the heart and the cusps fill with blood, closing the semilunar valves and preventing arterial blood from reentering the heart.

Mitral Valve Opened	# 03767	
Mitral Chordae	# 03776	
Pulmonary Valve, Normal	# 03863	

Cardiac Circulation

Even though the heart chambers are almost continually bathed with blood, this contained blood does not nourish the myocardium. The functional blood supply of the heart is provided by the right and left coronary arteries. The **coronary arteries** issue from the base of the aorta just above the aortic semilunar valve and encircle the heart in the **atrioventricular groove** at the junction of the atria and ventricles. They then ramify over the heart's surface, the right coronary artery supplying the posterior surface of the ventricles and the lateral aspect of the right side of the heart, largely through its **posterior interventricular** and **marginal artery** branches. The left coronary artery supplies the anterior ventricular walls and the laterodorsal part of the left side of the heart via its two major branches, the **anterior interventricular artery** and the **circumflex artery** (see Figure 30.1a). The coronary arteries and their branches are compressed during systole and fill when the heart is relaxed. The myocardium is drained by the **cardiac veins,** most of which empty into the **coronary sinus,** which in turn empties into the right atrium.

Coronary Arteries, SA Nodal Artery	# 53988	
Coronary Arteries, Normal	# 03929	

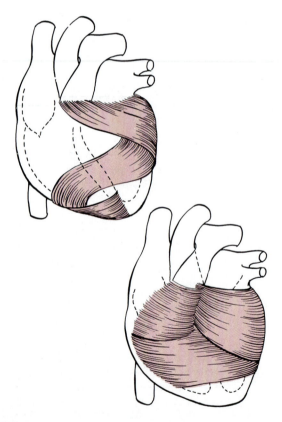

F30.3

Longitudinal view of the heart chambers showing the spiral arrangement of the cardiac muscle fibers.

MICROSCOPIC ANATOMY OF CARDIAC MUSCLE

Cardiac muscle is found in only one place—the heart. The heart acts as a vascular pump, propelling blood to all tissues of the body; cardiac muscle is thus very important to life. Cardiac muscle is involuntary, thus ensuring a constant blood supply.

The cardiac cells, only sparingly invested in connective tissue, are arranged in spiral or figure-8-shaped bundles (Figure 30.3). When the heart contracts, its internal chambers become smaller (or are temporarily obliterated), forcing the blood into the large arteries leaving the heart.

1. Observe the three-dimensional model of cardiac muscle, examining its branching cells and the areas where the cells interdigitate, the **intercalated discs.** These two structural features provide a continuity to cardiac muscle not seen in other muscle tissues and allow close coordination of heart activity.

2. Note the similarities and differences between cardiac muscle and skeletal muscle.

3. Obtain and observe a longitudinal section of cardiac muscle under high power. Identify the nucleus, striations, intercalated discs, and sarcolemma of the individual cells and then label these structures in Figure 30.4.

Cardiac Muscle   # 14625
Intercalated Disks

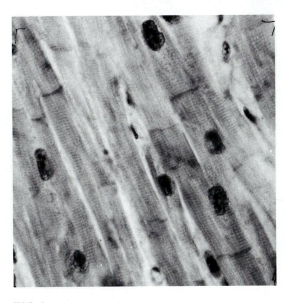

F30.4

Photomicrograph of cardiac muscle (160×).

DISSECTION OF THE SHEEP HEART

Dissection of the sheep heart is valuable because it is similar in size and structure to the human heart. Also, a dissection experience allows you to view structures in a way not possible with models and diagrams. Refer to Figure 30.5 as you proceed with the dissection.

1. Obtain a preserved sheep heart, a dissection tray, dissecting instruments and, if desired, protective skin cream or gloves. Rinse the sheep heart in cold water to remove excessive preservatives and to flush out any trapped blood clots. Now you are ready to make your observations.

2. Observe the texture of the pericardium. Also, note its point of attachment to the heart. Where is it attached?

_____

3. If the serous pericardial sac is still intact, slit open the parietal pericardium and cut it from its attachments. Observe the visceral pericardium (epicardium). Using a sharp scalpel, carefully pull a little of this serous membrane away from the myocardium. How does its position, thickness, and apposition to the heart differ from those of the parietal pericardium?

_____

_____

_____

4. Examine the external surface of the heart. Notice the accumulation of adipose tissue, which in many cases marks the separation of the chambers and the location of the coronary arteries that nourish the myocardium. Carefully scrape away some of the fat with a scalpel to expose the coronary blood vessels.

(Text continued on p. 303)

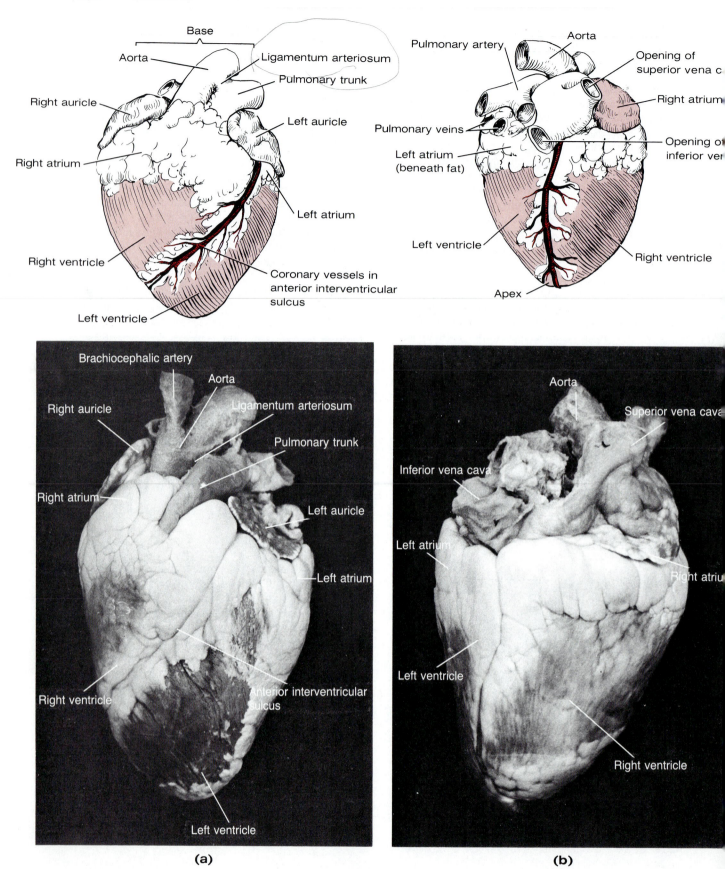

Base

Aorta

Ligamentum arteriosum

Pulmonary trunk

Right auricle

Left auricle

Right atrium

Left atrium

Right ventricle

Coronary vessels in anterior interventricular sulcus

Left ventricle

Pulmonary artery

Aorta

Opening of superior vena c

Right atrium

Pulmonary veins

Left atrium (beneath fat)

Opening of inferior ver

Left ventricle

Right ventricle

Apex

Brachiocephalic artery

Aorta

Ligamentum arteriosum

Right auricle

Pulmonary trunk

Right atrium

Left auricle

Left atrium

Right ventricle

Anterior interventricular sulcus

Left ventricle

Aorta

Superior vena cava

Inferior vena cava

Left atrium

Right atriu

Left ventricle

Right ventricle

(a)   (b)

F30.5

Anatomy of the sheep heart. (a) Anterior view. (b) Posterior view. Diagrammatic views at top; photographs at bottom.

5. Identify the base and apex of the heart, and then identify the two wrinkled **auricles,** earlike flaps of tissue projecting from the atrial chambers. The balance of the heart muscle is ventricular tissue. To identify the left ventricle, compress the ventricular chambers on each side of the longitudinal fissures carrying the coronary blood vessels. The side that feels thicker and more solid is the left ventricle. The right ventricle feels much thinner and somewhat flabby when compressed. This difference reflects the greater demand placed on the left ventricle, which must pump blood through the much longer systemic circulation, a pathway with much higher resistance than the pulmonary circulation served by the right ventricle. Hold the heart in its anatomical position (Figure 30.5a), with the anterior surface uppermost. In this position the left ventricle composes the entire apex and the left side of the heart.

6. Identify the pulmonary trunk and the aorta extending from the superior aspect of the heart. The pulmonary trunk is the more anterior, and you may see its division into the right and left pulmonary arteries if it has not been cut too closely to the heart. The thicker-walled aorta, which branches almost immediately, is located just beneath the pulmonary trunk. The first branch of the sheep aorta, the **brachiocephalic artery,** is identifiable unless the aorta has been cut immediately as it leaves the heart. The brachiocephalic artery splits to form the right carotid and subclavian arteries, which supply the right side of the head and right forelimb, respectively. Carefully clear away some of the fat between the pulmonary trunk and the aorta to expose the **ligamentum arteriosum,** a cordlike remnant of the **ductus arteriosus.** (In the fetus the ductus arteriosus allows blood to pass directly from the pulmonary trunk to the aorta, thus bypassing the nonfunctional fetal lungs.)

Ductus Arteriosus,   # 08570
Patent

7. Cut through the wall of the aorta until you see the aortic semilunar valve. Identify the two openings to the coronary arteries just above the valve. Insert a probe into one of these holes to see if you can follow the course of a coronary artery across the heart.

8. Turn the heart to view its posterior surface. The heart will appear as shown in Figure 30.5b. Notice that the right and left ventricles appear equal-sized in this view. Identify the four thin-walled pulmonary veins entering the left atrium. (It may or may not be possible to locate the pulmonary veins from this vantage point, depending on how they were cut as the heart was removed.) Identify the superior and inferior venae cavae entering the right atrium. Compare the approximate diameter of the superior vena cava with the diameter of the aorta.

Which is larger? _____

Which has thicker walls? __*inferior*_____

Why do you suppose these differences exist?

_____

_____

_____

9. Insert a probe into the superior vena cava and use scissors to cut through its wall so that you can view the interior of the right atrium. Do not extend your cut entirely through the right atrium or into the ventricle. Observe the right atrioventricular valve.

How many flaps does it have? _____

Pour some water into the right atrium and allow it to flow into the ventricle. Slowly and gently squeeze the right ventricle to watch the closing action of this valve. (If you squeeze too vigorously, you'll get a face full of water!) Drain the water from the heart before continuing.

10. Return to the pulmonary trunk and cut through its anterior wall until you can see the pulmonary semilunar valve. Pour some water into the base of the pulmonary trunk to observe the closing action of this valve. How does its action differ from that of the atrioventricular valve?

_____

_____

_____

After observing semilunar valve action, drain the heart once again. Return to the superior vena cava, and continue the cut made in its wall through the right atrium and right atrioventricular valve into the right ventricle. Parallel the anterior border of the interventricular septum until you "round the corner" to the dorsal aspect of the heart (Figure 30.6).

11. Reflect the cut edges of the superior vena cava, right atrium, and right ventricle to obtain the view seen in Figure 30.6. Observe the comblike ridges of muscle throughout most of the right atrium. This is called **pectinate muscle** (*pectin* means "comb"). Identify, on the ventral atrial wall, the large opening of the inferior vena cava and follow it to its external opening with a probe. Notice that the atrial walls in the vicinity of the venae

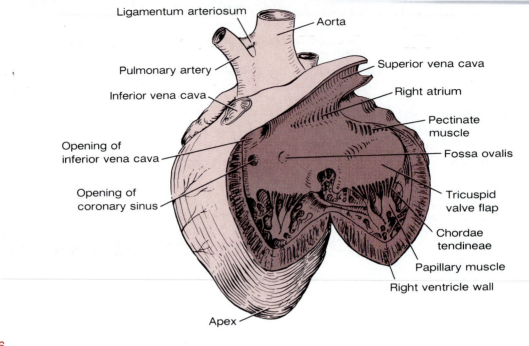

Ligamentum arteriosum

Aorta

Pulmonary artery

Superior vena cava

Inferior vena cava

Right atrium

Pectinate muscle

Opening of inferior vena cava

Fossa ovalis

Opening of coronary sinus

Tricuspid valve flap

Chordae tendineae

Papillary muscle

Right ventricle wall

Apex

F30.6

Right side of the sheep heart opened and reflected to reveal internal structures (diagrammatic view).

cavae are smooth and lack the roughened appearance (pectinate musculature) of the other regions of the atrial walls. Just below the inferior vena caval opening, identify the opening of the **coronary sinus,** which returns venous blood of the coronary circulation to the right atrium. Nearby, locate an oval depression, the **fossa ovalis,** in the interatrial septum. This depression marks the site of an opening in the fetal heart, the **foramen ovale,** which allows blood to pass from the right to the left atrium, thus bypassing the fetal lungs.

12.   Identify the papillary muscles in the right ventricle, and follow their attached chordae tendineae to the flaps of the tricuspid valve. Notice the pitted and ridged appearance (**trabeculae carneae**) of the inner ventricular muscle.

13.   Make a longitudinal incision through the aorta and continue it into the left ventricle. Notice how much thicker the myocardium of the left ventricle is as compared to that of the right ventricle. Compare the *shape* of the left ventricular cavity to the shape of the right ventricular cavity.

_____

_____

_____

_____

Are the papillary muscles and chordae tendineae observed in the right ventricle also present in the left ventricle?

_____

Count the number of cusps in the left atrioventricular valve. How does this compare with the number seen in the right atrioventricular valve?

_____

_____

_____

How do the sheep valves compare with their human counterparts?

_____

14.   Continue your incision from the left ventricle superiorly into the left atrium. Reflect the cut edges of the atrial wall, and attempt to locate the entry points of the pulmonary veins into the left atrium. Follow them to the heart exterior with a probe. Notice how thin-walled these vessels are.

15.   Properly dispose of the organic debris, and clean the dissecting tray and instruments.

Conduction System of the Heart and Electrocardiography

THE INTRINSIC CONDUCTION SYSTEM

Heart contraction results from a series of electrical potential changes (depolarization waves) that travel through the heart preliminary to each beat. The ability of cardiac muscle to beat is intrinsic—it does not depend on impulses from the nervous system to initiate its contraction and will continue to contract rhythmically even if all nerve connections are severed. However, two types of controlling systems exert their effects on heart activity. One of these involves nerves of the autonomic nervous system, which accelerate or decrease the heart beat rate depending on which division is activated. The second system is the **intrinsic conduction system,** or **nodal system,** of the heart, consisting of specialized noncontractile myocardial tissue. This conduction system ensures that heart muscle depolarizes in an orderly and sequential manner (from atria to ventricles) and that the heart beats as a coordinated unit.

The components of the intrinsic conduction system include the **SA (sinoatrial) node,** located in the right atrium just inferior to the entrance to the superior vena cava; the **AV (atrioventricular) node** in the lower atrial septum at the junction of the atria and ventricles; the **AV bundle (bundle of His)** and right and left **bundle branches,** located in the interventricular septum; and the **Purkinje fibers,** which ramify within the muscle bundles of the ventricular walls. The Purkinje fiber network is much denser and more elaborate in the left ventricle because of the larger size of this chamber (Figure 31.1).

The SA node, which has the highest rate of discharge, provides the stimulus for contraction. Because it sets the rate of depolarization for the heart as a whole, the SA node is often referred to as the *pacemaker.* From the SA node, the impulse spreads throughout the atria

and to the AV node. This electrical wave is immediately followed by atrial contraction. At the AV node, the impulse is momentarily delayed (approximately 0.1 sec), allowing the atria to complete their contraction. It then passes through the AV bundle, the right and left bundle branches, and the Purkinje fibers, finally resulting in ventricular contraction. Note that the atria and ventricles are separated from one another by a region of electrically inert connective tissue; so the depolarization wave

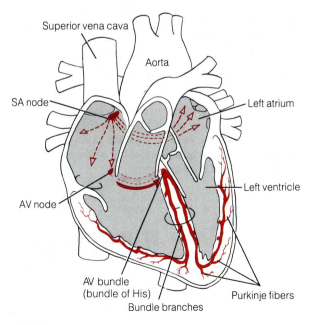

F31.1

The intrinsic conduction system of the heart. Dashed-line arrows indicate transmission of the impulse from the SA node through the atria. Solid arrow indicates transmission of the impulse from the AV node to the AV bundle.

5. Repeat the recording procedure for leads II (voltage difference between the right arm and left leg) and III (voltage difference between the left arm and left leg).

6. Each student should take a representative segment of one of the lead recordings and label the record with the name of the subject and the lead used. Identify and label the P, QRS, and T waves. The calculations you perform for your recording should be based on the following information: Because the paper speed was 25 mm/sec, each millimeter of paper corresponds to a time interval of 0.04 sec. Thus, if an interval requires 4 mm of paper, its duration is 4 mm × 0.04 sec/mm = 0.16 sec.

Compute the heart rate. Measure the distance (mm) from the beginning of one QRS complex to the beginning of the next QRS complex, and plug this value into the equation below to find the time for one heartbeat.

_____ mm × 0.04 sec/min = _____ sec/beat

Now find the beats per minute, or heart rate, by using the figure just computed for seconds per beat in the following equation:

$$\text{Beats/min} = \frac{1}{\rule{2cm}{0.4pt}\ \text{sec/beat}} \times 60 \text{ sec/min}$$

Beats/min = _____

Is the obtained value within normal limits? _____

Measure the QRS interval and compute its duration.

_____

Measure the Q-T interval and compute its duration.

_____

Measure the P-R interval and compute its duration.

_____

Are the computed values within normal limits?

_____

7. At the bottom of this page, attach segments of the ECG recordings from leads I through III. Make sure you indicate the paper speed, lead, and subject's name on each tracing. To the recording on which you based your previous computations, add your calculations for the duration of the QRS, P-R intervals, and Q-T intervals above the respective area of tracing. Also record the heart rate on that tracing.

"RUNNING IN PLACE" RECORDING

1. Make sure the electrodes are securely attached to prevent electrode movement while recording the ECG.

2. Set the paper speed to 25 mm/sec, and prepare to make the recording using lead I.

3. Record the ECG while the subject is running in place for 3 min. Then have the subject sit down, but continue to record the ECG for an additional 4 minutes. *Mark the recording* at the end of the 3 minutes of running and at 1 minute after cessation of activity.

4. Stop the recording. Compute the beats/min during the third minute of running, at 1 minute after exercise, and at 4 minutes after exercise. Record below:

_____ beats/min while running in place

_____ beats/min at 1 minute after exercise

_____ beats/min at 4 minutes after exercise

5. Compare this recording with the previous recording from lead I. Which intervals are shorter in the "running" recording?

_____

Does the subject's heart rate return to baseline levels by 4 minutes after exercise?

_____

"BREATH-HOLDING" RECORDING

1. Position the subject comfortably in the sitting position.

2. Using lead I and a paper speed of 25 mm/sec, *begin* the recording. After approximately 10 seconds have passed, notify the subject to begin breath holding and mark the record to indicate the onset of the 1-minute breath-holding interval.

3. Stop the recording after 1 minute and remind the subject to breathe. Compute the beats/min during the 1-minute experimental (breath-holding) period.

Beats/min during breath holding _____

4. Compare this recording with the lead I recording obtained under baseline conditions.

What differences are seen? _____

_____

Attempt to *explain* the physiologic reason for the differences you have seen. (Hint: a good place to start might be to check "hypoventilation" or the role of the *respiratory system* in acid-base balance of the blood.)

_____

_____

_____

_____

Anatomy of Blood Vessels

OBJECTIVES

1. To describe the tunics of arterial and venous walls and state the function of each layer.

2. To correlate differences observed in artery, vein, and capillary structure with the functions these vessels perform.

3. To recognize a cross-sectional view of an artery and vein when provided with a microscopic view or appropriate diagram.

4. To list and/or identify the major arteries arising from the aorta, and to indicate the body region supplied by each.

5. To list and/or identify the major veins draining into the superior and inferior venae cavae, and to indicate the body regions drained.

6. To point out and/or discuss the unique features of special circulations in the body:

    - The pattern of blood flow in the hepatic portal system and its importance
    - The vascular supply of the brain and the importance of the circle of Willis
    - Components of the pulmonary circulation
    - Structures unique to the fetal circulation and the importance of each

7. To point out anatomical differences between the vascular system of the human and the laboratory dissection specimen.

MATERIALS

Anatomical charts of human arteries and veins (or a three-dimensional model of the human circulatory system)

Anatomical charts of the following specialized circulations: pulmonary circulation, hepatic portal circulation, arterial supply and circle of Willis of the brain (or a brain model showing this circulation), fetal circulation

Compound microscope

Prepared microscope slides showing cross sections of an artery and vein

Dissection animals

Dissecting pans and instruments

Protective skin cream or disposable gloves

Blood circulates within the blood vessels, which constitute a closed transport system. As the heart contracts, blood is propelled into the large arteries leaving the heart. It moves into successively smaller arteries and then to the arterioles, which feed the capillary beds in the tissues. Capillary beds are drained by the venules, which in turn empty into veins that ultimately converge on the great veins entering the heart. Thus arteries, carrying blood away from the heart, and veins, which drain the tissues and return blood to the heart, function simply as conducting vessels or conduits. Only the tiny capillaries that connect the arterioles and venules and ramify throughout the tissues directly serve the needs of the body's cells. It is through the capillary walls that exchanges between tissue cells and blood occur.

Respiratory gases, nutrients, and wastes move along diffusion gradients; thus, oxygen and nutrients diffuse from the blood to the tissue cells, and carbon dioxide and metabolic wastes move from the cells to the blood.

In this exercise you will examine the microscopic structure of blood vessels and will identify the major arteries and veins of the systemic circulation and other special circulations.

MICROSCOPIC STRUCTURE OF THE BLOOD VESSELS

Except for the microscopic capillaries, the walls of blood vessels are constructed of three coats, or tunics (Figure 32.1). The **tunica intima,** or **interna,** which lines the lumen of a vessel, is a single thin layer of *endothelium* (squamous cells underlain by a scant basal lamina) that is continuous with the endocardium of the heart. Its cells fit closely together, forming an extremely smooth blood vessel lining that helps to decrease resistance to blood flow.

The **tunica media** is the more bulky middle coat and is composed primarily of smooth muscle and elastic tissue. The smooth muscle, under the control of the sympathetic nervous system, plays an active role in reducing or increasing the diameter of blood vessels,

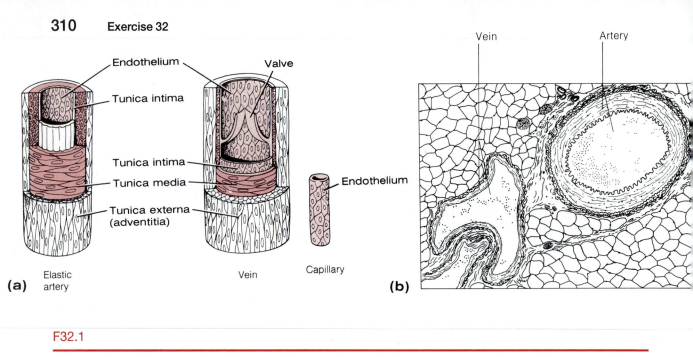

F32.1

Structure of arteries, veins, and capillaries. (a) Diagrammatic view. (b) Line drawing of a small artery (right) and vein (left), cross-sectional view, shown in Plate 26 in the Histology Atlas.

which in turn increases or decreases the peripheral resistance and blood pressure.

The **tunica externa,** or **adventitia,** the outermost tunic, is composed of areolar or fibrous connective tissue. Its function is basically supportive and protective.

In general, the walls of arteries are much thicker than those of veins. The tunica media in particular tends to be considerably heavier and contains substantially more smooth muscle and elastic tissue. This anatomical difference reflects a functional difference in the two types of vessels. Arteries, which are closer to the pumping action of the heart, must be able to expand as an increased volume of blood is propelled into them and then recoil passively as the blood flows off into the circulation during diastole. Their walls must be sufficiently strong and resilient to withstand such pressure fluctuations. Since these larger arteries have such large amounts of elastic tissue in their media, they are often referred to as *elastic arteries.* Smaller arteries, further along in the circulatory pathway, are exposed to less extreme pressure fluctuations. They have somewhat less elastic tissue but still have substantial amounts of smooth muscle in their media. For this reason, they are called *muscular arteries.*

By contrast, veins, which are far removed from the heart in the circulatory pathway, are not subjected to such pressure fluctuations and are essentially low-pressure vessels. Thus, veins may be thinner-walled without jeopardy. However, the low-pressure condition itself requires structural modifications to ensure that venous return equals cardiac output. Thus, the lumens of veins tend to be substantially larger than those of corresponding arteries.

Because blood returning to the heart often flows against gravity, there are other aids to venous return. Valves in the larger veins function to prevent backflow of blood in much the same manner as the semilunar valves of the heart. Skeletal muscle activity also promotes venous return; as the skeletal muscles surrounding the veins contract and relax, the blood is "milked" through the veins toward the heart. (Anyone who has had to stand relatively still for an extended time will be happy to show you their swollen ankles, caused by blood pooling in their feet during the period of muscle inactivity!) Finally, pressure changes that occur in the thorax during breathing also facilitate the return of blood to the heart.

● To demonstrate how efficiently venous valves prevent backflow of blood, perform the following simple experiment. Allow one hand to hang by your side until the blood vessels on the dorsal aspect become distended. Place two fingertips against one of the distended veins and, pressing firmly, move the superior finger proximally along the vein and then release this finger. The vein will remain flattened and collapsed despite gravity. Then remove the distal fingertip and observe the rapid filling of the vein.

The transparent walls of the tiny capillaries are only one cell layer thick, consisting of just the endothelium underlain by a basal lamina, that is, the tunica intima. Because of this exceptional thinness, exchanges are easily made between the blood and tissue cells.

1. Obtain a slide showing a cross-sectional view of blood vessels and a microscope.

2. Using Figure 32.1b as a guide, scan the section to identify a thick-walled artery. Very often, but not always, its lumen will appear scalloped due to the constriction of its walls by the elastic tissue of the media.

3. Identify a vein. Its lumen may appear elongated or irregularly shaped and collapsed, and its walls will be considerably thinner. Notice the difference in the relative amount of elastic fibers in the media of the two vessels. Also, note the thinness of the intima layer, which is composed of flat squamous-type cells.

4. Make a drawing of your observations of the two vessel types below, and label the tunics. Try to indicate the proper size relationships relative to wall thickness and the tunic widths.

Artery

Vein

Artery	# 15218	
Vein	# 15219	
Capillary	# 14687	

MAJOR SYSTEMIC ARTERIES OF THE BODY

The **aorta** is the largest artery of the body. Extending upward as the ascending aorta from the left ventricle, it arches posteriorly and to the left (aortic arch) and then courses downward as the descending aorta through the thoracic cavity. It penetrates the diaphragm to enter the abdominal cavity just anterior to the vertebral column.

Figure 32.2 depicts the course of the aorta and its major branches. As you locate the arteries on the figure, be aware of ways in which you can make your memorization task easier. In many cases the name of the artery reflects the body region traversed (axillary, subclavian, brachial, popliteal), the organ served (renal, hepatic), or the bone followed (tibial, femoral, radial, ulnar). Once you have identified these arteries on the figure, attempt to locate and name them (without a reference) on a large anatomical chart or a three-dimensional model of the circulatory system vessels.

All arteries described here are shown in the figure, but some that are not described are also named and illustrated. Ask your instructor which arteries you are required to identify.

Ascending Aorta

The only branches of the ascending aorta are the **right and the left coronary arteries,** which supply the myocardium. The coronary arteries are described in Exercise 30 in conjunction with heart anatomy.

Aortic Arch

The **brachiocephalic,** (literally, "arm-head") **artery** is the first branch of the aortic arch. It persists briefly before dividing into the right **common carotid artery** and the right **subclavian artery.** The common carotid divides to form the **internal carotid artery,** which serves the brain, and the **external carotid artery,** which supplies the extracranial tissues of the neck and head. The subclavian artery gives off three branches to the head and neck, the most important being the **vertebral artery,** which runs up the posterior neck to supply a portion of the brain. In the axillary region, the subclavian artery becomes the **axillary artery** and then the **brachial artery** as it enters the arm. At the elbow, the brachial artery divides into the **radial** and **ulnar arteries,** which follow the same-named bones to supply the forearm and hand.

(Text continues on p. 313)

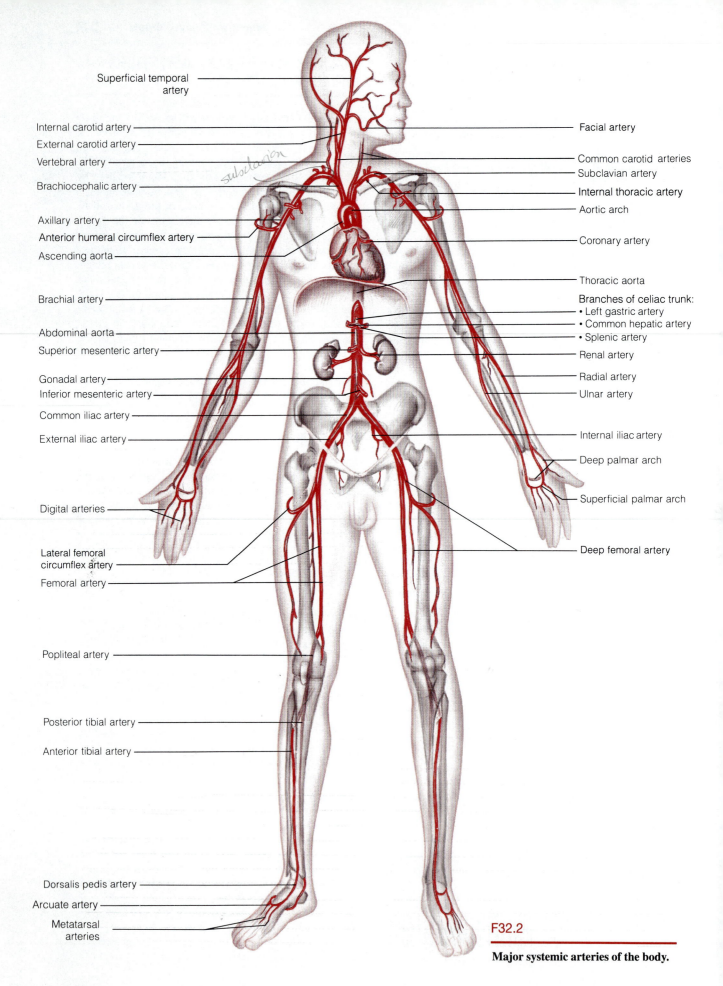

Superficial temporal
artery

Internal carotid artery

External carotid artery

Vertebral artery

subclavian

Brachiocephalic artery

Axillary artery

Anterior humeral circumflex artery

Ascending aorta

Brachial artery

Abdominal aorta

Superior mesenteric artery

Gonadal artery

Inferior mesenteric artery

Common iliac artery

External iliac artery

Digital arteries

Lateral femoral
circumflex artery

Femoral artery

Popliteal artery

Posterior tibial artery

Anterior tibial artery

Dorsalis pedis artery

Arcuate artery

Metatarsal
arteries

Facial artery

Common carotid arteries

Subclavian artery

Internal thoracic artery

Aortic arch

Coronary artery

Thoracic aorta

Branches of celiac trunk:
• Left gastric artery
• Common hepatic artery
• Splenic artery

Renal artery

Radial artery

Ulnar artery

Internal iliac artery

Deep palmar arch

Superficial palmar arch

Deep femoral artery

F32.2

Major systemic arteries of the body.

312

The **left common carotid artery,** the second branch of the aortic arch, supplies the left side of the head and neck in the same manner the right common carotid serves the right side. The third branch is the **left subclavian artery,** which supplies the left upper extremity and subdivides as described for the right subclavian artery.

Aorta   # 04475

Descending Aorta

Not shown in Figure 32.2 are the 9 or 10 pairs of *intercostal arteries* that supply the muscles of the thoracic wall. The intercostal arteries are small branches of the descending aorta, as are the *phrenic arteries,* which supply the diaphragm. Other more major branches of the descending aorta supply the abdominal region. The **celiac trunk** is an unpaired artery that subdivides into three branches: the **left gastric** artery supplying the stomach, the **splenic artery** supplying the spleen, and the **common hepatic artery,** which provides the functional blood supply of the liver. The largest branch of the descending aorta, the **superior mesenteric artery,** supplies most of the small intestine and the first half of the large intestine. The small paired **suprarenal arteries** emerge at approximately the same level as the superior mesenteric artery and run laterally to supply the adrenal glands. (These are not shown in Figure 32.2.) The paired **renal arteries** supply the kidneys, and the **gonadal arteries,** arising from the ventral surface of the aorta slightly below the renal arteries, run inferiorly to serve the gonads. They are called **ovarian arteries** in the female and **testicular** (or **internal spermatic) arteries** in the male. Since these vessels must travel through the inguinal canal to supply the testes in the male, they are considerably longer in the male than in the female. The small unpaired artery supplying the second half of the large intestine is the **inferior mesenteric artery.**

In the pelvic region, the descending aorta divides into the two large **common iliac arteries.** Each of these vessels extends for about 2 inches into the pelvis before it divides into the **internal iliac artery,** which supplies the pelvic organs (bladder, rectum, and some reproductive structures, such as the uterus, uterine tubes, and vas deferens), and the **external iliac artery,** which continues into the thigh, where its name changes to the **femoral artery.** A branch of the femoral artery, the **deep femoral artery,** supplies the posterior thigh. In the knee region, the femoral artery briefly becomes the **popliteal artery;** its subdivisions—the **anterior** and **posterior tibial arteries**—supply the leg, ankle, and foot. The posterior tibial gives off one main branch, the **peroneal artery** (not shown), which serves the lateral calf (peroneal muscles). The anterior tibial artery terminates at the **dorsalis pedis** artery, which supplies the dorsum of the foot and continues on as the **arcuate artery.** The dor-

salis pedis is often palpated in patients with circulation problems of the leg to determine the circulatory efficiency to the limb as a whole.

● Palpate your own dorsalis pedis artery.

External Carotid   # 46765
Artery, Branches

Brachial Artery   # 18448
(Cyan)

Radial Artery   # 18491
(Both Arrows)

External Iliac Artery   # 46945

MAJOR SYSTEMIC VEINS OF THE BODY

Arteries are generally located in deep, well-protected body areas. However, many veins follow a more superficial course and are often easily seen and palpated on the body surface (Figure 32.3). Most deep veins parallel the course of the major arteries; thus in many cases the naming of the veins and arteries is identical except for the designation of the vessels as veins. Whereas the major systemic arteries branch off the aorta, the veins tend to converge on the venae cavae, which enter the right atrium of the heart. Veins draining the head and upper extremities empty into the **superior vena cava,** and those draining the lower body empty into the **inferior vena cava.**

Veins Draining into the Superior Vena Cava

Veins draining into the superior vena cava are named from the superior vena cava distally; **but remember that the flow of blood is in the opposite direction.**

The **right** and **left brachiocephalic veins** drain the head, neck, and upper extremities and unite to form the superior vena cava. (Note that although there is only one brachiocephalic artery, there are two brachiocephalic veins.)

Branches of the brachiocephalic veins include the **internal jugular veins,** large veins that drain the superior sagittal sinus and other dural sinuses of the brain; the **vertebral veins,** which drain the posterior aspect of the head; and the **subclavian veins,** which receive venous blood from the upper extremity. The **external jugular vein** joins the subclavian vein near its origin to return the venous drainage of the extracranial tissues of the head and neck. As the subclavian vein traverses the

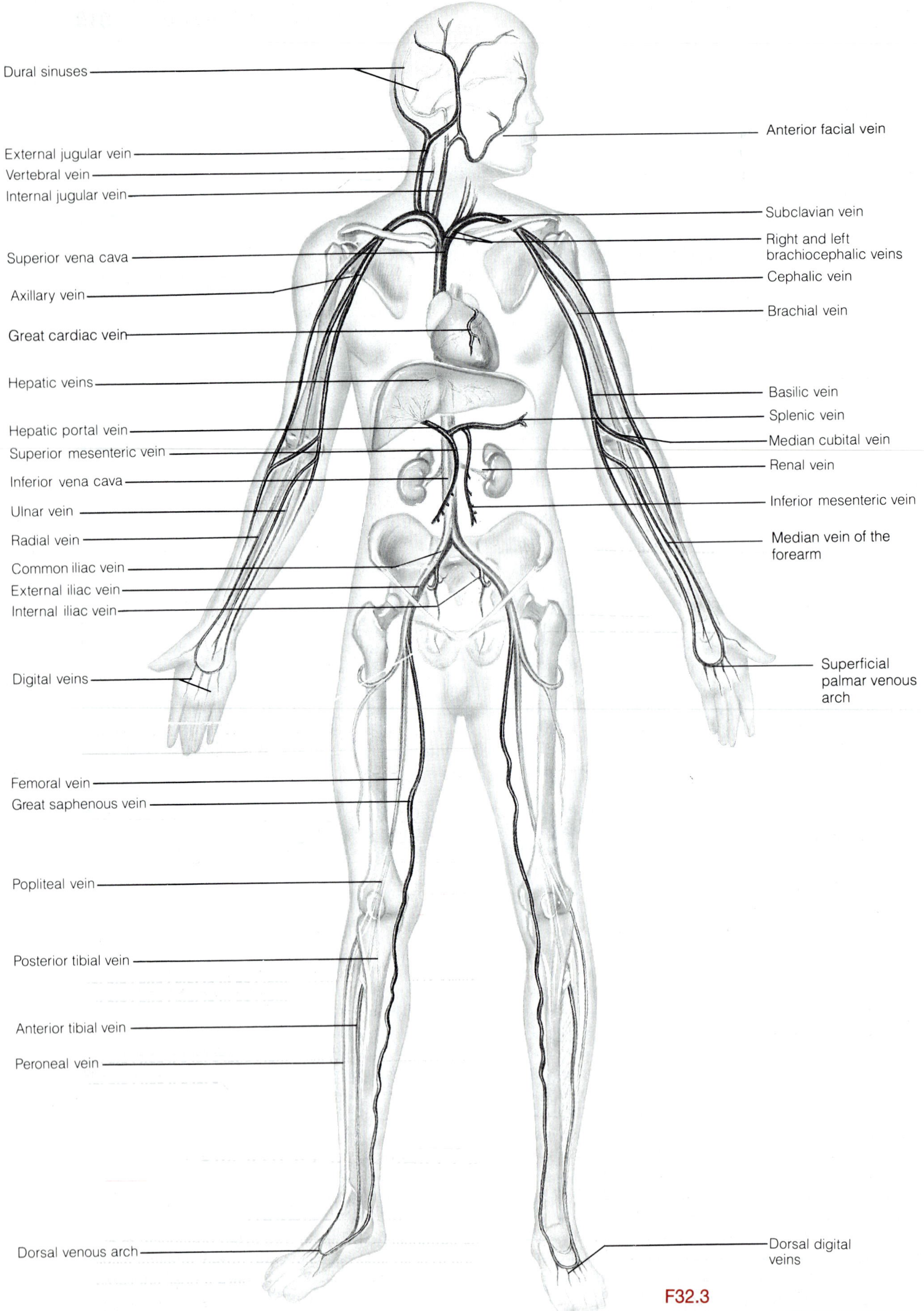

Dural sinuses

Anterior facial vein

External jugular vein
Vertebral vein
Internal jugular vein

Subclavian vein

Right and left
brachiocephalic veins

Superior vena cava

Cephalic vein

Axillary vein

Brachial vein

Great cardiac vein

Hepatic veins

Basilic vein

Splenic vein

Hepatic portal vein

Median cubital vein

Superior mesenteric vein

Renal vein

Inferior vena cava

Inferior mesenteric vein

Ulnar vein

Radial vein

Median vein of the
forearm

Common iliac vein
External iliac vein
Internal iliac vein

Digital veins

Superficial
palmar venous
arch

Femoral vein
Great saphenous vein

Popliteal vein

Posterior tibial vein

Anterior tibial vein

Peroneal vein

Dorsal venous arch

Dorsal digital
veins

F32.3

Major systemic veins of the body.

axilla, it becomes the **axillary vein** and then the **brachial vein** as it courses along the posterior aspect of the humerus. The brachial vein is formed by the union of the deep **radial** and **ulnar veins** of the forearm. The superficially located venous drainage of the arm includes the **cephalic vein,** which courses along the lateral aspect of the arm and empties into the axillary vein; the **basilic vein,** found on the medial aspect of the arm and entering the brachial vein; and the **median cubital vein,** which runs between the cephalic and basilic veins in the anterior aspect of the elbow (this vein is often the site of choice for removing blood for testing purposes).

The **azygos vein,** part of the *azygos system* that drains the intercostal muscles of the thorax and provides an accessory venous system to drain the abdominal wall, enters the dorsal aspect of the superior vena cava immediately before it enters the right atrium. The azygos system, depicted in Figure 32.4, also includes the **hemiazygos** and **accessory hemiazygos veins,** which together drain the left aspect of the thorax and empty into the azygos vein. The azygos vein drains the right aspect of the thorax.

Superior Sagittal Sinus	# 31436
Veins, Cerebral Superficial	# 44701

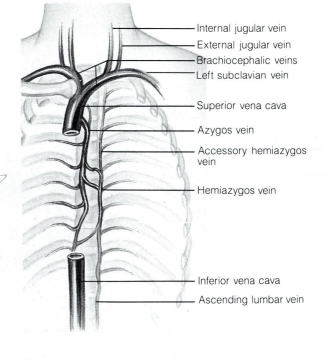

F32.4

The azygos system.

Internal jugular vein
External jugular vein
Brachiocephalic veins
Left subclavian vein
Superior vena cava
Azygos vein
Accessory hemiazygos vein
Hemiazygos vein
Inferior vena cava
Ascending lumbar vein

Veins Draining into the Inferior Vena Cava

The inferior vena cava, a much longer vessel than the superior vena cava, returns blood to the heart from all body regions below the diaphragm (see Figure 32.3). It begins in the lower abdominal region with the union of the paired **common iliac veins,** which drain venous blood from the legs and pelvis. Each common iliac vein in turn is formed by the union of the **internal iliac vein,** draining the pelvis, and the **external iliac vein,** which receives venous blood from the lower limb. Veins of the leg include the **anterior** and **posterior tibial veins,** which serve the calf and foot. The posterior tibial vein becomes the **popliteal vein** in the knee region and the **femoral vein** in the thigh. The femoral vein empties into the external iliac vein in the inguinal region. The **great saphenous vein,** a superficial vein, is the longest vein of the body. Beginning in the foot with the **dorsal venous arch,** it extends up the medial side of the leg, knee, and thigh to empty into the femoral vein. Moving superiorly into the abdominal cavity, the inferior vena cava receives blood from the **right gonadal vein** (testicular or spermatic vein in the male; ovarian vein in the female), which drains the right gonad. (The left testicular or ovarian vein drains into the left renal vein.) The **right** and **left renal veins** drain the kidneys, and the **right** and **left hepatic veins** drain the liver. The unpaired veins draining the digestive tract organs empty into a special vessel, the **hepatic portal vein,** which carries this blood

through the liver before it enters the systemic venous system. (The hepatic portal system is discussed separately on p. 317.)

     Identify the important arteries and veins on the large anatomical chart or model without referring to the figures.

Axillary Vein	# 18412
Greater Saphenous Vein and Nerve	# 47906

SPECIAL CIRCULATIONS

Pulmonary Circulation

The pulmonary circulation (discussed previously in relation to heart anatomy on p. 299) differs in many ways from the systemic circulation, because it does not serve the metabolic needs of the body tissues with which it is associated (in this case, lung tissue). It functions instead

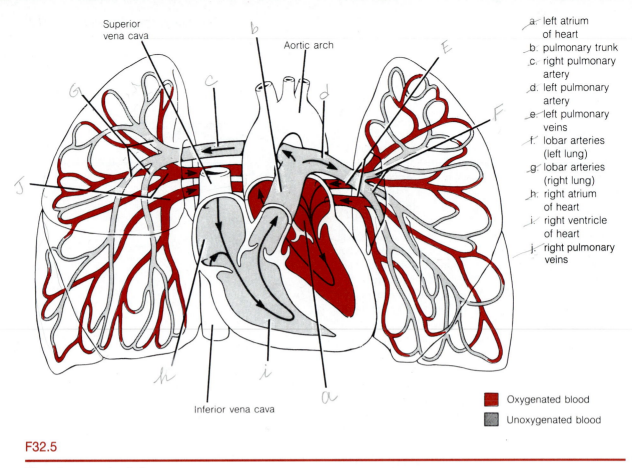

Superior
vena cava

Aortic arch

b

G

c

E

d

J

F

a. left atrium
of heart
b. pulmonary trunk
c. right pulmonary
artery
d. left pulmonary
artery
e. left pulmonary
veins
f. lobar arteries
(left lung)
g. lobar arteries
(right lung)
h. right atrium
of heart
i. right ventricle
of heart
j. right pulmonary
veins

h

i

a

Inferior vena cava

■ Oxygenated blood
■ Unoxygenated blood

F32.5

The pulmonary circulation.

to bring the blood into close contact with the alveoli of the lungs to permit gas exchanges that rid the blood of excess carbon dioxide and replenish its supply of vital oxygen. The arteries of the pulmonary circulation are structurally much like veins; thus they create a low pressure bed in the lungs. (If the arterial pressure in the systemic circulation is 120/80, the pressure in the pulmonary artery is likely to be approximately 25/10.) The functional blood supply of the lungs is provided by the **bronchial arteries,** which diverge from the thoracic portion of the descending aorta.

Pulmonary circulation begins with the large **pulmonary trunk,** which leaves the right ventricle and divides into the **right** and **left pulmonary arteries** about 2 inches above its origin (Figure 32.5). The right and left pulmonary arteries plunge into the lungs, where they subdivide into the **lobar arteries** (three on the right and two on the left), which accompany the main bronchi into the lobes of the lungs. Within the lungs, the lobar arteries branch extensively to form the arterioles, which finally terminate in the capillary networks surrounding the alveolar sacs of the lungs. Diffusion of the respiratory gases occurs across the walls of the alveoli and **pulmonary capillaries.** The pulmonary capillary beds are drained by venules, which converge to form sequentially larger veins and finally the four **pulmonary veins** (two leaving each lung), which return the blood to the left atrium of the heart.

- Using the terms provided in Figure 32.5, **label** all structures provided with leader lines.

Arterial Supply of the Brain and the Circle of Willis

A continuous blood supply to the brain is crucial, since deprivation for even a few minutes causes irreparable damage to the delicate brain tissue. The brain is supplied by two pairs of arteries arising from the region of the aortic arch—the *internal carotid arteries* and the *vertebral arteries*. Figure 32.6 is a diagram of the brain's arterial supply.

Basilar Artery   # 04544

- The internal carotid and vertebral arteries are labeled. As you read the description of the blood supply below, **complete the labeling of this diagram.**

The **internal carotid arteries,** branches of the common carotid arteries, follow a deep course through the neck and along the pharynx, entering the skull through the carotid canals of the temporal bone. Within the cranium, each divides into the **anterior** and **middle cerebral** arteries, which supply the bulk of the cerebrum. The internal carotid arteries also contribute to the formation of the **circle of Willis,** an arterial anastomosis at the base of the brain surrounding the pituitary gland and the optic chiasma, by forming a **posterior communicating artery** on each side. The circle is completed by the **anterior communicating artery,** a short shunt connecting the right and left anterior cerebral arteries.

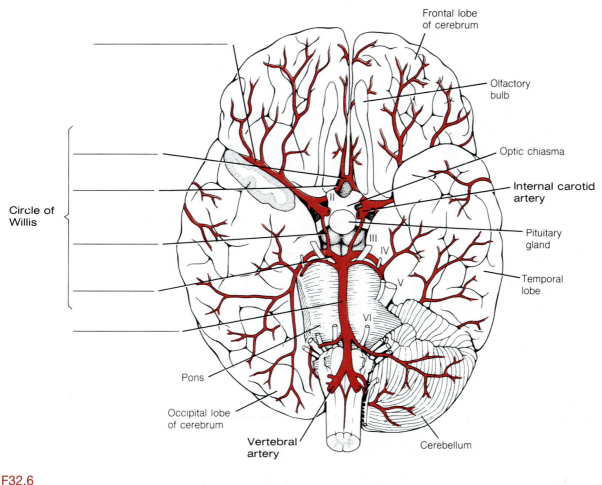

Frontal lobe
of cerebrum

Olfactory
bulb

Optic chiasma

**Internal carotid
artery**

Pituitary
gland

Temporal
lobe

Circle of
Willis

Pons

Occipital lobe
of cerebrum

Vertebral
artery

Cerebellum

Arterial supply of the brain. (Cerebellum is not shown on the left side of the figure.)

The paired **vertebral arteries** diverge from the subclavian arteries and pass superiorly through the foramina of the transverse process of the cervical vertebrae to enter the skull through the foramen magnum. Within the skull, the vertebral arteries unite to form a single **basilar artery,** which continues superiorly along the ventral aspect of the brain stem, giving off branches to the pons, cerebellum, and inner ear. At the base of the cerebrum, the artery divides to form the **posterior cerebral arteries,** which supply portions of the temporal and occipital lobes of the cerebrum and also become part of the circle of Willis by joining with the posterior communicating arteries.

The uniting of the blood supply of the internal carotid arteries and the vertebral arteries via the circle of Willis is a protective device that theoretically provides an alternate set of pathways for blood to reach the brain tissue in the case of arterial occlusion or impaired blood flow anywhere in the system. In actuality, the communicating arteries are tiny, and in many cases the communicating system is defective.

Hepatic Portal Circulation

Blood vessels of the hepatic portal circulation drain the digestive viscera, spleen, and pancreas and deliver this blood to the liver for processing via the **hepatic portal vein.** If a meal has recently been eaten, the hepatic portal blood will contain a high concentration of nutrient substances. Since the liver is a key body organ involved in maintaining proper sugar, fatty acid, and amino acid concentrations in the blood, this system ensures that these substances pass through the liver before entering the systemic circulation. As blood percolates through the liver sinusoids, some of the nutrients are removed to be stored or processed in various ways for release to the general circulation. At the same time, the hepatocytes are detoxifying alcohol and other possibly harmful chemicals present in the blood, and the liver's macrophages are removing bacteria and other debris from the passing blood. The liver in turn is drained by the hepatic veins that enter the inferior vena cava.

The **inferior mesenteric vein,** draining the transverse and terminal portions of the large intestine, drains

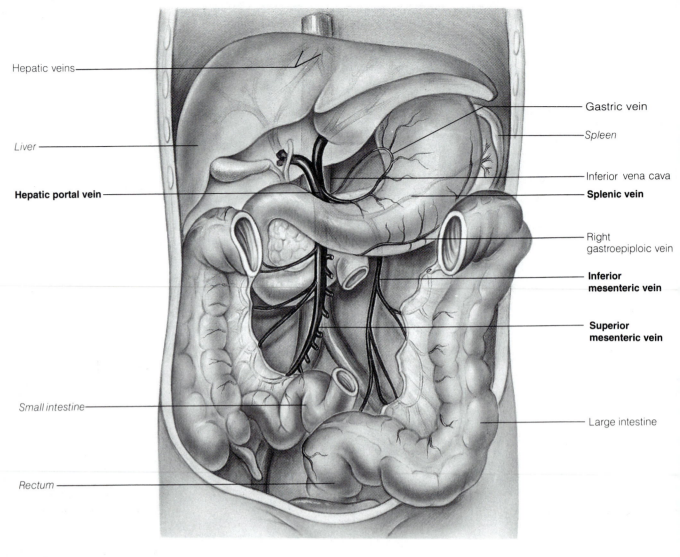

Hepatic veins

Liver

Hepatic portal vein

Small intestine

Rectum

Gastric vein

Spleen

Inferior vena cava

Splenic vein

Right gastroepiploic vein

Inferior mesenteric vein

Superior mesenteric vein

Large intestine

F32.7

Hepatic portal circulation of the human.

into the **splenic vein,** which drains the spleen, pancreas, and greater curvature of the stomach. The splenic vein and the **superior mesenteric vein,** which receives blood from the small intestine and the ascending colon, join to form the hepatic portal vein. The **gastric vein,** which drains the lesser curvature of the stomach, drains directly into the hepatic portal vein.

- **Locate** the vessels named above on Figure 32.7.

Fetal Circulation

In a developing fetus, the lungs and digestive system are not yet functional, and all nutrient, excretory, and gaseous exchanges must occur through the placenta (see Figure 32.8). Nutrients and oxygen move across placental barriers from the mother's blood into fetal blood, and carbon dioxide and other metabolic wastes move from the fetal blood supply to the mother's blood.

Fetal blood travels through the umbilical cord, which contains three blood vessels: two smaller umbilical arteries and one large umbilical vein. The **umbilical vein** carries blood rich in nutrients and oxygen to the fetus; the **umbilical arteries** carry carbon dioxide and waste-laden blood from the fetus to the placenta. The umbilical arteries, which transport blood away from the fetal heart, meet the umbilical vein at the *umbilicus* (navel, or belly button) and wrap around the vein within the cord en route to their placental attachments. Newly oxygenated blood flows in the umbilical vein superiorly toward the fetal heart. En route, some of this blood perfuses the liver, but a larger proportion is ducted through the relatively nonfunctional liver to the inferior vena cava via a vessel called the **ductus venosus,** which carries the blood to the right atrium of the heart.

Because fetal lungs are nonfunctional and collapsed, two shunting mechanisms ensure that blood al-

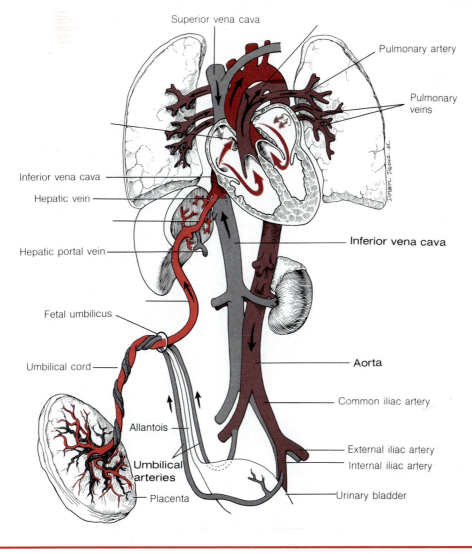

Superior vena cava

Pulmonary artery

Pulmonary veins

Inferior vena cava

Hepatic vein

Inferior vena cava

Hepatic portal vein

Fetal umbilicus

Aorta

Umbilical cord

Common iliac artery

Allantois

External iliac artery

Internal iliac artery

Umbilical arteries

Urinary bladder

Placenta

F32.8

The fetal circulation.

most entirely bypasses the lungs. Much of the blood entering the right atrium is shunted into the left atrium through a flaplike opening in the interatrial septum—the **foramen ovale.** The left ventricle then pumps the blood out the aorta to the systemic circulation. Blood that does enter the right ventricle and is pumped out of the pulmonary trunk encounters a second shunt, the **ductus arteriosus,** a short vessel connecting the pulmonary trunk and the aorta. Because the collapsed lungs present an extremely high-resistance pathway, blood more readily enters the systemic circulation through the ductus arteriosus.

The aorta carries blood to the tissues of the body; this blood ultimately finds its way back to the placenta via the umbilical arteries. The only fetal vessel that carries highly oxygenated blood is the umbilical vein; all other vessels contain varying degrees of oxygenated and deoxygenated blood.

At birth, or shortly after, the foramen ovale closes and becomes the **fossa ovalis,** and the ductus arteriosus collapses and is converted to the fibrous **ligamentum arteriosum.** Lack of blood flow through the umbilical vessels leads to their eventual obliteration, and the circulatory pattern becomes that of the adult. Remnants of

the umbilical arteries persist as the **medial umbilical ligaments** on the inner surface of the anterior abdominal wall, of the umbilical vein as the **ligamentum teres** or **round ligament** of the liver, and of the ductus venosus as a fibrous band called the **ligamentum venosus** on the inferior surface of the liver.

The pathway of fetal blood flow is indicated with arrows on Figure 32.8. Appropriately **label** all specialized fetal circulatory structures provided with leader lines.

DISSECTION OF FETAL PIG BLOOD VESSELS

Opening the Ventral Body Cavity

To identify the blood vessels of the circulatory system of the pig, it is necessary to open the ventral body cavity. The outline drawing provided in the inset on Figure 32.9a indicates where to make the incisions.

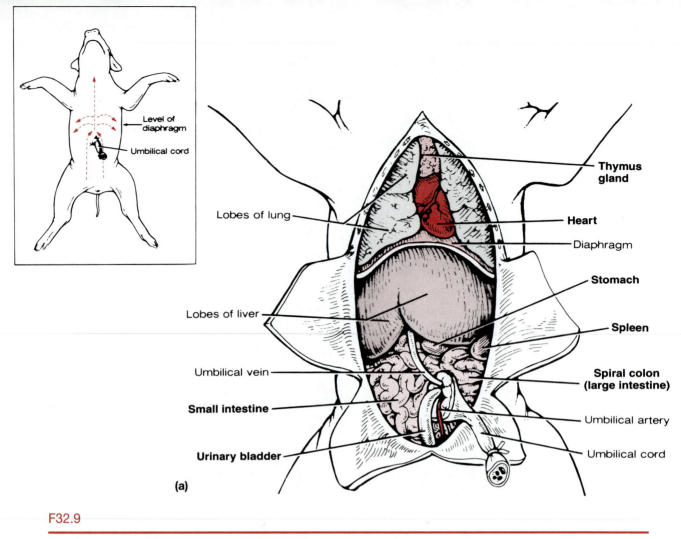

F32.9

Ventral body cavity organs of the fetal pig, greater omentum removed. (a) Diagrammatic view. (Inset indicates incision lines for opening ventral body cavity.)

(continued)

1. Place the pig dorsal side down on the dissecting pan and secure its forelimbs and hindlimbs with cord. Using scissors, make two longitudinal incisions through the ventral body wall beginning just superior and lateral to the midline of the pubic bone. Cut to and then around each side of the umbilical cord until the cuts meet medially. Continue anteriorly to the rib cage with a single midline incision.

2. Angle the scissors slightly (½ inch) to the right or left of the sternum, and continue the cut through the rib cartilages just lateral to the body midline, to the base of the throat.

3. Make two lateral cuts on either side of the ventral body surface, anterior and posterior to the diaphragm. Leave the diaphragm intact. Spread the thoracic walls laterally to expose the thoracic organs.

4. If the body cavity contains a dark fluid, flush it out with tap water before continuing.

5. Using Figure 32.9 as a guide, identify the organs of the thoracic and abdominal cavities.

THORACIC CAVITY ORGANS

Thymus: a large, brownish elongated mass of tissue seen extending over the heart and superior thoracic organs
Heart: in the mediastinum enclosed by the pericardium
Lungs: flank the heart
Thyroid gland: an oval, reddish organ (gland) seen at the base of the throat

ABDOMINAL CAVITY ORGANS

Liver: a large, brown, multilobed organ posterior to the diaphragm
Stomach: lies to the left and nearly covered by the liver
Spleen: a brown organ curving around the lateral aspect of the stomach

320

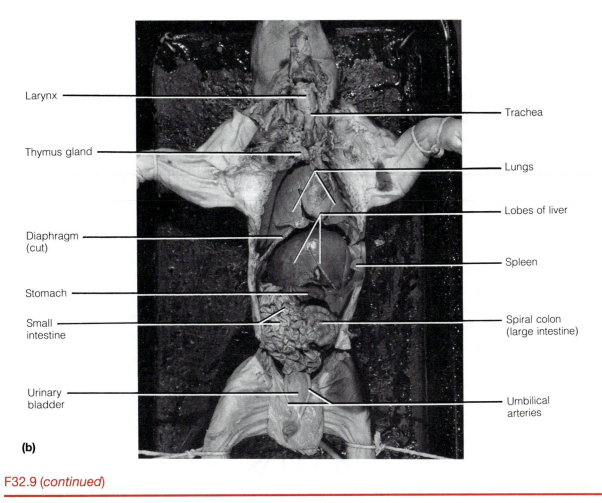

Larynx

Thymus gland

Diaphragm
(cut)

Stomach

Small
intestine

Urinary
bladder

Trachea

Lungs

Lobes of liver

Spleen

Spiral colon
(large intestine)

Umbilical
arteries

(b)

F32.9 (*continued*)

Ventral body cavity organs of the fetal pig, greater omentum removed. (b) Photograph (see corresponding Plate C in the Pig Anatomy Atlas).

Small intestine: continues posteriorly from the stomach

Large intestine: a large composite mass of coils lying within the coils of the small intestine

Urinary bladder: the large saclike structure seen attached to and entering the umbilical cord in the lower abdominal wall

Preparing to Identify the Blood Vessels of the Body

1. Carefully clear away any thymus tissue or fat obscuring the heart and the large vessels associated with the heart. Before identifying the blood vessels, try to locate the *phrenic nerve* (from the cervical plexus), which innervates the diaphragm. The phrenic nerves can be seen ventral to the root of the lung on each side, passing to the diaphragm. Also attempt to locate the *vagus nerve* (cranial nerve X) passing laterally along the trachea and dorsal to the root of the lung.

2. Slit the parietal pericardium and reflect it superiorly; then cut it away from its heart attachments. Review the structures of the heart. Notice its pointed inferior end (apex) and its broader superior base. Identify the two atria, which appear darker than the inferior ventricles. Identify the coronary arteries in the sulcus on the ventral surface of the heart; these should be injected with red latex. (As an aid to blood vessel identification, laboratory specimens prepared for dissection have the arteries injected with red latex and the veins injected with blue latex. Exceptions to this will be noted as they are encountered.)

3. Identify the two large venae cavae—the **anterior** and **posterior venae cavae**—entering the right atrium. (These vessels are homologous to the superior and inferior venae cavae, respectively, in the human.) The caval veins drain the same relative body areas as in humans. The anterior vena cava is the largest dark-colored vessel entering the base of the heart. Also identify the **pulmonary trunk** (usually injected with blue latex) extending anteriorly from the right ventricle and the **right** and **left pulmonary arteries.** Trace the pulmonary arteries until they enter the lungs. Locate the **pulmonary veins** entering the left atrium and the **ascending aorta** arising from the left ventricle running dorsally to the an-

Subtract the respective baseline readings of systolic and diastolic blood pressure from the highest single reading of systolic and diastolic pressure obtained during cold immersion (that is, if the highest experimental reading is 140/88 and the baseline reading is 120/70, then the differences in blood pressure would be indicated as: systolic pressure, 20 mm Hg; and diastolic pressure, 18 mm Hg). These differences are called the **index of response.** According to their index of response, subjects can be classified as follows:

hyporeactors: (stable blood pressure)—exhibit a rise of diastolic and/or systolic pressure ranging from 0 to 22 mm Hg; or a drop in pressures
hyperreactors: (labile blood pressure)—exhibit a rise of 23 mm Hg or more in the diastolic and/or systolic blood pressure

Is the subject tested a hypo- or hyperreactor?

_____

SKIN COLOR AS AN INDICATOR OF LOCAL CIRCULATORY DYNAMICS

Careful observation of skin color under carefully controlled conditions reveals (with surprising accuracy) the state of the local circulation, and allows inferences concerning the larger blood vessels and the circulation as a whole. The experiments on local circulation outlined below illustrate a number of fundamental factors that affect blood flow to the tissues.

Clinical expertise when conducting a physical examination depends upon good observation skills, accurate recording of data, and logical interpretation of the findings. A single example will be given to demonstrate this statement: A massive hemorrhage may be internal and hidden (thus, not obvious), but will still threaten the blood delivery to the brain and other vital organs. One of the earliest compensatory reactions of the body to such a threat is constriction of cutaneous blood vessels, which reduces blood flow to the skin and diverts it into the circulatory mainstream to serve other, more vital tissues. As a result, the skin of the face and particularly of the extremities becomes pale, cold, and finally moist with perspiration. Therefore, a pale, cold, clammy skin should immediately lead the careful diagnostician to suspect that the circulation is dangerously inefficient. Other conditions, such as local arterial obstruction and venous congestion, as well as certain pathologies of the heart and lungs, also alter skin texture, color, and circulation in characteristic ways.

The local blood supply to the skin (indeed, to any tissue) is influenced by (1) local metabolites, (2) oxygen supply, (3) local temperature, (4) autonomic nervous system impulses, (5) local vascular reflexes, (6) certain hormones, and (7) substances released by injured tissues. A number of these factors are examined in the simple experiments that follow. Each experiment should be conducted by students in groups of three or four. One student will act as the subject; the others will conduct the tests, and make and record observations.

Vasodilation and Flushing of the Skin Due to Local Metabolites

1. Obtain a blood pressure cuff (sphygmomanometer) and stethoscope. A watch with a second hand will also be needed.

2. The subject should bare both arms by rolling up the sleeves as high as possible and then lay his forearms side by side on the bench top.

3. Observe the general color of the subject's forearm skin, and the normal contour and size of his veins. Notice whether skin color is bilaterally similar. Record your observations:

_____

_____

4. Apply the blood pressure cuff to one arm, and inflate it to 250 mm Hg. Keep it inflated for 1 min. During this period, repeat the observations made above and record the results:

_____

_____

5. Release the pressure in the cuff (leaving the deflated cuff in position), and again record the forearm skin color and the condition of the forearm veins. Make this observation immediately after deflation and then again 30 sec later.

immediately after deflation _____

_____

30 sec after deflation _____

_____

The above observations constitute your baseline information. Now conduct the following tests.

6. Instruct the subject to raise his cuffed arm above his head and to clench his fist as tightly as possible. While his hand and forearm muscles are tightly contracted, rapidly inflate the cuff to 240 mm Hg or more. This maneuver partially empties the hand and forearm of blood, and stops most blood flow to the hand and forearm. Once the cuff has been inflated, the subject is to relax his fist and return his forearm to the bench top so that it can easily be compared to the other forearm.

7.   Leave the cuff inflated for exactly 1 min. During this interval, compare the skin color in the "ischemic" (blood-deprived) hand to that of the "normal" (non-cuffed-limb) hand. Quickly release the pressure immediately after the 1-min count.

What are the subjective effects* of stopping blood flow to the arm and hand for 1 min?

_____

_____

What are the objective effects (color of skin and venous condition)?

_____

_____

How long does it take for the subject's ischemic hand to resume its normal color?

_____

Effects of Venous Congestion

1.   Again, but with a different subject, observe and record the appearance of the skin and veins on the forelimbs resting on the bench top. This time, pay particular attention to the color of the fingers, particularly the distal phalanges, and the nail beds. Record this information:

_____

_____

2.   Wrap the blood pressure cuff around one of the subject's arms, and inflate it to 40 mm Hg. Maintain this pressure for 5 min. Make a record of the subjective and objective findings just before the 5 min are up, and then again immediately after release of the pressure at the end of 5 min.

subjective (arm cuffed) _____

_____

objective (arm cuffed) _____

_____

subjective (pressure released) _____

_____

* Subjective effects are sensations—such as pain, coldness, warmth, tingling, and weakness—experienced by the subject. They are "symptoms" of a change in function.

objective (pressure released) _____

_____

3.   With still another subject, conduct the following simple experiment: Raise one arm above the head, and let the other hang by the side for 1 min. After 1 min, quickly lay both arms on the bench top, and compare their color.

color of raised arm _____

color of dependent arm _____

From this and the two preceding observations, analyze the factors that determine tint of color (pink or blue) and intensity of skin color (deep pink or blue as opposed to light pink or blue). Record your conclusions:

_____

_____

_____

_____

_____

Collateral Blood Flow

In some diseases, blood flow to an organ through one or more arteries may be completely and irreversibly obstructed. Fortunately, in most cases a given body area is supplied both by one main artery and by anastomosing channels connecting the main artery with one or more neighboring blood vessels. Consequently, an organ may remain viable even though its main arterial supply is occluded, as long as the **collateral vessels** are still functional.

    The effectiveness of collateral blood flow in preventing ischemia can be easily demonstrated.

1.   Check the subject's hands to be sure they are *warm* to the touch. If not, choose another, "warm-handed" subject, or warm the subject's hands in 35°C water for 10 min before beginning.

2.   Palpate the subject's radial and ulnar arteries approximately 1 in. above the wrist flexure, and mark their locations with a felt marker.

3.   Instruct the subject to supinate one forearm and to hold it in a partially flexed (about a 30° angle) position, with the elbow resting on the bench top.

4.   Face the subject and grasp his or her forearm with both of your hands, the thumb and fingers of one hand compressing the marked radial artery and the thumb and fingers of the other hand compressing the ulnar artery.

The Lymphatic System and Immune Response

OBJECTIVES

1. To name the components of the lymphatic system.

2. To relate the function of the lymphatic system to that of the blood vascular system.

3. To describe the formation and composition of lymph, and to describe how it is transported through the lymphatic vessels.

4. To relate the importance of immunologic memory, specificity, and differentiation of self from nonself to immune function.

5. To differentiate between the roles of B cells and T cells in the immune response.

6. To describe the structure and function of lymph nodes, and to indicate the localization of T cells, B cells, and macrophages in a typical lymph node.

7. To describe (or draw) the structure of the immunoglobulin monomer, and to name the five immunoglobulin subclasses.

8. To discuss the immunologic "abnormality" evidenced by many rheumatoid arthritis sufferers.

MATERIALS

Large anatomical chart of the human lymphatic system
Dissection animal, tray, and dissection instruments
Prepared microscope slides of lymph nodes
Compound microscope

Microscope slide
Wax marking pencil
Applicator sticks
Arthritis screening test (Wampole)
pH paper
Plastic (disposable) gloves
Disposable autoclave bag

THE LYMPHATIC SYSTEM

General Description

The **lymphatic system** consists of a network of successively larger lymphatic vessels (lymphatics), lymph nodes, and a number of other lymphoid organs, such as the tonsils, thymus, and spleen (Figure 35.1). We will focus on the lymphatic vessels and lymph nodes in this section. The overall function of the lymphatic system is twofold. It returns tissue fluid (lymph) to the blood vessels. Because lymph flows only toward the heart, it is a one-way system. In addition, it protects the body by removing foreign material such as bacteria from the lymphatic stream and by serving as a site for lymphocyte "policing" of body fluids and lymphocyte multiplication. The function of these white blood cells in body immunity is described later in this exercise.

Distribution and Function of Lymphatic Vessels and Lymph Nodes

As blood circulates through the body, the hydrostatic and osmotic pressures operating at the capillary beds result in an outward flow of fluid at the arterial end of the

bed and in its return at the venous end. However, not all of the lost fluid is returned to the bloodstream by this mechanism; and the fluid that lags behind in the tissue spaces must eventually return to the blood if the vascular system is to operate properly. (If it does not, fluid accumulates in the tissues, producing a condition called edema.) It is the microscopic, blind-ended **lymphatic capillaries,** which ramify through all the tissues of the body, that pick up this leaked fluid (primarily water and a small amount of dissolved proteins) and carry it through successively larger vessels—**lymphatic collecting vessels** to **lymphatic trunks**—until the lymph finally returns to the venous system through one of the two large ducts in the thoracic region. The **right lymphatic duct** drains lymph from the right upper extremity, head, and thorax; the large **thoracic duct** receives lymph from the rest of the body (Figure 35.1b). In humans, both ducts empty the lymph into the venous circulation at the junction of the internal jugular vein and the subclavian vein, on their respective sides of the body.

Like veins of the blood vascular system, the lymphatic collecting vessels have three tunics and are equipped with valves. However, the lymphatics tend to be thinner-walled, to have *more* valves, and to anastomose more than veins. Since the lymphatic system is a pumpless system, lymph transport depends largely on

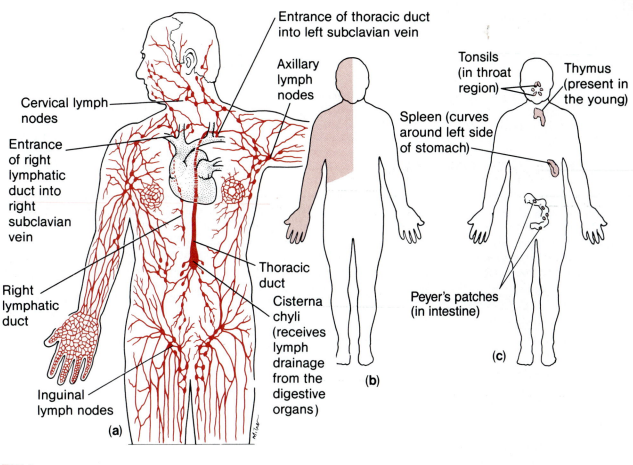

Cervical lymph nodes

Entrance of thoracic duct into left subclavian vein

Axillary lymph nodes

Entrance of right lymphatic duct into right subclavian vein

Right lymphatic duct

Thoracic duct

Cisterna chyli (receives lymph drainage from the digestive organs)

Inguinal lymph nodes

(a)

(b)

Tonsils (in throat region)

Thymus (present in the young)

Spleen (curves around left side of stomach)

Peyer's patches (in intestine)

(c)

F35.1

Lymphatic system. (a) Distribution of lymphatic vessels and lymph nodes. (b) Dark area represents body area drained by the right lymphatic duct. (c) Body location of the tonsils, thymus, spleen, and Peyer's patches.

the milking action of the skeletal muscles and on pressure changes within the thorax during breathing.

As lymph is transported, it filters through oval or bean-shaped **lymph nodes,** which cluster along the lymphatic vessels of the body. There are thousands of lymph nodes; but because they are usually embedded in connective tissue, they are not ordinarily seen. Within the lymph nodes are **phagocytic cells (macrophages),** which destroy bacteria, cancer cells, and other foreign matter in the lymphatic stream, thus rendering many harmful substances or cells harmless before the lymph enters the bloodstream. Particularly large collections of lymph nodes are found in the inguinal, axillary, and cervical regions of the body. Although we are not usually aware of the filtering and protective nature of the lymph nodes, most of us have experienced "swollen glands" during an active infection. This swelling is a manifestation of the trapping function of the nodes.

The tonsils, thymus, and spleen are generally considered to be lymphoid organs because they resemble the lymph nodes histologically, and house similar cell populations (lymphocytes and macrophages).

Study the large anatomical chart to observe the general plan of the lymphatic system. Notice the distribution of the lymph nodes, the various lymphatics, the lymphatic trunks, and the location of the right lymphatic duct and the thoracic duct. Also identify the **cisterna chyli,** the enlarged terminus of the thoracic duct that receives lymph from the digestive viscera.

Thoracic Duct	# 44526	
Lymphatics, Inguinal Nodes	# 47144	
Cervical Nodes	# 53412	

MAIN LYMPHATIC DUCTS OF THE FETAL PIG

1.   Obtain your pig and a dissecting tray and instruments. Because the lymphatic vessels are extremely thin-walled, it is difficult to locate them in a dissection; however, the large thoracic duct can be localized and identified.

2.   Move the thoracic organs to the side to find the **thoracic duct** traveling through the thorax just to the left of the mid-dorsal line and abutting the dorsal aspect of the descending aorta. It is usually about the size of pencil lead and commonly red-brown with a segmented or beaded appearance caused by the valves within it. Trace it anteriorly to the site where it passes behind the left brachiocephalic vein and then bends and enters the venous system at the junction of the left subclavian and external jugular veins. If the venous system is well injected, some of the blue latex may have slipped past the valves and entered the first portion of the thoracic duct.

3.   While in this region, also attempt to identify the short **right lymphatic duct** draining into the right subclavian vein, and note the collection of lymph nodes in the axillary region.

4.   Clean the dissecting instruments and tray, and properly wrap and return the animal to storage before continuing with the laboratory exercise.

THE IMMUNE RESPONSE

The **immune system** is a functional system that recognizes something as foreign and acts to destroy or neutralize it. This is known as the **immune response.** When operating effectively, the immune response protects us from bacterial and viral infections, bacterial toxins, and cancer. When it fails or malfunctions, the body is quickly devastated by pathogens or its own assaults.

Major Characteristics of the Immune Response

The most important characteristics of the immune response are its (1) **memory,** (2) **specificity,** and (3) **ability to differentiate self from nonself.** Not only does the immune system have a "memory" for previously encountered antigens (molecules foreign to the body—the chicken pox virus for example), this memory is remarkably accurate and highly specific.

An almost limitless variety of macromolecules is *antigenic*—that is, capable of provoking an immune response and reacting with its products. Nearly all foreign proteins, many polysaccharides, and many small molecules (haptens), when linked to our own body proteins, exhibit this capability. The cells that recognize antigens and initiate the immune response are lymphocytes. (As described in Exercise 29, lymphocytes are the most numerous members of the leukocyte or white blood cell (WBC) population.) Each immunocompetent lymphocyte is virtually monospecific; that is, it has receptors on its surface allowing it to bind with only one or a few very similar antigens. Following such binding, the lymphocyte proliferates; and its members differentiate—some forming memory cells and others becoming effector or regulatory cells. Upon subsequent meetings with the same antigen, the immune response proceeds considerably faster because the "troops are already mobilized and awaiting further orders," so to speak.

As a rule, our own proteins are tolerated, a fact that reflects the ability of the immune system to distinguish our own tissues (self) from foreign antigens (nonself). Nevertheless, an inability to recognize self can and does occasionally happen and our own tissues are attacked by the immune system. This phenomenon is called *autoimmunity.*

The immune response is genetically controlled by the immune response (Ir) gene complex, which is located on the same chromosome(s) as the MHC genes that direct the production of cell-surface proteins that identify as "self" the cells upon which they are located. Together the Ir and MHC genes form part of the *major histocompatibility complex,* a gene segment crucial in the regulation of immune system capability and activity.

Organs, Cells, and Cell Interactions of the Immune Response

The immune system utilizes as part of its arsenal the **lymphoid organs,** including the thymus, lymph nodes, spleen, tonsils, and bone marrow, and the cells that travel between these regions and the rest of the body. Of these, the thymus and bone marrow are considered to be the *primary lymphoid organs;* the others are *secondary lymphoid areas.*

The stem cells which give rise to the immune system arise in the bone marrow, and their subsequent differentiation into one of the two populations of immunocompetent lymphocytes occurs in the primary lymphoid organs. The **B cells** differentiate in bone marrow, and the **T cells** differentiate in the thymus. While in their "programming organs," the lymphocytes become *immunocompetent,* an event indicated by the appearance of specific cell-surface proteins that enable the lymphocytes to respond (by binding) to a particular antigen. Although the mechanism of this specialization is still far from clear, it is known that the mechanism is *not* antigen-driven.

After differentiation, the B and T cells leave the bone marrow and thymus, respectively; enter the bloodstream; and travel to peripheral (secondary) lymphoid organs, where clonal selection occurs. **Clonal selection** is triggered when an antigen binds to the specific cell-surface receptors of a T or B cell. This event causes the lymphocyte to proliferate rapidly, forming a clone of like cells, all bearing the same antigen-specific receptors. Then, in the presence of certain regulatory signals,

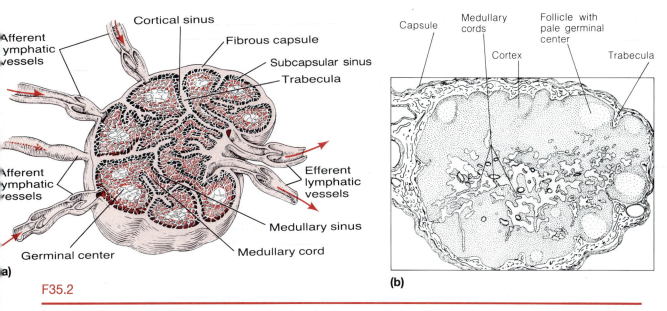

(a)

F35.2

(b)

Structure of lymph node. (a) Cross section of a lymph node, diagrammatic view. Note that the afferent vessels outnumber the efferent vessels, which slows the rate of lymph flow. The arrows indicate the direction of the lymph flow. (b) Line drawing of a photomicrograph (Plate 27 in the Histology Atlas) showing part of a lymph node.

the members of the clone specialize. In the case of B cell clones, some become memory B cells; the others form antibody-producing **plasma cells.** Because the B cells act indirectly through the antibodies that their progeny release into the bloodstream (or other body fluids), they are said to provide **humoral immunity.**

T cell clones are more diverse. Although all T cell clones also contain memory cells, some clones contain *killer,* or *cytotoxic,* T cells (effector cells that directly attack virus-infected tissue cells). Others contain regulatory cells such as the *helper cells* (that interact with and help activate the B cells and killer T cells) and still others contain *suppressor cells* that can inhibit the immune response. Because the T cells act directly to destroy virus-infected cells, many bacteria, and cancer cells, and to reject foreign grafts, T cells are said to mediate **cellular immunity.**

Absence or failure of thymic differentiation of T lymphocytes results in a marked depression of both antibody and cell-mediated immune functions. Additionally, the observation that the thymus naturally involutes with age has been correlated with the relatively immune-deficient status of elderly individuals. ■

All lymphoid tissues except the thymus and bone marrow contain both T and B cell–dependent regions. The lymph node is used as the example in the following microscopic study.

MICROSCOPIC ANATOMY OF A LYMPH NODE

Obtain a prepared slide of a lymph node and a compound microscope. As you examine the slide, notice the following anatomical features, depicted in Figure 35.2. The node is enclosed within a fibrous **capsule,** from which connective tissue septa (**trabeculae**) extend inward to divide the node into several compartments. Very fine strands of reticular connective tissue issue from the trabeculae, forming the stroma of the gland within which cells are found.

In the outer region of the node, the **cortex,** some of the cells are arranged in globular masses, referred to as **germinal centers.** The germinal centers contain rapidly dividing B lymphocytes. The rest of the cortical cells are primarily T lymphocytes that circulate continuously, moving from the blood into the node and then exiting from the node in the lymphatic stream.

In the internal portion of the gland, the **medulla,** the *medullary strands or cords,* cells are arranged in cordlike fashion. Most of the medullary cells are macrophages. Macrophages are important not only for their phagocytic function, but also because they play an essential role in "presenting" the antigens to the T cells.

Lymph enters the node through a number of afferent vessels, circulates through sinuses within the node, and leaves the node through efferent vessels at the **hilus.** Since each node has fewer efferent than afferent vessels, the lymph flow stagnates somewhat within the node. This allows time for the generation of an immune response and for the macrophages to remove debris from the lymph before it reenters the blood vascular system.

In the space provided here, draw a pie-shaped section of a lymph node, showing the detail of cells in a germinal center, sinusoids, and afferent and efferent vessels. Label all elements.

Before leaving the topic of the lymphoid organs, compare and contrast the structure of the lymph node examined here with the microscopic anatomy of the spleen and tonsils illustrated in Plates 28 and 29 in the Histology Atlas.

Lymph Node and Subcapsular Sinus	# 15189
Lymph Node, Primary Nodule	# 15190
Lymph Node, Germinal Center	# 15191

ANTIBODIES AND TESTS FOR THEIR PRESENCE

Antibodies, produced by sensitized B cells and their progeny plasma cells in response to an antigen, are a heterogenous group of proteins that comprise the general class of plasma proteins called **gamma globulins.** The antibodies can be further categorized into their immunoglobulin subgroups, which are found not only in plasma, but also (to greater or lesser extents) in all body secretions. Five major classes of immunoglobulins (Igs) have been identified: IgM, IgG, IgD, IgA, and IgE. The immunoglobulin classes share a common basic structure, but differ functionally and in their localization in the body.

All Igs are composed of one or more monomers (structural units). A monomer consists of four protein chains bound together by disulfide bridges (Figure 35.3). Two of the chains are quite large and have a high molecular weight; these are the **heavy chains.** The other two chains have a low molecular weight and are called the **light chains.** The two heavy chains have a *constant*

(C) region, in which the amino acid sequence is identical in both chains, and a *variable (V) region,* which differs in the Igs formed in response to different antigens. The same is true of the two light chains; each has a constant and a variable region.

The intact Ig molecule has a three-dimensional shape that is generally Y-shaped. Together, the variable regions of the light and heavy chains in each "arm" construct one antigen-binding site. Thus, each Ig monomer bears two identical sites that bind to a specific (and the same) antigen. Binding of the immunoglobulins to their complementary antigen(s) effectively immobilizes the antigens until they can be phagocytized or lysed by complement fixation.

Although the role of the immune system is to protect the body, symptoms of certain diseases may reflect excessively high antibody synthesis (as in multiple myeloma, a cancer of the bone marrow and adjacent bony structures) and/or the production of abnormal antibodies (such as **rheumatoid factor** present in the blood of many rheumatoid arthritis sufferers). The simple experiment described below tests for the presence of the rheumatoid factor in plasma.

Test for Rheumatoid Factor

Although the precise cause of rheumatoid arthritis is not yet known, the disease process itself involves an astonishing number of the body's immune elements—T cells, rheumatoid factor, and antirheumatoid antibodies, to name a few. Thus, rheumatoid arthritis is believed to involve an autoimmune reaction, and rheumatoid factor

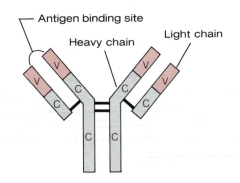

F35.3

Structure of an immunoglobulin monomer. Each monomer is composed of four protein chains (two heavy chains and two light chains) connected by disulfide bonds. Both the heavy and light chains have regions of constant amino acid sequence (C regions) and regions of variable amino acid sequence (V regions). The variable regions differ in each type of antibody and construct the antigen-binding sites. Each immunoglobulin monomer has two such antigen-specific sites.

Immunoglobin	# 05244

(while not fully diagnostic for the disease) is found in the serum of many rheumatoid arthritis victims. Perhaps the initial disease trigger is a genetic defect that leads to the local formation of the abnormal antibody—which in turn prompts the clustering, at certain body joints, of T cells, protective antibodies, and other inflammatory cells.

Although rheumatoid arthritis is a systemic disease that may involve many body organs and tissues, it is characterized by the manner in which the joints are affected. The synovial membranes become inflamed and then thicken as they accumulate inflammatory cells (Figure 35.4). This is followed by the formation of **pannus,** an abnormal tissue that clings to the articular cartilages and eventually destroys them. The final stage involves the elaboration of fibrous tissue that connects the bone ends. Because this fibrous tissue eventually ossifies, the bone ends become firmly fused, and often deformed. Not all cases progress to joint immobilization (the severely crippling stage), but all cases do involve some restriction of joint movement and extreme pain.

The test for the rheumatoid factor involves mixing a drop of plasma with serum containing antibodies against the abnormal antibody (that is, antirheumatoid-factor antibodies). If rheumatoid factor is present, agglutination will occur, indicating the formation of antigen-antibody complexes.

F35.4

Scanning electron micrograph of the synovial membrane from a joint affected by rheumatoid arthritis. Notice the inflammatory cells, exhibiting numerous microvilli, that have accumulated on the membrane surface (3500×).

1. Obtain the arthritis screening test materials, a microscope slide, a wax marker, two applicator sticks, and plastic gloves.

2. With the wax marker, label one end of the slide "control" and the other end "test." Don the gloves.

3. Place a drop of test plasma on the end of the slide marked "test" and a drop of the positive control plasma on the end marked "control."

4. Add one drop of reagent 1 to each sample, and mix with an applicator stick. (Use opposite ends of the applicator stick to mix each sample, and then discard the applicator stick in the disposable autoclave bag provided at the supply area.)

5. Add 2 drops of reagent 2 to each sample. Using opposite ends of a fresh applicator stick, mix each sample thoroughly; and then spread the samples over a 1-inch-square area on the slide.

6. Gently rock the slide back and forth for 3 minutes, and then check each sample for the presence of agglutination.

Which sample gave the positive test for the presence of rheumatoid factor?

_____

7. Dispose of the second applicator stick and the gloves in the autoclave bag.

white pulp
red pulp

Thymus

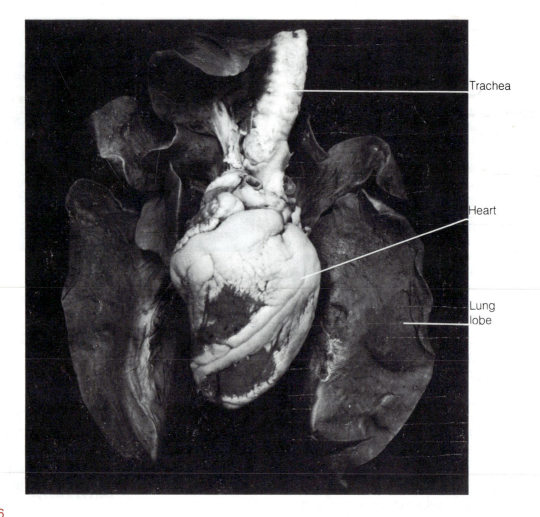

Trachea

Heart

Lung lobe

F36.6

Sheep pluck.

SHEEP PLUCK DEMONSTRATION

A *sheep pluck* (Figure 36.6) includes the larynx, trachea with attached lungs, the heart and pericardium, and portions of the major blood vessels found in the mediastinum (aorta, pulmonary artery and vein, venae cavae).

Don plastic gloves, obtain a sheep pluck, and iden-tify the lower respiratory system organs. Once you have completed your observations, insert a hose from an air compressor (vacuum pump) into the trachea and al-ternately allow air to flow in and out of the lungs. Notice how the lungs inflate. This observation is educational in a preserved pluck but it is a spectacular sight in a fresh one. Another advantage of using a fresh pluck is that the lung pluck changes color (becomes redder) as hemoglo-bin in trapped RBCs becomes loaded with oxygen.

If air compressors are not available, the same effect may be obtained by using a length of laboratory rubber tubing to blow into the trachea. Obtain a cardboard mouthpiece and fit it into the cut end of the laboratory tubing before attempting to inflate the lungs.

Dispose of the mouthpiece and gloves in the auto-clave bag immediately after use.

Mediastinum   # 03680
Human

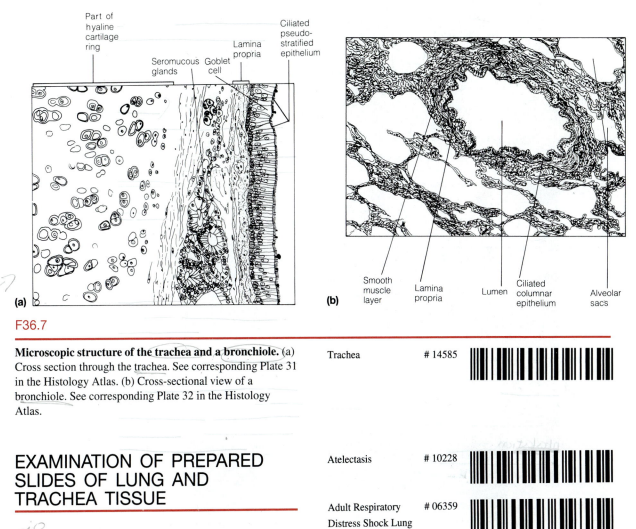

(a) Part of hyaline cartilage ring — Seromucous glands — Goblet cell — Lamina propria — Ciliated pseudo-stratified epithelium

(b) Smooth muscle layer — Lamina propria — Lumen — Ciliated columnar epithelium — Alveolar sacs

F36.7

Microscopic structure of the trachea and a bronchiole. (a) Cross section through the trachea. See corresponding Plate 31 in the Histology Atlas. (b) Cross-sectional view of a bronchiole. See corresponding Plate 32 in the Histology Atlas.

EXAMINATION OF PREPARED SLIDES OF LUNG AND TRACHEA TISSUE

1. Obtain and examine a cross section of the trachea wall. Identify the smooth muscle layer, the hyaline cartilage supporting rings, and the pseudostratified ciliated epithelium. Using Figure 36.7 as a guide, also try to identify a few goblet cells in the epithelium. In the space below, draw a section of the trachea wall and label all tissue layers.

Trachea	# 14585	‖‖‖‖‖‖‖‖
Atelectasis	# 10228	‖‖‖‖‖‖‖‖
Adult Respiratory Distress Shock Lung	# 06359	‖‖‖‖‖‖‖‖

2. Obtain a slide of lung tissue for examination. The alveolus is the main structural and functional unit of the lung and is the actual site of gas exchange (see Figure 36.3c). Identify the thin squamous epithelium of the alveolar walls, a bronchiole (Figure 36.7b), and if possible one of the smaller bronchi. Draw your observations of a small section of the alveolar tissue in the space below. Label the alveoli.

Bronchus	# 17521	‖‖‖‖‖‖
Arteriosclerosis, Lung	# 11672	‖‖‖‖‖‖

3. Examine slides of pathologic lung tissues, and compare them to the normal lung specimens.

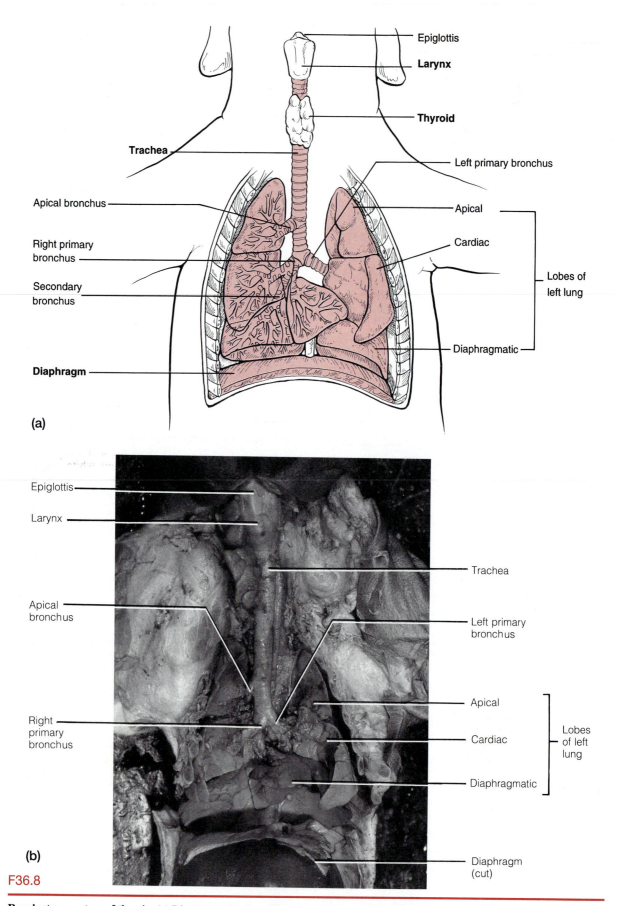

(a)

(b)

F36.8

Respiratory system of the pig. (a) Diagrammatic view. (Heart is removed and right lung is partially dissected to show some right bronchus branching.) (b) Photograph corresponding to Plate E in the Fetal Pig Anatomy Atlas.

DISSECTION OF FETAL PIG RESPIRATORY SYSTEM

1. Before beginning the dissection, don gloves or put on protective skin cream if desired. Examine the external nares and nasal cavity of the pig. The **nostrils,** or **external nares,** of the pig are relatively small, and are located on the flat anterior surface of the **rostrum,** or snout. To view the interior of the **nasal cavity,** which is long and narrow in the pig, make a transverse cut through the snout posterior to the external nares. Examine the medial wall of the nasal passages. Notice that the mucous membrane is thrown into convolutions in this area, since it overlies the turbinate bones which project laterally from the nasal septum. What function does this mucosa perform for the respiratory system?

warms air

moistens air

carries dust particles, bacteria

and debris out

2. To examine the continuity between the oropharynx and the nasopharynx, place a probe deep into the nasal cavity so that it enters the **nasopharynx.** Leave the probe in place. Open the mouth of the pig, and observe the posterior aspect of the oral cavity. You should be able to see the tip of the probe hanging downward into the **oropharynx** where the nasal (respiratory) and oral (digestive) passageways unite temporarily. Cut through the skin on the lateral cheeks to produce the view seen in Plate D of the Fetal Pig Anatomy Atlas and identify the epiglottis.

3. Secure the animal to the dissecting tray, and expose the respiratory structures by retracting the cut muscle and the rib cage. (Do not sever nerves and blood vessels located on either side of the trachea if these have not previously been studied.) If you have not opened the thoracic cavity previously, make a medial longitudinal incision through the neck muscles and thoracic musculature to view the thoracic organs.

4. Using Figure 36.8 as a guide, identify the following structures.

Trachea: determine by finger examination whether the cartilage rings are complete or incomplete posteriorly.

Thymus gland: a large gland overlying the heart.

Thyroid gland: located on the trachea inferior to the larynx.

Larynx: remove attached muscle from the larynx and pull it anteriorly for ease of examination. Identify the *thyroid* and *cricoid cartilages* and the flaplike *epiglottis.* Find the hyoid bone, located anterior to the larynx. Make a longitudinal incision through the ventral wall of the larynx and locate the true and false vocal cords on the inner wall.

Vagus nerve: a conspicuous white band that lies alongside the trachea.

5. To examine the contents of the thoracic cavity, follow the trachea as it bifurcates into the two primary bronchi, which plunge into the lungs. Note that in the pig, the trachea gives off an additional **apical bronchus** at the level of the fourth rib before it diverges into the right and left primary bronchi. The apical bronchus supplies the apical lobe of the right lung; the right primary bronchus supplies the cardiac, intermediate, and diaphragmatic lobes of the right lung; and the left primary bronchus supplies the left apical, cardiac, and diaphragmatic lobes of the left lung. Note the pericardial sac containing the heart located in the mediastinum (if it is still present). Examine the pleura, and note its exceptionally smooth texture. Locate the **diaphragm** and the **phrenic nerve.** The phrenic nerve, an obvious white "thread" running along the pericardium to the diaphragm, controls the activity of the diaphragm in breathing. Lift one lung and find the esophagus beneath the parietal pleura. Follow it through the diaphragm to the stomach.

6. Make a longitudinal incision in the outer tissue of one lung lobe beginning at a primary bronchus. Attempt to follow part of the respiratory tree from this point down into the smaller subdivisions. Carefully observe the cut lung tissue (under a dissection scope if one is available), noting the richness of the vascular supply. As you work, observe that the fetal lung tissue feels firm and solid rather than spongy, the texture of the adult human lung. This textural difference reflects the fact that the fetal lungs are nonfunctional, that is, they have not yet been inflated. Cut off a section of the fetal lung and notice how dense it is. Place the lung segment in a beaker of water and observe what happens. Does it float or sink? Explain the significance of your observation.

sink

Respiratory System Physiology

MECHANICS OF RESPIRATION

Pulmonary ventilation, or **breathing,** consists of two phases: **inspiration,** during which air is taken into the lungs, and **expiration,** during which air passes out of the lungs. As the inspiratory muscles (external intercostals and diaphragm) contract during inspiration, the size of the thoracic cavity increases. The diaphragm moves from its relaxed dome shape to a flattened position, increasing the superoinferior volume, and the external intercostals lift the rib cage, increasing the anteroposterior and lateral dimensions (Figure 37.1). Since the lungs adhere to the thoracic walls like flypaper because of the cohesive character of the pleurae, the intrapulmonary (within the lungs) volume also increases, lowering the air (gas) pressure inside the lungs. The gases then expand to fill the available space, creating a partial vac-

uum that causes air to flow into the lungs—constituting the act of inspiration. During expiration, the inspiratory muscles relax, and the natural tendency of the elastic lung tissue to recoil acts to decrease the intrathoracic and intrapulmonary volumes. As the gas molecules within the lungs are forced closer together, the intrapulmonary pressure rises to a point higher than atmospheric pressure. This causes gases to flow from the lungs to equalize the pressure inside and outside the lungs—the act of expiration.

 Observe the model lung, which demonstrates the principles involved in the filling and emptying of the lungs. It is a simple apparatus with a bottle "thorax," a rubber membrane "diaphragm," and "balloon lungs."

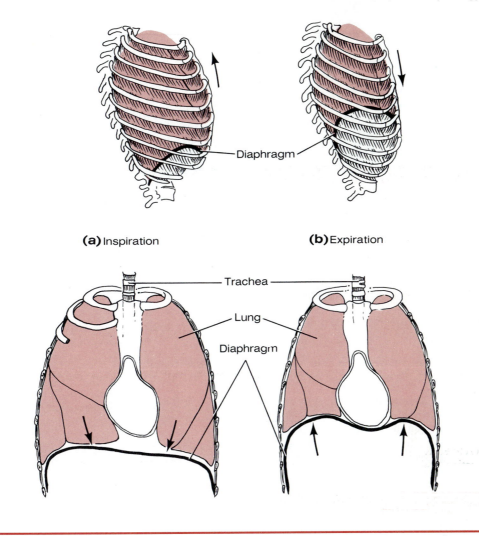

(a) Inspiration   **(b)** Expiration

F37.1

Rib cage and diaphragm positions during breathing. (a) At the end of a normal inspiration; chest expanded, diaphragm depressed. (b) At the end of a normal expiration; chest depressed, diaphragm elevated.

1. Go to the demonstration area and work the model lung by moving the rubber diaphragm up and down. Notice the changes in balloon (lung) size as the volume of the thoracic cavity is alternately increased and decreased.

2. Check the appropriate columns in the chart concerning these observations in the Exercise 37 Review Sheet on p. RS 159 at the back of this book.

3. After observing the operation of the model lung, conduct the following tests on your lab partner. Use the tape measure to determine chest circumference by placing the tape around the chest as high up under the armpits as possible. Record the measurements in inches in the appropriate space for each of the conditions below.

Quiet breathing:

inspiration _____ expiration _____

Forced breathing:

inspiration _____ expiration _____

Do the results coincide with what you expected on the

basis of what you have learned thus far? _____

RESPIRATORY VOLUMES AND CAPACITIES— SPIROMETRY

A person's size, sex, age, and physical condition produce variations in respiratory volumes. Normal quiet breathing moves about 500 ml of air in and out of the lungs with each breath. As you have seen in the previous experiment, a person can usually forcibly inhale or exhale much more air than is normally exchanged in quiet breathing. The terms given to the measurable respiratory

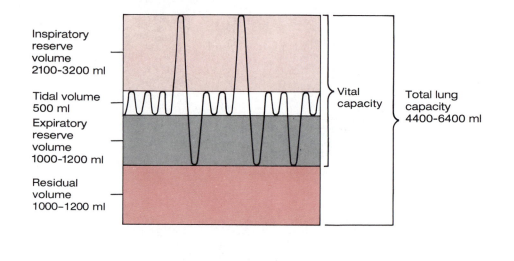

F37.2

Idealized tracing of the various respiratory volumes.

volumes are defined just below. These terms and their normal values for an adult male should be memorized.

Tidal volume (TV): amount of air inhaled or exhaled with each breath under resting conditions (500 ml).

Inspiratory reserve volume (IRV): amount of air that can be forcefully inhaled after a normal tidal volume exhalation (2800 ml).

Expiratory reserve volume (ERV): amount of air that can be forcefully exhaled after a normal tidal volume exhalation (1200 ml).

Vital capacity (VC): maximum amount of air that can be exhaled after a maximal inspiratory effort; VC = TV + IRV + ERV; (4800 ml).

An idealized tracing of the various respiratory volumes and their relationships to each other are shown in Figure 37.2.

Respiratory volumes will be measured with an apparatus called a **spirometer.** There are two major types of spirometers, which give comparable results—the hand-held dry, or wheel, spirometers (such as the Buhl spirometer illustrated in Figure 37.3) and "wet" spirometers, such as the Collins spirometer, which is available in both recording and nonrecording varieties. The somewhat more sophisticated wet spirometer consists of a cylinder within a tank into which air can be added or removed (Figure 37.4). The outer tank contains water and has a tube running through it to carry air above the water level. The floating bottomless inner cylinder is inverted over the water-containing tank and connected to a volume indicator.

In nonrecording spirometers, an indicator moves as air is *exhaled,* and only expired air volumes can be measured directly. By contrast, recording spirometers allow both inspired and expired gas volumes to be measured. Directions for both types of apparatus are provided below. Follow the steps in Procedure A if using a nonrecording spirometer, and those in Procedure B if using a wet recording spirometer.

Procedure A *— using non recording spirometer*

1. Without using the spirometer, count and record the subject's normal respiratory rate.

Respirations per minute _____ 19

2. Examine a spirometer indicator scale *before beginning* to make sure you know how to read the scale. Work in pairs, with one person acting as the subject while the other records the data of the volume determinations. The

F37.3

The Buhl Spiropet, an example of a hand-held dry spirometer. The dial face of the spirometer is rotated to zero prior to each test.

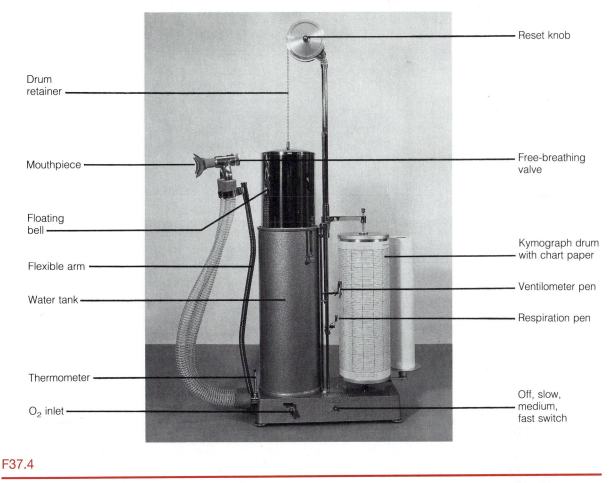

The Collins-9L "wet" recording spirometer.

subject should stand erect during testing. Reset the indicator to zero before beginning each trial. If you are using the hand-held spirometer, make sure its dial faces upward so that the volumes can be easily read during the tests.

Obtain a disposable cardboard mouthpiece. Insert it in the open end of the flexible tube of the wet spirometer (or over the fixed stem of the hand-held dry spirometer). Before beginning, the subject should practice exhaling through the mouthpiece without exhaling through the nose, or prepare to use the nose clips (clean them first with an alcohol swab).

3. Conduct the test three times for each required measurement. Record the data here, and then find the average volume figure for that respiratory measurement. After you have completed the trials and computed the averages, enter the average values on the table prepared on the chalkboard for tabulation of class data,* and copy all averaged data onto the Exercise 37 Review Sheet.

* Note to the Instructor: The format of class data tabulation can be similar to that shown here. However, it would be interesting to divide the class into smokers and nonsmokers and then compare the mean average VC and ERV for each group. Such a comparison might help to determine if smokers are handicapped in any way. It also might be a good opportunity for an informal discussion of the early warning signs of bronchitis and emphysema, which are primarily smokers' diseases.

4. Tidal volume (TV). The volume of air inhaled and exhaled with each normal respiration is approximately 500 ml. To conduct the test, inhale a normal breath, and then exhale a normal breath of air into the spirometer mouthpiece. (Do not force the expiration!) Record the volume and repeat the test twice.

trial 1 _____ ml   trial 2 _____ ml

trial 3 _____ ml   average TV _____ ml

5. Compute the subject's **minute respiratory volume (MRV)** using the following formula:

$$MRV = TV \times \text{respirations/min}$$

$$MRV = \text{_____ ml/min}$$

6. Expiratory reserve volume (ERV). The volume of air that can be forcibly exhaled after a normal expiration ranges between 1000 and 1200 ml.

Inhale and exhale normally two or three times, then insert the spirometer mouthpiece and exhale forcibly as much of the additional air as you can. Record your results, and repeat the test twice again.

trial 1 _____ ml   trial 2 _____ ml

trial 3 _____ ml   average ERV _____ ml

The ERV is dramatically reduced in conditions in which the elasticity of the lungs is decreased by a chronic obstructive pulmonary disease (COPD) such as **emphysema.** Since energy must be used to *deflate* the lungs in such conditions, expiration is physically exhausting to individuals suffering from COPD. ■

7. Vital capacity (VC). The total exchangeable air of the lungs (the sum of TV + IRV + ERV) is normally 4500 ml to 4800 ml. Breathe in and out normally two or three times, and then bend over and exhale all the air possible. Then, as you raise yourself to the upright position, inhale as fully as possible. (It is very important to *strain* to inhale the maximum amount of air that you can.) Quickly insert the mouthpiece, and exhale as forcibly as possible. Record your results and repeat the test two times.

trial 1 _____ ml   trial 2 _____ ml

trial 3 _____ ml   average VC _____ ml

8. Inspiratory reserve volume (IRV). The IRV, or volume of air that can be forcibly inhaled following a normal inspiration, can now be computed using the average values obtained for TV, ERV, and VC and plugging them into the equation:

$$IRV = VC - (TV + ERV)$$

Record your average IRV: _____ ml

The normal IRV is substantial, ranging from 2100 to 3200 ml. How does your computed value compare?

_____

Steps 9 and 10, which provide common directions for both nonrecording and recording spirometers, continue after the Procedure B directions.

Procedure B *using wet recording spirometer*

1. In preparation for recording, familiarize yourself with the spirometer by comparing it to Figure 37.4.

2. Examine the chart paper, noting that its horizontal lines represent milliliter units. To apply the chart paper to the recording drum, lift the drum retainer and then remove the kymograph drum. Wrap a sheet of chart paper around the drum, making sure that the right edge overlaps the left. Fasten it with tape, and then replace the kymograph drum and lower the drum retainer into its original position in the hole in the top of the drum.

3. Raise and lower the floating bell several times, noting as you do so that the *ventilometer pen* moves up and down on the drum. This pen, which writes in black ink, will be used for recording and should be positioned or adjusted so that it records in the approximate middle of the chart paper. This adjustment is made by repositioning the floating bell using the *reset knob* on the metal

pulley at the top of the spirometer apparatus. The other pen, the respirometer pen, which records in red ink, will not be used for these tests and should be moved away from the drum's recording surface.

4. Clean the nose clips with an alcohol swab. While you wait for the alcohol to air dry, count and record your normal respiratory rate.

Respirations per minute _____

After the alcohol has air dried, apply the nose clips to your nose. This will enforce mouth breathing.

5. Open the *free breathing valve.* Insert a disposable cardboard mouthpiece into the end of the breathing tube, and then insert the mouthpiece into your mouth. Practice breathing for several breaths to get used to the apparatus. At this time, you are still breathing room air.

6. Set the spirometer switch to SLOW (32 mm/min). Close the free breathing valve, and breathe in a normal manner for 2 minutes to record your tidal volume—the amount of air inspired or expired with each normal respiratory cycle. This recording should show a regular pattern of inspiration-expiration spikes and should gradually move upward on the chart paper. (A downward slope indicates that there is an air leak somewhere in the system—most likely at the mouthpiece.) Notice that on an apparatus using a counterweighted pen, such as the Collins Vitalometer shown in Fig. 37.4, inspirations are recorded by upstrokes and expirations are recorded by downstrokes.*

7. To record your vital capacity, take the deepest possible inspiration you can and then exhale to the greatest extent possible (really *push* the air out). The recording obtained should resemble that shown in Figure 37.5. Repeat the vital capacity maneuver twice again. Then turn off the spirometer and remove the chart paper from the kymograph drum.

8. Determine and record your measured, averaged, and corrected respiratory volumes here. Because the pressure and temperature inside the spirometer are influenced by room temperature and differ from those in the body, all measured values are to be multiplied by a **BTPS** (body temperature, atmospheric pressure, and water saturation) **factor.** At room temperature, the BTPS factor is typically 1.1 or very close to that value. Hence, you will multiply your measured values by 1.1 to obtain your corrected respiratory volume values. Copy the averaged and corrected values onto the Exercise 37 Review Sheet.

● Tidal volume. Select a typical resting tidal breath recording. Subtract the millimeter value of the trough (exhalation) from the millimeter value of the peak (inspiration). Record this value below as *measured TV 1.* Select two other TV tracings to deter-

* If a Collins survey spirometer is used, the situation is exactly opposite: Upstrokes are expirations and downstrokes are inspirations.

mine the TV values for the TV 2 and TV 3 measurements. Then determine your average TV and multiply it by 1.1 to obtain the BTPS-corrected average TV value.

measured TV 1 ___ ml   average TV _____ ml

measured TV 2 ___ ml   corrected average TV

measured TV 3 ___ ml   _____ ml

Also compute your **minute respiratory volume (MRV)** using the following formula:

$$MRV = TV \times respirations/min$$

$$MRV = \text{_____ ml/min}$$

- Inspiratory capacity (IC). In the first vital capacity recording, find the expiratory trough immediately preceding the maximal inspiratory peak achieved during vital capacity determination. Subtract the milliliter value of that expiration from the value corresponding to the peak of the maximal inspiration that immediately follows. For example, according to Figure 37.5, these values would be:

$$6650 - 3650 = 3000 \text{ ml}$$

Record your computed value and the results of the two subsequent tests on the appropriate lines below. Then calculate the measured and corrected inspiratory capacity averages and record.

measured IC 1 ___ ml   average IC _____ ml

measured IC 2 ___ ml   corrected average IC

measured IC 3 ___ ml   _____ ml

- Inspiratory reserve volume. Subtract the corrected average tidal volume from the corrected average for the inspiratory capacity and record below.

IRV = corrected average IC − corrected average TV

corrected average IRV _____ ml

- Expiratory reserve volume. Subtract the number of milliliters corresponding to the trough of the maximal expiration obtained during the vital capacity maneuver from milliliters corresponding to the last *normal* expiration before the VC maneuver is performed. For example, according to Figure 37.5, these values would be:

$$3650 \text{ ml} - 2050 \text{ ml} = 1650 \text{ ml}$$

Record your measured and averaged values (three trials) below.

measured ERV 1 ___ ml   average ERV _____ ml

measured ERV 2 ___ ml   corrected average ERV

measured ERV 3 ___ ml   _____ ml

- Vital capacity. Add your corrected values for ERV and IC together to obtain the corrected average VC. Record below and on the Exercise 37 Review Sheet.

corrected average VC _____ ml

[*Now continue with step 9, whether you are following Procedure A or Procedure B.*]

9. Figure out how closely your measured average vital capacity volume compares with the *predicted values* for someone your age, sex, and height. Obtain the predicted figure from Appendix C either from Table 1 (male values) or Table 2 (female values). Notice that you will have to convert your height in inches to centimeters (cm) to find the corresponding value. This is easily done by multiplying your height in inches by 2.54.

Computed height: _____ cm

Predicted VC value (obtained from the appropriate table): _____ ml

Use the following equation to compute your VC as a percentage of the predicted VC value:

$$\% \text{ of predicted VC} = \frac{\text{averaged measured VC}}{\text{predicted value}} \times 100$$

% predicted VC value: _____ %

10. A respiratory volume that cannot be experimentally demonstrated here is the residual volume (RV), which is the amount of air remaining in the lungs after a maximal expiratory effort. The presence of residual air (usually about 1200 ml) that cannot be voluntarily flushed from the lungs is important because it allows gas exchange to go on continuously—even between respirations.

Although the residual volume cannot be measured directly, it can be approximated by using one of the following factors:

For ages 16–34   Factor = 0.250

For ages 35–49   Factor = 1.305

For ages 50–69   Factor = 1.445

Compute your predicted RV using the following equation:

$$RV = VC \times factor$$

Figure 37.2 is an idealized tracing of the respiratory volumes described and tested in this exercise. Examine it carefully. Do your test results compare closely to the values in the tracing?

11. Dispose of the used cardboard mouthpiece in the autoclave bag before continuing.

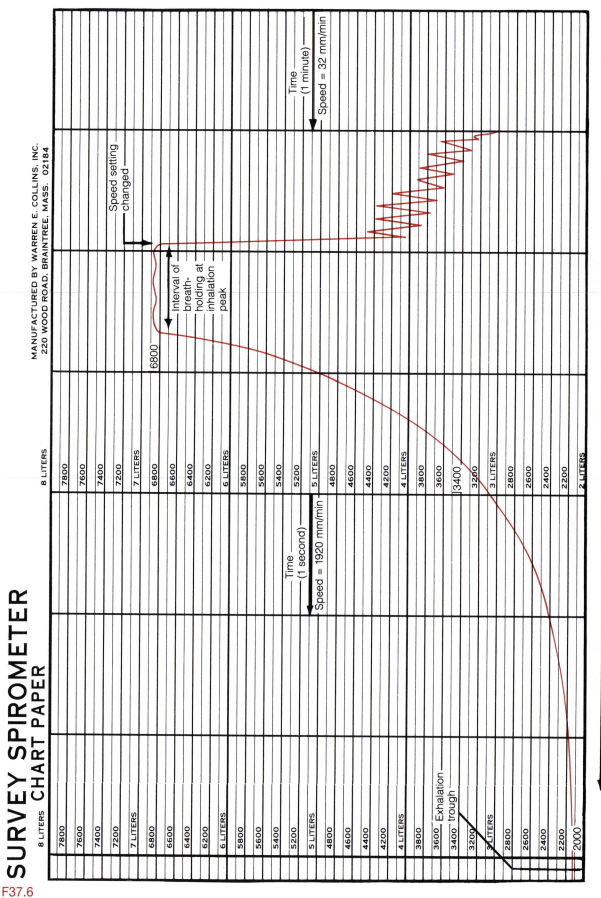

A recording of the forced vital capacity (FVC) and forced expiratory volume (FEV) or timed vital capacity test.

chemical factors. The chest pneumograph is a coiled rubber hose that is attached around the thorax. As the subject breathes, chest movements produce pressure changes within the pneumograph that are transmitted to a recorder.

The instructor will demonstrate the method of setting up the pneumograph and discuss the interpretation of the results. Work in pairs so that one person can mark the record to identify the test for later interpretation. Ideally, the student being tested should face away from the recording apparatus to prevent voluntary modification of the record.

1. Attach the pneumograph tubing firmly, but not restrictively, around the thoracic cage at the level of the sixth rib, leaving room for chest expansion during testing. If the subject is female, position the tubing above the breasts to prevent slippage during testing. Set the pneumograph speed at 1 or 2, and the time signal at 10-second intervals. Record quiet breathing for 1 minute with the subject in a sitting position.

Record breaths per minute: _____

2. Make a vital capacity tracing: Record a maximal inhalation followed by a maximal exhalation. This should correlate to the vital capacity measurement obtained earlier and will provide a baseline for comparison during the rest of the pneumograph testing. Stop the recording apparatus and indicate the following on the graph by marking the graph appropriately: tidal air volume, expiratory reserve volume, inspiratory reserve volume, and vital capacity (the total of the three measurements). Also mark, with arrows, the direction the recording stylus moves during inspiration and during expiration.

Measure in mm the height of the vital capacity recording. Divide the vital capacity measurement average recorded on the Exercise 37 Review Sheet by the millimeter figure to obtain the milliliters of air represented by one mm on the recording. For example, if your vital capacity reading is 4000 ml and the vital capacity tracing occupies a vertical distance of 40 mm on the pneumograph recording, then a vertical distance of 1 mm equals 100 ml of air.

Record your computed value: _____ ml air/mm

3. Record the subject's breathing as he or she performs activities from the list below. Make sure the record is marked accurately to identify each test conducted. Record your results on the Exercise 37 Review Sheet.

talking	swallowing water
yawning	coughing
laughing	lying down
standing	running in place

doing a math problem (concentrating)

4. Without recording, have the subject breathe normally for 2 minutes, then inhale deeply and hold his or her breath for as long as he or she can.

Time the breath-holding interval: _____ sec

As the subject exhales, turn on the recording apparatus and record the recovery period (time to return to normal breathing—usually slightly over 1 minute):

Time of recovery period: _____ sec

Did the subject have the urge to inspire or expire during breath holding?

_____

Without recording, repeat the above experiment, but this time exhale completely and forcefully after taking the deep breath. What was observed this time?

_____

_____

Explain the results. (Hint: the vagus nerve is the sensory nerve of the lungs and plays a role here.)

_____

_____

_____

_____

5. Have the subject hyperventilate (breathe deeply and forcefully at the rate of 1 breath/4 sec) for about 30 seconds.* Record both during and after hyperventilation. How does the pattern obtained during hyperventilation compare with that recorded during the vital capacity tracing?

Is the respiratory rate recorded after hyperventilation faster or slower than during normal quiet breathing?

_____

6. Repeat the above test, but do not record until after hyperventilating. After hyperventilation, the subject is to hold his or her breath as long as he or she can. Can the breath be held for a longer or shorter period of time after hyperventilation?

_____

---

* A sensation of dizziness may develop. (As the carbon dioxide is washed out of the blood by overventilation, the blood pH increases, leading to a decrease in blood pressure and reduced cerebral circulation.) The subject may experience a lack of desire to breathe after forced breathing is stopped. (If the period of breathing cessation— **apnea**—is extended, cyanosis of the lips may occur.)

7. Without recording, have the subject breathe into a paper bag for 3 minutes, then record breathing movements.

⚠️ *Caution:* During the bag-breathing exercise the subject's partner should watch the subject carefully for any untoward reactions.

Is the breathing rate faster *or* slower than that recorded during normal quiet breathing?

_____

After hyperventilating? _____

8. Run in place for 2 minutes; then have your partner determine the length of your breath-holding.

_____ sec

9. To prove that respiration has a marked effect on circulation, conduct the following test. Have your lab partner note the rate and relative force of your radial pulse before beginning.

rate _____ beats/min   relative force _____

Inspire forcibly. Immediately close your mouth and nose to retain the inhaled air, and then make a forceful and prolonged expiration. Your lab partner should observe and record the condition of the blood vessels of your neck and face, and again immediately palpate the radial pulse.

Observations _____

_____

Radial pulse _____ beats/min   Relative force _____

Explain the changes observed. _____

_____

_____

🩸 Dispose of the paper bag in the autoclave bag. Keep the pneumograph records to interpret results and hand them in if requested by the instructor. Observation of the test results should enable you to determine which chemical factor, carbon dioxide or oxygen, has the greatest effect on modifying the respiratory rate and depth.

⑤ RESPIRATORY SOUNDS

As air flows in and out of the respiratory tree, it produces two characteristic sounds that can be picked up with a stethoscope. The **bronchial sounds** are produced by air rushing through the large respiratory passageways (the trachea and the bronchi). The second sound type, **vesicular breathing sounds,** apparently results from air filling the alveolar sacs and resembles the sound of a rustling or muffled breeze.

1. Place the diaphragm of the stethoscope on the throat of the test subject just below the larynx. Listen for bronchial sounds on inspiration and expiration.

2. Move the stethoscope downward toward the bronchi until you can no longer hear sounds.

3. Place the stethoscope over the following chest areas and listen for vesicular sounds during respiration (heard primarily during inspiration)

- At various intercostal spaces
- At the *triangle of auscultation* (a small depressed area of the back where the muscles fail to cover the rib cage; located just medial to the inferior part of the scapula)
- Under the clavicle

▲ Diseased respiratory tissue, mucus, or pus can produce abnormal chest sounds such as rales (a rasping sound) and wheezing (a whistling sound). ∎

ROLE OF THE RESPIRATORY SYSTEM IN ACID-BASE BALANCE OF BLOOD

As you have already learned, pulmonary ventilation is necessary for continuous oxygenation of the blood and removal of carbon dioxide (a waste product of cellular respiration) from the blood. Blood pH must be relatively constant for the cells of the body to function optimally. Therefore the carbonic acid–bicarbonate buffer system of the blood is extremely important, because it helps stabilize arterial blood pH at 7.4 ± 0.02.

When carbon dioxide diffuses into the blood from the tissue cells, much of it enters the red blood cells, where it combines with water to form carbonic acid:

$$H_2O + CO_2 \xrightarrow[\text{Enzyme present in RBC}]{\text{Carbonic anhydrase}} H_2CO_3$$

Some carbonic acid is also formed in the plasma, but its formation there is very slow because of the lack of the carbonic anhydrase enzyme. Shortly after it forms, carbonic acid dissociates to release bicarbonate (HCO_3^-) and hydrogen (H^+) ions. The hydrogen ions that remain in the cells are neutralized, or buffered, when they combine with hemoglobin molecules. If they were not neutralized, the intracellular pH would become very acidic due to the accumulation of H^+ ions. Once formed, the bicarbonate ions diffuse out of the red blood cells into the plasma, where they become part of the carbonic acid–bicarbonate buffer system. As HCO_3^- follows its concentration gradient into the plasma, an electrical imbalance develops in the RBCs that draws Cl^- into them

[handwritten top margin: ↓Ph = acidic   ↑ Ph = alkaline / + H⁺ = ↓ ph   + basic = ↑ pH]

from the plasma. This exchange phenomenon is called the *chloride shift*.

Acids (more precisely, H⁺) released into the blood by the body cells tend to lower the pH of the blood and cause it to become too acidic. On the other hand, basic substances that enter the blood tend to cause the blood to become more alkaline and the pH to rise. Both of these tendencies are resisted in large part by the carbonic acid–bicarbonate buffer system. If H⁺ concentration in the blood begins to increase, the H⁺ ions combine with bicarbonate ions to form carbonic acid (a weak acid that does not tend to dissociate at physiologic or acid pH) and is thus removed.

$$H^+ + HCO_3^- \longrightarrow H_2CO_3$$

Likewise, as blood H⁺ concentration drops below what is desirable and blood pH rises, H_2CO_3 dissociates to release bicarbonate ions (weak bases that are poorly functional under alkaline conditions) and H⁺ ions to the blood. The released H⁺ lowers the pH again.

$$H_2CO_3 \longrightarrow H^+ + HCO_3^-$$

In the case of excessively slow or shallow breathing (hypoventilation) or fast deep breathing (hyperventilation), the amount of carbonic acid in the blood can be greatly modified—it may increase dramatically during hypoventilation and decrease substantially during hyperventilation. In either situation, the buffering ability of the blood may be inadequate, and respiratory acidosis or alkalosis can result. It is therefore important to maintain the normal rate and depth of breathing for proper control of blood pH.

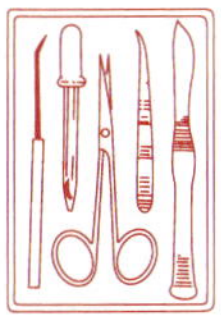

To observe the ability of a buffer system to stabilize the pH of a solution, obtain five 250-ml beakers, and a wash bottle containing distilled water. Set up the following experimental samples:

Beaker 1
(150 ml distilled water)   pH _7.07_

Beaker 2
(150 ml distilled water and
1 drop concentrated HCl) *acid*   pH _2.8_

Beaker 3
(150 ml distilled water and
1 drop concentrated NaOH) *base*   pH _11.25_

Beaker 4
(150 ml standard buffer solution
[pH 7] and 1 drop concentrated HCl)   pH _6.9_

Beaker 5
(150 ml standard buffer solution
[pH 7] and 1 drop concentrated NaOH)   pH _7.26_

[handwritten bottom margin: hypoventilation – ↑ H₂CO₃ / hyperventilation – ↓ H₂CO₃]

Using a pH meter standardized with a buffer solution of pH 7, determine the pH of the contents of each beaker and record above. After *each and every* pH recording, the pH meter switch should be turned to *standby*, and the electrodes rinsed thoroughly with a stream of distilled water from the wash bottle.

Add 3 more drops of concentrated HCl to beaker 4, stir, and record the pH: _6.65_

Add 3 more drops of concentrated NaOH to beaker 5, stir, and record the pH: _10.76_

How successful was the buffer solution in resisting pH changes when a strong acid (HCl) or a strong base (NaOH) was added?

successful.

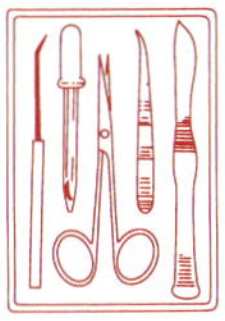

To observe the ability of the carbonic acid–bicarbonate buffer system of blood to resist pH changes, perform the following simple experiment.

Obtain two small beakers (50 ml), animal plasma, graduated cylinder, glass stirring rod, and a dropper bottle of 0.01 *M* HCl. Using the pH meter standardized with the buffer solution of pH 7.0, measure the pH of the animal plasma. Use only enough plasma to allow immersion of the electrodes and measure the volume used carefully.

pH of the animal plasma: _____

Add 2 drops of the 0.01 *M* HCl solution to the plasma; stir and measure the pH again.

pH of plasma plus 2 drops of HCl: _____

Turn the pH meter switch to standby, rinse the electrodes, and then immerse them in a quantity of distilled water (pH 7) exactly equal to the amount of animal plasma used. Measure the pH of the distilled water.

pH of distilled water: _____

Add 2 drops of 0.01 *M* HCl, swirl, and measure the pH again.

pH of distilled water plus the two drops of HCl: _____

Is the plasma a good buffer? _____

What component of the plasma carbonic acid–bicarbonate buffer system was operating to counteract a change in pH when HCl was added? *when acid increases*

[handwritten: $H^+ + HCO_3 \rightarrow H_2CO_3$]

CILIARY ACTION OF THE RESPIRATORY MUCOSA

If time is limited, your instructor may demonstrate this procedure. Otherwise, work together in groups of four to six students.

 1. Obtain dissecting instruments, pins and pan, room temperature frog Ringer's solution, bits of cork, disposable gloves, and a millimeter ruler, and bring them to the laboratory bench.

2. Don the gloves, and obtain a doubly pithed frog from your instructor or pith the frog by following instructions provided by your instructor. Then, cut the lower jaw away with scissors.

3. Use the fine scissors to make a longitudinal cut through the ventral wall of the pharynx, and continue the incision until you have cut the length of the trachea.

4. Flush the pharynx and trachea with saline. Using fine dissecting pins, pin the opened pharynx and trachea to the dissecting pan.

5. Place a tiny piece of cork (size of the head of a common pin) about halfway down the trachea and observe its movement toward the upper end. Time how long it takes for the bit of cork to move 0.5 cm.

Record your findings: _____

6. Obtain some cold saline (15°C), and flush the trachea and pharynx with it two or three times. Again observe and record the length of time required for the cork to move 0.5 cm.

_____

7. Flush the tissues several times with room-temperature saline, and then raise one end of the dissecting pan so that the pharyngeal region is higher than the trachea. Again watch the movement of the cork. Record the time required for it to move 0.5 cm.

_____

8. Dispose of the remains of the frog in the proper organic waste container, and clean the dissecting equipment.

Anatomy of the Digestive System

The **digestive system** provides the body with the nutrients, water, and electrolytes essential for metabolic processes and health. The organs of this system are responsible for food ingestion, digestion, absorption, and the elimination of the undigested remains as feces.

The digestive system consists of a hollow tube extending from the mouth to the anus, into which various accessory organs or glands empty their secretions (Figure 38.1). Food material within this tube, the *alimentary canal,* is technically outside the body, since it has contact only with the cells lining the tract. For the ingested food to become available to the body cells, it must first be broken down *physically* (chewing, churning) and *chemically* (enzymatic hydrolysis) into its smaller diffusible molecules—a process called **digestion.** The digested end products can then pass through the epithelial cells lining the tract into the blood for distribution to the body cells—a process termed **absorption.** In one sense, the digestive tract can be viewed as a disassembly line, in which food is carried from one stage of its digestive processing to the next by muscular activity, and its nutrients are made available to the cells of the body en route.

The organs of the digestive system are traditionally separated into two major groups: the **alimentary canal, or gastrointestinal tract,** and the **accessory digestive organs.** The alimentary canal is approximately 30 feet long in a cadaver but considerably less in a living person. It consists of the mouth, pharynx, esophagus, stomach, small and large intestines, rectum, and anus. The accessory structures include the salivary glands, gallbladder, liver, and pancreas, which secrete their products into the alimentary canal. These individual organs are described shortly.

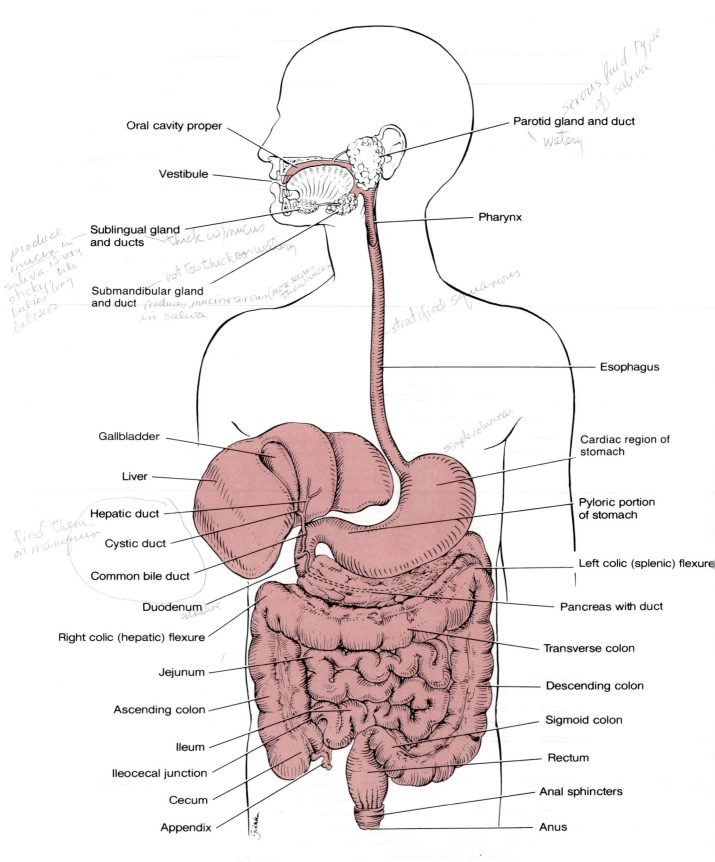

Oral cavity proper

Vestibule

Parotid gland and duct

serous fluid type of saliva
Watery

Sublingual gland and ducts

thick w/mucus

produce mucin in saliva. is very sticky. long babies bubbles

not too thick or watery

Pharynx

Submandibular gland and duct

Produce mucin + serous (more serous then mucin) in saliva

stratified squamous

Esophagus

simple columnar

Gallbladder

Liver

Hepatic duct

Cystic duct

find them on manikin

Common bile duct

Duodenum

alkaline

Right colic (hepatic) flexure

Jejunum

Ascending colon

Ileum

Ileocecal junction

Cecum

Appendix

Cardiac region of stomach

Pyloric portion of stomach

Left colic (splenic) flexure

Pancreas with duct

Transverse colon

Descending colon

Sigmoid colon

Rectum

Anal sphincters

Anus

F38.1

The human digestive system: alimentary tube and accessory organs. (Liver and gallbladder are reflected superiorly and to the right.)

GENERAL HISTOLOGICAL PLAN OF THE ALIMENTARY CANAL

Because the alimentary canal has a shared basic structure (particularly from the esophagus to the anus), it makes sense to review that structure as we begin studying this group of organs. Once done, all that need be emphasized as the individual organs are described is their specializations for unique functions in the digestive process.

Essentially the alimentary canal walls have four basic **tunics** (layers). From the lumen outward, these are the *mucosa*, the *submucosa*, the *muscularis externa,* and the *serosa* or *adventitia* (Figure 38.2). Each of these tunics has a predominant tissue type and a specific function in the digestive process.

Mucosa (mucous membrane): The mucosa is the wet epithelial membrane abutting the alimentary canal lumen. It consists of a surface *epithelium* (in most cases, a simple columnar), a *lamina propria* (areolar connective tissue on which the epithelial layer rests), and a *muscularis mucosae* (a scant layer of smooth muscle fibers that provide for local movements of the mucosa). The major functions of the mucosa are secretion (of enzymes, mucus, hormones, etc.), absorption of digested foodstuffs, and protection (against bacterial invasion). A particular mucosal region may be involved in one or all three functions.

Submucosa: Superficial to the mucosa, the submucosa is moderately dense connective tissue containing blood and lymphatic vessels, scattered lymph nodules, and nerve fibers. Its intrinsic nerve supply is

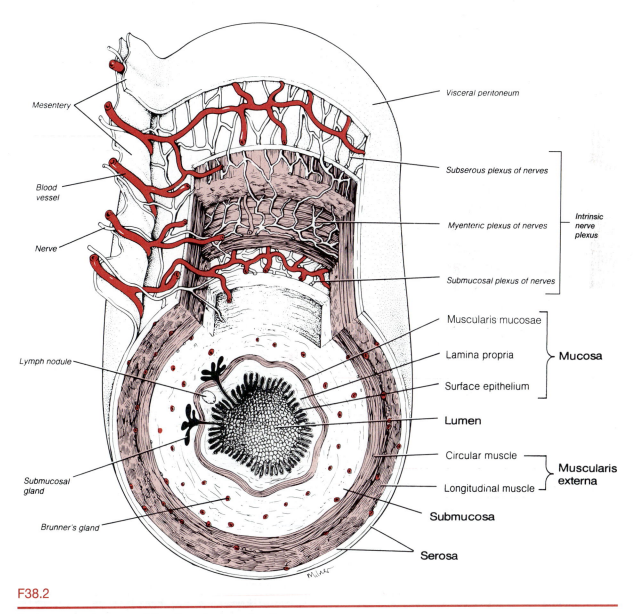

F38.2

Basic structural pattern of the alimentary canal wall.

called the *submucosal plexus.* Its major functions are nutrition and protection.

Muscularis externa: The muscularis externa, also simply called the *muscularis,* typically is a bilayer of smooth muscle, with the deeper layer running circularly and the more superficial layer running longitudinally. Another intrinsic nerve plexus, the *myenteric plexis,* is associated with this tunic and is a major regulator of GI motility effected by the smooth muscle muscularis.

Serosa: The outermost serosa is equal to the *visceral peritoneum.* It consists of mesothelium associated with a thin layer of areolar connective tissue. The *subserous plexus* is associated with this tunic. In areas *outside* the abdominopelvic cavity, the serosa is replaced by an **adventitia,** a layer of coarse fibrous connective tissue that binds the organ to surrounding tissues. (Such is the case with the esophagus.) The major function of the serosa is to reduce friction as the mobile GI tract organs work and slide across one another and the cavity walls. The adventitia anchors and protects the surrounded GI tract organ.

ORGANS OF THE ALIMENTARY CANAL

The sequential pathway and fate of food as it passes through the alimentary canal organs are described in the next sections. Identify each structure in Figure 38.1 and on the torso model as you work.

Oral Cavity or Mouth

Food enters the digestive tract through the **oral cavity,** or **mouth.** Within this mucous membrane-lined cavity are the gums, teeth, tongue, and openings of the ducts of the salivary glands. The **lips (labia)** protect the opening of the chamber anteriorly, the **cheeks** form its lateral walls, and the **palate,** its roof. The anterior portion of the palate is referred to as the **hard palate,** since bone (the palatine processes of the maxillae and the palatine bones) underlies it. The posterior **soft palate** is a fibromuscular structure that is unsupported by bone. The **uvula,** a fingerlike projection of the soft palate, extends downward from its posterior margin. The soft palate rises to close off the oral cavity from the nasal and pharyngeal passages during swallowing. The floor of the oral cavity is occupied primarily by the muscular **tongue,** which is largely supported by the **mylohyoid muscle** and is attached to the hyoid bone, mandible, styloid processes, and pharynx. A membrane called the **lingual frenulum** secures the inferior midline of the tongue to the floor of the mouth. The space between the lips and cheeks and the teeth is the **vestibule;** the area that lies within the teeth and gums is the **oral cavity** proper. (Figures 38.3 and 38.4 depict the structures of the oral cavity.)

On each side of the mouth at its posterior end are masses of lymphoid tissue, the **palatine tonsils.** Each lies in a concave area bounded anteriorly and posteriorly by membranes, the **palatoglossal arch** (anterior membrane) and the **palatopharyngeal arch** (posterior membrane). Another mass of lymphoid tissue, the **lingual tonsil,** covers the base of the tongue, posterior to the oral cavity proper. The tonsils, in common with other lymphoid tissues, are part of the body's defense system.

Palate, Soft   # 46995

Very often in young children, the palatine tonsils become inflamed and enlarge, partially blocking the entrance to the pharynx posteriorly and making swallowing difficult and painful. This condition is called **tonsilitis.** ∎

Three pairs of salivary glands duct their secretion, saliva, into the oral cavity. One component of saliva, salivary amylase, begins the digestion of starchy foods within the oral cavity. (The salivary glands are discussed in more detail on p. 389.)

As food enters the mouth, it is mixed with saliva and masticated (chewed). The cheeks and lips help hold the food between the teeth during mastication, and the highly mobile tongue manipulates the food for chewing and initiates swallowing. Thus the mechanical and chemical breakdown of food begins before the food has left the oral cavity. As noted in Exercise 26, the surface of the tongue is covered with papillae, many of which contain taste buds, the receptors for taste sensation. So, in addition to its manipulative function, the tongue provides for the enjoyment and appreciation of the food ingested.

Pharynx

When the tongue initiates swallowing, the food passes posteriorly into the pharynx, a common passageway for food, fluid, and air. The pharynx is often subdivided anatomically into the **nasopharynx** (behind the nasal cavity), the **oropharynx** (behind the oral cavity extending from the soft palate to the epiglottis overlying the larynx), and the **laryngopharynx** (extending from the epiglottis to the base of the larynx), which is continuous with the esophagus.

The walls of the pharynx consist largely of two layers of skeletal muscles: an inner layer of longitudinal muscle (the levator muscles) and an outer layer of circular constrictor muscles, which initiate wavelike contractions that propel the food inferiorly into the esophagus. Its mucosa, like that of the oral cavity, contains a friction-resistant stratified squamous epithelium.

Oronasopharynx,   # 53340
Bisected Diagram

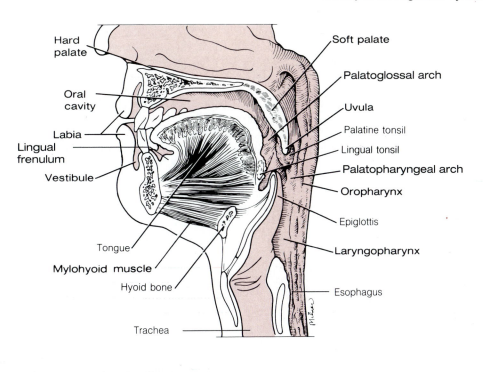

Sagittal view of the head showing oral, nasal, and pharyngeal cavities.

Esophagus

The **esophagus,** or gullet, extends from the pharynx through the diaphragm to the cardiac sphincter in the superior aspect of the stomach. It is approximately 10 inches long in humans and is essentially a food passageway that conducts food to the stomach in a wavelike peristaltic motion. The esophagus has no digestive or absorptive function. The walls at the superior end of the esophagus contain skeletal muscle, which is replaced by smooth muscle in the area nearing the stomach. Since the esophagus is located in the thoracic rather than the abdominal cavity, its outermost layer is an *adventitia,* rather than the serosa that would cover an abdominal cavity organ.

Esophagus,   # 19351
Endoscopy, Normal

Stomach

The **stomach** (Figures 38.1 and 38.5) is on the left side of the abdominal cavity and is hidden by the liver and diaphragm. Different regions of the saclike stomach are the **cardiac region** (the area surrounding the **cardiac sphincter** through which food enters the stomach from the esophagus), the **fundus** (the expanded portion of the stomach, superolateral to the cardiac region), the **body** (midportion of the stomach, inferior to the fundus), and the **pylorus** (the terminal part of the stomach, which is

continuous with the small intestine through the **pyloric sphincter**).

The concave medial surface of the stomach is called the **lesser curvature,** and its convex lateral surface is called the **greater curvature.** Extending from these curvatures are two mesenteries, called *omenta.* The **lesser omentum** extends from the liver to attach to the lesser curvature of the stomach. The **greater omentum,** a sac-

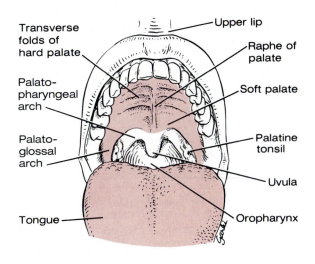

Anterior view of the oral cavity.

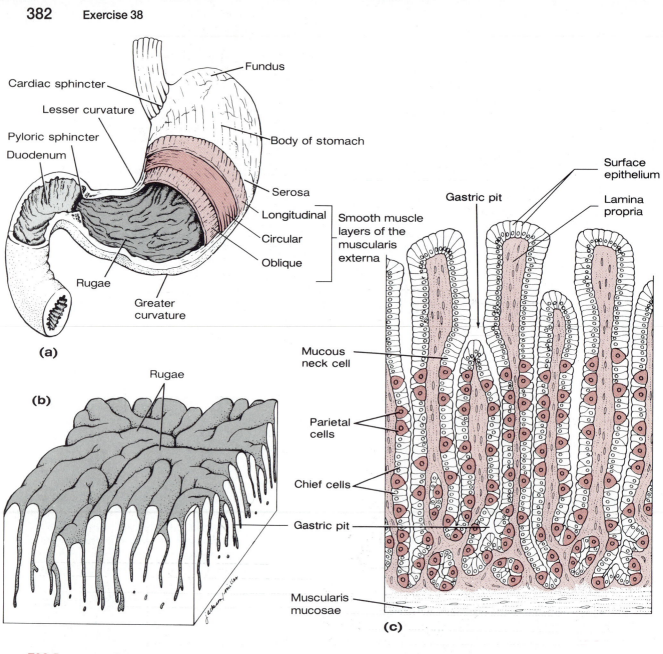

F38.5

Anatomy of the stomach. (a) Gross internal and external anatomy. (b) Section of the stomach wall showing rugae and gastric pits. (c) Enlarged view of gastric pits (longitudinal section).

like mesentery, extends from the greater curvature of the stomach, reflects downward over the abdominal contents to cover them in an apronlike fashion, and then blends with the **mesocolon** attaching the transverse colon to the posterior body wall. Figure 38.6 illustrates the omenta as well as the other peritoneal attachments of the abdominal organs.

The stomach is a temporary storage region for food as well as a site for the mechanical and chemical breakdown of food. It contains a third obliquely oriented layer of smooth muscle in its muscularis externa that allows it to churn, mix, and pummel the food, physically reducing it to smaller fragments. Gastric glands of the mucosa secrete hydrochloric acid (HCl) and hydrolytic enzymes

secreted by parietal cells

(primarily pepsinogen, the inactive form of *pepsin,* a protein-digesting enzyme), which begin the enzymatic, or chemical, breakdown of protein foods. The mucosal glands also secrete a viscous mucus that prevents the stomach itself from being digested by the proteolytic enzymes. Most digestive activity occurs in the pyloric region of the stomach. After the food has been processed in the stomach, it resembles a creamy mass (chyme), which enters the small intestine through the pyloric sphincter.

secreted by chief cells

Esophagus, Stomach   # 11811
and Duodenum

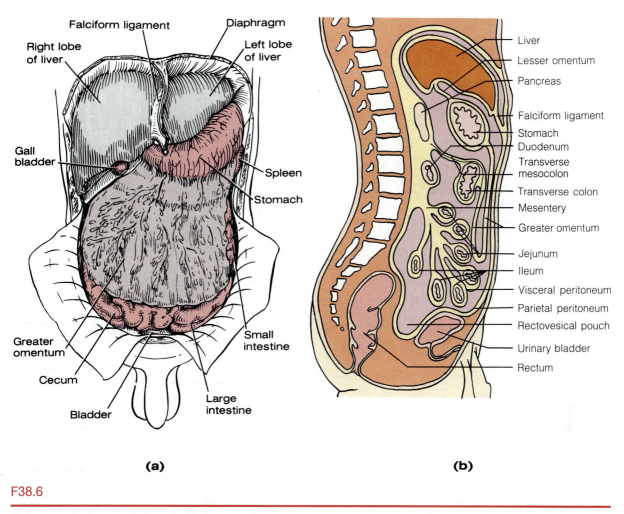

(a)

(b)

F38.6

Peritoneal attachments of the abdominal organs. (a) Anterior view, omentum in place. (b) Sagittal view of a male torso.

Stomach, Rugae   # 09332

Obtain a microscope and the following slides, in preparation for the histological study you will be conducting now and later in the lab: salivary glands (submandibular or sublingual); pancreas; cross sections of the duodenum, ileum, and stomach, and longitudinal sections of a tooth and the gastroesophageal junction.

1. **Stomach:** The stomach slide will be viewed first. Refer to Figure 38.7a as you scan the tissue under low power to locate the muscularis externa; then move to high power to more closely examine this layer. Try to pick out the three smooth muscle layers. How does the extra (oblique) layer of smooth muscle found in the stomach correlate with the stomach's churning movements?

_____

_____

_____

_____

Identify the gastric glands and the gastric pits (see Figures 38.5 and 38.7b). If the section is taken from the stomach fundus and is appropriately stained, you can identify, in the gastric glands, the blue-staining **chief,** or **zymogenic, cells,** which produce pepsinogen, and the red-staining **parietal cells,** which secrete HCl. Draw a small section of the stomach wall and label it appropriately.

2. **Gastroesophageal junction:** Examine the slide under low power, and scan it to locate the junction between the end of the esophagus and the beginning of the

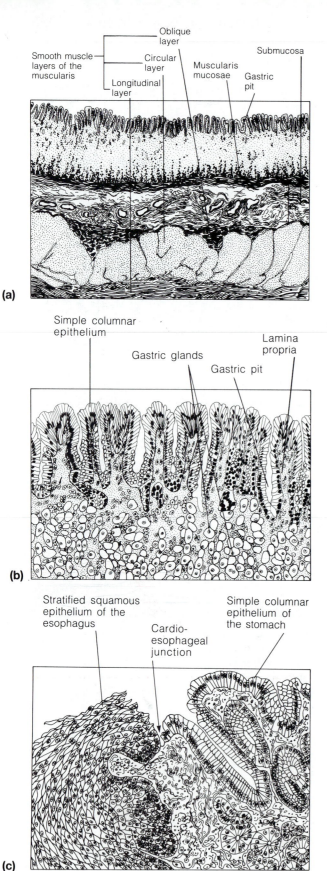

(a)

Smooth muscle layers of the muscularis
Oblique layer
Circular layer
Longitudinal layer
Muscularis mucosae
Submucosa
Gastric pit

(b)

Simple columnar epithelium
Gastric glands
Gastric pit
Lamina propria

(c)

Stratified squamous epithelium of the esophagus
Cardio-esophageal junction
Simple columnar epithelium of the stomach

F38.7

Histology of selected regions of the stomach and gastroesophageal junction. (a) Low-power view of the stomach wall. See corresponding Plate 33 in the Histology Atlas. (b) High-power view of gastric pits and glands. See corresponding Plate 34 in the Histology Atlas. (c) Gastroesophageal junction, longitudinal section. See corresponding Plate 35 in the Histology Atlas.

stomach, the gastroesophageal junction. Compare your observations to Figure 38.7c. What is the functional importance of the epithelial differences seen in the two organs?

_____

_____

_____

_____

Small Intestine

The **small intestine** is a convoluted tube, 6 to 7 meters (m) long, extending from the pyloric sphincter to the ileocecal valve. The small intestine is suspended by a double layer of peritoneum, the fan-shaped **mesentery,** from the posterior abdominal wall (see Figure 38.6), and it lies, framed laterally and superiorly by the large intestine, in the abdominal cavity. The small intestine has three subdivisions: (1) the **duodenum** extends from the pyloric sphincter for about 25 cm (10 inches) and curves around the head of the pancreas; most of the duodenum lies in a retroperitoneal position. (2) The **jejunum,** continuous with the duodenum, extends for 2.5 to 3 m (about 8 feet). Most of the jejunum occupies the umbilical region of the abdominal cavity. (3) The **ileum,** the terminal portion of the small intestine, is about 4 m (12 feet) long and joins the large intestine at the **ileocecal valve.** It is located inferiorly and somewhat to the right in the abdominal cavity, but its major portion lies in the hypogastric region.

Brush border enzymes, hydrolytic enzymes bound to the microvilli of the columnar epithelial cells and, more importantly, enzymes produced by the pancreas and ducted into the duodenum via the **pancreatic duct** complete the enzymatic digestion process in the small intestine. Bile (formed in the liver) also enters the duodenum via the **common bile duct** in the same area (see Figure 38.1). At the duodenum, the ducts join to form the bulblike **hepatopancreatic ampulla (of Vater)** and empty their products into the duodenal lumen through the **duodenal papilla,** an orifice controlled by a muscular valve called the **hepatopancreatic sphincter (of Oddi).**

Nearly all nutrient absorption occurs in the small intestine, where three structural modifications that increase the mucosa absorptive area appear—the microvilli, villi, and plicae circulares. **Microvilli** are minute projections of the surface plasma membrane of the columnar epithelial lining cells of the mucosa; the **villi** are the fingerlike projections of the mucosa tunic that give it a velvety appearance and texture (Figure 38.8). The **plicae circulares** are deep folds of the mucosa and submucosa layers that extend partially or totally around the intestine. These structural modifications, which increase the surface area, decrease in frequency and elaboration toward the end of the small intestine. Any residue remaining undigested and unabsorbed at the terminus of the small intestine enters the large intestine through the

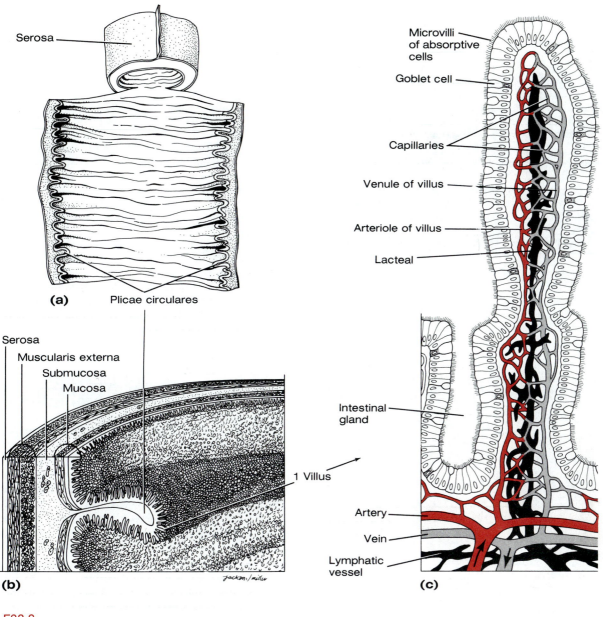

(a) — Serosa, Plicae circulares

(b) — Serosa, Muscularis externa, Submucosa, Mucosa, 1 Villus

jackson/miller

(c) — Microvilli of absorptive cells, Goblet cell, Capillaries, Venule of villus, Arteriole of villus, Lacteal, Intestinal gland, Artery, Vein, Lymphatic vessel

F38.8

Structural modifications of the small intestine. (a) Plicae circulares (circular folds) seen on the inner surface of the small intestine. (b) Enlargement of one plica circulare to show villi. (c) Detailed anatomy of a villus.

ileocecal valve. In contrast, the amount of lymphoid tissue in the submucosa of the small intestine (**Peyer's patches**) increases along the length of the small intestine and is very apparent in the ileum. This reflects the fact that the remaining undigested food residue contains large numbers of bacteria that must be prevented from entering the bloodstream.

Superior Mesenteric   # 47973
Vessels

Small Bowel,   # 15596
Unfixed

1. **Duodenum:** Secure the slide of the duodenum (cross section) to the microscope stage. Observe the tissue under low power to identify the four basic tunics of the intestinal wall—that is, the three layers of the **mucosa** lining, the **submucosa** (areolar connective tissue layer deep to the mucosa), the **muscularis externa** (composed of circular and longitudinal smooth muscle layers), and the **serosa** (the outermost layer, also called the *visceral peritoneum*). (See Figure 38.9a.) Identify the scattered mucus-producing **duodenal glands** (Brunner's glands) in the submucosa.

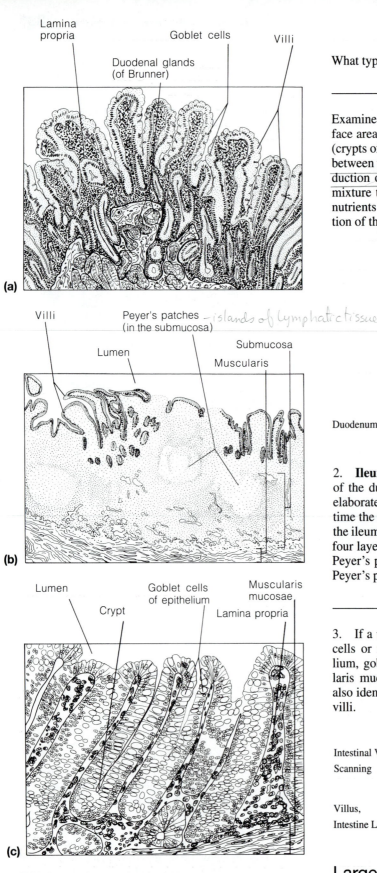

(a)

Lamina propria

Duodenal glands (of Brunner)

Goblet cells

Villi

(b)

Villi

Peyer's patches — *islands of lymphatic tissue*
(in the submucosa)

Lumen

Submucosa

Muscularis

(c)

Lumen

Crypt

Goblet cells of epithelium

Muscularis mucosae

Lamina propria

F38.9

Histology of selected regions of the small and large intestines. (a) Duodenum of the small intestine (XS). See corresponding Plate 36 in the Histology Atlas. (b) Ileum of the small intestine (XS). See corresponding Plate 37 in the Histology Atlas. (c) Large intestine (XS). See corresponding Plate 38 in the Histology Atlas.

What type of epithelium do you see here? _____

_____

Examine the large leaflike *villi,* which increase the surface area for absorption. Note also the *intestinal crypts* (crypts of Lieberkühn), invaginated areas of the mucosa between the villi where the cells are involved in the production of intestinal juice, a watery mucus-containing mixture that serves as a carrier fluid for absorption of nutrients from the chyme. Sketch and label a small section of the duodenal wall, showing all layers and villi.

Duodenum   # 10163 |||||| ||| ||| | |||||

2. **Ileum:** The structure of the ileum is similar to that of the duodenum, except that the villi tend to be less elaborate (most of the absorption has occurred by the time the ileum is reached). Obtain and secure a slide of the ileum for viewing. Observe the villi, and identify the four layers of the wall and the large generally spherical Peyer's patches (Figure 38.9b). What tissue comprises Peyer's patches?

_____

3. If a *villus model* is available, identify its following cells or regions before continuing: absorptive epithelium, goblet cells, lamina propria, slips of the muscularis mucosae, capillary bed, and lacteal. If possible, also identify the intestinal crypts which lie between the villi.

Intestinal Villi   # 19368 |||||| ||| ||| | |||||
Scanning

Villus,   # 44475 |||||| ||| ||| | |||||
Intestine Lacteal

Large Intestine

The **large intestine** (see Figure 38.10) is about 1.5 m (5 feet) long and extends from the ileocecal valve to the anus. It encircles the small intestine on three sides and consists of the following subdivisions: the **cecum, appendix, colon, rectum,** and **anal canal.**

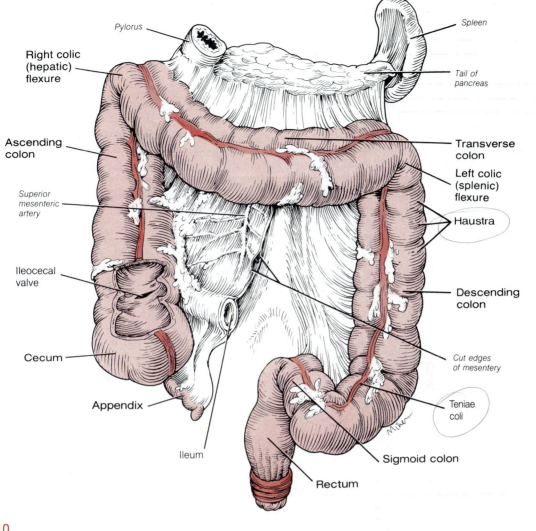

Pylorus

Right colic
(hepatic)
flexure

Spleen

Tail of
pancreas

Ascending
colon

Transverse
colon

Left colic
(splenic)
flexure

Superior
mesenteric
artery

Haustra

Ileocecal
valve

Descending
colon

Cecum

Cut edges
of mesentery

Appendix

Teniae
coli

Ileum

Sigmoid colon

Rectum

F38.10

The large intestine. (Section of the cecum removed to show the ileocecal valve.)

Appendix	# 24810
Transverse Colon	# 47991

The blind tubelike appendix, which hangs from the cecum, is a trouble spot in the large intestine. Since it is generally twisted, it provides an ideal location for bacteria to accumulate and multiply. Inflammation of the appendix, or **appendicitis,** is the result. ■

The colon is divided into several distinct regions. The **ascending colon** travels up the right side of the abdominal cavity and makes a right-angle turn at the **right colic (hepatic) flexure** to cross the abdominal cavity as the **transverse colon.** It then turns at the **left colic (splenic) flexure** and continues down the left side of the abdominal cavity as the **descending colon,** where it

takes an S-shaped course as the **sigmoid colon.** The sigmoid colon, rectum, and the anal canal lie in the pelvis anterior to the sacrum and thus are not considered abdominal cavity structures. Except for the transverse and sigmoid colons, which are secured to the dorsal body wall by mesocolons (see Figure 38.6), the colon is retroperitoneal.

The anal canal terminates in the **anus,** the opening to the exterior of the body. The anus, which has an external sphincter of skeletal muscle (the voluntary sphincter) and an internal sphincter of smooth muscle (the involuntary sphincter), is normally closed except during defecation when the undigested remains of the food and bacteria are eliminated from the body as feces.

In the large intestine, the longitudinal muscle layer of the muscularis externa is reduced to three longitudinal muscle bands called the **teniae coli.** Since these bands are shorter than the rest of the wall of the large intestine, they cause the wall to pucker into small pocketlike sacs called **haustra.**

The major function of the large intestine is to consolidate and propel the unusable fecal matter toward the anus and eliminate it from the body. While it does that "chore," it (1) provides a site for the manufacture, by intestinal bacteria, of some vitamins (B and K), which it then absorbs into the bloodstream; and (2) reclaims most of the remaining water (and some of the electrolytes) from undigested food, thus conserving body water.

Watery stools, or diarrhea, result from any condition that rushes undigested food residue through the large intestine before it has had sufficient time to absorb the water (as in irritation of the colon by bacteria). Conversely, when food residue remains in the large intestine for extended periods (as with atonic colon or failure of the defecation reflex), excessive water is absorbed and the stool becomes hard and difficult to pass (constipation). ■

- Examine Figure 38.9c to compare the histology of the large intestine to that of the small intestine just studied.

Colon Mucosa   # 10502

ACCESSORY DIGESTIVE ORGANS

Teeth

By the age of 21, two sets of teeth have developed (Figure 38.11). The initial set, called the **deciduous,** or **milk teeth,** normally appears between the ages of 6 months and 2½ years. The first of these to erupt are the lower central incisors, an event which is usually applauded by the child's parents. The child begins to shed the deciduous teeth around the age of 6. The second set of teeth, the **permanent teeth,** gradually replace them. As the deeper permanent teeth progressively enlarge and develop, the roots of the deciduous teeth are resorbed, leading to their final shedding, and during the sixth to twelfth years, the child has mixed dentition—both permanent and deciduous teeth. Generally, by the age of 12, all of the deciduous teeth have been shed, or exfoliated.

The teeth are classified as **incisors, canines** (eye teeth), **premolars** (bicuspids), and **molars.** Teeth names reflect differences in relative structure and function. The incisors are chisel-shaped and exert a shearing action used in biting. The canines are cone-shaped or fanglike, the latter description being much more applicable to the canines of animals whose teeth are used for the tearing of food. Incisors, canines, and premolars typically have single roots, though the first upper premolars may have two. The lower molars have two roots but the upper molars usually have three. The premolars have two cusps (grinding surfaces); the molars have relatively flat, broad superior surfaces specialized for the fine grinding of food.

Dentition is described by means of a **dental formula,** which designates the numbers, types, and position of the teeth in one side of the jaw. (Since tooth arrangement is bilaterally symmetrical, it is only necessary to designate one side of the jaw.) The complete dental formula for the deciduous teeth from the medial aspect of each jaw and proceeding posteriorly is as follows:

$$\frac{\text{Upper teeth: 2 incisors, 1 canine, 0 premolars, 2 molars}}{\text{Lower teeth: 2 incisors, 1 canine, 0 premolars, 2 molars}} \times 2$$

This formula is generally abbreviated to read as follows:

$$\frac{2,1,0,2}{2,1,0,2} \times 2 = 20 \text{ (number of deciduous teeth)}$$

The 32 permanent teeth are then described by the following dental formula:

$$\frac{2,1,2,3}{2,1,2,3} \times 2 = 32 \text{ (number of permanent teeth)}$$

Although 32 is designated as the normal number of permanent teeth, not everyone develops a full complement. In many people, the No. 3 molars, commonly called the *wisdom teeth,* never erupt.

 Identify the four types of teeth (incisors, canines, premolars, and molars) on the jaw model or human skull.

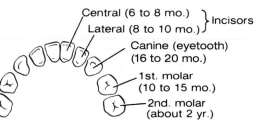

Deciduous (milk) teeth

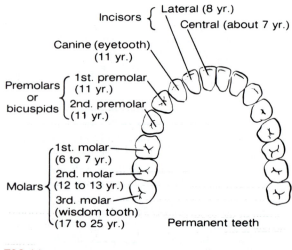

Permanent teeth

F38.11

Human deciduous teeth and permanent teeth.
(Approximate time of teeth eruption shown in parentheses.)

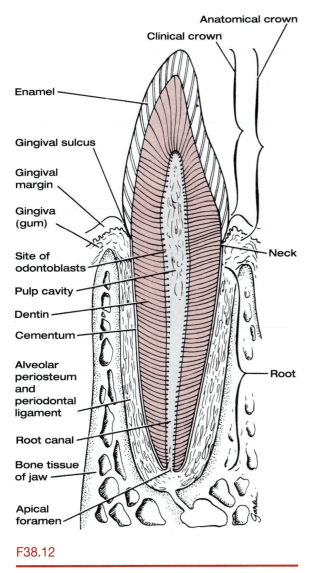

Anatomical crown
Clinical crown
Enamel
Gingival sulcus
Gingival margin
Gingiva (gum)
Site of odontoblasts
Pulp cavity
Dentin
Cementum
Alveolar periosteum and periodontal ligament
Root canal
Bone tissue of jaw
Apical foramen
Neck
Root

F38.12

Longitudinal section of human canine tooth.

A tooth consists of two major regions, the **crown** and the **root.** A longitudinal section made through a tooth shows the following basic anatomical plan (Figure 38.12). The crown is the superior portion of the tooth; the portion of the crown visible above the **gum,** or **gingiva,** is referred to as the **clinical crown.** The entire area covered by **enamel** is called the **anatomical crown.** The crevice between the end of the anatomical crown and the upper margin of the gingiva is referred to as the **gingival sulcus** and its apical border is the **gingival margin.** Enamel is the hardest substance in the body and is fairly brittle. It consists of 95% to 97% inorganic calcium salts (chiefly $CaPO_4$) and thus is heavily mineralized. That portion of the tooth embedded in the alveolar portion of the jaw is the root, and the root and crown are connected by a slight constriction, the **neck.** The outermost surface of the root is covered by **cementum,** which is similar to bone in composition and less brittle than enamel. The cementum attaches the tooth to the **periodontal ligament** which holds the tooth in the alveolar socket and

exerts a cushioning effect. **Dentin,** which comprises the bulk of the tooth, consists of bonelike material and is medial to the enamel and cementum. The **pulp cavity** occupies the central portion of the tooth. **Pulp,** connective tissue liberally supplied with blood vessels, nerves, and lymphatics, occupies this cavity and provides for tooth sensation and supplies nutrients to the tooth tissues. Specialized cells, **odontoblasts,** reside in the outer margins of the pulp cavity and produce the dentin. As the pulp cavity extends into distal portions of the root it becomes the **root canal.** An opening at the root apex, the **apical foramen,** provides a route of entry into the tooth for the blood vessels, nerves, and other structures from the tissues beneath.

Observe a slide of a longitudinal section of a tooth, and compare your observations with the structures detailed in Figure 38.12. Identify as many of these structures as possible.

Teeth, Skull   # 48743

Tooth, Innervation,   # 00950
Molar, Model

Salivary Glands

The three pairs of major **salivary glands** (see Figure 38.1) that empty their secretions into the oral cavity are the large **parotid glands,** located anteriorly to the ear and ducting into the mouth over the second upper molar through the parotid duct; the **submandibular glands,** located inside the maxillary arch in the floor of the mouth and ducting under the tongue to the base of the lingual frenulum; and the small **sublingual glands,** located most anteriorly in the floor of the mouth and emptying under the tongue via several small ducts.

Food in the mouth and mechanical pressure (chewing rubber bands or wax) stimulate the salivary glands to secrete saliva. Saliva consists primarily of mucin (a viscous glycoprotein), which moistens the food and helps to bind it together into a mass called a **bolus,** and a clear serous fluid containing the enzyme, *salivary amylase.* Salivary amylase begins the digestion of starch (a large polysaccharide), breaking it down into disaccharides, or double sugars, and glucose. The secretion of the parotid glands is mainly serous, whereas the submandibular and sublingual glands are mixed glands that produce mucin and serous components.

Parotid Duct,   # 46803
Prosected Head

Submandibular Gl.,   # 46804
Prosected Head

Salivary Gland   # 15174

Sublingual   # 14818
Salivary Gland

Examine the salivary gland tissue under low power and then high power to become familiar with the appearance of a glandular tissue. Note the clustered arrangement of the cells around their ducts. The cells are basically triangular, with their pointed ends facing the duct orifice. If possible, differentiate between the mucus-producing cells, which look hollow or have a clear cytoplasm, and the serous cells, which produce the clear, enzyme-containing fluid and have granules in their cytoplasm. The serous cells often form "caps" (*demilunes*) around the more central mucous cells. Figure 38.13 may be helpful in this task. Draw your version of a small portion of the salivary gland tissue and label it appropriately.

Mucous   Serous
cells   demilunes   Duct
(light)   (darker)

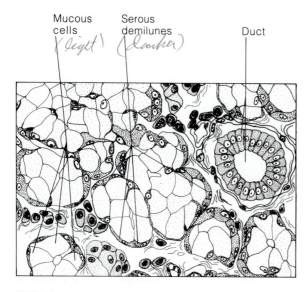

F38.13

A mixed salivary gland. (Corresponds to the photomicrograph in Plate 39 in the Histology Atlas.)

Liver and Gallbladder

The **liver** (see Figure 38.1), the largest gland in the body, is located inferior to the diaphragm, more to the right than the left side of the body. As noted earlier, it hides the stomach from view in a superficial observation of abdominal contents. The human liver has four lobes and is suspended from the diaphragm and anterior abdominal wall by the **falciform ligament** (see Figure 38.6a).

The liver is one of the body's most important organs, and it performs many metabolic roles. However, its digestive function is to produce bile, which leaves the liver through the **hepatic duct** and then enters the duodenum through the **common bile duct.** Bile has no enzymatic action but emulsifies fats (spreads thin or breaks up large fat particles into smaller ones), thus creating a larger surface area for more efficient lipase activity. Without bile, very little fat digestion or absorption occurs.

When digestive activity is not occurring in the digestive tract, bile backs up the cystic duct and enters the **gallbladder,** a small, green sac on the inferior surface of the liver. It is stored there until needed for the digestive process. While in the gallbladder, bile is concentrated by the removal of water and some ions. When fat-rich food enters the duodenum, a hormonal stimulus causes the gallbladder to contract, releasing the stored bile and making it available to the duodenum.

If the hepatic or common bile duct is blocked (for example, by wedged gallstones), bile is prevented from entering the small intestine, begins to accumulate, and eventually backs up into the liver. This exerts pressure on the liver cells, and bile begins to enter the bloodstream. As the bile circulates through the body, the tissues become yellow or **jaundiced.**

Blockage of the ducts is just one cause of jaundice; more often it results from actual liver problems such as **hepatitis** (an inflammation of the liver) or **cirrhosis,** a condition in which the liver is severely damaged, becoming hard and fibrous. Cirrhosis is almost guaranteed in those who drink excessive alcohol for many years. ■

As demonstrated by its highly organized anatomy, the liver (Figure 38.14) is very important in the initial processing of the nutrient-rich blood draining the digestive organs. Its structural and functional units are called **lobules.** Each lobule is a basically cylindrical structure consisting of cordlike arrays of parenchyma cells, which radiate outward from a central vein running upward in the longitudinal axis of the lobule. At each of the six corners of the lobule is a **portal triad,** so named because three basic structures are always present there: a branch of the *hepatic artery* (the functional blood supply of the liver), a branch of the *hepatic portal vein* (carrying nutrient-rich blood from the digestive viscera), and a *bile duct.* Between the liver parenchyma cells are blood-filled spaces, or **sinusoids,** through which blood from the hepatic portal vein and hepatic artery percolates past the parenchyma cells. Special phagocytic cells, **Kupffer cells,** line the sinusoids and remove debris such as bacteria from the blood as it flows past, while the paren-

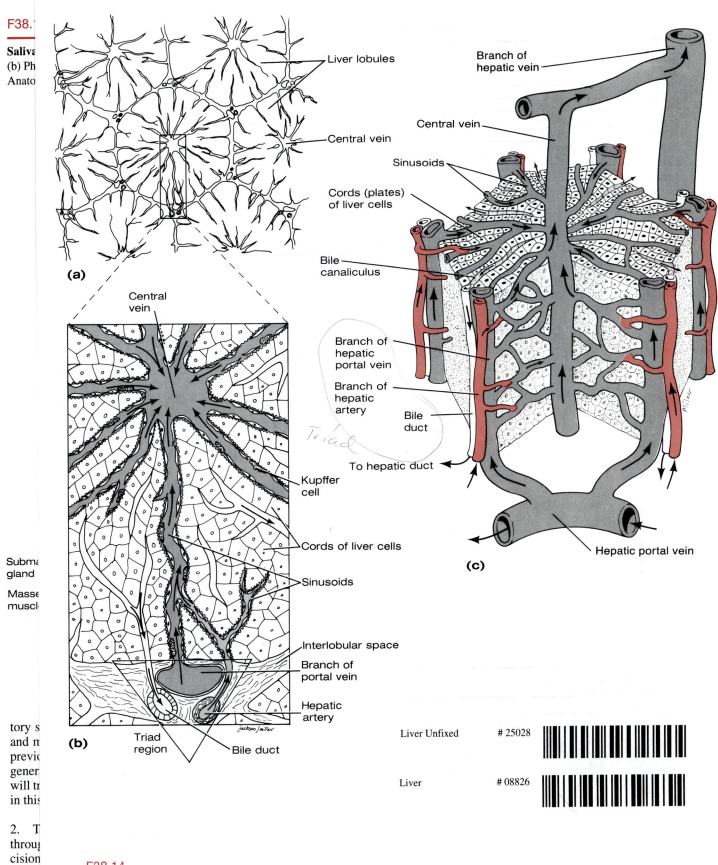

Saliva
(b) Ph
Anato

Subma
gland

Masse
muscl

tory s
and n
previc
gener
will tr
in this

2. T
throug
cision
terior
produ
to ide
reflec

(a)

Central
vein

Kupffer
cell

Cords of liver cells

Sinusoids

Interlobular space

Branch of
portal vein

Hepatic
artery

Triad
region

Bile duct

(b)

jackson/miller

Liver lobules

Central vein

Branch of
hepatic vein

Central vein

Sinusoids

Cords (plates)
of liver cells

Bile
canaliculus

Branch of
hepatic
portal vein

Branch of
hepatic
artery

Bile
duct

Triad

To hepatic duct

Hepatic portal vein

(c)

Liver Unfixed   # 25028

Liver   # 08826

F38.14

Microscopic anatomy of the liver, diagrammatic view. (a) Several liver lobules (cross section). (b) Enlarged view of a portion of one liver lobule (cross section). (c) Portion of one liver lobule (three-dimensional representation). Arrows show direction of bile and blood flow.

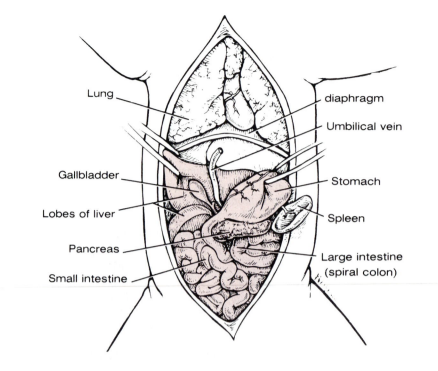

(a)

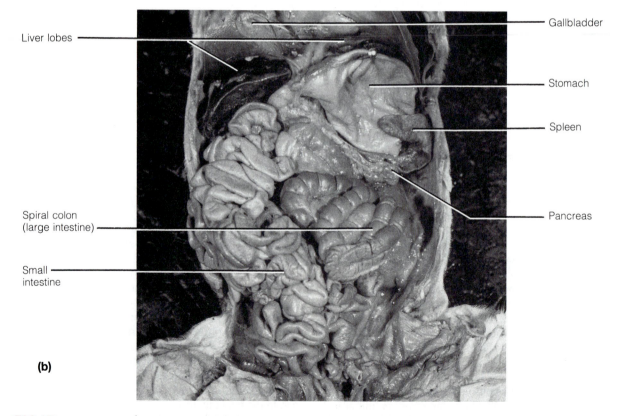

(b)

F38.17

Digestive organs of the fetal pig. (a) Diagrammatic view; greater omentum removed, liver reflected superiorly. (b) Photograph of digestive organs of the fetal pig. See corresponding Plate G in the Fetal Pig Anatomy Atlas.

and located at the base of the tongue anterior to the sub-mandibular gland. The ducts of these two salivary glands run deep and parallel to each other and empty on the side of the frenulum of the tongue. These need not be identified in the pig.

3.   To expose and identify the structures of the oral cavity, use bone cutters to cut through the mandible just anterior to the angle to free the lower jaw from the max-illa. Observe the **teeth** of the pig. The dental formula for the fetal pig is as follows:

$$\frac{3,1,4,0}{3,1,4,0} \times 2 = 32$$

Notice that many of the fetal teeth are incompletely de-veloped, or may not have emerged through the gums yet. If you have a very young fetus with no teeth in evi-dence, cut into the gum tissue to determine whether the deciduous teeth are present. Identify the **hard** and **soft palates,** and use a probe to trace the hard palate to its posterior limits. Does the pig have a uvula?

Identify the **oropharynx** at the rear of the oral cav-ity and the nasopharynx, the continuation of the nasal cavities, superior to it. Identify the **tongue** and rub your fingers across its surface to feel the papillae. As in hu-mans, the tongue plays a role in the manipulation of food in the mouth, and its papillae house the taste buds.

Locate the **lingual frenulum** that attaches the tongue to the floor of the mouth. Trace the tongue pos-teriorly until you locate the **epiglottis,** which appears as a small white tissue tab and which closes the respiratory passageway when swallowing occurs. Also identify the **esophagus** posterior to the epiglottis.

4.   Locate the abdominal alimentary canal structures. If you have not opened the abdominal cavity previously, make a midline incision from the rib cage to the umbil-ical cord and then make two lateral cuts to encircle the umbilicus. Continue these cuts, staying lateral to the body midline, posteriorly until the pubic bone is reached. Make four lateral cuts, two parallel to the rib cage and two at the inferior margin of the abdominal cavity so that the abdominal wall can be reflected back for examination of the abdominal contents. Also cut the umbilical vein at the lower margin of the liver (Figure 38.17). Observe the shiny membrane lining the inner surface of the abdominal wall, which is the **parietal peritoneum.** Identify the large reddish-brown **liver** just beneath the diaphragm. The pig's liver has four main lobes (right lateral and right central and left lateral and left central) plus a small posterior caudate lobe. How does this compare to the number of liver lobes seen in the human liver?

Lift the liver and examine its inferior surface to lo-cate the greenish **gallbladder** embedded in its ventral surface. In preserved specimens, the gallbladder is often shrunken and nearly colorless.

Identify the *falciform ligament,* a delicate layer of mesentery, separating the main lobes of the liver and at-taching the liver superiorly to the abdominal wall. No-tice that this structure surrounds the umbilical vein of the fetus. (Later in life, the remnant of the umbilical vein becomes the round ligament.)

Displace the left lobes of the liver to expose the **stomach.** Identify the point of entry of the esophagus into the stomach and the stomach's cardiac, fundic, body, and pyloric regions. What is the general shape of the stomach?

_____

Locate the **lesser omentum,** the serous membrane attaching the lesser curvature of the stomach to the liver. Make an incision through the stomach wall, and wash out its green contents. (This green substance seen in the fetal digestive tract is called **meconium.** It is composed of the bile-stained mucus and sloughed-off epithelial cells of the digestive tract, as well as sebaceous secre-tions and swallowed amniotic fluid residues.) Notice that the stomach wall is quite thick near the stomach-intestinal junction and that a fold partially occludes the lumen in that region. This fold is the **pyloric sphincter,** which controls passage of stomach contents into the du-odenum. Examine the inner surface of the stomach wall. Can you see the **rugae**? After birth, as nutrients are in-gested and the stomach fills, the rugae gradually disap-pear and are no longer visible. Lift the stomach and pull away the thin peritoneal membrane beneath it to locate the **pancreas,** which appears as a loose glandular organ between the stomach and duodenum. Locate the pancre-atic duct, which extends from the duodenum into the pancreas tissue.

Trace the course of the **small intestine** from the du-odenum to the right, where it takes a left turn near the right kidney. Follow it as it curves anteriorly to become the jejunum and then proceeds to its distal (ileal) end. Lift the small intestine to observe the manner in which it is attached to the posterior body wall by the **mesen-tery.** Observe the mesentery closely. What types of structures do you see in this double peritoneal fold?

_____

_____

Other than providing support for the intestine, what other functions are provided for by the mesentery?

_____

_____

With a scalpel, slice open the distal portion of the ileum and flush out the inner surface with water. Feel the inner surface with your finger tip. How does it feel?

_____

Use a hand lens to see if you can see any **villi** and to locate the areas of lymphatic tissue called **Peyer's patches,** which appear as scattered white patches on the inner intestinal surface. (It may be helpful to examine the opened surface under water.) Return to the duodenal end of the small intestine. Make an incision into the duodenum. As before, flush the surface with water, and feel the inner surface. Does it feel any different from the ileal mucosa?

_____ If so, describe the difference. _____

_____

Again use the hand lens to observe the villi. What differences between the villi are noted in the two areas of the small intestine examined?

_____

Make an incision into the junction between the ileum and the cecum, and identify the **ileocecal valve,** which protrudes into the lumen of the cecum. What is the function of this valve?

_____

Does the pig have an appendix? _____

Trace the continuation of the **large intestine,** or **colon,** from the ileocecal valve to where it forms a tight double coil in the pig and then courses across the body cavity to the region of the left kidney and descends along the midline to the pelvic region, where it becomes the **rectum.** Identify the external anal opening.

Identify the two portions of the peritoneum: the parietal peritoneum, which lines the abdominal wall (identified previously), and the visceral peritoneum, which is the outermost layer of the wall of the abdominal organs (serosa).

5. Prepare your pig for storage by wrapping it in paper towels wet with embalming fluid, returning it to the plastic bag, and attaching your name label. Wash the dissecting tray and instruments before continuing or leaving the laboratory.

Chemical and Physical Processes of Digestion

OBJECTIVES

1. To list the digestive system enzymes involved in the digestion of proteins, fats, and carbohydrates; to state their site of origin; and to summarize the environmental conditions promoting their optimal functioning.

2. To name the end products of digestion of proteins, fats, and carbohydrates.

3. To perform the appropriate chemical tests to determine if digestion of a particular foodstuff has occurred.

4. To cite the function(s) of bile in the digestive process.

5. To discuss the role of temperature and pH in the regulation of enzyme activity.

6. To define *enzyme, catalyst, control, substrate,* and *hydrolase.*

7. To explain why swallowing is both a voluntary and a reflex activity.

8. To discuss the role of the tongue and larynx in swallowing.

9. To state the function of the gastroesophageal sphincter.

10. To describe the following digestive system movements: pendular, segmental, peristaltic, and mass.

MATERIALS

PART I: Enzyme Action

General supply area:
 10-ml and 50-ml graduated cylinders
 Test tubes and test tube rack
 Glass stirring rods
 100-ml beakers
 Wide-range pH paper
 Wax markers
 Distilled water
 Water bath set at 37°C
 Chart on chalkboard for recording class results
Supply area 1:
 0.1% alpha-amylase solution*
 1% boiled starch solution, freshly prepared†
 1% maltose solution
 1 N HCl and 1 N NaOH in dropper bottles
 IKI (Lugol's iodine) and Benedict's solutions in dropper bottles
 500-ml beaker
 Hot plate
 Ice bath

Supply area 2:
 2% pepsin solution
 Alternative substrates:
  Procedure A: albumin solution, freshly prepared, consisting of one part egg white to three parts water
  Procedure B: hard-boiled egg white
 0.5 to 1.0% HCl and 10 N NaOH in dropper bottles
 20% NaOH and 10% $CuSO_4$ in separate stoppered flasks
 Medicine dropper
 Single-edge razor blades
Supply area 3:
 1.5% pancreatin
 Phenol red pH indicator
 0.2% NaOH
 0.1 N HCl
 2% bile solution or "artificial bile" (10% solution of enzyme grade Tween-20)**
 Vegetable oil in dropper bottle

PART II: Physical Processes

Supply area 4:
 Water pitcher
 Paper cups
 Stethoscope
 Alcohol swabs
 Disposable autoclave bag
Supply area 5:
Rats or guinea pigs that have fasted for 24 hours. (The rats should be force-fed cream and meat extract 2 hours before the laboratory experiment.)
Large bell jar
Ether
Absorbent cotton or gauze pads
Dissecting instruments and pan
Plastic gloves
Hand lens
Physiologic saline (mammalian) warmed to 37°C in a water bath

---

*The alpha-amylase should be a low-maltose preparation for best results.

†Prepare by adding 1 g starch to 100 ml distilled water; boil and cool; add a pinch of salt (NaCl). Prepare fresh daily.

**The emulsifier Tween-20 (polyoxyethylene-20-sorbitan mono-laurate), available from Fischer Biotech, allows better visualization of color change than does the bile solution.

(handwritten note in left margin, vertical:) digestive enzymes are hydrolytic enzymes

CHEMICAL DIGESTION OF FOODSTUFFS: ENZYMATIC ACTION

Because nutrients can only be absorbed when broken down to their monomer forms, food digestion is a prerequisite to food absorption. You have already studied mechanisms of passive and active absorption in Exercise 5. Before proceeding, review that material on pages 33–39.

Enzymes are large protein molecules produced by body cells. They are biological catalysts, which increase the rate of a chemical reaction without themselves becoming part of the product. The digestive enzymes are hydrolytic enzymes, or *hydrolases,* which break down organic food molecules by adding water to the molecular bonds, thus cleaving the bonds between the subunits, or monomers.

The various hydrolytic enzymes are highly specific in their action. Each enzyme hydrolyzes only one or a small group of substrate molecules, and very specific environmental conditions are necessary for it to function optimally. Since digestive enzymes actually function outside the body cells, in the digestive tract, their hydrolytic activity can also be studied in a test tube. Such an *in vitro* study provides a convenient laboratory environment for investigating the effect of such variations on enzymatic activity.

Figure 39.1 is a flowchart of the progressive digestion of proteins, fats, and carbohydrates, and indicates specific enzymes involved and their site of formation. Acquaint yourself with this flowchart before beginning this experiment, and refer to it as necessary during the laboratory session.

Work in groups of 3 or 4, with each group taking responsibility for setting up and conducting one of the following experiments. Each group should then communicate its results to the rest of the class by recording them in a chart on the chalkboard. Additionally, all members of the class should observe the controls, as well as the positive and negative examples of all experimental results. All members of the class should be able to explain the tests used and the results observed and anticipated for each experiment.

Starch Digestion By Salivary Amylase

From the general supply area, obtain a test tube rack, 10 test tubes, 10-ml graduated cylinder, wide-range pH paper, a glass stirring rod, and wax marking pencils. From supply area 1, obtain a hot plate and a 500-ml beaker, dropper bottles of 1 N NaOH and HCl, 10 ml of starch solution, 10 ml of amylase solution, and dropper bottles of IKI and Benedict's solutions. Two students should prepare the controls (steps 1 to 4) while the other two prepare the experimental samples (steps 5 and 6).

Since in this experiment you will investigate the hydrolysis of starch to maltose by **salivary amylase** (the enzyme produced by the salivary glands and secreted into the mouth), it is important to be able to identify the presence of these substances to determine to what extent the enzymatic activity has occurred. Thus controls must be prepared to provide a known standard against which comparisons can be made. Starch decreases and sugar increases as digestion occurs according to the following equation:

$$\text{Starch} + \text{water} \xrightarrow{\text{amylase}} X \text{ maltose}$$

1.   With the wax marker, mark a test tube No. 1. Place 1 ml of starch solution in the test tube, and add 2–3 drops of IKI solution. The presence of a blue-black color when IKI is added indicates the presence of starch and is referred to as a **positive starch test.** As the starch is progressively hydrolyzed, the color of the solution will change from blue-black to blue-red, and then to faint red, and finally disappears when all the starch has been digested.

2.   To obtain a *negative starch test,* place 1 ml of distilled water in test tube 2; and add 2–3 drops of IKI. The unchanged color of the solution indicates the absence of starch. What color did you obtain with water and IKI?

_____

3.   To obtain a **positive sugar test,** place 1 ml of maltose solution in test tube 3; and add 5 drops of Benedict's solution. Mix well. Place the test tube in a water bath (a beaker of water on a hot plate), and boil until a color change is noted (but no longer than 5 min). The presence of a bright yellow to deep red precipitate (cuprous oxide) indicates a positive test for maltose, sucrose, or any other reducing sugar. (A change to green is also considered a positive test for sugar but indicates the presence of a smaller amount.)

4.   To obtain a *negative sugar test,* place 1 ml of distilled water in test tube 4, add 5 drops of Benedict's solution, and boil for 5 minutes. Notice that the solution's color remains unchanged from the blue of Benedict's solution, indicating the absence of sugar.

5.   Mark six test tubes with the numbers 5 through 10, and prepare them for incubation as described in Chart 1 (p. 400). You can assume that all of the experimental samples at the time of preparation will give a *negative* test for sugar. Since the enzyme solution in sample 8 must be boiled before incubation begins, the preparation of that sample should be started first. Note and record the time that incubation begins in each case.

6.   As the tubes become colorless (negative starch test), discontinue their incubation. Perform *Benedict's test* on each sample. (Add 1 ml of the incubated solution to a clean test tube, and then add 5 drops of Benedict's solution to the tube. Boil until a color change is noted

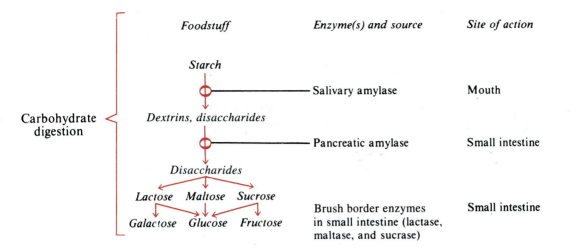

Absorption: The monosaccharides (glucose, galactose, and fructose) are absorbed into the capillary blood in the villi and transported to the liver via the hepatic portal vein

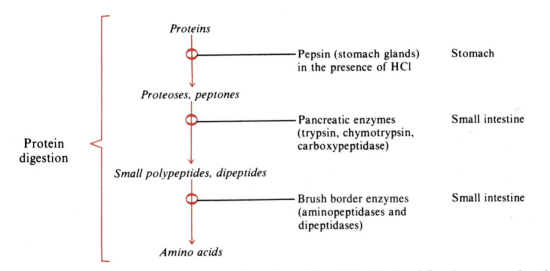

Absorption: The amino acids are absorbed into the capillary blood in the villi and transported to the liver via the hepatic portal vein

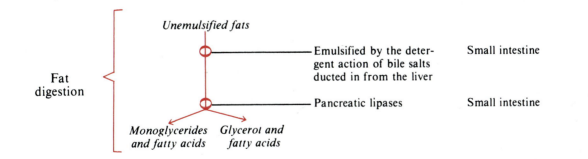

Absorption: Absorbed primarily into the lacteals of the villi and transported to the systemic circulation via the lymph in the thoracic duct. (Glycerol and short-chain fatty acids are absorbed into the capillary blood in the villi and transported to the liver via the hepatic portal vein.)

F39.1

Flow chart of digestion and absorption of foodstuffs.

Chart 1   Salivary Amylase Digestion of Starch

Tube no.	Additives	Incubation condition	Time of initiation	Time for negative IKI test*	Benedict's test +	Benedict's test −
5	4 drops IKI, 1 ml amylase solution; incubate	37°C	8:55	*negative* dark gold brown		
6	4 drops IKI, 1 ml starch solution, 1 ml amylase solution; incubate	37°C	began black-blue	at 37° gold POSITIVE		
7	4 drops IKI, 1 ml starch solution, 1 ml amylase solution; incubate	0°C (ice bath)				
8	5 ml amylase solution; boil 4 min before adding 4 drops IKI and 1 ml starch solution; incubate	37°C				
9	4 drops IKI, 1 ml starch solution, 1 ml amylase solution; add 1 N HCl until a pH of 3 is achieved (stir after each addition); incubate *acidic*	37°C				
10	4 drops IKI, 1 ml starch solution, 1 ml amylase solution; add 1 N NaOH until a pH of 9 is achieved (stir after each addition); incubate *alk*	37°C				

handwritten left margin: explain / mix enzyme last / pH first / mix enzyme last

* If the sample is still positive for the presence of starch at the end of the incubation period, put a (+) in this column.

[or for a maximum of 5 minutes].) After 1 hour of incubation, discontinue the incubation of any remaining tubes; and conduct Benedict's test on their contents. Record the results on Chart 1 and on the chalkboard.

Pepsin Digestion of Protein

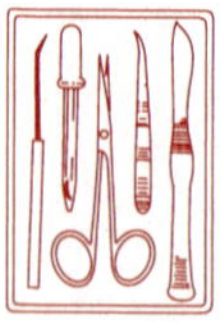

Obtain a test tube rack, seven test tubes, wax marking pencils, and wide-range pH paper from the general supply area, and one of each of the materials/supplies listed under *Supply area 2*. If albumin solution is provided, you will be conducting Procedure A. If hard-boiled egg white is provided, follow the instructions for Procedure B.

Pepsin, produced by the chief cells of the stomach glands, hydrolyzes proteins to smaller fragments (peptides and polypeptides), i.e.:

$$\text{Protein} + \text{water} \xrightarrow{\text{pepsin}} X \text{ peptides}$$

Procedure A:

One student should prepare the control sample according to the directions in step 1 while the other members of the group set up the experimental samples (steps 2 and 3).

1. To prepare a control sample that indicates the presence of protein, perform a *biuret test*. Add 3 ml of albumin solution (diluted egg white) to a test tube marked A, and then add 10 drops of 20% NaOH and 5 drops of 10% $CuSO_4$. Mix well with a glass stirring rod. If the mixture turns *violet*, protein is present. In the presence of polypeptides, the biuret test yields a *pink* color. A negative biuret test (no color change) indicates complete protein digestion.

2. To prepare the experimental samples, mark five test tubes with numbers 1 to 5. Preparation and incubation conditions for the experimental samples are listed in Chart 2. Determine the pH of each sample *before* adding the albumin solution and record the resultant pH on Chart 2. After adding the albumin, shake the tubes vigorously. Except for test tube 4, which is to be incubated at room temperature, place all tubes in the water bath set at 37°C and continue incubation for 2 hours. Shake the tubes occasionally.

3.   Perform the biuret test on the contents of each test tube after the 2-hour incubation period. Record the results on Chart 2 and on the chalkboard. A − indicates a negative test (complete protein digestion); + indicates a test that is slightly positive (incomplete protein digestion; polypeptides present); ++ indicates a strongly positive test (virtually no protein digestion has occurred).

Procedure B:

In this procedure, no control sample will be prepared. Instead, extent of protein digestion will be estimated by visual inspection only.

1.   Mark five test tubes with the numbers 1 to 5.

2.   Using a razor blade, cut five slices of egg white. The slices should be fingernail size and paper thin. The thinness of the egg white is critical to the success of this experiment.

3.   The preparation and incubation conditions for the experimental samples are identical to those indicated for Procedure A, except that slices of egg white instead of albumin solution are to be used as the substrate. Determine the pH of each sample *before* adding the slice of egg white, and record it in Chart 2.

Except for Sample 4, which is to be incubated at room temperature, place all the samples in a water bath set at 37°C and continue incubation for 2 hours. Shake the tubes vigorously before incubating, and then occasionally during incubation when you check to determine if there is any evidence of digestive activity. The egg white will become increasingly transparent and will decrease in mass as digestion proceeds.

4.   At the end of 2 hours of incubation, observe each sample, and record its relative transparency on Chart 2 according to the following scale:

+ + +   no egg white observed
    + +   egg white present, but decreased in mass and very transparent
        +   egg white slightly transparent
        −   appearance of egg white exhibits no difference from untreated egg white

Chart 2   Pepsin Digestion of Protein

Tube no.	Additives	pH of sample	Procedure A Biuret test			Procedure B Transparency			
			−	+	+ +	−	+	+ +	+ + +
1	2 ml pepsin solution, 2 ml 0.5%–1.0% HCl, 2 ml albumin solution or 1 slice egg white; incubate at 37°C								
2	2 ml pepsin solution, 2 ml distilled water, 2 ml albumin solution or 1 slice egg white; incubate at 37°C								
3 *alkaline pH 5/6 9*	2 ml pepsin solution, 2 drops 10 N NaOH, 2 ml albumin solution or 1 slice egg white; incubate at 37°C								
4	2 ml pepsin solution, 2 ml 0.5%–1.0% HCl, 2 ml albumin solution or 1 slice egg white; incubate at room temperature								
5	2 ml distilled water, 2 ml 0.5%–1.0% HCl, 2 ml albumin solution or 1 slice egg white; incubate at 37°C								

Chart 3   Pancreatic Lipase Digestion of Fats

Tube no.	Additives	Incubation		Change in color	Change in odor
		Began	Ended		
2	3 ml pancreatin, 3 ml distilled water, 3 drops phenol red; add 0.2% NaOH until pink; 5 drops of oil; incubate at 37°C				
3	3 ml pancreatin, 3 ml bile solution, 3 drops phenol red; add 0.2% NaOH until pink; 5 drops of oil; incubate at 37°C				
4	3 ml pancreatin, 3 ml bile solution, 3 drops phenol red; add 0.2% NaOH until pink; 5 drops of oil; incubate at room temperature				
5	3 ml distilled water, 3 ml bile solution, 3 drops phenol red; add 0.2% NaOH until pink; 5 drops of oil; incubate at 37°C				

Pancreatic Lipase Digestion of Fats and the Action of Bile

The treatment that fats and oils go through during digestion in the small intestine is a bit more complicated than that of carbohydrates or proteins—it requires pretreatment with bile to physically emulsify the fats first. Hence, two sets of reactions are required.

First:

$$\text{Fats/oils} \xrightarrow[\text{(emulsification)}]{\text{bile}} \text{minute fat/oil droplets}$$

Then:

$$\text{Fat/oil droplets} \xrightarrow{\text{lipase}} \text{monoglycerides and fatty acids}$$

The term **pancreatin** describes the enzymatic product of the pancreas, which includes protein, carbohydrate, nucleic acid, and fat-digesting enzymes. It is used here to investigate the properties of **pancreatic lipase,** which hydrolyzes fats and oils to their component monoglycerides and two fatty acids (and occasionally to glycerol and three fatty acids).

The fact that some of the end products of fat digestion (fatty acids) are organic acids that decrease the pH provides an easy way to recognize that digestion is ongoing or completed. You will be using a pH indicator called *phenol red* to follow these changes; it changes from *red* to *yellow* as the test tube contents become acid.

1. From the general supply area, obtain a test tube rack, seven test tubes, a glass stirring rod, and a 10-ml graduated cylinder. Also obtain one sample each of the substances and supplies listed under *Supply area 3*. One student should prepare the

control (step 2), another should set up the demonstration of the action of bile on fats (step 3), while the other two group members prepare the experimental samples (step 4).

2. To prepare the control, add 3 ml of 1.5% pancreatin solution, 3 ml of bile solution (real or artificial), and 3 drops of phenol red indicator to test tube 1. Add 0.2% NaOH dropwise, stirring with a glass rod after each addition until the contents of the tube turn pink. Put in 5 drops of vegetable oil, and then add 0.1 N HCl, drop by drop (stirring after each addition) until the tube contents turn yellow. This color change indicates that the test tube contains an acidic product and will identify the tubes in which fat hydrolysis has occurred. Mark the tube "control" with a wax marker and put it in the test tube holder for future reference.

3. Although bile, a secretory product of the liver, is not an enzyme, it is important to fat digestion because of its emulsifying action (the physical breakdown of larger particles into smaller ones) on fats. Emulsified fats provide a larger surface area for enzymatic activity. To demonstrate the action of bile on fats, prepare two test tubes; label them A and B. To tube A, add 6 ml H_2O and 5 drops of vegetable oil. To tube B, add 3 ml of H_2O, 3 ml of bile solution, and 5 drops of vegetable oil. Shake each tube vigorously, and allow the tubes to stand in a test tube rack at room temperature for 10 to 15 minutes. Observe both tubes. If emulsification has *not* occurred, the oil will be floating on the surface of the water. If emulsification *has* occurred, the fat droplets will be suspended throughout the water, forming an emulsion.

In which tube has emulsification occurred? _____

4. Prepare the experimental samples as indicated in Chart 3. (Remember to stir when adding the sodium hydroxide [NaOH] solution to turn the phenol red indicator pink.) Then shake each test tube well, before beginning its incubation at room temperature or in a 37°C water bath. Incubate until a color change (pink to yellow) becomes apparent. Shake the tubes occasionally during the incubation period. Note the time incubation begins, the time it ends, and any changes in the color and odor of the samples. Record results on the chalkboard and in Chart 3. After 1 hour, discontinue incubation of any remaining samples, whether or not a color change has occurred. (If there was no color change, write N.C.)

PHYSICAL PROCESSES: MECHANISMS OF FOOD PROPULSION AND MIXING

Although enzyme activity is a very important part of the overall digestion process, foods must also be processed physically (churning and chewing), and moved by mechanical means along the tract if digestion and absorption are to be completed. Just about any time organs exhibit mobility, muscles are involved, and movements of and in the gastrointestinal tract are no exception. Although we tend to think only of smooth muscles when visceral activities are involved, both skeletal and smooth muscles are involved in digestion. This fact is amply demonstrated by the two simple sets of demonstrations that follow.

Deglutition (Swallowing)

Swallowing, or **deglutition,** which is largely the result of skeletal muscle activity, occurs in two phases: *buccal* (mouth) and *pharyngeal-esophageal.* The initial phase—the buccal—is voluntarily controlled and initiated by the tongue. Once begun, the process continues involuntarily in the pharynx and esophagus, through peristalsis, resulting in the delivery of the swallowed contents to the stomach.

 Obtain a pitcher of water, a stethoscope, a paper cup, and an autoclave bag before making the following observations:

1. While swallowing a mouthful of water, consciously note the movement of your tongue during the process. Record your observations.

_____

_____

_____

_____

_____

2. Repeat the swallowing process while your laboratory partner watches the externally visible movements of your larynx. (This movement is more obvious in a male, who has a larger Adam's apple.)

Record your observations. _____

_____

_____

What do these movements accomplish? _____

_____

_____

_____

3. Before donning the stethoscope your partner should clean the earpieces with an alcohol swab. Then he or she should place the diaphragm of the stethoscope over your abdominal wall, approximately 1 inch below the xiphoid process and slightly to the left, to listen for sounds as you again take two or three swallows of water. There should be two audible sounds—one when the water splashes against the closed gastroesophageal sphincter and the second when the peristaltic wave of the esophagus arrives at the sphincter and the sphincter opens, allowing the water to gurgle into the stomach. Determine, as accurately as possible, the time interval between these two sounds and record it below.

Interval between arrival of water at the sphincter and opening of the sphincter:

_____ sec

This interval gives a fair indication of the time it takes for the peristaltic wave to travel down the 10-inch-long esophagus. (Actually the time interval is slightly less than it seems, because pressure causes the sphincter to relax before the peristaltic wave reaches it.)

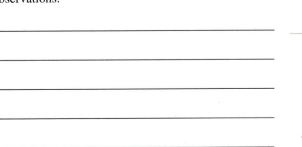 Dispose of the used paper cup in the autoclave bag before continuing.

Observation of Digestive System Movements in a Small Animal

Visceral smooth muscle (*unitary smooth muscle*) composes the muscularis externa portion of the walls of organs of the digestive tract. Smooth muscle activity produces various types of movement in the digestive viscera, which promote digestion, absorption, and food movement. You will observe the three major types of movement: *pendular, segmental,* and *peristaltic.*

Pendular movements, which cause the intestine to sway from side to side, do not appear to play a role in moving the chyme along the tract.

40 EXERCISE

Anatomy of the Urinary System

Metabolism of nutrients by the body produces wastes (carbon dioxide, nitrogenous wastes, ammonia, and so on) that must be eliminated from the body if normal function is to continue. Although excretory processes involve several organ systems (the lungs excrete carbon dioxide and the skin glands excrete salts and water), it is the **urinary system** that is primarily concerned with the removal of nitrogenous wastes from the body. In addition to this purely excretory function, the kidney maintains the electrolyte, acid-base, and fluid balances of the blood and is thus a major, if not *the* major, homeostatic organ of the body.

To perform its functions, the kidney acts first as a blood "filter," and then as a blood "processor." It allows toxins, metabolic wastes, and excess ions to leave the body in the urine, while simultaneously retaining needed substances and returning them to the blood. Malfunction of the urinary system, particularly of the kidneys, leads to a failure in homeostasis which, unless corrected, results in death.

GROSS ANATOMY OF THE HUMAN URINARY SYSTEM

The urinary system (Figure 40.1) consists of the paired kidneys and ureters and the single urinary bladder and urethra. The kidneys perform the functions described above and manufacture urine in the process. The remaining organs of the system provide temporary storage reservoirs or transportation channels for urine.

Kidney and Ureter, Model   # 11870

Examine the human torso model, a large anatomical chart, or a three-dimensional model of the urinary system to locate and study the anatomy and relationships of the urinary organs.

1. Locate the paired **kidneys** on the dorsal body wall in the superior lumbar region. Note that they are not positioned at exactly the same level; because it is "crowded" by the liver, the right kidney is slightly lower than the left kidney. In a living person, fat deposits hold the kidneys in place in a retroperitoneal position.

⬤ When the fatty material surrounding the kidneys is reduced or deficient in amount (in cases of rapid weight loss or in very thin individuals), the kidneys are less securely anchored to the body wall and may drop to

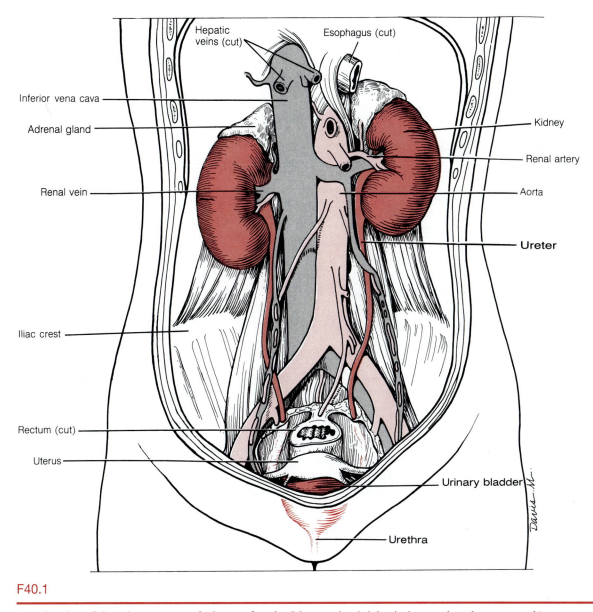

Hepatic veins (cut)

Esophagus (cut)

Inferior vena cava

Adrenal gland

Renal vein

Iliac crest

Rectum (cut)

Uterus

Kidney

Renal artery

Aorta

Ureter

Urinary bladder

Urethra

F40.1

Anterior view of the urinary organs of a human female. (Most unrelated abdominal organs have been removed.)

a lower or more inferior position in the abdominal cavity. This phenomenon is called **ptosis.** ■

2.   Observe the **renal arteries** as they diverge from the descending aorta and plunge into the indented medial region (**hilus**) of each kidney. Note also the **renal veins,** which drain the kidneys (circulatory drainage) and the two **ureters,** which drain urine from the kidneys and conduct it by peristalsis to the bladder for temporary storage.

3.   Locate the **urinary bladder,** and observe the point of entry of the two ureters into this organ. Also locate the single **urethra,** which drains the bladder. The triangular region of the bladder, which is delineated by these three openings (two ureteral and one urethral orifice), is referred to as the **trigone** (Figure 40.2). Although the

formation of urine by the kidney is a continuous process, urine is usually removed from the body when voiding is convenient. In the meantime the bladder provides temporary storage for urine.

Voiding, or **micturition,** is the process in which urine empties from the bladder. Two sphincter muscles or valves, the **internal urethral sphincter** (more superiorly located) and the **external urethral sphincter** (more inferiorly located) control the emptying of urine from the bladder. Ordinarily, the bladder continues to collect urine until about 200 ml have accumulated, at which time the stretching of the bladder wall activates stretch receptors. Impulses transmitted to the central nervous system subsequently produce reflex contractions of the bladder wall through parasympathetic nervous system pathways (i.e., via the pelvic splanchnic nerves). As the contractions increase in force and fre-

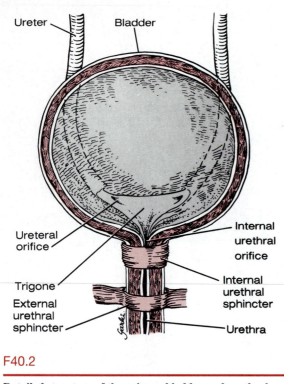

F40.2

Detailed structure of the urinary bladder and urethral sphincter.

quency, the stored urine is forced past the internal sphincter, which is a smooth muscle involuntary sphincter, into the superior part of the urethra. It is then that a person feels the urge to void. The inferior external sphincter consists of skeletal muscle and is voluntarily controlled. If it is not convenient to void, the opening of this sphincter can be inhibited. Conversely, if the time is convenient, the sphincter may be relaxed and the stored urine flushed from the body. If voiding is inhibited, the reflex contractions of the bladder cease temporarily and urine continues to accumulate in the bladder. After another 200 to 300 ml of urine have been collected, the *micturition reflex* will again be initiated.

Lack of voluntary control over the external sphincter is referred to as **incontinence.** Incontinence is a normal phenomenon in children 2 years old or younger, as they have not yet gained control over the voluntary sphincter. In adults and older children, incontinence is generally a result of spinal cord injury, emotional problems, bladder irritability, or some other pathologic condition of the urinary tract. ■

4.   Follow the course of the urethra to the body exterior. In the male, it is approximately 20 cm (8 inches) long, travels the length of the **penis,** and opens at its tip. Its three named regions—the *prostatic, membranous,* and *spongy (penile) urethrae*—are described in more detail in Exercise 42 and illustrated in Figure 42.1 (p. 423). The urethra of males has a dual function: it is a urine conduit to the body exterior, and it provides a passageway for the ejaculation of semen. Thus, in the male,

the urethra is part of both the urinary and reproductive systems. In females, the urethra is very short, approximately 4 cm (1½ inches) long. There are no common urinary-reproductive pathways in the female, and the female urethra serves only to transport urine to the body exterior. Its external opening, the **external urethral orifice,** lies anterior to the vaginal opening.

Bladder, Unfixed,   # 15588

GROSS INTERNAL ANATOMY OF THE PIG OR SHEEP KIDNEY

1.   Obtain a preserved sheep or pig kidney, dissecting pan, and instruments. Observe the kidney to identify the **renal capsule,** a smooth transparent membrane that adheres tightly to the kidney tissue.

2.   Find the ureter, renal vein, and renal artery at the hilus (indented) region. The renal vein has the thinnest wall and will be collapsed. The ureter is the largest of these structures and has the thickest wall.

3.   Make a cut through the longitudinal axis (frontal section) of the kidney and locate the anatomical areas described below and depicted in Figure 40.3.

Kidney cortex: the outer kidney region, which is lighter in color. If the kidney is double-injected with latex, you will see a predominance of red and blue latex specks in this region indicating its rich vascular supply.

Medullary region: deep to the cortex; a darker, reddish-brown color. The medulla is segregated into triangular regions that have a striped, or striated, appearance—the **medullary (renal) pyramids.** The base of each pyramid faces toward the cortex; its **apex,** or **papilla,** points to the innermost kidney region.

Renal columns: areas of tissue, more like the cortex in appearance, which segregate and dip inward between the pyramids.

Renal pelvis: medial to the hilus; a relatively flat, basinlike cavity that is continuous with the **ureter,** which exits from the hilus region. Fingerlike extensions of the pelvis should be visible. The larger, or primary, extensions are called the **major calyces;** subdivisions of the major calyces are the **minor calyces.** Notice that the minor calyces terminate in cuplike areas that enclose the apexes of the medullary pyramids and collect urine draining from the pyramidal tips into the pelvis.

4.   If the preserved kidney is doubly or triply injected, follow the renal blood supply from the renal artery to the **glomeruli.** The glomeruli appear as little red and blue specks in the cortex region. (See Figures 40.3 and 40.4 and the discussion below.)

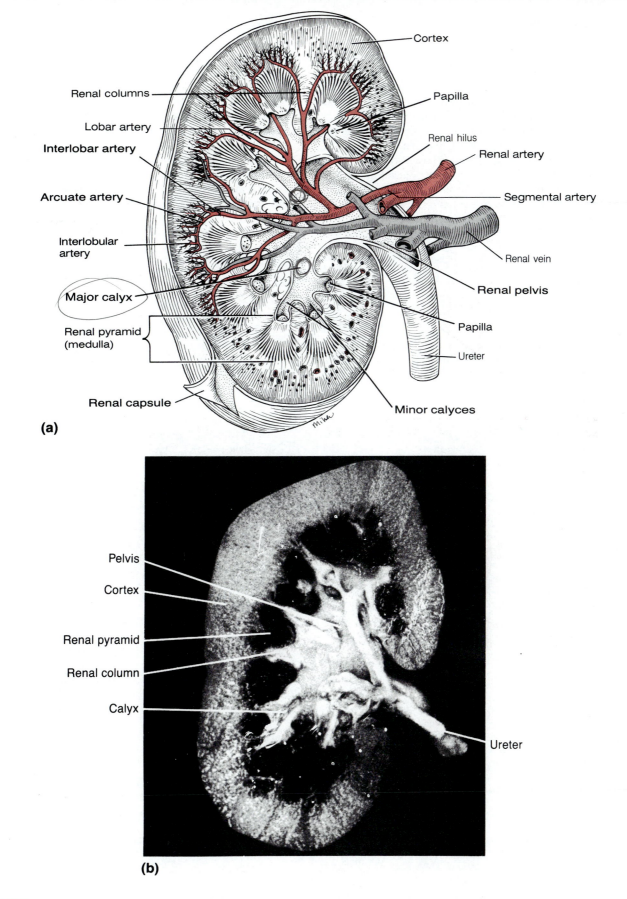

(a)

Cortex

Renal columns

Papilla

Lobar artery

Renal hilus

Interlobar artery

Renal artery

Segmental artery

Arcuate artery

Renal vein

Interlobular artery

Renal pelvis

Major calyx

Papilla

Renal pyramid (medulla)

Ureter

Renal capsule

Minor calyces

(b)

Pelvis

Cortex

Renal pyramid

Renal column

Calyx

Ureter

Frontal section of a kidney. (a) Diagrammatic view, showing larger arteries supplying the kidney tissue. (b) Photograph of a pig kidney.

Because the kidneys continuously cleanse the blood and adjust its composition, it is not surprising that they have a rich vascular supply. Approximately a fourth of the total blood flow of the body is delivered to the kidneys each minute by the large **renal arteries.** As a renal artery approaches the kidney, it breaks up into five branches called **segmental arteries** which enter the hilus. Each segmental artery, in turn, divides into several **lobar arteries.** The lobar arteries branch to form **interlobar arteries,** which ascend toward the cortex in the renal column areas. At the top of the medullary region, these arteries give off arching branches, the **arcuate ar-** **teries,** which curve over the bases of the medullary pyramids. Small **interlobular arteries** branch off the arcuate arteries and ascend into the cortex, giving off the individual **afferent arterioles,** which provide the capillary networks (**glomeruli** and **peritubular capillary beds**) that supply the nephrons, or functional units, of the kidney. Blood draining from the nephron capillary networks in the cortex enters the **interlobular veins** and then drains through the **arcuate veins** and the **interlobar veins** to finally enter the **renal vein** in the pelvis region. (There are no lobar or segmental veins.)

← wrong, yes there are!

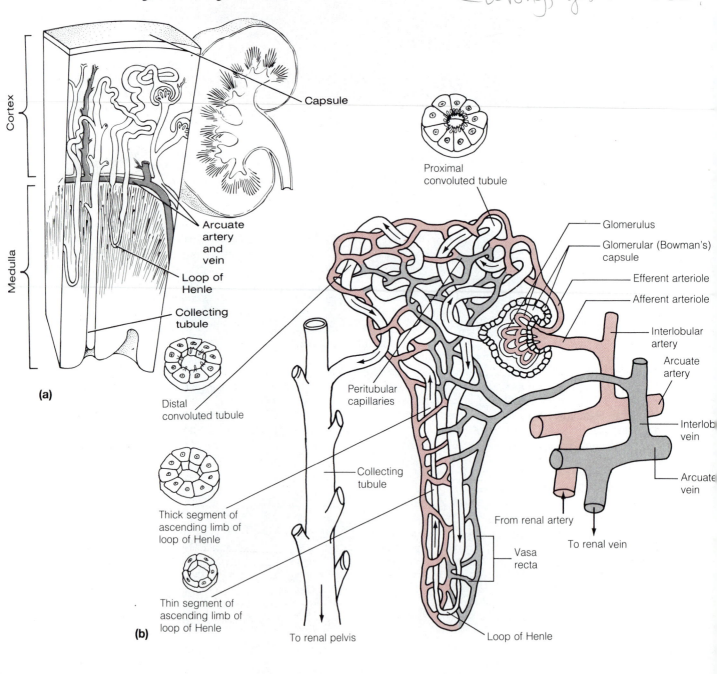

(a)

Cortex

Medulla

Capsule

Arcuate artery and vein

Loop of Henle

Collecting tubule

Distal convoluted tubule

Thick segment of ascending limb of loop of Henle

Thin segment of ascending limb of loop of Henle

(b)

Proximal convoluted tubule

Glomerulus

Glomerular (Bowman's) capsule

Efferent arteriole

Afferent arteriole

Interlobular artery

Arcuate artery

Interlob vein

Arcuate vein

Peritubular capillaries

Collecting tubule

From renal artery

To renal vein

Vasa recta

To renal pelvis

Loop of Henle

F40.4

Structure of a nephron. (a) Wedge-shaped section of kidney tissue, indicating the position of the nephrons in the kidney. (b) Detailed nephron anatomy and associated blood supply.

Kidney, Unfixed	# 15573
Kidney Cut Surface, Unfixed	# 11813
Kidney, Tubules (Distal & Proximal)	# 14928
Glomerulus, (Vascular Pole)	# 14936
Kidney Cortex, (Glomerulus)	# 14926

MICROSCOPIC ANATOMY OF THE KIDNEY AND BLADDER

Obtain prepared slides of kidney and bladder tissue, and a compound microscope.

Kidney

Each kidney contains over one million nephrons, which are the anatomical units responsible for forming urine. Figure 40.4 depicts the detailed structure and the relative positioning of the nephrons in the kidney.

Each nephron consists of two major structures: a **glomerulus** (a capillary knot) and a **renal tubule.** During embryologic development, each renal tubule begins as a blind-ended tubule that gradually encloses an adjacent capillary cluster, or glomerulus. The enlarged end of the tubule encasing the glomerulus is the **glomerular (Bowman's) capsule,** and its inner, or visceral, wall consists of highly specialized cells called **podocytes.** Podocytes have long, branching processes (*foot processes*) that interdigitate with those of other podocytes and cling to the endothelial wall of the glomerular capillaries, thus forming a very porous epithelial membrane surrounding the glomerulus. The glomerulus-capsule complex is sometimes called the **renal corpuscle.**

The rest of the tubule is approximately 3 cm (1.25 inches) long. As it emerges from the glomerular capsule, it becomes highly coiled and convoluted, drops down into a long hairpin loop, and then again coils and twists before entering a collecting tubule. In order from the glomerular capsule, the anatomical areas of the tubule are: the **proximal convoluted tubule, loop of Henle** (descending and ascending limbs), and the **distal convoluted tubule.** The wall of the renal tubule is composed almost entirely of cuboidal epithelial cells, with the exception of part of the descending limb (and sometimes part of the ascending limb) of the loop of Henle, which is simple squamous epithelium. The lumen surfaces of the cuboidal cells in the proximal convoluted tubule have dense microvilli (a cellular modification that greatly increases the surface area exposed to the lumen contents, or filtrate). Microvilli also occur on

cells of the distal convoluted tubule but in greatly reduced numbers, revealing its less significant role in reclaiming filtrate contents.

Most nephrons, called **cortical nephrons,** are located entirely within the cortex. However, parts of the loops of Henle of the **juxtamedullary nephrons** (located close to the cortex-medulla junction), penetrate well into the medulla. The **collecting tubules,** each of which receives urine from many nephrons, run downward through the medullary pyramids, giving them their striped appearance. As the collecting tubules approach the renal pelvis, they fuse to form larger *papillary ducts,* which empty the final urinary product into the calyces and pelvis of the kidney.

The function of the nephron depends on several unique features of the renal circulation. The capillary vascular supply consists of two distinct capillary beds, the **glomerulus** and the **peritubular capillary bed.** Vessels leading to and from the glomerulus, the first capillary bed, are both arterioles: **the afferent arteriole** feeds the bed while the **efferent arteriole** drains it. The glomerular capillary bed has no parallel elsewhere in the body. It is a high-pressure bed along its entire length. Its high pressure is a result of two major factors: (1) the bed is *fed and drained* by arterioles (arterioles are high-resistance vessels as opposed to venules, which are low-resistance vessels), and (2) the afferent feeder arteriole is larger in diameter than the efferent arteriole that drains the bed. The high hydrostatic pressure created by these two anatomical features forces out fluid and blood components smaller than proteins from the glomerulus into the glomerular capsule; that is, it forms the filtrate which is processed by the nephron tubule.

The peritubular capillary bed arises from the efferent arteriole draining the glomerulus. This set of capillaries cling intimately to the renal tubule and empty into the interlobular veins that leave the cortex. The peritubular capillaries are *low-pressure* very porous capillaries adapted for absorption rather than filtration and readily take up the solutes and water reabsorbed from the filtrate by the tubule cells. The juxtamedullary nephrons have additional looping vessels, called the **vasa recta** ("straight vessels"), that parallel their long loops of Henle in the medulla (see Figure 40.4). Hence, the two capillary beds of the nephron have very different, but complementary, roles: The glomerulus produces the filtrate and the peritubular capillaries reclaim most of that filtrate.

Urine formation is a result of three processes: *filtration, reabsorption,* and *secretion* (Figure 40.5). **Filtration** is the role of the glomerulus and is largely a passive process in which a portion of the blood passes from the glomerular bed into the glomerular capsule. This filtrate then enters the proximal convoluted tubule where tubular reabsorption and secretion begin. During **tubular reabsorption,** many of the filtrate components move through the tubule cells and return to the blood in the peritubular capillaries. Some of this reabsorption is passive, such as that of water which passes by osmosis, but the reabsorption of most substances depends on active transport processes and is highly selective. Which substances are reabsorbed at a particular time depends on

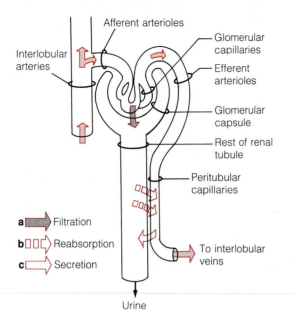

Afferent arterioles

Glomerular capillaries

Interlobular arteries

Efferent arterioles

Glomerular capsule

Rest of renal tubule

Peritubular capillaries

a ▬▶ Filtration

b ▢▢▢▷ Reabsorption

c ▢▷ Secretion

To interlobular veins

Urine

F40.5

The kidney depicted as a single, large nephron. A kidney actually has millions of nephrons acting in parallel. The three major mechanisms by which the kidneys adjust the composition of plasma are (a) glomerular filtration, (b) tubular reabsorption, and (c) tubular secretion. Red arrows show the path of blood flow through the renal microcirculation.

Observe a model of the nephron before continuing on with the microscope study of the kidney.

Hold the longitudinal section of the kidney up to the light to identify cortical and medullary areas. Then secure the slide on the microscope stage and scan the slide under low power. Move the slide so that you can see the cortical area. Identify a glomerulus, which appears as a ball of tightly packed material containing many small nuclei (Figure 40.6). It is usually delineated by a vacant-appearing region (corresponding to the space between the visceral and parietal layers of the glomerular capsule) that surrounds it. Notice that the renal tubules are cut at various angles. Also try to differentiate between the thin-walled loop of Henle portion of the tubules and the cuboidal epithelium of the proximal convoluted tubule, which has dense microvilli.

Bladder

Scan the bladder tissue. Identify its three layers—mucosa, muscular layer, and fibrous adventitia. Observe the mucosa with its highly specialized transitional epithelium. The plump, transitional epithelial cells have the ability to slide over one another, thus decreasing the thickness of the mucosa layer as the bladder fills and stretches to accommodate the increased urine volume. Depending on the degree of stretching of the bladder, the mucosa may be three to eight cell layers thick. Examine the heavy muscular wall (detrusor muscle), which consists of three irregularly arranged muscular layers. The innermost and outermost muscle layers are arranged longitudinally; the middle layer is arranged circularly. Attempt to differentiate the three muscle layers.

Draw a small section of the bladder wall, and label all regions or tissue areas.

the composition of the blood and needs of the body at that time. Substances that are almost entirely reabsorbed from the filtrate include water, glucose, and amino acids. Various ions are selectively reabsorbed or allowed to go out in the urine according to what is required to maintain appropriate blood pH and electrolyte composition. Waste products (urea, creatinine, uric acid, and drug metabolites) are reabsorbed to a much lesser degree or not at all. Most (75% to 80%) of tubular reabsorption occurs in the proximal convoluted tubule; the balance occurs in other areas, especially the distal convoluted and collecting tubules.

Tubular secretion is essentially the reverse process. Substances such as hydrogen and potassium ions, creatinine, and ammonia move either from the blood of the peritubular capillaries through the tubular cells or from the tubular cells into the filtrate to be disposed of in the urine. This process is particularly important for the disposal of substances not already in the filtrate (such as drug metabolites), and as an adjunct method for controlling blood pH.

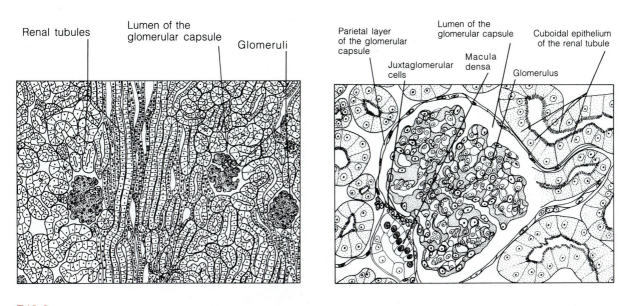

F40.6

Microscopic structure of the kidney. (a) Low-power view of the renal cortex. (b) Detailed structure of the glomerulus. (See corresponding Plates 43 and 44 in the Histology Atlas.)

Compare your sketch of the bladder wall to the structure of the ureter wall shown in Plate 45 in the Histology Atlas. How are the two organs similar histologically?

_____

_____

_____

What is/are the most obvious differences?

_____

_____

DISSECTION OF THE FETAL PIG URINARY SYSTEM

The structures of the reproductive and urinary systems are often considered together as the *urogenital system,* since they have common embryologic origins. How-

ever, the emphasis in this dissection is on identifying the structures of the urinary tract (Figures 40.7 and 40.8) with only a few references to contiguous reproductive structures. (Exercise 42 is a study of the anatomy of the reproductive system.)

1. Obtain your dissection specimen, and pin or tie its limbs to the dissection tray. Reflect the abdominal viscera (small intestine) to locate the kidneys high on the dorsal body wall. Notice that the kidneys in the pig, as well as in the human, are retroperitoneal (behind the peritoneum).

2. Carefully remove the peritoneum, and clear away the bed of fat that invests the kidneys. Locate the adrenal (suprarenal) glands, which appear as bandlike pale orange glands lying on the anteromedial surface of each kidney.

3. Identify the renal artery (red latex–injected), the renal vein (blue latex–injected), and the ureter at the hilus region of the kidney.

(Text continues on p. 414)

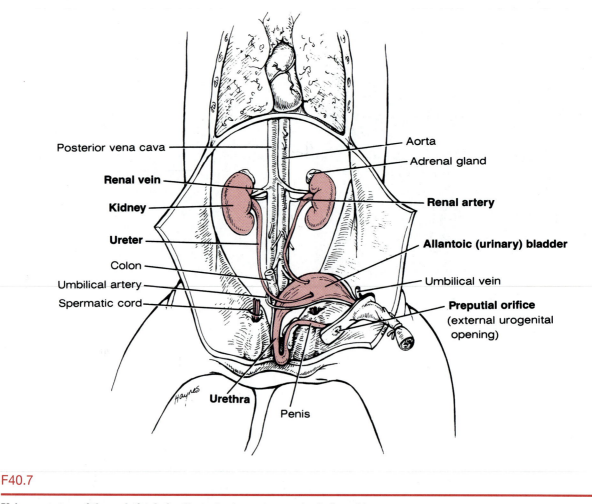

Posterior vena cava

Aorta

Adrenal gland

Renal vein

Kidney

Renal artery

Ureter

Colon

Allantoic (urinary) bladder

Umbilical artery

Umbilical vein

Spermatic cord

Preputial orifice
(external urogenital
opening)

Haynes

Urethra

Penis

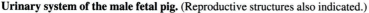

F40.7

Urinary system of the male fetal pig. (Reproductive structures also indicated.)

4. Trace the ureters posteriorly along the dorsal body wall to where they turn ventrally to enter the **allantoic bladder,** or fetal urinary bladder, a collapsed elongated sac lying between the umbilical arteries. Trace the posterior portion of the bladder to the point where it narrows to become the urethra, which enters the pelvic cavity. Backtrack to the point where the ureters enter the allantoic bladder, and then trace the bladder into the umbilical cord, where it continues as the **allantoic stalk.** After birth, when the allantois becomes nonfunctional, the allantoic bladder becomes the urinary bladder.

5. Cut through the bladder wall and examine the region of the urethral exit to see if you can discern any evidence of the internal sphincter.

6. Using a probe, trace the urethra as it exits from the bladder to its terminus in the *urogenital sinus,* which also opens into the vagina in the female pig and into the penis of the male. (In the human female, the urethra does not empty into the vagina but has a separate external opening located superior to the vaginal orifice.) Identify the external urogenital opening in the male pig located just below the umbilicus. Do not expose the urethra along its entire length at this time, because you may damage the reproductive structures, which will be studied later.

7. Before cleaning up the dissection materials, observe a pig of the opposite sex.

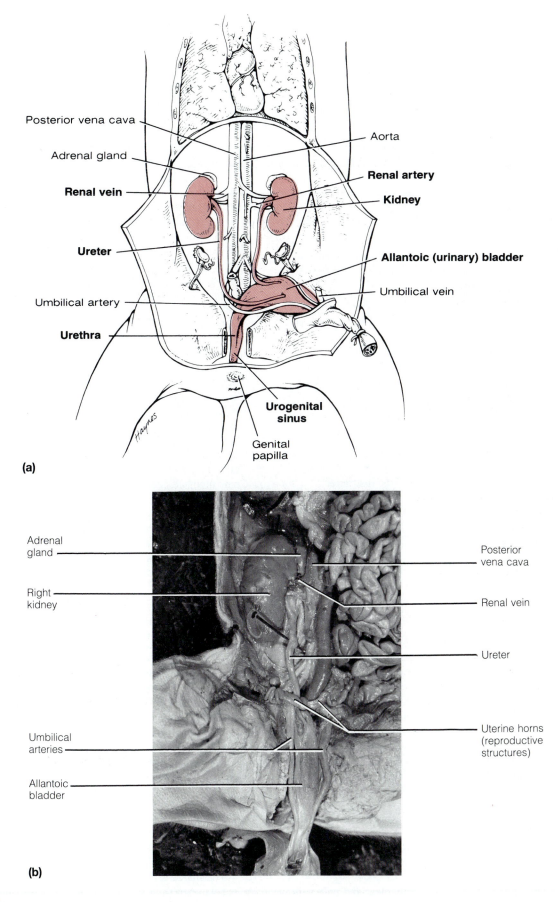

(a)

(b)

Urinary system of the female fetal pig. (a) Diagrammatic view. (b) Photograph. Some reproductive structures also indicated. See dissection photo, Plate H in the Fetal Pig Anatomy Atlas.

Urinalysis

Blood composition depends on three major factors: dietary intake, cellular metabolism, and urinary output. In 24 hours, the kidney's two million nephrons filter approximately 150 to 180 liters of blood plasma through their glomeruli into the tubules, where it is selectively processed by tubular reabsorption and secretion. In the same period, urinary output, which contains by-products of metabolism and excess ions, is 1.0 to 1.8 liters. In healthy individuals, the kidneys can maintain blood constancy despite wide variations in diet and metabolic activity. With certain pathologic conditions, urine composition often changes dramatically.

CHARACTERISTICS OF URINE

Freshly voided urine is generally clear and pale yellow to amber in color. This normal yellow color is due to *urochrome,* a pigment metabolite arising from the body's destruction of hemoglobin (via bilirubin or bile pigments). As a rule, color variations from pale yellow to deeper amber indicate the relative concentration of solutes to water in the urine. The greater the solute concentration, the deeper the color. Abnormal urinary color may be due to certain foods, such as beets, various drugs, bile, or blood.

The odor of freshly voided urine is characteristic and slightly aromatic, but bacterial action gives it an ammonialike odor when left standing. Some drugs, vegetables (such as asparagus), and various disease processes (such as diabetes mellitus) alter the characteristic odor of urine. For example, the urine of a person with uncontrolled diabetes mellitus (and elevated levels of ketones) smells fruity or acetonelike.

The pH of urine ranges from 4.5 to 8.0, but its average value, 6.0, is slightly acidic. Diet may markedly influence the pH of the urine. For example, a diet high in protein (meat, eggs, cheese) and whole wheat products increases the acidity of urine. Such foods are called *acid ash foods.* On the other hand, a vegetarian diet (*alkaline ash diet*) increases the alkalinity of the urine. A bacterial infection of the urinary tract may also result in urine with a high pH.

Specific gravity is the relative weight of a specific volume of liquid compared with an equal volume of distilled water. The specific gravity of distilled water is 1,000, because 1 ml weighs 1 g. Since urine contains dissolved solutes, it weighs more than water, and its customary specific gravity ranges from 1.001 to 1.030. Urine with a specific gravity of 1.001 contains few solutes and is considered very dilute. Dilute urine commonly results when a person drinks excessive amounts of water, uses diuretics, or suffers from diabetes insipidus or chronic renal failure. Conditions that produce urine with a high specific gravity include limited fluid intake, fever, and kidney inflammation, called *pyelonephritis.* If urine becomes excessively concentrated, some of the substances normally held in solution begin to precipitate or crystallize, forming **kidney stones,** or **renal calculi.**

Normal constituents of urine (in order of decreasing concentration) include water; urea;* sodium,† potassium, phosphate, and sulfate ions; creatinine,* and uric acid.* Much smaller but highly variable amounts of calcium, magnesium, and bicarbonate ions are also found in the urine. Abnormally high concentrations of any of these urinary constituents may indicate a pathological condition.

ABNORMAL URINARY CONSTITUENTS

Abnormal urinary constituents are substances not normally present in the urine when the body is operating properly.

Glucose

The presence of glucose in the urine, a condition called **glycosuria,** is indicative of abnormally high blood sugar levels. Normally blood sugar levels are maintained between 80 and 120 mg/100 ml of blood. At this level all glucose in the filtrate is reabsorbed by the tubular cells and returned to the blood. Glycosuria may result from carbohydrate intake so excessive that normal physiologic and hormonal mechanisms cannot clear it from the blood quickly enough. In such cases of glycosuria, the active transport reabsorption mechanisms of the tubules for glucose are exceeded, but only temporarily.

Pathologic glycosuria occurs in conditions such as uncontrolled diabetes mellitus, in which the body cells are unable to absorb glucose from the blood because the pancreatic islet cells produce inadequate amounts of the hormone insulin, or there is some abnormality of the insulin receptors. Under such circumstances, the body cells increase their metabolism of fats, and the excess and unusable glucose spills out in the urine.

Albumin

Albuminuria, or the presence of albumin in urine, is an abnormal finding. Albumin is the single most abundant blood protein and is very important in maintaining the osmotic pressure of the blood. Albumin, like other blood proteins, normally is too large to pass through the glomerular filtration membrane; thus albuminuria is generally indicative of an abnormally increased permeability of the glomerular membrane. Certain nonpathologic conditions, such as excessive exertion, pregnancy, or overabundant protein intake, can temporarily increase the membrane permeability, leading to **physiologic albuminuria.** Pathologic conditions resulting in the appearance of albumin in the urine include events that damage the glomerular membrane, such as kidney trauma due to blows, the ingestion of heavy metals, bacterial toxins, glomerulonephritis, and hypertension.

Ketone Bodies

Ketone bodies (acetoacetic acid, beta-hydroxybutyric acid, and acetone) normally appear in the urine in very small amounts. **Ketonuria,** the presence of these intermediate products of fat metabolism in excessive amounts, usually indicates that abnormal metabolic processes are occurring. The result may be acidosis and its complications. Ketonuria is an expected finding during starvation, when inadequate food intake forces the body to use its fat stores. Ketonuria coupled with a finding of glycosuria is generally diagnostic for diabetes mellitus.

Red Blood Cells

Hematuria, the appearance of red blood cells, or erythrocytes, in the urine, almost always indicates pathology of the urinary tract, since erythrocytes are too large to pass through the glomerular pores. Possible causes include irritation of the urinary tract organs by calculi (kidney stones), which produces frank bleeding; infections; or physical trauma to the urinary organs. In healthy menstruating females, it may reflect accidental contamination of the urine sample with the menstrual flow.

Hemoglobin

Hemoglobinuria, the presence of hemoglobin in the urine, is a result of the fragmentation, or hemolysis, of red blood cells and liberation of the hemoglobin into the plasma with its subsequent appearance in the kidney filtrate. Hemoglobinuria may indicate various pathologic conditions, including hemolytic anemias, transfusion reactions, burns, or renal disease.

---

* Urea, uric acid, and creatinine are the most important nitrogenous wastes found in urine. Urea is an end product of protein breakdown; uric acid is a metabolite of purine breakdown; and creatinine is associated with muscle metabolism of creatine phosphate.

† Sodium ions appear in relatively high concentration in the urine because of reduced urine volume, not because large amounts are being secreted. Sodium is the major positive ion in the plasma; under normal circumstances, most of it is actively reabsorbed.

Bile Pigments

Bilirubinuria, the appearance of bilirubin (bile pigments) in urine is an abnormal finding and most often reflects liver pathology such as hepatitis or cirrhosis. Bilirubinuria is indicated by a yellow foam that results when the urine sample is shaken.

White Blood Cells

Pyuria is the presence of white blood cells or other pus constituents in the urine. It indicates an inflammatory process in the urinary tract.

Casts

Any complete discussion of the varieties and implications of casts is beyond the scope of this exercise; however, because they always represent a pathologic condition of the kidney or urinary tract, they should be mentioned. **Casts** are hardened cell fragments, usually cylindrical, which are flushed out of the urinary tract. White blood cell casts are a common finding with pyelonephritis, red blood cell casts are commonly seen with glomerulonephritis, and fatty casts indicate severe renal damage.

ANALYSIS OF URINE SAMPLES

In this part of the exercise, you will use various types of prepared dip sticks and perform chemical tests to determine the characteristics of normal urine as well as to identify abnormal urinary components. You will investigate your own (student-collected) specimen or a "normal" urine sample provided by your instructor, *and* an unknown specimen of urine. Make the following determinations on both samples and record your results by circling the appropriate item or description or by adding data to complete Table 41.1. If you have more than one unknown sample, accurately identify each sample used by number.

Obtain and wear plastic disposable gloves throughout this laboratory session. When you have completed the laboratory procedures: (1) dispose of the gloves and used pH paper strips in the autoclave bag; (2) put used glassware in the bleach-containing laboratory bucket; (3) wash the lab bench down with 10% bleach solution.

Determination of the Physical Characteristics of Urine

1. Determine the color, transparency, and odor of your sample and one of the numbered pathologic samples, and circle the appropriate descriptions in Table 41.1.

2. Obtain a roll of wide-range pH paper to determine the pH of each sample. Use a fresh piece of paper for each test, and dip the strip into the urine to be tested two or three times before comparing the color obtained with the chart on the dispenser. Record your results in Table 41.1. (If you will be using one of the combination dip sticks—Chemstrip or Multistix—this pH determination can be done later.)

3. To determine specific gravity, obtain a urinometer cylinder and float. Mix the urine well, and fill the urinometer cylinder about two-thirds full with urine.

4. Examine the urinometer float to determine how to read its markings. In most cases, the scale has numbered lines separated by a series of unnumbered lines. The numbered lines give the reading for the first two decimal places. You must determine the third decimal place by reading the lower edge of the meniscus—the curved surface representing the urine-air junction—on the stem of the float.

5. Carefully lower the urinometer float into the urine. Make sure it is floating freely before attempting to take the reading. Record the specific gravity of both samples in the table. *Do not dispose of this urine if the samples that you have are less than 200 ml in volume* because you will need to make several more determinations.

Determination of Inorganic Constituents in Urine

SULFATES   Add 5 ml of urine to a test tube, and then add a few drops of dilute hydrochloric acid and 2 ml of 10% barium chloride solution. The appearance of a white precipitate (barium sulfate) indicates the presence of sulfates in the sample. Clean the test tubes well after use. Record your results. Are sulfates a *normal* constituent of urine?

PHOSPHATES   Add 5 ml of urine to a test tube, and then add three or four drops of dilute nitric acid and 3 ml of ammonium molybdate. Mix well with a glass stirring rod, and then heat gently in a hot water bath. The formation of a yellow precipitate indicates the presence of phosphates in the sample.

CHLORIDES   Place 5 ml of urine in a test tube, and add several drops of silver nitrate ($AgNO_3$). The appearance of a white precipitate (silver chloride) is a positive test for chlorides. Record your results.

Determination of Organic Constituents in Urine

Individual dip sticks or combination dip sticks (Chemstrip or Multistix) may be used for many of the tests in this section. If the combination dip sticks are used, be prepared to take the readings on several factors (pH, protein [albumin], glucose, ketones, blood/hemoglobin, and leukocytes [pus]) at the same time. Generally speaking, results for all of these tests may be read *during* the second minute after immersion, but readings taken after 2 minutes have passed should be considered invalid. Pay careful attention to the directions for method and time

TABLE 41.1 Urinalysis Results*

Observation or test	Normal values	Student urine specimen	Unknown specimen (# F)
Physical characteristics			
Color	Pale yellow	Yellow: pale medium dark other _____	Yellow: pale (medium) dark other _____
Transparency	Transparent	Clear slightly cloudy cloudy	Clear (slightly cloudy) cloudy
Odor	Characteristic	Describe _____	Describe _____ aromatic _____
pH	4.5–8.0	_____	_____ 6.00 _____
Specific gravity	(1.001–1.030)	_____	_____ ~~1.00T~~ 1.011 _____
Inorganic components			
Sulfates	Present	Present Absent	(Present) Absent
Phosphates	Present	Present Absent	(Present) Absent
Chlorides	Present	Present Absent	(Present) Absent
Organic components			
Urea	Present	Present Absent	Present Absent
Glucose Dip stick: _____	Negative	Record results: _____	Record results: _____ negative _____
Clinitest _____	Negative	Record results: _____	Record results: _____ negative _____
Albumin Dip stick: _____	Negative	Record results: _____	Record results: _____ trace _____
Ketone bodies Dip stick: _____	Negative	Record results: _____	Record results: _____ negative _____
RBCs/hemoglobin Dip stick: _____	Negative	Record results: _____	Record results: _____ negative _____
WBCs (leukocytes) Dip stick: _____	Negative	Record results: _____	Record results: _____
Bilirubin Dip stick: _____	Negative	Record results: _____	Record results: _____
Ictotest	Negative (no color change)	Negative Positive (purple)	Negative Positive (purple)

*In recording urinalysis data, circle the appropriate description if provided; otherwise record the results you observed. Identify dip sticks used.

of immersion and disposal of excess urine from the strip, regardless of the dip stick used.

UREA   Put two drops of urine on a clean microscope slide and *carefully* add one drop of concentrated nitric acid to the urine. Slowly warm the mixture on a hot plate until it begins to dry at the edges, but do not allow it to boil or to evaporate to dryness. When the slide has cooled, examine the edges of the preparation under low power to identify the rhombic or hexagonal crystals of urea nitrate, which form when urea and nitric acid react chemically. Keep the light low for best contrast. Record your results.

GLUCOSE   Use a combination dip stick or obtain a vial of Clinistix, and conduct the dip stick test according to the instructions on the vial. Record the results in Table 41.1.

Because the Clinitest reagent is routinely used in clinical agencies for glucose determinations in pediatric patients (children), it is worthwhile to conduct this test as well. Obtain the Clinitest tablets and the associated color chart. Using a medicine dropper, put 5 drops of urine into a test tube; then rinse the dropper and add 10 drops of water to the tube. Add a Clinitest tablet. Wait 15 seconds and then compare the color obtained to the color chart. Record the results.

ALBUMIN   Use a combination dip stick or obtain the Albustix dip sticks, and conduct the determinations as indicated on the vial. Record your results.

BLOOD/HEMOGLOBIN   Test your urine samples for the presence of hemoglobin by using a Hemastix dip stick or a combination dip stick according to the directions on the vial. Usually a short drying period is required before making the reading, so read the directions carefully. Record your results.

BILIRUBIN   Using a Bilistix dip stick, determine if there is any bilirubin in your urine samples. Record your results.

Also conduct the Ictotest for the presence of bilirubin. Using a medicine dropper, place one drop of urine in the center of one of the special test mats provided with the Ictotest reagent tablets. Place one of the reagent tablets over the drop of urine, and then add two drops of water directly to the tablet. If the mixture turns purple when you add water, bilirubin is present. Record your results.

MICROSCOPIC ANALYSIS OF URINE SEDIMENT (OPTIONAL)

If a centrifuge is available, a microscopic analysis of the urine sediment can be done. The instructor will provide directions for the use of the centrifuge. After centrifugation, pour off the supernatant (the fluid that appears above the sediments at the bottom of the tube), and place a drop of the sediment on a clean glass slide. Add a drop of Sedi-stain, and cover the specimen with a coverslip.

Using the lowest light source possible, examine the slide under low power to determine if any of the sediments illustrated in Figures 41.1 and 41.2 (and described here) can be seen.

Unorganized sediments (Figure 41.1): chemical substances that form crystals or precipitate from solution; for example, calcium oxalates, carbonates, and phosphates; uric acid; ammonium ureates; and cholesterol. Also, if one has been taking antibiotics or certain drugs such as sulfa drugs, these may be detectable in the urine in crystalline form. Normal urine contains very small amounts of crystals, but conditions such as urinary retention or urinary tract infection may result in the appearance of much larger amounts (and their possible consolidation into calculi). The high-power lens may be needed to view the various crystals that tend to be much more minute than the organized (cellular) sediments.

Organized sediments (Figure 41.2): include epithelial cells (rarely of any pathologic significance), pus cells (white blood cells), red blood cells, and casts. Urine is normally negative for organized sediments, and the presence of the last three categories mentioned, other than trace amounts, always indicates kidney pathology (infectious or noninfectious in nature).

Draw a few of your observations below and attempt to identify them by comparing them with Figures 41.1 and 41.2.

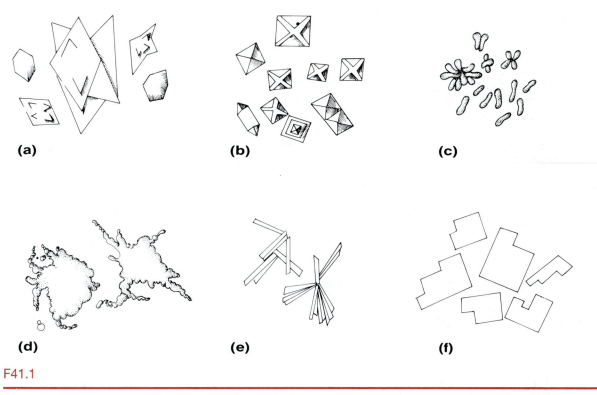

F41.1

Examples of unorganized sediments. (a) Uric acid crystals, (b) calcium oxalate crystals, (c) calcium carbonate crystals, (d) ammonium ureate crystals, (e) calcium phosphate crystals, (f) cholesterol crystals.

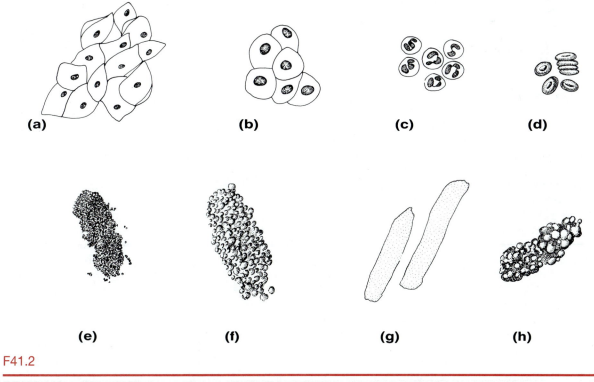

F41.2

Examples of organized sediments. (a) Squamous epithelial cells, (b) transitional epithelial cells, (c) white blood cells (pus), (d) red blood cells, (e) granular casts, (f) red blood cell casts, (g) hyaline casts, (h) fatty casts.

Anatomy of the Reproductive System

1. To discuss the general function of the reproductive system.

2. To identify and name the structures of the male and female reproductive systems when provided with an appropriate model or diagram, and to discuss the general function of each.

3. To define *semen,* discuss its composition, and name the organs involved in its production.

4. To trace the pathway followed by a sperm from its site of formation to the external environment.

5. To name the exocrine and endocrine products of the testes and ovaries, indicating the cell types or structures responsible for the production of each.

6. To identify homologous structures of the male and female systems.

7. To discuss the microscopic structure of the penis, epididymis, uterine tube, and uterus, and to relate structure to function.

8. To define *ejaculation, erection,* and *gonad.*

9. To discuss the function of the fimbriae and ciliated epithelium of the uterine (fallopian) tubes.

10. To identify the fundus, body, and cervical regions of the uterus.

11. To define *endometrium, myometrium,* and *ovulation.*

12. To identify the major reproductive structures of the male and female dissection animal, and to recognize and discuss pertinent differences between the reproductive structures of the human and the dissection animal.

Models or large laboratory charts of the male and female reproductive tracts

Prepared microscope slides of cross sections of the penis, epididymis, uterine tube, and uterus showing endometrium (proliferative phase)

Compound microscope

Dissection animal, tray, and instruments

Bone clippers

Protective skin cream or plastic gloves

Most simply stated, the biologic function of the **reproductive system** is to perpetuate the species. Thus the reproductive system is unique, since the other organ systems of the body function primarily to sustain the existing individual.

The essential organs of reproduction are those that produce the germ cells—the testes and the ovaries. The reproductive role of the male is to manufacture sperm and to deliver them to the female reproductive tract. The female, in turn, produces eggs. If the time is suitable, the combination of sperm and egg produces a fertilized egg, which is the first cell of a new individual. Once fertilization has occurred, the female uterus provides a nurturing, protective environment in which the embryo, later called the fetus, develops until birth.

Although the drive to reproduce is strong in all animals, in humans this drive is also intricately related to nonbiologic factors. Emotions and social considerations often enhance or thwart its expression.

GROSS ANATOMY OF THE HUMAN MALE REPRODUCTIVE SYSTEM

The primary reproductive organs of the male are the **testes,** the male *gonads,* which have both an exocrine (sperm production) and an endocrine (testosterone production) function. All other reproductive structures are conduits or sources of secretions, which aid in the safe delivery of the sperm to the body exterior or female reproductive tract.

As the following organs and structures are described, locate them on Figure 42.1, and then identify them on a three-dimensional model of the male reproductive system or on a large laboratory chart.

The paired oval testes lie in the **scro-**

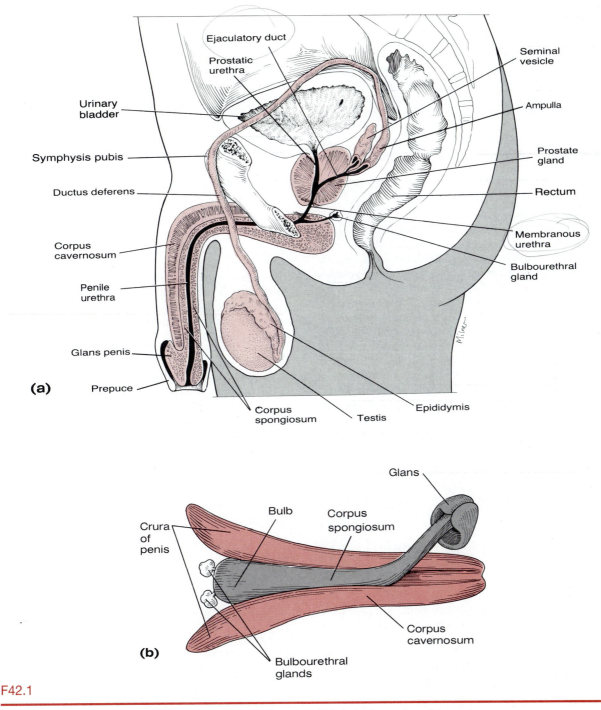

(a)

Ejaculatory duct

Prostatic
urethra

Urinary
bladder

Symphysis pubis

Ductus deferens

Corpus
cavernosum

Penile
urethra

Glans penis

Prepuce

Corpus
spongiosum

Testis

Epididymis

Seminal
vesicle

Ampulla

Prostate
gland

Rectum

Membranous
urethra

Bulbourethral
gland

(b)

Crura
of
penis

Bulb

Corpus
spongiosum

Glans

Corpus
cavernosum

Bulbourethral
glands

F42.1

Reproductive system of the human male. (a) Midsagittal section. (b) Inferior intact view of the penis.

tal sac outside the abdominopelvic cavity. The temperature there (approximately 94°F, or 34°C) is slightly
lower than body temperature, a requirement for production of viable sperm.

The accessory structures forming the *duct system*
are the epididymis, the ductus deferens, the ejaculatory
duct, and the urethra. The **epididymis** is an elongated
structure running up the posterolateral aspect of the testis and capping its superior aspect. The epididymis

forms the first portion of the duct system and provides a
site for immature sperm that enter it from the testis to
complete their maturation process. The **ductus deferens**
(sperm duct) arches upward from the epididymis, passes
through the inguinal canal into the pelvic cavity, and
courses over the superior aspect of the urinary bladder.
In life, the ductus deferens (also called the *vas deferens*)
is enclosed along with blood vessels and nerves in a
connective tissue sheath called the **spermatic cord.** The

terminus of the ductus deferens enlarges to form the region called the **ampulla,** which empties into the **ejaculatory duct.** Contraction of the ejaculatory duct propels the sperm through the prostate gland to the **prostatic urethra,** which in turn empties into the **membranous urethra** and then into the **penile urethra,** which runs through the length of the penis to the body exterior.

The spermatic cord is easily palpated through the skin of the scrotum. When a *vasectomy* is performed, a small incision is made in each side of the scrotum, and each ductus deferens is cut through or cauterized. Although sperm are still produced, they can no longer reach the body exterior; thus a man is sterile after this procedure (and 12 to 15 ejaculations to clear the conducting tubules).

The *accessory glands* include the prostate gland, the paired seminal vesicles, and bulbourethral glands. These glands produce **seminal fluid,** the liquid medium in which sperm leave the body. The **seminal vesicles,** which produce about 60% of seminal fluid, lie at the posterior wall of the urinary bladder close to the terminus of the ductus deferens. They produce a viscous secretion containing fructose (a simple sugar) and other substances that nourish the sperm passing through the tract or promote the fertilizing capability of sperm in some way. The duct of each seminal vesicle merges with a ductus deferens to form the ejaculatory duct (mentioned above); thus sperm and seminal fluid enter the urethra together.

The **prostate gland** encircles the urethra just inferior to the bladder. It secretes a milky alkaline fluid into the urethra, which plays a role in activating the sperm.

Reprod. System, Male, Model	# 11839	
Prostate	# 15129	

 Hypertrophy of the prostate gland, a troublesome condition commonly seen in old age, constricts the urethra so that urination is difficult. ■

The **bulbourethral glands (Cowper's glands)** are tiny, pea-shaped glands inferior to the prostate. They produce a thick, clear, alkaline mucus that drains into the membranous urethra. This secretion is believed to wash the residual urine out of the urethra when ejaculation of **semen** (sperm plus seminal fluid) occurs. The relative alkalinity of all of these glandular secretions also buffers the sperm against the acidity of the female reproductive tract.

The **penis,** part of the external genitalia of the male along with the scrotal sac, is the copulatory organ of the male and is designed to deliver sperm into the female reproductive tract. It consists of a shaft, which terminates in an enlarged tip, the **glans** (see Figure 42.1b). The skin covering the penis is loosely applied, and it reflects downward to form a circular fold of skin, the **prepuce,** or **foreskin,** around the proximal end of the glans. (The foreskin is removed in the surgical procedure called *circumcision.*) Internally, the penis consists primarily of three elongated cylinders of erectile tissue, which become engorged with blood during sexual excitement. This causes the penis to become rigid and enlarged so that it may more adequately serve as a penetrating device. This event is called **erection.** The paired dorsal cylinders are the **corpora cavernosa.** The single ventral **corpus spongiosum** surrounds the penile urethra.

MICROSCOPIC ANATOMY OF SELECTED MALE REPRODUCTIVE ORGANS

Testis

Each testis is covered by a dense connective tissue capsule called the **tunica albuginea** (literally, white tunic). Extensions of this sheath enter the testis, dividing it into a number of lobes, each of which houses one to four highly coiled **seminiferous tubules,** the sperm-forming factories (Figure 42.2). The seminiferous tubules of each lobe converge to empty the sperm into another tubular region, the **rete testis,** at the mediastinum of the testis. Sperm traveling through the rete testis then enter the epididymis, located on the exterior aspect of the testis, as previously described. Lying between the seminiferous tubules and softly padded with connective tissue are the **interstitial cells,** which produce testosterone, the hormonal product of the testis. You will conduct a microscopic study of testes tissue in Exercise 43.

Spermatic Cord	# 47968	

Epididymis

Obtain a microscope and a cross section of the epididymis. Notice the abundant tubule cross sections resulting from the fact that the coiling epididymis tubule has been cut through many times in the specimen. Look for sperm in the lumen of the tubule. Using Figure 42.3a as a guide, examine the composition of the tubule wall carefully. Identify the *stereocilia* of the pseudostratified columnar epithelial lining. (These nonmotile microvilli absorb excess fluid and pass nutrients to the sperm in the lumen.) Now identify the smooth muscle layer. What do you think the function of the smooth muscle is?

_____

_____

Epididymis   # 20762

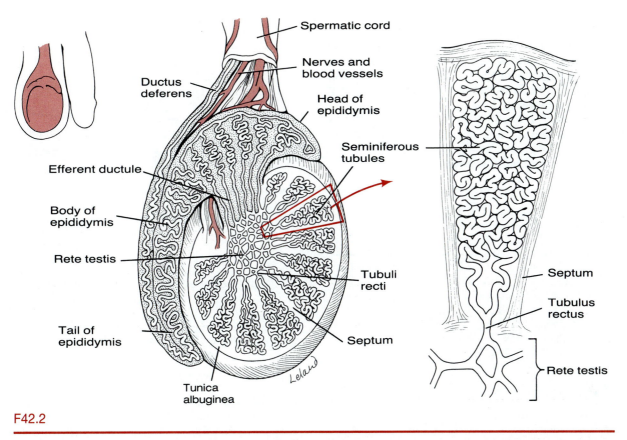

Spermatic cord

Nerves and blood vessels

Ductus deferens

Head of epididymis

Efferent ductule

Seminiferous tubules

Body of epididymis

Rete testis

Tubuli recti

Septum

Tail of epididymis

Tunica albuginea

Septum

Tubulus rectus

Rete testis

Leland

F42.2

Longitudinal-section view of the testis showing seminiferous tubules. (Epididymis and part of the ductus deferens also shown.)

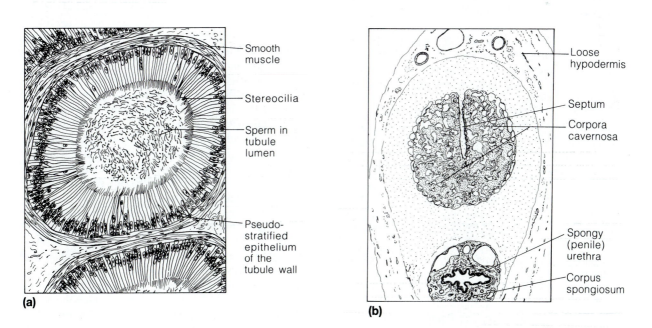

Smooth muscle

Stereocilia

Sperm in tubule lumen

Pseudo-stratified epithelium of the tubule wall

Loose hypodermis

Septum

Corpora cavernosa

Spongy (penile) urethra

Corpus spongiosum

(a)

(b)

F42.3

Microscopic anatomy of selected organs of the male reproductive duct system. (a) Epididymis (see corresponding Plate 46 in the Histology Atlas). (b) Cross-sectional view of the penis (see also Plate 47).

Penis

Obtain a cross section of the penis. Scan the tissue under low power to identify the urethra and the cavernous bodies. Compare your observations to Figure 42.3b. Observe the lumen of the urethra carefully. What type of epithelium do you see?

_____

Explain the function of this type of epithelium.

_____

_____

_____

_____

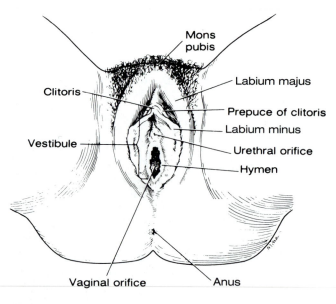

F42.4

External genitalia of the human female.

GROSS ANATOMY OF THE HUMAN FEMALE REPRODUCTIVE SYSTEM

The **ovaries** (female gonads) are the primary reproductive organs of the female. Like the testes of the male, the ovaries produce both an exocrine product (the eggs, or ova) and endocrine products (estrogens and progesterone). The other accessory structures of the female reproductive system transport, house, nurture, or otherwise serve the needs of the reproductive cells and/or the developing fetus.

The reproductive structures of the female are generally considered in terms of internal organs and external organs, or external genitalia.

As you read the descriptions of these structures, locate them on Figures 42.4 and 42.5 and then on the female reproductive system model or large laboratory chart.

The **external genitalia (vulva)** consist of the mons pubis, labia majora and minora, the clitoris, urethral and vaginal orifices, the hymen, and the greater vestibular glands. The **mons pubis** is a rounded fatty eminence overlying the pubic symphysis. Running inferiorly and posteriorly from the mons pubis are two elongated, pigmented, hair-covered skin folds, the **labia majora,** which enclose two smaller hair-free folds, the **labia minora.** (Terms indicating only one of the two folds in each case are *labium majus* and *minus,* respectively.) The labia majora are homologous to the scrotum of the male. The labia minora, in turn, enclose a region called the **vestibule,** which contains many structures: the clitoris, most anteriorly, followed by the urethral orifice and the vaginal orifice. The diamond-shaped region between the anterior end of the labial folds, the ischial tuberosities laterally, and the anus posteriorly is called the **perineum.**

The **clitoris** is a small protruding structure, homologous to the male penis, and like its counterpart is com-

posed of highly sensitive, erectile tissue. It is hooded by skin folds of the anterior labia minora, referred to as the **prepuce of the clitoris.** The urethral orifice, which lies posterior to the clitoris, is the outlet for the urinary system and has no reproductive function in the female. The vaginal opening is partially closed by a thin fold of mucous membrane called the **hymen** and is flanked by the mucus secreting **greater vestibular (Bartholin's) glands,** which lubricate the distal end of the vagina during coitus. (These glands are not depicted in the illustrations.)

The internal female organs include the vagina, uterus, uterine tubes, ovaries, and the ligaments and supporting structures that suspend these organs in the pelvic cavity. The **vagina** extends for approximately 10 cm (4 inches) from the vestibule to the uterus superiorly. It serves as the copulatory organ and the birth canal and permits passage of the menstrual flow. The pear-shaped **uterus,** situated between the bladder and the rectum, is a highly muscular organ with its narrow end, the **cervix,** directed inferiorly. The major portion of the uterus is referred to as the **body;** its superior rounded region above the entrance of the uterine tubes is called the **fundus.** A fertilized egg is implanted in the uterus, which houses the embryo or fetus during its development.

In some cases, the fertilized egg may implant in a uterine tube or even on the abdominal viscera, creating an **ectopic pregnancy.** Such implantations are usually unsuccessful and may even endanger the mother's life, because the uterine tubes cannot accommodate the increasing size of the fetus. ■

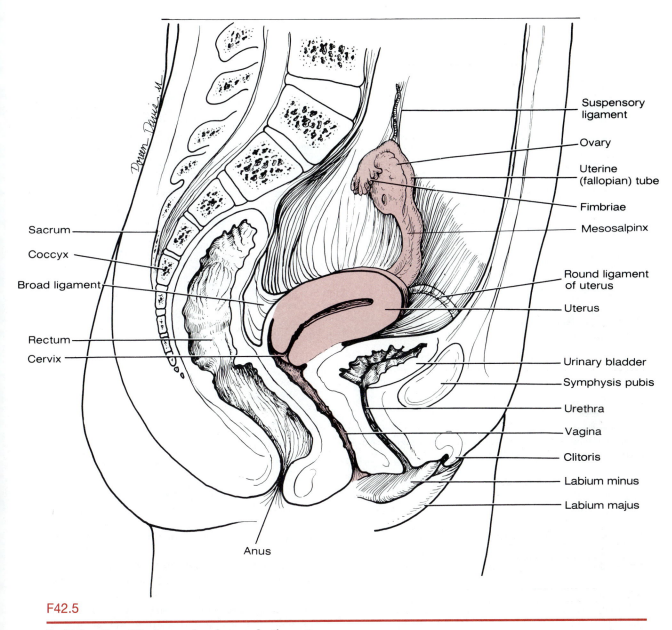

F42.5

Sagittal section of the human female reproductive system.

The apical portion of the **endometrium,** the thick mucosal lining of the uterus, sloughs off periodically (about every 28 days) in response to cyclic changes in the levels of ovarian hormones in the woman's blood. This sloughing-off process, which is accompanied by bleeding, is referred to as **menstruation,** or **menses.**

The **uterine,** or **fallopian, tubes** enter the superior region of the uterus and extend laterally for about 10 cm (4 inches) toward the **ovaries** in the peritoneal cavity. The distal ends of the tubes are funnel-shaped and have fingerlike projections called **fimbriae.** Unlike the male duct system, there is no actual contact between the female gonad and the initial part of the female duct system—the uterine tube.

Because of this open passageway between the female reproductive organs and the peritoneal cavity, reproductive system infections, such as gonorrhea, can spread to cause widespread inflammations of the pelvic viscera, a condition called **pelvic inflammatory disease** or **PID.** ■

Pelvic Inflammatory   # 10901
Disease

Within the ovaries, the female gametes (eggs) develop in sac-like structures called *follicles.* The growing follicles also produce *estrogens.* When a developing egg

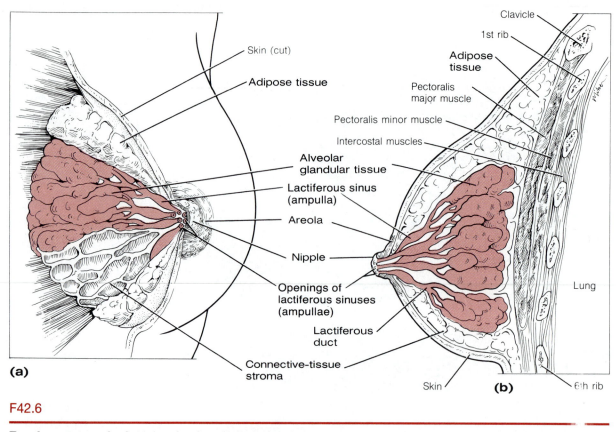

F42.6

Female mammary gland. (a) Anterior view. (b) Sagittal section.

has reached the appropriate stage of maturity, it is ejected from the ovary in an event called **ovulation.** The ruptured follicle is then converted to a second type of endocrine gland, called a *corpus luteum,* which secretes progesterone (and some estrogens).

The flattened almond-shaped ovaries lie adjacent to the uterine tubes but are not connected to them; consequently, an ovulated egg* enters the pelvic cavity. The waving fimbriae of the uterine tubes create fluid currents that, if successful, draw the egg into the lumen of the uterine tube, where it begins its passage to the uterus, propelled by the cilia of the tubule walls. The usual and most desirable site of fertilization is the uterine tube, because the journey to the uterus takes about 3 to 4 days and an egg is viable for up to 24 hours after it is expelled from the ovary. Thus, sperm must swim upward through the vagina and uterus, and into the uterine tubes to reach the egg. This must be an arduous journey, because they must swim against the downward current created by ciliary action—rather like swimming against the tide!

The internal female organs are all retroperitoneal, except the ovaries. They are supported and suspended

somewhat freely by ligamentous folds of peritoneum. The peritoneum takes an undulating course: from the pelvic cavity floor it moves superiorly over the top of the bladder, reflects over the anterior and posterior surfaces of the uterus, and then over the rectum, and up the posterior body wall. The fold that encloses the uterine tubes and uterus and secures them to the lateral body walls is referred to as the **broad ligament.** The portion of the broad ligament specifically anchoring the uterus is called the **mesometrium** and that anchoring the uterine tubes, the **mesosalpinx.** The **round ligaments,** fibrous cords that run from the uterus to the labia majora, also help attach the uterus to the body wall. The ovaries are supported medially by the **ovarian ligament** (extending from the uterus to the ovary), laterally by the **suspensory ligaments,** and posteriorly by a fold of the broad ligament, the **mesovarium.**

The **mammary glands** or breasts exist, of course, in both sexes, but they have a reproduction-related function only in females. Since the function of the mammary glands is to produce milk to nourish the newborn infant, their importance is more closely associated with events that occur when reproduction has already been accomplished. Periodic stimulation by the female sex hormones, especially estrogens, increases the size of the female mammary glands at puberty. During this period, the duct system becomes more elaborate, and fat is de-

---

* To simplify this discussion, the ovulated cell is called an egg. What is actually expelled from the ovary is an earlier stage of development called a secondary oocyte. These matters are explained in more detail in Exercise 43.

posited—fat deposition being the more important contributor to increased breast size.

The rounded, skin-covered mammary glands lie anterior to the pectoral muscles of the thorax, attached to them by connective tissue. Slightly below the center of each breast is a pigmented area, the **areola,** which surrounds a centrally protruding **nipple** (Figure 42.6).

Internally each mammary gland consists of 15 to 20 **lobes** separated by connective tissue and adipose, or fatty, tissue, which radiate around the nipple. Within each lobe are smaller chambers called **lobules,** containing the clusters of **alveolar glands** that produce the milk during lactation. The alveolar glands of each lobule pass the milk into a number of **lactiferous ducts,** which join to form an expanded storage chamber, the **lactiferous sinus,** or **ampulla,** as they approach the nipple. The ampullae open to the outside at the nipple.

MICROSCOPIC ANATOMY OF SELECTED FEMALE REPRODUCTIVE ORGANS*

Uterine Tube

Obtain a prepared slide of a cross-sectional view of a uterine tube for examination. Notice the highly folded mucosa (the folds nearly fill the tubule lumen) as illustrated in Figure 42.7. Then switch to high power to examine the ciliated secretory epithelium. Draw your observations of the tubule mucosa below.

Serosa Smooth muscle Highly folded mucosa Lumen

F42.7

Cross-sectional view of a uterine tube. Notice its highly folded mucosa. (See also corresponding Plate 48 in the Histology Atlas.)

* A microscopic study of the ovary is described in Exercise 43, p. 438. If that exercise is not to be conducted in its entirety, the instructor might want to include the ovary study in the scope of this exercise.

Reprod. System, Female, Anterior	# 11832	
Female Genital Organs Unfixed	# 15779	
Ovary and FallopianTube	# 15783	
Uterus, Unfixed	# 15789	
Vagina, Unfixed	# 15780	
Breast, Serratus Anterior	# 47746	
Oviduct, Ampulla	# 20677	

(Text continues on next page)

Physiology of Reproduction: Gametogenesis and the Female Cycles

OBJECTIVES

1. To define *meiosis, gametogenesis, oogenesis, spermatogenesis, spermiogenesis, synapsis, haploid, diploid,* and *menses,* and to state the similarities and differences between spermatogenesis and oogenesis.

2. To relate the stages of spermatogenesis to the cross-sectional structure of the seminiferous tubule.

3. To discuss the microscopic structure of the ovary and to be prepared to identify primary, secondary, and vesicular follicles and the corpus luteum, and to state the hormonal products of the last two structures.

4. To relate the stages of oogenesis to follicle development in the ovary.

5. To cite similarities and differences between mitosis and meiosis.

6. To describe the anatomical structure of the sperm and relate it to function.

7. To discuss the phases and control of the menstrual cycle.

8. To discuss the effect of FSH and LH on the ovary and to describe the feedback relationship between anterior pituitary gonadotropins and ovarian hormones.

9. To describe the effect of FSH and LH (ICSH) on testicular function.

MATERIALS

Prepared microscope slides of testis, ovary, human sperm, and uterine endometrium (showing menstrual, proliferative, and secretory stages)

Three-dimensional models illustrating meiosis, spermatogenesis, and oogenesis

Compound microscope

Demonstration Area: microscopes set up to demonstrate the following stages of oogenesis in *Ascaris megalocephala:*

1. Primary oocyte with fertilization membrane, sperm nucleus, and aligned tetrads apparent
2. Formation of the first polar body
3. Secondary oocyte with dyads aligned
4. Formation of the ovum and second polar body
5. Fusion of the male and female pronuclei to form the fertilized egg

special type of nuclear ÷ that occurs only in testes & ovaries. Yields 4 daughter nuclei that differ genetically & in composition from the mother nucl is used only for the production of eggs & sperm (gametes)

MEIOSIS

Every human being, so far, has developed from the union of gametes. The gametes, produced only in the testis or ovary, are unique cells, since they have only half the normal chromosome number (designated as **n,** or the **haploid complement**) seen in all other body cells. In humans, gametes have 23 chromosomes instead of the 46 of other tissue cells. Theoretically, every gamete has a full set of genetic instructions, a conclusion borne out by the observation that some animals can develop from an egg that is artificially stimulated, as by a pinprick, rather than by sperm entry. (This is less true of the sperm, because it has an incomplete sex chromosome.) **Gametogenesis,** the process of gamete formation, involves the reduction of chromosome number by half. This event is important to maintain the character-

istic chromosomal number of the species generation after generation; otherwise there would be a doubling of chromosome number with each succeeding generation and the cells would become so chock-full of genetic material there would be little room for anything else.

Egg and sperm chromosomes that carry genes for the same traits are called **homologous chromosomes,** and when the sperm and egg fuse to form the **zygote,** or fertilized egg, it is said to contain 23 pairs of homologous chromosomes, or the **diploid (2n)** chromosome number of 46. The zygote, once formed, then divides to produce the cells needed to construct the multicellular human body. All cells of the developing human body have a chromosome content exactly identical in quality and quantity to that of the fertilized egg; this is assured by the nuclear division process called **mitosis.** (Mitosis was considered in depth in Exercise 4. You may want to review it at this time.)

To produce gametes with the reduced (haploid) chromosomal number, **meiosis,** a specialized type of nuclear division, occurs in the ovaries and testes during gametogenesis. Before meiosis begins, the chromosomes are replicated in the *mother cell* or stem cell just as they are before mitosis. As a result, the mother cell briefly has double the normal diploid genetic complement. The stem cell then undergoes two consecutive nuclear divisions, termed *meiosis I* and *II,* or the first and second maturation divisions, without replicating the chromosomes before the second division. The result is that four haploid daughter cells are produced, rather than the two diploid daughter cells produced by mitotic division.

The entire process of meiosis is quite complex and is dealt with here only to the extent necessary to reveal important points of difference between this type of nuclear division and mitosis. Essentially, each meiotic division involves the same phases and events seen in mitosis (prophase, metaphase, anaphase, and telophase), but during the first maturation division (meiosis I) an event not seen in mitosis occurs as the mother cell goes into prophase. The homologous chromosomes, each now a duplicated structure, begin to pair so that they become closely aligned along their entire length. This pairing is called **synapsis.** As a result, 23 **tetrads** (groupings of four chromatids) form, become attached to the spindle fibers, and begin to align themselves on the spindle equator. While in synapsis, two of the four strands (one from each homologue) in each tetrad wrap and coil around each other, forming many points of **crossover,** or **chiasmata.** (Perhaps this could be called the conjugal bed of the cell!) When anaphase of meiosis I begins, the homologues separate from one another, breaking and exchanging parts at points of crossover, and move apart toward opposite poles of the cell. The centromeres holding the "sister" chromatids or **dyads** together do not break at this point (Figure 43.1).

During the second maturation division, events parallel those in mitosis, except that the daughter cells do not replicate their chromosomes before this division, and each daughter cell has only half of the homologous chromosomes rather than a complete set. The crossover events and the way in which the homologues align on the spindle equator during the first maturation division introduce an immense variability in the resulting gametes, which explains why we are all unique.

 Obtain a model depicting the events of meiosis, and follow the sequence of events during the first and second maturation divisions. Identify prophase, metaphase, anaphase, and telophase in each; the tetrads and chiasmata during the first maturation division; and the dyads (groupings of two chromatids connected by centromeres) in the second maturation division. Note ways in which the daughter cells resulting from meiosis I differ from the mother cell and how the gametes differ from both cell populations. (Use the key on the model, your textbook, or an appropriate reference as necessary to aid you in these observations.)

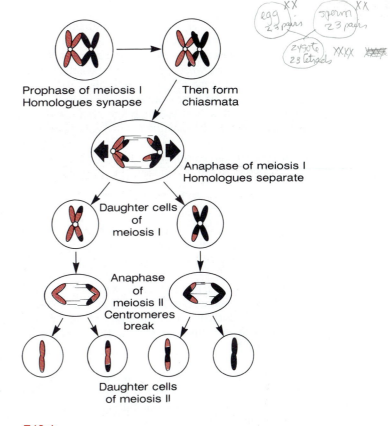

F43.1

Events of meiosis involving one pair of homologous chromosomes. (Male homologue is black; female homologue is red.)

If your instructor wishes you to observe meiosis in *Ascaris* to provide cellular material for comparison, continue with the microscopic study described next. Otherwise, skip to the study of spermatogenesis.

DEMONSTRATION OF OOGENESIS IN *ASCARIS* (OPTIONAL)

Generally speaking, oogenesis (the process of gametogenesis resulting in egg production) in mammals is difficult to demonstrate in a laboratory situation. However, the process of oogenesis and mechanics of meiosis may be studied rather easily in the transparent eggs of *Ascaris megalocephala,* an invertebrate roundworm parasite found in the intestine of mammals. Such a study is significant, because the process in *Ascaris** is much the same as in humans and, since its diploid chromosome number is 4, the chromosomes are easily counted.

Go to the demonstration area where the slides are set up and make the following observations:

---

* In *Ascaris,* meiosis does not begin until the sperm has penetrated the primary oocyte, whereas in humans, meiosis I occurs before sperm penetration.

1.   Scan the first demonstration slide to identify a primary oocyte, the cell type that begins the meiotic process. It will have what appears to be a relatively thick cell membrane; this is the *fertilization membrane* that the oocyte produces after sperm penetration. Find and study a primary oocyte that is undergoing the first maturation division. Look for a barrel-shaped spindle with two tetrads (two groups of four beadlike chromosomes) in it. Most often the spindle is located at the periphery of the cell. (The sperm nucleus may or may not be seen, depending on how the cell was cut.)

2.   Observe slide 2. Locate a cell in which half of each tetrad (a dyad) is being extruded from the cell surface into a smaller cell called the first polar body.

3.   On slide 3, attempt to locate a secondary oocyte (a daughter cell produced during meiosis I) undergoing the second maturation division. In this view, two dyads (two groups of two beadlike chromosomes) will be seen on the spindle.

4.   Locate a cell in which the second polar body is being formed on slide 4. In this case, both it and the ovum will now contain two chromosomes, the haploid number for *Ascaris*.

5.   On the fifth slide, identify a fertilized egg or a cell in which the sperm and ovum nuclei (actually *pronuclei*) are fusing to form a single nucleus containing four chromosomes.

SPERMATOGENESIS

Human sperm production or **spermatogenesis** begins at puberty and continues without interruption throughout life. The average male ejaculation contains a quarter-billion to a half-billion sperm. Since only one sperm fertilizes an ovum, it seems that nature has tried to assure that the perpetuation of the species will not be endangered for lack of sperm.

As explained in Exercise 42, spermatogenesis (the process of gametogenesis in males) occurs in the seminiferous tubules of the testes. The primitive stem cells or **spermatogonia,** found at the tubule periphery, undergo extensive mitotic activity to build up and retain the stem cell line. Before puberty, all divisions are mitotic divisions that produce more spermatogonia. At puberty, however, under the influence of FSH (follicle-stimulating hormone) secreted by the anterior pituitary gland, each mitotic division of a spermatogonium produces one spermatogonium and another cell, now called a **primary spermatocyte,** which is destined to undergo meiosis. As meiosis occurs, the dividing cells approach the lumen of the tubule. Thus the progression of meiotic events can be followed from the tubule periphery to the lumen. It is important to recognize that the **spermatids,**

which are actually the product of meiosis (since they are haploid cells), are not functional gametes; they are non-motile cells and have too much excess baggage to function well in a reproductive capacity. Another process, called **spermiogenesis,** which follows meiosis, strips away the extraneous cytoplasm from the spermatid and converts it to a motile, streamlined sperm.

1.   Obtain a slide of the testis and a microscope. Examine the slide under low power to identify the cross-sectional views of the cut seminiferous tubules. Then rotate the high power lens into position and observe the wall of one of the cut tubules. As you work, refer to Figure 43.2 and to Plate 49 in the Histology Atlas to make the following identifications.

Seminiferous Tubule   # 15003

2.   Scrutinize the cells at the periphery of the tubule. The cells in this area are the spermatogonia, which undergo frequent mitoses to increase their number and maintain their population. About half of the spermatogonia's "offspring," called *type B cells,* differentiate to form primary spermatocytes. The primary spermatocytes begin meiosis, which leads to the formation of spermatids having half the usual genetic composition. The remaining daughter cells resulting from mitotic divisions of spermatogonia, the *type A cells,* remain at the tubule periphery to maintain the germ cell line.

3.   Observe the cells in the middle of the tubule wall. There you should see a large number of cells (spermatocytes) that are obviously undergoing a nuclear division process. Look for the chromosomes, visible only during nuclear division, that have the appearance of coiled springs. Attempt to differentiate between the larger primary spermatocytes and the somewhat smaller secondary spermatocytes.

Can you see tetrads? _____

Evidence of crossover? _____

Where would you expect to see the tetrads, closer to the spermatogonia or to the lumen?

_____

In the primary or secondary spermatocytes? _____

_____

_____

4.   Examine the cells at the tubule lumen. Identify the small round-nucleated spermatids, many of which may appear lopsided and look as though they are starting to

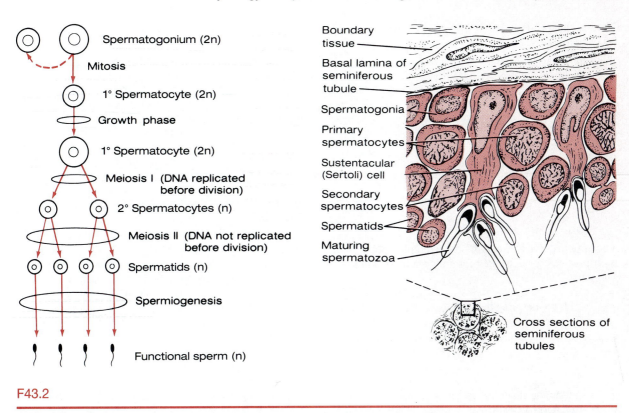

Spermatogenesis. Left, flowchart of meiotic and spermiogenesis events. Right, diagrammatic view of seminiferous tubule. Redrawn with permission from C. R. Leeson and T. S. Leeson, *Histology,* 4th ed. (Philadelphia: W. B. Saunders, 1981).

lose their cytoplasm. See if you can find a spermatid embedded in an elongated cell type, a **sustentacular (Sertoli) cell,** which extends inward from the periphery of the tubule. The sustentacular cells nourish the spermatids as they begin their transformation into sperm. Also in the adluminal area, locate sperm, which can be identified by their tails. The sperm develop directly from the spermatids by the loss of extraneous cytoplasm and the development of a propulsive tail.

Sertoli Cell   # 15008

5. Identify the **interstitial cells** lying external to and between the seminiferous tubules. LH (luteinizing hormone), also called *interstitial cell-stimulating hormone* in males, prompts these cells to produce testosterone which acts synergistically with FSH to stimulate sperm production.

Interstitial   # 15010
Cells, Leydig

In the next stage of sperm development, spermiogenesis, all the superficial cytoplasm is sloughed off, and the remaining cell organelles are compacted into the

three regions of the mature sperm. At the risk of oversimplifying, these anatomical regions are the *head,* the *midpiece,* and the *tail,* which correspond roughly to the activating and genetic region, the metabolic region, and the locomotor region respectively. The mature sperm is a streamlined cell equipped with an organ of locomotion and a high rate of metabolism that enables it to move long distances in jig time to get to the egg. It is a prime example of the correlation of form and function.

The sperm head contains the DNA, or genetic material, of the chromosomes. Essentially it is the nucleus of the spermatid. Anterior to the nucleus is the **acrosome,** which contains enzymes involved in sperm penetration of the egg.

In the midpiece of the sperm is a centriole from which arise the filaments that structure the sperm tail. Wrapped tightly around the centriole are mitochondria, which apparently provide the ATP needed for the contractile activity of the tail filaments.

The tail is composed of filaments that arise from the centriole and are constructed of contractile proteins, much like those in muscle. The filaments, when powered by ATP, propel the sperm.

6. Obtain a prepared slide of human sperm and view it under high power or with the oil immersion lens. See the photograph of sperm in Plate 50 in the Histology Atlas. Identify the head, acrosome, and tail regions.

Draw and appropriately label two or three sperm in the space below.

Very often deformed sperm, for example sperm with multiple heads or tails, are present in such preparations. Did you observe any?

___ _____ If so, describe them. _____

_____

_____

7.   Examine the model of spermatogenesis to identify the spermatogonia, the primary and secondary spermatocytes, the spermatids, and the functional sperm.

OOGENESIS AND THE OVARIAN CYCLE

The gonadotropic hormones produced by the anterior pituitary influence the development of ova in the ovaries and their cyclic production of female sex hormones. Within an ovary, each immature ovum develops within a saclike structure called a *follicle,* where it is encased by one or more layers of smaller cells called **follicle cells** (when one layer is present) or **granulosa cells** (when there is more than one layer).

The process of *oogenesis,* or female gamete formation, which occurs in the ovary, is very similar to spermatogenesis occurring in the testis, but there are some important differences. The process, schematically outlined in Figure 43.3, begins with the primitive stem cells called **oogonia,** located in the vascular connective tissue of the ovarian cortices of the developing female fetus. During fetal development, the oogonia undergo mitosis thousands of times until their number reaches 700,000 or more. They then become encapsulated by a single layer of squamouslike follicle cells and form the **primordial follicles** of the ovary. By the time the female child is born, most of her oogonia have increased in size and have become **primary oocytes,** which are in the prophase stage of meiosis I. Thus at birth, the total potential for producing germ cells in the female is already determined since the primitive stem-cell line no longer exists or will exist for only a brief period after birth.

From birth until puberty, the primary oocytes are quiescent. Then, under the influence of FSH, one or

sometimes more of the follicles begin to undergo maturation approximately every 28 days.

As a follicle grows, its epithelium changes from squamous to cuboidal cells and it comes to be called a **primary follicle.** The primary follicle begins to produce estrogen, and the primary oocyte completes its first maturation division, producing two haploid daughter cells that are very disproportionate in size. One of these is the **secondary oocyte,** which contains nearly all of the cytoplasm in the primary oocyte; the other is the tiny **first polar body.** The first polar body then completes the second maturation division, producing two more polar bodies. These eventually disintegrate for lack of sustaining cytoplasm.

As the follicle containing the secondary oocyte continues to enlarge, blood levels of estrogen rise. Initially, estrogen exerts a negative feedback influence on the release of gonadotropins by the anterior pituitary. However, approximately in the middle of the 28-day cycle, as the follicle reaches the mature **vesicular,** or **Graafian, follicle** stage, rising estrogen levels become highly stimulatory and a sudden burstlike release of LH (and, to a lesser extent, FSH) by the anterior pituitary triggers ovulation. The secondary oocyte is extruded and begins its journey down the uterine tube to the uterus. If penetrated en route by a sperm, the secondary oocyte will undergo meiosis II, producing one large **ovum** and a tiny second polar body. When the second maturation division is complete, the chromosomes of the egg and sperm combine to form the diploid nucleus of the fertilized egg. If sperm penetration does not occur, the secondary oocyte simply disintegrates without ever producing the female gamete in human females.

Thus in the female, meiosis produces only one functional gamete, in contrast to the four produced in the male. Another major difference is in the relative size and structure of the functional gametes. The sperm are tiny and are equipped with tails for locomotion. They have few organelles and virtually no nutrient-containing cytoplasm; hence the nutrients contained in semen are essential to their survival. In contrast, the egg is a relatively large nonmotile cell, well stocked with cytoplasmic reserves that nourish the developing embryo until implantation can be accomplished. Essentially all the zygote's organelles are "delivered" by the egg.

Once the secondary oocyte has been extruded from the ovary, LH transforms the ruptured follicle into the **corpus luteum,** which begins producing progesterone and estrogen. Rising blood levels of the two ovarian hormones inhibit FSH release by the anterior pituitary. As FSH declines, its stimulatory effect on follicular production of estrogen ends, and estrogen blood levels begin to decline. Since increased estrogen levels triggered LH release by the anterior pituitary, lower estrogen levels result in declining levels of LH in the blood. Because corpus luteum secretory function is maintained by high blood levels of LH, as LH blood levels begin to drop toward the end of the 28-day cycle, progesterone production ends and the corpus luteum begins to degenerate and is replaced by scar tissue (**corpus albicans**). The graphs in Figure 43.5 depict the hormone relationships described here.

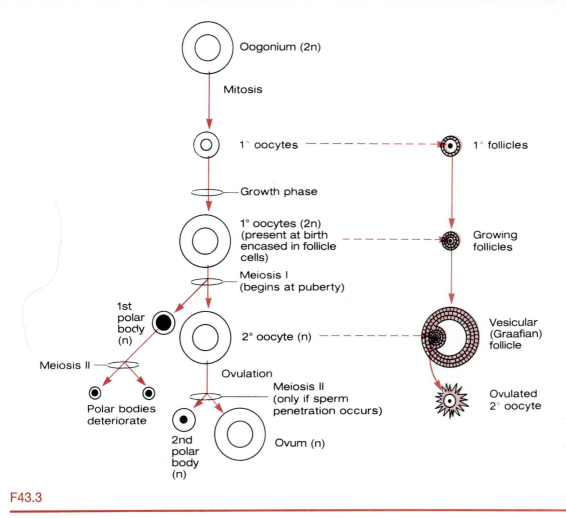

F43.3

Oogenesis. Left, flowchart of meiotic events. Right, correlation with follicular development and ovulation in the ovary.

 Because many different stages of ovarian development exist within the ovary at any one time, a single microscopic preparation will contain follicles at many different stages of development. Obtain a cross section of ovary tissue, and identify the following structures. Refer to Figure 43.4 as you work.

Germinal epithelium: outermost layer of the ovary.

Primary follicle: one or a few layers of cuboidal follicle cells surrounding the larger central developing ovum.

Secondary (growing) follicles: follicles consisting of several layers of follicle (granulosa) cells surrounding the central developing ovum, and beginning to show evidence of fluid accumulation and **antrum** (central cavity) formation.

Vesicular (Graafian) follicle: at this stage of development, the follicle has a large antrum containing fluid produced by the granulosa cells. The developing ovum is pushed to one side of the follicle and is surrounded by a capsule of several layers of granulosa cells called the **corona radiata** (radiating crown). When the immature ovum (secondary oocyte) is released, it enters the uterine tubes with its corona radiata intact. The connective tissue stroma (background tissue) adjacent to the mature follicle forms a capsule that encloses the follicle and is called the **theca.** (See also Plate 24 in the Histology Atlas.)

Corpus luteum: a solid glandular structure or a structure containing a scalloped lumen that develops from the ovulated follicle. (See Plate 25 in the Histology Atlas.)

Examine the model of oogenesis and compare it with the spermatogenesis model. Note differences in the size and structure of the functional gametes.

Primary Follicle	# 14970
Secondary Follicle, Ovary	# 20668
Graafian Follicle Focus on Ovum	# 24695
Corpus Luteum,	# 20672

439

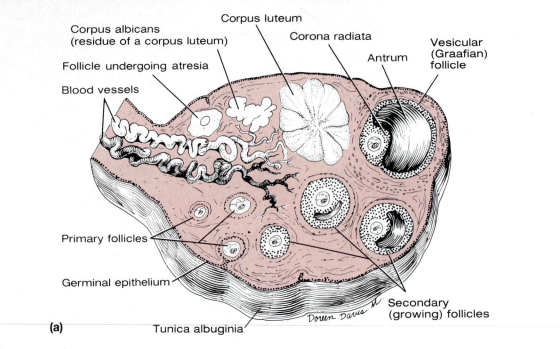

Corpus albicans
(residue of a corpus luteum)

Follicle undergoing atresia

Blood vessels

Corpus luteum

Corona radiata

Antrum

Vesicular
(Graafian)
follicle

Primary follicles

Germinal epithelium

Secondary
(growing) follicles

(a)

Tunica albuginia

Doreen Davis, M

F43.4

Anatomy of the ovary. (a) Diagrammatic view of the human ovary. (b) Line drawing of a photomicrograph of the ovary. (See corresponding Plate 51 in the Histology Atlas.)

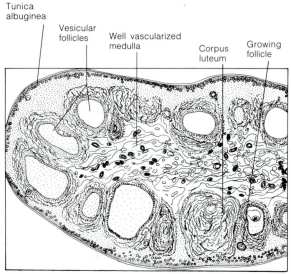

Tunica
albuginea

Vesicular
follicles

Well vascularized
medulla

Corpus
luteum

Growing
follicle

(b)

THE MENSTRUAL CYCLE

The **menstrual cycle,** sometimes referred to as the **uterine cycle,** is hormonally controlled by estrogen and progesterone secreted by the ovary. It is normally divided into three stages: menstrual, proliferative, and secretory. The stages shown in the bottom portion of Figure 43.5 are described as follows:

Menstrual stage (menses): approximately days 1 to 5. Sloughing off of the thick functionalis portion of the endometrial lining of the uterus, accompanied by bleeding.

Proliferative stage: approximately days 6 to 14. Under the influence of estrogens produced by the growing follicle of the ovary, the endometrium is repaired, glands and blood vessels proliferate, and the endometrium thickens. Ovulation occurs at the end of this stage.

Secretory stage: approximately days 15 to 28. Under the influence of progesterone produced by the corpus luteum, the vascular supply to the endometrium increases further. The glands increase in size and begin to secrete nutrient substances to sustain a developing embryo, if present, until implantation can occur. If fertilization has occurred, the embryo will produce a hormone much like LH, which will maintain the function of the corpus luteum. Otherwise,

as the corpus luteum begins to deteriorate, lack of ovarian hormones in the blood causes blood vessels supplying the endometrium to kink and become spastic, setting the stage for menses to begin by the 28th day.

Although the foregoing explanation assumes a classic 28-day cycle, the length of the menstrual cycle is highly variable, sometimes as short as 21 days or as long as 38. Only one interval is relatively constant in all females: the time from ovulation to the onset of menstruation is almost always 14 days.

Obtain slides showing the menstrual, secretory, and proliferative phases of the uterine endometrium. Observe each carefully, comparing their relative thicknesses and vascularity. As you work, refer to the corresponding photomicrographs (Plates 52 through 54) in the Histology Atlas.

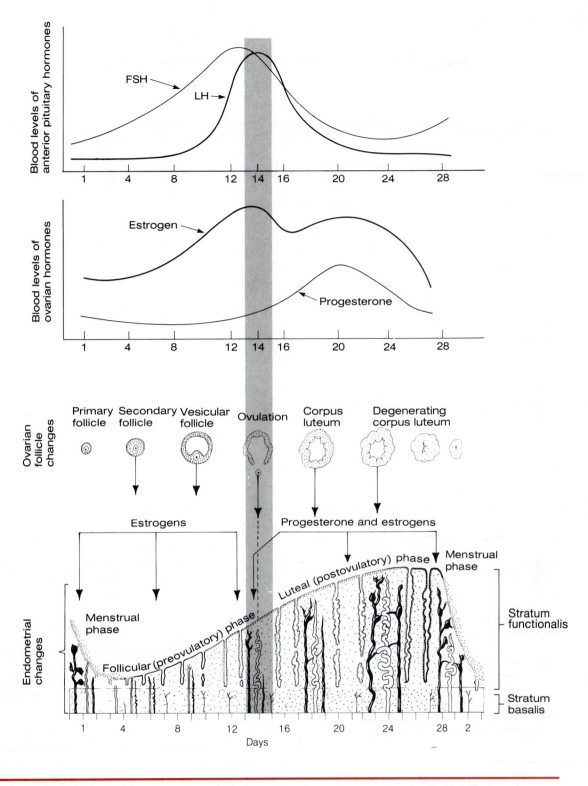

F43.5

Hormonal interactions of the female cycles. Relative levels of anterior pituitary hormones correlated with follicular and hormonal changes in the ovary. The menstrual cycle (endometrial changes) is depicted at the bottom of the figure.

Survey of Embryonic Development

OBJECTIVES

1. To define *fertilization* and *zygote*.

2. To define and discuss the function of *cleavage* and *gastrulation*.

3. To name the three primary germ layers and discuss the importance of each.

4. To identify the following structures of a human chorionic vesicle when provided with an appropriate diagram, and to state the function of each.

inner cell mass	trophoblast
amnion	allantois
yolk sac	chorionic villi

5. To describe the process and timing of implantation in the human.

6. To define *decidua basalis* and *decidua capsularis*.

7. To state the germ-layer origin of several body organs and organ systems of the human: circulatory system, nervous system, skeleton, skeletal muscles, and lining of the digestive and respiratory tracts.

8. To describe developmental direction.

9. To describe the gross anatomy and general function of the human placenta.

MATERIALS

Human development models or plaques (if available)

Life Before Birth, Educational Reprint #27, available from Time-Life Educational Materials, Box 834, Radio City P.O., New York, N.Y. 10019

Pregnant cat, rat, or pig uterus (one per laboratory session) with uterine wall dissected to allow student examination

Dissecting instruments

Model of pregnant human torso

Fresh or formalin-preserved placenta (obtained from a clinical agency)

Microscope slide of placenta tissue

Compound microscope

Because reproduction is such a familiar event, we tend to lose sight of the wonder of the process. One part of that process, the development of the embryo, is the concern of embryologists who study the changes in structure that occur from the time of fertilization until the time of birth.

Early development in all animals involves three basic types of activities, which are integrated to ensure the formation of a viable offspring: (1) an increase in cell number and subsequent cell growth; (2) cellular specialization; and (3) morphogenesis, the formation of functioning organ systems. This exercise provides a rather broad overview of the changes in structure that take place during embryonic development in humans.

DEVELOPMENTAL STAGES OF THE HUMAN

Go to the demonstration area where the models of human development are on display. If these are not available, use Figure 44.1 for this study. Observe the models to identify the various stages of human development as they are described, and respond to the questions posed below.

1. Observe the fertilized egg, or zygote, which appears as a single cell immediately surrounded by a jellylike *zona pellucida* and then a crown of granulosa cells (the *corona radiata*). After a secondary oocyte is penetrated by a sperm, and meiosis is completed to yield the ovum (egg) nucleus, the egg and the sperm nuclei fuse to form a single nucleus. This process is called **fertilization.** Shortly after sperm penetration, a granular barrier forms beneath the zona pellucida to prevent the entry of additional sperm.

2. Next, observe the cleavage stages. Once fertilization has occurred, the zygote begins to divide, forming a mass of successively smaller and smaller cells, called **blastomeres.** This series of mitotic divisions without intervening growth periods is referred to as **cleavage,** and it results in a multicellular embryonic body. Essentially, the cleavage stage of embryonic development provides a large number of building blocks (cells) with which to build the forming body. If this is a little difficult to understand, consider trying to erect a building with one huge block of granite rather than with small bricks. As the division process continues, a solid ball of cells forms. (At the 32-cell stage, it is called the **morula,** and the embryo resembles a raspberry in form.) Then the cell mass hollows out to become the embryonic form

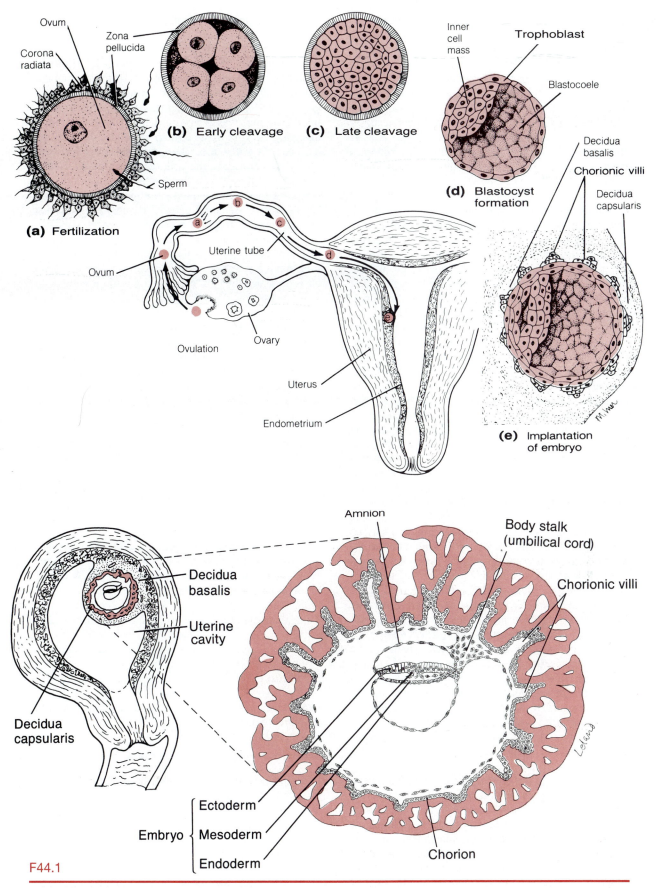

(a) Fertilization

(b) Early cleavage

(c) Late cleavage

(d) Blastocyst formation

(e) Implantation of embryo

F44.1

Early embryonic development of the human. Top (a–e), from fertilization to blastocyst implantation in the uterus. Below, embryo of approximately 22 days. Embryonic membranes and germ layers present.

called the **blastula,** which is a ball of cells surrounding a central cavity. The blastula, which is more commonly called the **blastocyst** in humans, is the final product of cleavage.

Only a portion of the blastula cells in the human contribute to the formation of the embryonic body—those seen on the top of the blastocyst forming the so-called **inner cell mass (ICM).** The rest of the blastocyst enclosing the central cavity and overriding the ICM is referred to as the **trophoblast.** The trophoblast becomes an extraembryonic membrane called the **chorion,** which forms the fetal portion of the *placenta.*

3. Observe the *implanting* blastocyst shown on the model or in the figure. By approximately the seventh day after ovulation, the developing embryo is at the blastocyst stage and is floating free in the uterine cavity. About that time, the blastocyst adheres to the uterine wall over the ICM area, and implantation begins. The trophoblast cells secrete enzymes that erode the uterine mucosa at the point of attachment to reach the vascular supply in the submucosa. By the fourteenth day after ovulation, implantation is completed and the uterine mucosa has grown over the burrowed-in embryo. The portion of the uterine wall beneath the ICM, destined to take part in placenta formation, is called the **decidua basalis** and that surrounding the rest of the blastocyst is called the **decidua capsularis.** Identify these regions.

By the time implantation has been completed, the blastocyst has undergone **gastrulation.** As a result of gastrulation, a three-layered embryo called a **gastrula** forms. Each of the gastrula's three layers corresponds to a *primary germ layer* from which specific body tissues develop. The innermost layer, the **endoderm,** and the middle layer, the **mesoderm,** form the internal organs. The outermost layer, the **ectoderm,** forms the surface tissues of the body and neural tissue. Within the next 6 weeks, virtually all of the body organ systems will have been laid down at least in rudimentary form by the germ layers. The ectoderm gives rise to the epidermis of the skin and the nervous system; the endoderm forms the mucosa of the digestive and respiratory tracts and associated structures; and the mesoderm forms virtually everything lying between the two (skeleton, walls of the digestive organs, urinary system, muscular and circulatory systems, and others).

All the groundwork has been completed by the eighth week, and by the ninth week of development, the embryo is referred to as a **fetus.** From this point on, the major activities are growth and tissue and organ specialization.

4. Again observe the blastocyst to follow the formation of the embryonic membranes and the placenta (see Figure 44.1). Notice the villus extensions of the trophoblast. By the time implantation has been completed, the trophoblast has differentiated into the **chorion,** and the large elaborate villi extending from the chorion are lying in the blood-filled sinusoids in the uterine tissue. This composite of uterine tissue and **chorionic villi** is called the **placenta,** and all exchanges to and from the embryo occur through the chorionic membranes.

Three embryonic membranes (originating in the ICM) have also formed by this time: the amnion, the allantois, and the yolk sac. Identify each. The **amnion** encases the young embryonic body in a fluid-filled chamber that protects the embryo from mechanical trauma and prevents adhesions during rapid embryonic growth. The **yolk sac** in humans has lost its original function, which was to pass nutrients to the embryo after digesting the yolk mass, primarily because the placenta has taken over that task. (Also, the human egg has very little yolk.) However, the yolk sac is not totally useless since the embryo's first blood cells originate here, and the primordial germ cells migrate from it into the embryo's body to seed the gonadal tissue. The **allantois,** which protrudes from the posterior end of the yolk sac, is also a largely redundant structure in humans because of the placenta. In birds and reptiles, it is a repository for embryonic wastes; in the human, it is the structural basis on which the mesoderm migrates to form the body stalk, or **umbilical cord,** which attaches the embryo to the placenta. (Refer ahead to p. 446 to refresh your memory of the structure of the umbilical cord if necessary.)

5. Go to the demonstration area to view the photographic series, *Life Before Birth.* This series, by Lennart Nilsson, illustrates human development in a way you will long remember. After viewing it, respond to the following questions.

In your own words, what do the chorionic villi look like?

_____

_____

_____

What organs or organ systems appear *very* early in embryonic development?

_____

_____

_____

Does development occur in a rostral to caudal (head to toe) direction, or vice versa?

_____

Does development occur in a distal to proximal direction, or vice versa?

_____

Does spontaneous movement occur *in utero?* _____

How does the mother recognize this? _____

_____

The very young embryo has been described as resembling "an astronaut suspended and floating in space." Do you think this definition is appropriate?

_____ Why or why not? _____

_____

_____

_____

What is vernix caseosa? _____

_____

_____

What is lanugo? _____

_____

_____

IN UTERO DEVELOPMENT

1. Go to the appropriate demonstration area and observe the fetuses in the Y-shaped animal uterus. Identify the following fetal or fetal-related structures:

Placenta. (a composite structure formed from the uterine mucosa and the fetal chorion).

Describe its appearance. _____

_____

_____

Umbilical cord. Describe its relationship to the placenta and fetus.

_____

_____

_____

Amniotic sac. Identify the transparent amnion surrounding a fetus. Open one amniotic sac and note the amount, color, and consistency of the fluid.

_____

_____

Remove a fetus and observe the degree of development of the head, body, and extremities. Is the skin thick or thin?

_____

What is the basis for your response? _____

_____

_____

2. Observe the model of a pregnant human torso. Identify the placenta. How does it differ in shape from the animal placenta observed?

_____

_____

_____

Identify the umbilical cord. In what region of the uterus does implantation usually occur, as indicated by the position of the placenta?

_____

_____

What might be the consequence if it occurred lower?

_____

_____

_____

Why would a feet-first position (breech presentation) be less desirable than the positioning of the model?

_____

_____

_____

GROSS AND MICROSCOPIC ANATOMY OF THE PLACENTA

no slide on lab test!

The placenta is a remarkable temporary organ. It is composed of maternal and fetal tissues and is responsible for providing nutrients and oxygen to the embryo and fetus while removing carbon dioxide and metabolic wastes.

1. Notice that the placenta on display has two very different-appearing surfaces—one smooth and the other spongy, roughened, and torn-looking.

Which is the fetal side? _____ —

Basis of your conclusion? _____

_____

_____

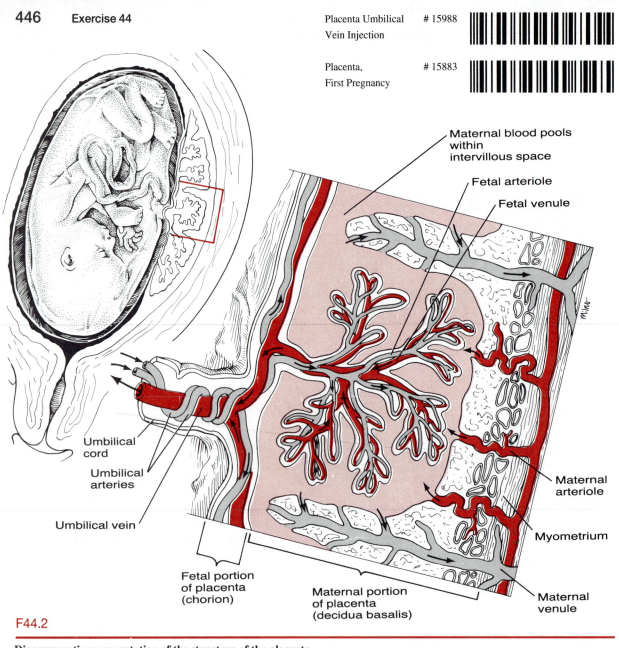

Maternal blood pools within intervillous space

Fetal arteriole

Fetal venule

Maternal arteriole

Myometrium

Maternal venule

Umbilical cord

Umbilical arteries

Umbilical vein

Fetal portion of placenta (chorion)

Maternal portion of placenta (decidua basalis)

F44.2

Diagrammatic representation of the structure of the placenta.

Identify the umbilical cord. Within the cord, identify the umbilical vein and two umbilical arteries. What is the function of the umbilical vein?

_____

_____

The umbilical arteries? _____

_____

Are any of the fetal membranes still attached?

_____

If so, which? _____

_____

2.   Obtain a microscope slide of placental tissue. Observe the tissue carefully, comparing it to Figure 44.2. Identify the _intervillus spaces_ (maternal sinusoids), which are blood-filled in life. Identify the villi, and notice their rich vascular supply. Draw a small representative diagram of your observations below and label it appropriately.

Principles of Heredity

The field of genetics currently is bristling with excitement. Complex gene-splicing techniques have allowed researchers to precisely isolate genes coding for specific proteins and then to insert those genes into bacterial or tumor cells so that large amounts of particular proteins can be harvested. At present, growth hormone, insulin, and interferon produced by these genetic engineering techniques are available for clinical use, and the list is growing daily.

Comprehension of the science of genetics in relation to such studies requires arduous training. However, a basic understanding and appreciation of how genes regulate our various traits (dimples and hair color, for example) can be gained by anyone. The thrust of this exercise is to provide a "genetics sampler" or relatively simple introduction to the principles of heredity.

INTRODUCTION TO THE LANGUAGE OF GENETICS

In humans all cells, except eggs and sperm, contain 46 chromosomes, that is, the diploid number. This number is established when fertilization occurs as a result of the fusion of the egg and sperm, and the combination of the 23 chromosomes (or haploid complement) each is carrying. The diploid chromosomal number is maintained throughout life in nearly all cells of the body by the precise process of mitosis. As explained in Exercise 43, the diploid chromosomal number actually represents two complete (or nearly complete) sets of genetic instructions—one from the egg and the other from the sperm—or 23 pairs of *homologous chromosomes.*

Genes coding for the same traits on each pair of homologous chromosomes are called **alleles.** The alleles may be identical or different in their influence. For example, the members of the gene pair, or alleles, coding for hairline shape on your forehead may specify either straight across or widow's peak. When both alleles in a homologous chromosome pair have the same expression, the individual is said to be **homozygous** for that trait. When the alleles differ in their expression, the individual is **heterozygous** for the given trait; and typically only one of the alleles, called the **dominant gene,** will exert its effects. The allele with less potency, the **recessive gene,** will be present but masked. Whereas dominant genes, or alleles, will exert their effects in both homozygous and heterozygous conditions, as a rule recessive alleles *must* be present in double dose (homozygosity) to exert their influence. An individual's actual genetic makeup, that is, whether he is homozygous or heterozygous for the various alleles, is called **genotype.** The manner in which genotype is expressed (for example, the presence of a widow's peak or not, blue vs. brown eyes) is referred to as **phenotype.**

The complete story of heredity is much more complex than just outlined, and in actuality the expression of many traits (for example, eye color) is determined by the interaction of many allele pairs. However, our emphasis here will be to investigate only the less complex aspects of genetics.

DOMINANT-RECESSIVE INHERITANCE

One of the best ways to master the terminology and learn the principles of heredity is to work out the solutions to some genetic crosses in much the same manner as Gregor Mendel did in his classic experiments on pea plants. (Mendel, an Austrian monk of the mid-1800s, found evidence in these experiments that each gamete contributes just one allele to each pair in the zygote.) To work out the various simple monohybrid (one pair of alleles) crosses in this exercise, you will be given the genotype of the parents. You will then determine the possible genotypes of their offspring by using the *Punnet square,* and you will record both genotype and phenotype percentages. To illustrate the procedure, an example of one of Mendel's pea plant crosses is outlined next.

Alleles: T (determines *tallness;* dominant)
 t (determines *dwarfness;* recessive)
Genotypes of parents: TT(♂) × tt (♀)
Phenotypes of parents: Tall × dwarf

To use the Punnet, or checkerboard, square, write the alleles (actually gametes) of one parent across the top and the gametes of the other parent down the left side. Then combine the gametes across and down to achieve all possible combinations as shown below:

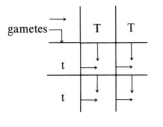

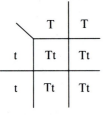

Results: Genotypes 100% Tt (all heterozygous)
 Phenotypes 100% Tall (since T, which determines tallness, is dominant and all contain the T allele).

1. Using the technique outlined above, determine the genotypes and phenotypes of the offspring of the following crosses:

a. Genotypes of parents: Tt (♂) × tt (♀)

% of each genotype: _____ 50% T _____ t

% of each phenotype: __50__ % tall

__50__ % dwarf

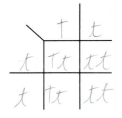

b. Genotypes of parents: Tt (♂) × Tt (♀)

% of each genotype: __50% homozygote__
__50% heterozygote__

% of each phenotype: __75__ % tall

__25__ % dwarf

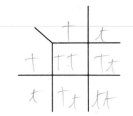

2. In guinea pigs, rough coat (R) is dominant over smooth coat (r). What will be the genotypes and phenotypes of the following monohybrid crosses?

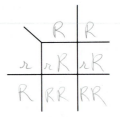

a. Genotypes of the parents: RR × rR

% of each genotype: __50% homozygote 50% heterozygote__

% of each phenotype: __100__ % rough

__50__ % smooth

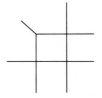

b. Genotypes of the parents: Rr × rr

% of each genotype: _____

% of each phenotype: _____ % rough

_____ % smooth

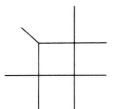

c. Genotypes of the parents: RR x rr

% of each genotype: _____

% of each phenotype: _____ % rough

_____ % smooth

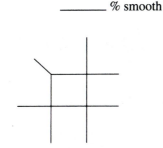

INCOMPLETE DOMINANCE

In actuality, the concepts of dominance and recessiveness are somewhat arbitrary and artificial in some instances, since so-called dominant genes may be expressed differently in homozygous and heterozygous individuals. This gives rise to a condition called *incomplete dominance* or *intermediate inheritance.* In such cases, both alleles express themselves in the offspring. The crosses are worked out in the same manner as indicated previously, but the heterozygous offspring exhibit a phenotype intermediate between that of the homozygous individuals. Some examples follow.

1. The inheritance of flower color in snapdragons illustrates the principle of incomplete dominance. The genotype RR is expressed as a red flower, Rr yields pink flowers, and rr produces white flowers. Work out the following crosses to determine phenotypes seen and both genotype and phenotype percentages.

    a. Genotypes of parents: RR × rr

Genotypes and %: _____

Phenotypes and %: _____

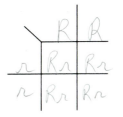

b. Genotypes of parents: Rr × rr

Genotypes and %: _____

Phenotypes and %: _100% pink flowers_

_____

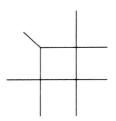

c. Genotypes of parents Rr × Rr

Genotypes and %: _____

Phenotypes and %: _____

_____

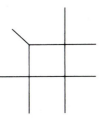

2. In humans, the inheritance of sickle-cell anemia/trait is determined by a single pair of alleles that exhibit incomplete dominance. Individuals homozygous for the sickling gene (s) are said to have *sickle-cell anemia.* In double dose (ss) the sickling gene causes the production of a very abnormal hemoglobin, which crystallizes and becomes sharp and spiky under conditions of oxygen deficit. This, in turn, leads to clumping and hemolysis of red blood cells in the circulation, which causes a great deal of pain and can be fatal. Heterozygous individuals (Ss) are said to have the *sickle-cell trait,* which is much less severe; however, they are carriers for the abnormal gene and may pass it on to their offspring. Individuals with the genotype SS form nor-

mal hemoglobin. Work out the following crosses:

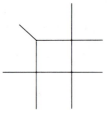

a. Parental genotypes: SS × ss

Genotypes and %: _____

Phenotypes and %: _____

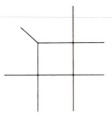

b. Parental genotypes: Ss × Ss

Genotypes and %: _____

Phenotypes and %: _____

_____

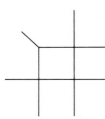

c. Parental genotypes: ss × Ss

Genotypes and %: _____

Phenotypes and %: _____

_____

SEX-LINKED INHERITANCE

Of the 23 pairs of homologous chromosomes, 22 pairs are referred to as **autosomes.** Autosomes contain genes that determine most body (somatic) characteristics. The 23rd pair, called the **sex chromosomes,** determine the sex of an individual, that is, whether an individual will be male or female. Normal females possess two sex chromosomes that look alike, the X chromosomes. Males possess two dissimilar sex chromosomes, referred to as X and Y. Possession of the Y chromosome determines maleness. A photomicrograph of a male's chromosome complement (male karyotype) is shown in Figure 45.1. The Y sex chromosome is only about a third as large as the X sex chromosome, and lacks many of the genes (directing characteristics other than sex) that are found on the X. Genes present *only* on the X sex chromosome are called *sex-linked* (or X-linked) genes. Some examples of X-linked genes include those that determine normal color vision (or, conversely, color blindness), and normal clotting ability (as opposed to hemophilia, or bleeder's disease). The alleles that determine color blindness and hemophilia are recessive alleles. In females, *both* X chromosomes must carry the recessive alleles for a woman to express either of these conditions, and thus they tend to be infrequently seen. However, should a male receive even one sex-linked recessive allele for these conditions, he will exhibit the recessive phenotype because his Y chromosome lacks any genes that might dominate or mask the recessive allele.

The critical understanding of X-linked inheritance is the *absence* of male to male (that is, father to son) transmission of X-linked genes. The X of the father *will* pass to each of his daughters but to none of his sons. Males always inherit sex-linked conditions from their mothers (through the X chromosome).

1. A heterozygous woman carrying the recessive gene for color blindness marries a man who is colorblind. Assume the dominant gene is X^C (allele for normal color vision) and the recessive gene is X^c (determines color blindness). The mother's genotype is $X^C X^c$ and the father's $X^c Y$. Do a Punnet square to determine the answers to the following questions.

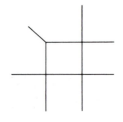

According to the laws of probability, what percent of their children will be color-blind?

_____ %

What is the proportion of color-blind individuals by

sex? _____ male; _____ female

What percentage will be carriers? _____ %

What is the sex of the carriers? _____

2. A heterozygous woman carrying the recessive gene for hemophilia marries a man who is not a hemo-

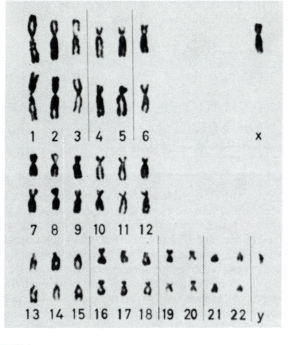

F45.1

Karyotype (chromosomal complement) of human male.
Each pair of homologous chromosomes is numbered (1–22) except the sex chromosomes, which are identified by their letters, X and Y. (Courtesy of T. T. Puck, 1972. *The Mammalian Cell as Microorganism.* San Francisco, Holden-Day.)

philiac. Assume the dominant gene is X^H and the recessive gene is X^h. The woman's genotype is $X^H X^h$ and her husband's genotype is $X^H Y$. What is the potential percentage and sex of their offspring that will be hemophiliacs?

_____ % males; _____ % females

What percentage can be expected to neither exhibit nor carry the allele for hemophilia?

_____ %

What is the anticipated sex and percentage of individuals that will be carriers for hemophilia?

_____ %; _____ sex

PROBABILITY

Because the segregation (or parceling out) of chromosomes to daughter cells (gametes) during meiosis and the combination of egg and sperm are random or chance events, the possibility that certain genomes will arise and be expressed is based on the laws of probability. The randomness of gene recombination from each parent de-

termines individual uniqueness and explains why siblings, however similar, never have totally corresponding traits (unless, of course, they are identical twins). The Punnet square method that you have been using to work out the genetics problems actually provides information on the *probability* of appearance of certain genotypes considering all possible events. Probability (P) is defined as:

$$P = \frac{\text{number of specific events/cases}}{\text{total number of events/cases}}$$

If an event is certain to happen, its probability is 1. If it happens one out of every two times, its probability is ½; if one out of 4 times, its probability is ¼, and so on.

When figuring the probability of separate events occurring together (or consecutively), the probability of each event must be multiplied together to get the final probability figure. For example, the probability of a penny coming up "heads" in each toss is ½ (because it has two sides—heads and tails). But the probability of a tossed penny coming up heads 4 times in a row is: ½ × ½ × ½ × ½ = ¹⁄₁₆.

1. Obtain two pennies and perform the following simple experiment to explore the laws of probability.

a. Toss one penny into the air 10 times, and record the number of heads/tails observed.

_____ heads   _____ tails

Probability: _____ /10ths tails; _____ /10ths heads

b. Now simultaneously toss two pennies into the air for 24 tosses, and record the results of each toss below. In each case, report the probability in the lowest fractional terms.

#HH_____   Probability_____

#HT _____   Probability_____

#TT _____   Probability_____

Does the first toss have any influence on the second?

_____

Does the third toss have any influence on the fourth?

_____

c. Do a Punnet square using HT for one coin and HT for the alleles of the other.

Probability of HH: _____

Probability of HT: _____

Probability of TT: _____

How closely do your coin-tossing results correlate with the percentages obtained from the Punnet square results?

_____

_____

2. Determine the probability of having a boy or girl offspring for each conception.

Parental genotypes: XY × XX

Probability of males: _____ %

Probability of females: _____ %

3. Dad wants a baseball team! What are the chances of his having nine sons in a row?

_____ (Sorry, Dad!)

GENETIC DETERMINATION OF SELECTED HUMAN CHARACTERISTICS

Many human traits are determined by a single pair of alleles easily identifiable by observation. For each of the characteristics described here, determine (as best you can) both your own phenotype and genotype, and record this information on Table 45.1. Since it is impossible to know whether you are homozygous or heterozygous for a trait when you exhibit its dominant expression, you are to record your genotype as A— (or B—, and so on, depending on the letter used to indicate the alleles) in such cases. If you exhibit the recessive trait, you are homozygous for the recessive allele and should record it accordingly as aa (bb, cc, and so on). When you have completed your observations, also record your data on the chart for tabulation of class results, on the chalkboard.

TABLE 45.1   Record of Human Genotypes/Phenotypes

Characteristic	Phenotype	Genotype
Tongue rolling (T,t)		
Attached earlobes (E,e)		
Interlocking fingers (I,i)		
PTC taste (P,p)		
Sodium benzoate taste (S,s)		
Sex (X,Y)		
Dimples (D,d)		
Widow's peak (W,w)		
Bent little finger (L,l)		
Double-jointed thumb (J,j)		
Middigital hair (H,h)		
Freckles (F,f)		
Blaze (B,b)		
ABO blood type (I^A, I^B, i)		

Tongue rolling: Extend your tongue and attempt to roll it into a U shape longitudinally. People with this ability have the dominant allele for this trait. Use T for the dominant allele, and t for the recessive allele (see Figure 45.2).

Attached earlobes: Have your lab partner examine your earlobes. If no portion of the lobe hangs free inferior to its point of attachment to the head, you are homozygous recessive (ee) for attached earlobes. If part of the lobe hangs free below the point of attachment, you possess at least one dominant gene (E) (see Figure 45.2).

Interlocking fingers: Clasp your hands together by interlocking your fingers. Now observe your clasped hands. Which thumb is uppermost? If the left thumb is uppermost, you possess a dominant allele (I) for this trait. If you clasped your right over your left thumb, you are illustrating the homozygous recessive (ii) phenotype.

PTC taste: Obtain a PTC taste strip. PTC or phenylthiocarbamide is a harmless chemical that some people can taste and others find tasteless. Chew the strip. If it tastes slightly bitter, you are a "taster" and possess the dominant gene (P) for this trait. If you cannot taste anything, you are a nontaster and are homozygous recessive (pp) for the trait. Approximately 70% of the people in the United States are tasters.

Sodium benzoate taste: Obtain a sodium benzoate taste strip and chew it. A different pair of alleles (from that determining PTC taste) determines the ability to taste sodium benzoate. If you can taste it, you have at least one of the dominant alleles (S). If not, you are homozygous recessive (ss) for the trait. Also record whether sodium benzoate tastes salty, bitter, or sweet to you (if a taster). Even though PTC and sodium benzoate taste are inherited independently, they interact to determine a person's taste sensations. Individuals who find PTC bitter and sodium benzoate salty tend to be devotees of sauerkraut, buttermilk, spinach, and other slightly bitter or salty foods.

Sex: The genotype XX determines the female phenotype, whereas XY determines the male phenotype.

Dimpled cheeks: The presence of dimples in one or both cheeks is due to a dominant gene (D). Absence of dimples indicates the homozygous recessive condition (dd) (see Figure 45.2).

Widow's peak: A distinct downward V-shaped hairline at the middle of the forehead is referred to as a widow's peak. It is determined by a dominant allele (W), whereas the straight or continuous forehead hairline is determined by the homozygous recessive condition (ww) (see Figure 45.2).

Bent little finger: Examine your little finger on each hand. If its terminal phalanx angles toward the ring finger, you are dominant for this trait. If one or both terminal digits are essentially straight, you are homozygous recessive for the trait. Use L for the dominant allele and l for the recessive allele.

Double-jointed thumb: A dominant gene determines a condition of loose ligaments that allows one to throw the thumb out of joint. The homozygous recessive condition determines tight joints. Use J for the dominant allele and j for the recessive allele.

Middigital hair: Critically examine the dorsum of the middle segment (phalanx) of fingers 3 and 4. If *no* hair is obvious, you are recessive (hh) for this condition. If hair is seen, you have the dominant gene (H) for this trait (which, however, is determined by multigene inheritance) (see Figure 45.2).

Freckles: The appearance of freckles is the result of a dominant gene. Use F as the dominant allele and f as the recessive allele (see Figure 45.2).

Blaze: A lock of hair different in color from the rest of scalp hair is called a blaze; it is determined by a dominant gene. Use B for the dominant gene and b for the recessive gene.

Blood type: Inheritance of the ABO blood type is based on the existence of 3 alleles designated as I^A, I^B, and i. Both I^A and I^B are dominant over i, but neither is dominant over each other. Thus the possession of I^A and I^B will yield type AB blood, whereas the possession of the I^A and i alleles will yield type A blood, and so on as explained in Exercise 29. There are four ABO blood groups or phenotypes. A, B, AB, and O, and their correlation to genotype is indicated as follows:

ABO blood group	Genotype
A	$I^A I^A$ or $I^A i$
B	$I^B I^B$ or $I^B i$
AB	$I^A I^B$
O	ii

Assuming you have previously typed your blood, record your phenotype and genotype in Table 45.1. If not, type your blood following the instructions on p. 294, and then enter your results in the table.

Dispose of any blood-soiled supplies by placing the glassware in the bleach-containing beaker and all other items in the autoclave bag.

Once class data have been tabulated, scrutinize the results. Is there a single trait that is expressed in an identical manner by all members of the class?

Because all human beings have 23 pairs of homologues and each pair segregates independently at meiosis, the number of possible combinations at segregation is over 8 million! On the basis of this information, what would you guess are the chances of *any* two individuals in the class having identical phenotypes for all 14 traits investigated?

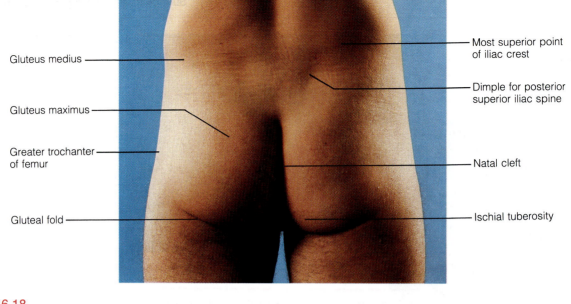

Gluteus medius

Gluteus maximus

Greater trochanter of femur

Gluteal fold

Most superior point of iliac crest

Dimple for posterior superior iliac spine

Natal cleft

Ischial tuberosity

F46.18

The gluteal region. This region extends from the iliac crests superiorly to the gluteal folds inferiorly. Therefore, it includes more than just the prominences (cheeks) of the buttock.

The gluteal region is a major site for administering intramuscular injections. When giving such injections, extreme care must be taken to avoid piercing a major nerve that lies just deep to the gluteus maximus muscle. Can you guess what nerve this is?

It is the thick *sciatic nerve,* which innervates much of the lower limb. Furthermore, the needle must avoid the gluteal nerves and gluteal blood vessels, which also lie deep to the gluteus maximus.

To avoid harming these structures, the injections are most often applied to the gluteus *medius* (not maximus) muscle superior to the cheeks of the buttocks, in a safe area called the **ventral gluteal site** (Figure 46.19b). To locate this site, mentally draw a line laterally from the posterior superior iliac spine (dimple) to the greater trochanter; the injection would be given 5 cm (2 inches)

superior to the midpoint of that line. Another safe way to locate the ventral gluteal site is to approach the lateral side of the patient's left hip with your extended right hand (or the right hip with your left hand), then place your thumb on the anterior superior iliac spine and your index finger as far posteriorly on the iliac crest as it can reach. The heel of your hand comes to lie on the greater trochanter, and the needle is inserted in the angle of the V formed between your thumb and index finger about 4 cm (1.5 inches) inferior to the iliac crest.

Gluteal injections are not given to small children because their "safe area" is too small to locate with certainty and because the gluteal muscles are thin at this age. Instead, infants and toddlers receive intramuscular shots in the prominent vastus lateralis muscle of the thigh.

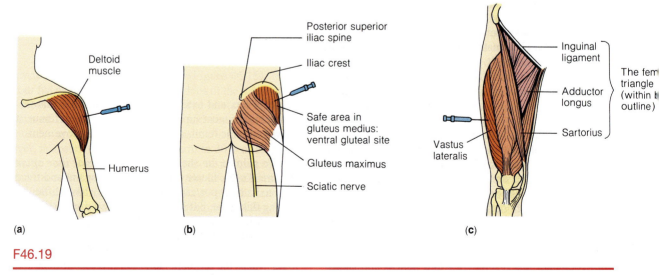

Deltoid muscle

Humerus

Posterior superior iliac spine

Iliac crest

Safe area in gluteus medius: ventral gluteal site

Gluteus maximus

Sciatic nerve

Inguinal ligament

Adductor longus

Sartorius

Vastus lateralis

The fem triangle (within outline)

(a)   (b)   (c)

F46.19

Three major sites of intramuscular injections. (a) Deltoid muscle of the arm. (b) Ventral gluteal site (gluteus medius). (c) Vastus lateralis in the lateral thigh. The femoral triangle is also shown.

470

Thigh

The thigh is pictured in Figures 46.20, 46.21, and 46.22. Much of the femur is clothed by thick muscles, so the thigh has few palpable bony landmarks.

1.   Distally, feel the *medial* and *lateral condyles of the femur* and the *patella* anterior to the condyles (see Figure 46.21c and a).

2.   Next, palpate your three groups of thigh muscles (Figures 46.20, 46.21a, and 46.21b): the *quadriceps femoris muscles* anteriorly, the *adductor muscles* medially, and the *hamstrings* posteriorly. The *vastus lateralis,* the lateral muscle of the quadriceps group, is a site for intramuscular injections. Such injections are administered about halfway down the length of this muscle (see Figure 46.19c).

3.   The anterosuperior surface of the thigh exhibits a three-sided depression called the **femoral triangle** (Figure 46.21a). As shown in Figure 46.19c, the superior border of this triangle is formed by the inguinal ligament, and its two inferior borders are defined by the *sartorius* and *adductor longus* muscles. The large *femoral artery* and *vein* descend vertically through the center of the femoral triangle. To feel the pulse of your femoral artery, press inward just inferior to your midinguinal point (halfway between the anterior superior iliac spine and the pubic tubercle). Be sure to push hard, because the artery lies somewhat deep. By pressing very hard on this point, one can stop the bleeding from a hemorrhage in the lower limb. The femoral triangle also contains most of the *inguinal lymph nodes* (which are easily palpated if swollen).

Leg and Foot

1.   Locate your patella again, then follow the thick *patellar ligament* inferiorly from the patella to its insertion on the superior tibia (Figure 46.21c). Here you can feel a rough projection, the *tibial tuberosity.* Continue running your fingers inferiorly along the tibia's sharp *anterior border* and its flat *medial*

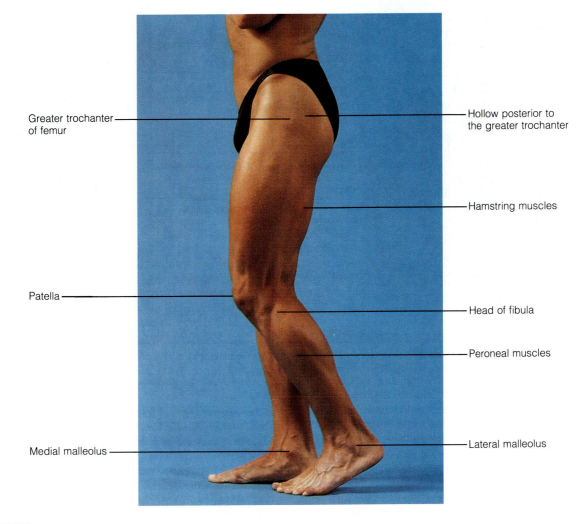

Greater trochanter of femur

Patella

Medial malleolus

Hollow posterior to the greater trochanter

Hamstring muscles

Head of fibula

Peroneal muscles

Lateral malleolus

F46.20

Lateral surface of the lower limb.

Surface Anatomy

1. Match each of the following descriptions with a key equivalent, and record the key letter or term in front of the description.

Key: a. buccal c. deltoid e. patellar
   b. calcaneal d. digital f. scapular

_____ cheek   _____ anterior aspect of knee

_____ pertaining to the fingers _____ heel of foot

_____ shoulder blade region _____ curve of shoulder

2. Indicate the following body areas on the accompanying diagram by placing the correct key letter at the end of each line.

Key:

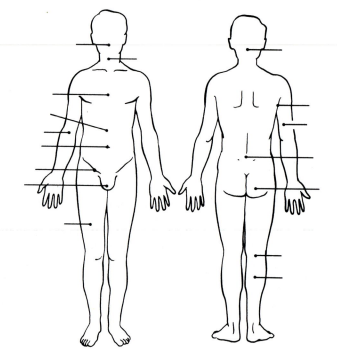

 a. abdominal
 b. antecubital
 c. axillary
 d. brachial
 e. cervical
 f. femoral
 g. gluteal
 h. inguinal
 i. lumbar
 j. occipital
 k. oral
 l. popliteal
 m. pubic
 n. sural
 o. thoracic
 p. umbilical

3. Correctly identify each of the nine areas of the abdominal surface by inserting the appropriate term for each of the letters indicated in the drawing on the next page.

a. _____ d. _____

b. _____ e. _____

c. _____ f. _____

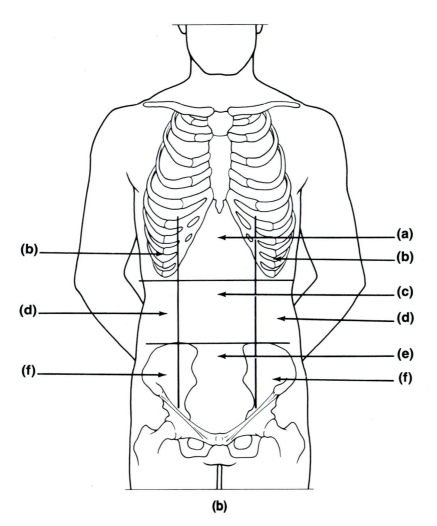

(a)

(b)

(b)

(c)

(d)

(e)

(f)

(d)

(f)

(b)

Body Cavities

1. Which body cavity would have to be opened for the following types of surgery? (Insert letter of key choice in same-numbered blank.)

   Key: a. abdominopelvic   c. dorsal   e. thoracic
         b. cranial   d. spinal   f. ventral

   1. surgery to remove a cancerous lung lobe
   2. removal of the uterus or womb
   3. removal of a brain tumor
   4. appendectomy
   5. stomach ulcer operation

   The abdominopelvic and thoracic cavities are subdivisions of the __6__ body cavity, while the cranial and spinal cavities are subdivisions of the __7__ body cavity. The __8__ body cavity is totally surrounded by bone, and thus affords its contained structures very good protection.

2. Name the serous membranes covering the lungs (#9), the heart (#10), and the organs of the abdominopelvic cavity (#11), and insert your responses in the blanks on the right.

3. What muscle subdivides the ventral body cavity? (#12)

1. _____

2. _____

3. _____

4. _____

5. _____

6. _____

7. _____

8. _____

9. _____

10. _____

11. _____

12. _____

RS3

4. Which of the following organ systems are represented in all three subdivisions of the ventral body cavity? (Circle all appropriate responses.)

respiratory   circulatory   reproductive   lymphatic
nervous   excretory (urinary) muscular   integumentary

5. Which organ system would not be represented in any of the body cavities? _____

6. What are the bony landmarks of the abdominopelvic cavity? _____

_____

7. Which body cavity affords the least protection to its internal structures? _____

8. What is the function of the serous membranes of the body? _____

_____

_____

9. A nurse informs you that she is about to take blood from the cubital region. What portion of your body should

you present to her? _____

10. What do peritonitis, pleurisy, and pericarditis (pathologic conditions) have in common? _____

_____

11. Why are these conditions accompanied by a great deal of pain? _____

_____

12. The mouth, or buccal cavity, and its extension, which stretches through the body inside the digestive system, is

not listed as an internal body cavity. Why is this so? _____

_____

_____

EXERCISE 2

Organ Systems Overview

1. Use the key below to indicate the body systems that perform the following functions for the body.

Key: a. cardiovascular   e. integumentary   i. reproductive
      b. digestive   f. lymphatic   j. respiratory
      c. endocrine   g. muscular   k. skeletal
      d. immune   h. nervous   l. urinary

_____ rids the body of nitrogen-containing wastes

_____ is affected by removal of the thyroid gland

_____ provides support and levers on which the muscular system acts

_____ includes the heart

_____ causes the onset of the menstrual cycle

_____ protects underlying organs from drying out and from mechanical damage

_____ protects the body; destroys bacteria and tumor cells

_____ breaks down ingested food into its building blocks

_____ removes carbon dioxide from the blood

_____ delivers oxygen and nutrients to the tissues

_____ moves the limbs; facilitates facial expression

_____ conserves body water or eliminates excesses

_____ and _____ facilitate conception and childbearing

_____ controls the body by means of chemical molecules called hormones

_____ is damaged when you cut your finger or get a severe sunburn

2. Using the above key, choose the *organ system* to which each of the following sets of organs or body structures belong:

_____ thymus, spleen, lymphatic vessels

_____ bones, cartilages, tendons

_____ pancreas, pituitary, adrenals

_____ trachea, bronchi, alveoli

_____ kidneys, bladder, ureters

_____ testis, vas deferens, urethra

_____ esophagus, large intestine, rectum

_____ arteries, veins, heart

RS5

3. Using the key below, place the following organs in their proper body cavity.

    Key: a.   abdominopelvic   b.   cranial   c.   spinal   d.   thoracic

    _____ 1.   stomach   _____ 7.   urinary bladder

    _____ 2.   esophagus   _____ 8.   heart

    _____ 3.   large intestine   _____ 9.   trachea

    _____ 4.   adrenal glands   _____ 10. brain

    _____ 5.   liver   _____ 11. rectum

    _____ 6.   spinal cord

4. Using the organs listed in item 3 above, record, by number, which would be found in the abdominal regions listed below:

    _____ hypogastric region   _____ epigastric region

    _____ right lumbar region   _____ left iliac region

    _____ umbilical region   _____ left hypochondriac region

5. The five levels of organization of a living body are cell, _____,

    _____, _____, and organism.

6. Define *organ*. _____

    _____

    _____ _____

7. During the course of this laboratory exercise, a rat was dissected. What is the *value* of observing the anatomy of a rat (or any other small mammal) when *human anatomy* is the actual topic of study?

    _____

    _____

    _____

RS6

EXERCISE 3

The Microscope

Care and Structure of the Compound Microscope

1. Label all indicated parts of the microscope.

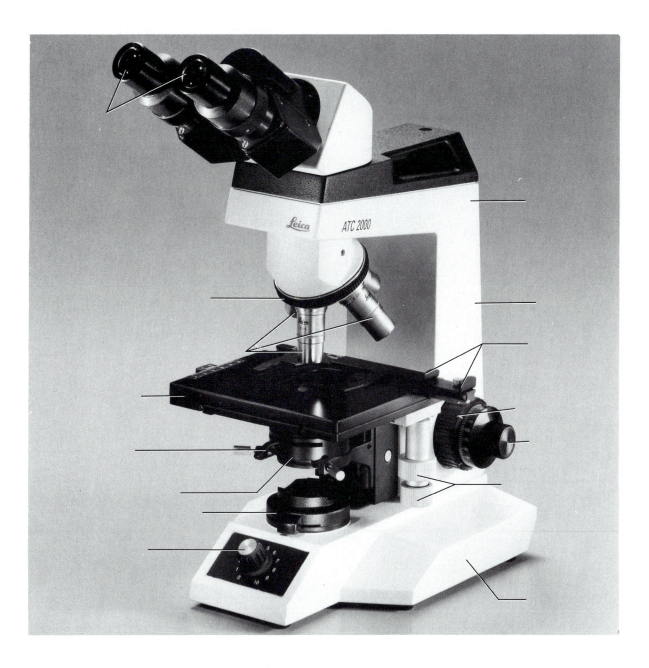

2. The following statements are true or false. If true, write *T* on the answer blank. If false, correct the statement by writing on the blank the proper word or phrase to replace that underlined.

_____ The microscope lens may be cleaned with any soft tissue.

_____ The coarse adjustment knob may be used in focusing with all three objectives.

_____ The microscope should be stored with the oil immersion lens in position over the stage.

_____ When beginning to focus, the low-power lens should be used.

_____ In low power, always focus toward the specimen.

_____ A coverslip should always be used with the high-power and oil lenses.

_____ The greater the amount of light delivered to the objective lens, the less the resolution.

3. Match the microscope structures given in column B with the statements in column A that identify or decribe them:

Column A

_____ platform on which the slide rests for viewing

_____ lens located at the superior end of the body tube

_____ secure(s) the slide to the stage

_____ delivers a concentrated beam of light to the specimen

_____ used for precise focusing once initial focusing has been done

_____ carries the objective lenses; rotates so that the different objective lenses can be brought into position over the specimen

_____ used to increase the amount of light passing through the specimen

Column B

a. coarse adjustment knob

b. condenser

c. fine adjustment knob

d. iris diaphragm

e. mechanical stage or spring clips

f. movable nosepiece

g. objective lenses

h. ocular

i. stage

4. Explain the proper technique for transporting the microscope.

_____

_____

5. Define the following terms.

real image: _____

_____

virtual image: _____

_____

6. Define *total magnification:* _____

_____

_____

7. Define *resolution:* _____

Viewing Objects Through the Microscope

1. Complete, or respond to, the following statements:

_____ The distance from the bottom of the objective lens in use to the specimen is called the _____.

_____ The resolution of the human eye is _____ μm.

_____ The area of the specimen seen when looking through the microscope is the _____.

_____ If a microscope has a 10× ocular and the total magnification at a particular time is 950×, the objective lens in use at that time is _____×.

_____ Why should the light be dimmed when looking at living (nearly transparent) cells?

_____ If, after focusing in low power, only the fine adjustment need be used to focus the specimen at the higher powers, the microscope is said to be _____.

_____ If, when using a 10× ocular and a 15× objective, the field size is 1.5 mm, the approximate field size with a 30× objective is _____ mm.

_____ If the size of the high-power field is 1.2 mm, an object that occupies approximately a third of that field has an estimated diameter of _____ mm.

_____ Assume there is an object on the left side of the field that you want to bring to the center (that is, toward the apparent right). In what direction would you move your slide?

_____ If the object is in the top of the field and you want to move it downward to the center, you would move the slide _____.

2. You have been asked to prepare a slide with letter *k* on it (as below). In the circle below, draw the *k* as seen in the low-power field.

k

4. In the following diagram, label all parts provided with a leader line.

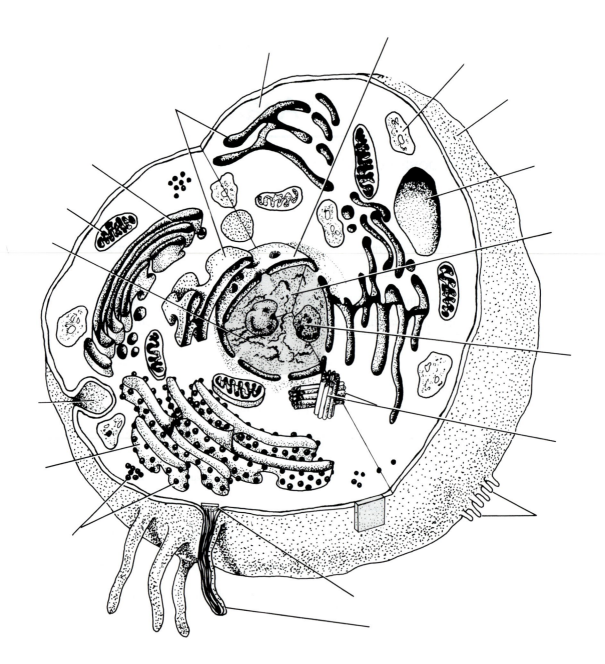

Observing Differences and Similarities in Cell Structure

1. List *one* important structural characteristic (a) of each of the following cell types observed in the laboratory, and then give the function (b) that structure complements or ensures:

squamous epithelium   a. _____

                       b. _____

sperm   a. _____

                       b. _____

smooth muscle   a. _____

                 b. _____

red blood cell   a. _____

                 b. _____

2. What is the significance of the red blood cell being anucleate (without a nucleus)? _____

_____

    Did it ever have a nucleus? _____When? _____

Cell Division: Mitosis and Cytokinesis

1. Identify the three phases of mitosis in the following photomicrograph.

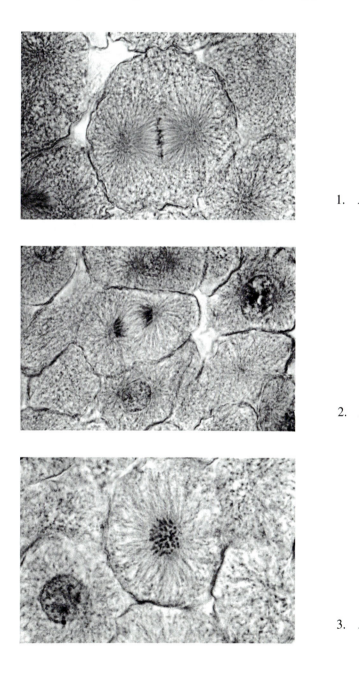

1. _____

2. _____

3. _____

Muscle Tissue

The three types of muscle tissue exhibit similarities as well as differences. Check the appropriate space in the chart below to indicate which muscle types exhibit each characteristic.

Characteristic	Skeletal	Cardiac	Smooth
Voluntarily controlled			
Involuntarily controlled			
Striated			
Has a single nucleus in each cell			
Has several nuclei per cell			
Found attached to bones			
Allows you to direct your eyeballs			
Found in the walls of the stomach, uterus, and arteries			
Contains spindle-shaped cells			
Contains branching cylindrical cells			
Contains long, nonbranching cylindrical cells			
Has intercalated discs			
Concerned with locomotion of the body as a whole			
Changes the internal volume of an organ as it contracts			
Tissue of the heart			

Nervous Tissue

1. What two physiologic characteristics are highly developed in nervous tissue? _____

   _____

2. In what ways are nerve cells similar to other cells? _____

   _____

   How are they different? _____

3. **Sketch** a neuron, recalling in your diagram the most important aspects of its structure. Below the diagram, describe how its particular structure relates to its function in the body.

_____

_____

For Review
Label the following tissue types here and on the next pages, and identify all major structures.

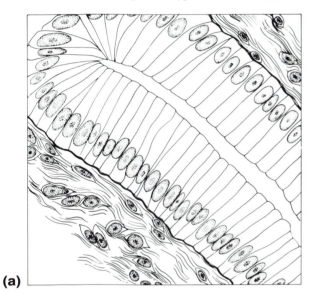

(a)

_____

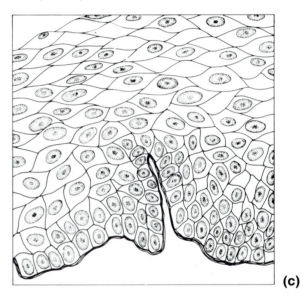

(c)

_____

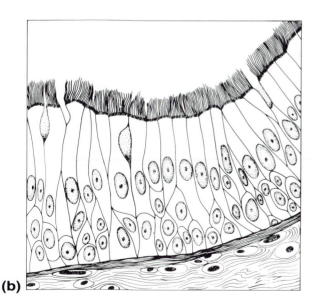

(b)

_____

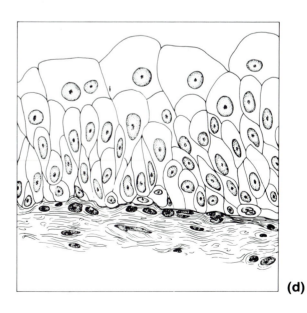

(d)

_____

2. Why does the clavicle often fracture when a person falls on his or her shoulder? _____

_____

3. Why is there generally no problem in the arm clearing the widest dimension of the thoracic cage?

_____

_____

4. What is the total number of phalanges in the hand? _____

5. What is the total number of carpals in the wrist? _____

In the proximal row, the carpals are (medial to lateral) _____

In the distal row, they are (medial to lateral) _____

6. Using items from the list at the right, identify the anatomical landmarks and regions of the scapula.

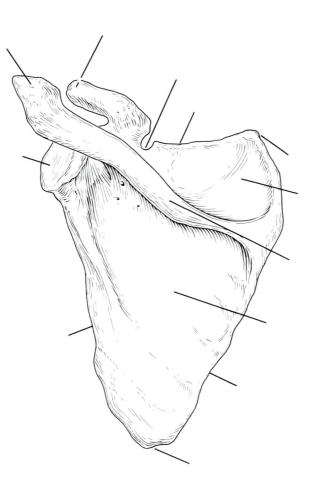

a. acromion

b. coracoid process

c. glenoid cavity

d. inferior angle

e. infraspinous fossa

f. lateral border

g. medial border

h. spine

i. superior angle

j. superior border

k. suprascapular notch

l. supraspinous fossa

Bones of the Pelvic Girdle and Lower Extremity

1. Compare the pectoral and pelvic girdles by choosing appropriate descriptive terms from the key.

   Key: a. flexibility most important   d. insecure axial and limb attachments
          b. massive   e. secure axial and limb attachments
          c. lightweight   f. weightbearing most important

   Pectoral: _____, _____, _____   Pelvic: _____, _____, _____

2. What organs are protected, at least in part, by the pelvic girdle? _____

   _____

3. Distinguish between the true pelvis and the false pelvis. _____

   _____

   _____

4. Name five differences between the male and female pelves. _____

   _____

   _____

   _____

   _____

5. Deduce why the pelvic bones of a four-legged animal such as the cat or pig are much less massive than those of

   the human. _____

   _____

6. A person instinctively curls over his abdominal area in times of danger. Why? _____

   _____

7. For what anatomical reason do many women appear to be slightly knock-kneed? _____

   _____

   _____

   _____

8. What does *fallen arches* mean? _____

   _____

9. Match the bone names and markings in column B with the descriptions in column A.

Column A

_____ , _____ , and

_____ fuse to form the coxal bone

_____ inferoposterior "bone" of the coxal bone

_____ point where the coxal bones join anteriorly

_____ superiormost margin of the coxal bone

_____ deep socket in the coxal bone that receives the head of the thigh bone

_____ joint between the axial skeleton and the pelvic girdle

_____ longest, strongest bone in body

_____ thin lateral leg bone

_____ heavy medial leg bone

_____ , _____ bones forming the knee joint

_____ point where the patellar ligament attaches

_____ kneecap

_____ shin bone

_____ medial ankle projection

_____ lateral ankle projection

_____ largest tarsal bone

_____ ankle bones

_____ bones forming the instep of the foot

_____ opening in hip bone formed by the pubic and ischial rami

_____ and _____ sites of muscle attachment on the proximal femur

_____ tarsal bone that "sits" on the calcaneus

Column B

a.   acetabulum

b.   calcaneus

c.   femur

d.   fibula

e.   gluteal tuberosity

f.   greater sciatic notch

g.   greater and lesser trochanters

h.   iliac crest

i.   ilium

j.   ischial tuberosity

k.   ischium

l.   lateral malleolus

m.   lesser sciatic notch

n.   linea aspera

o.   medial malleolus

p.   obturator foramen

q.   metatarsals

r.   patella

s.   pubic symphysis

t.   pubis

u.   sacroiliac joint

v.   talus

w.   tarsals

x.   tibia

y.   tibial tuberosity

Summary of Skeleton

1. Identify all indicated bones (or groups of bones) in the diagram of the articulated skeleton.

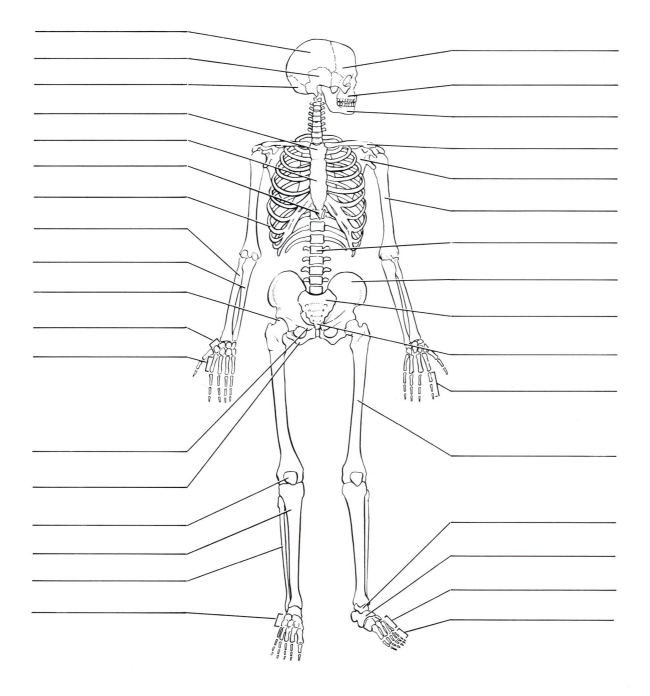

7. Using the terms listed at the right, identify each of the fontanels shown on the fetal skull below.

a. anterior fontanel

b. mastoid fontanel

c. posterior fontanel

d. sphenoidal fontanel

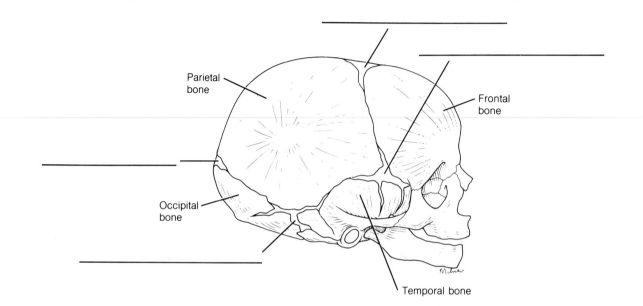

EXERCISE 13   # Articulations

Types of Joints

1. Use key responses to identify the joint types described below.

   Key: a. cartilaginous   b. fibrous   c. synovial

   _____ typically allows a slight degree of movement

   _____ includes joints between the vertebral bodies and the pubic symphysis

   _____ essentially immovable joints

   _____ sutures are the most remembered examples

   _____ characterized by cartilage connecting the bony portions

   _____ all characterized by a fibrous articular capsule lined with a synovial membrane
                     surrounding a joint cavity

   _____ all are freely movable or diarthrotic

   _____ bone regions are united by fibrous connective tissue

   _____ include the hip, knee, and elbow joints

2. Match the joint subcategories in column B with their descriptions in column A, and place an asterisk (*) beside
   all choices that are examples of synovial joints.

   Column A   **Column B**

   _____ joint between skull bones   a. ball and socket

   _____ joint between the axis and atlas   b. condyloid

   _____ hip joint   c. gliding

   _____ intervertebral joints (between articular processes)   d. hinge

   _____ joint between forearm bones and wrist   e. pivot

   _____ elbow   f. saddle

   _____ interphalangeal joints   g. suture

   _____ intercarpal joints   h. symphysis

   _____ joint between tarsus and tibia/fibula   i. synchondrosis

   _____ joint between skull and vertebral column   j. syndesmosis

   _____ joint between jaw and skull

   _____ joints between proximal phalanges and metacarpal bones

   _____ epiphyseal plate of a child's long bone

   _____ a multiaxial joint

   _____ , _____ biaxial joints

   _____ , _____ uniaxial joints

3. What characteristics do all joints have in common? _____

_____

4. Describe the structure and function of the following structures or tissues in relation to a synovial joint and label the structures indicated by leader lines in the diagram.

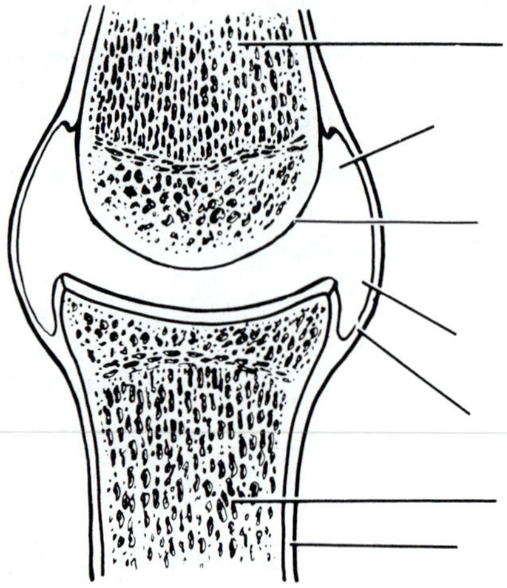

ligament _____

_____

tendon _____

_____

hyaline cartilage _____

_____

synovial membrane _____

_____

_____

bursa _____

5. Which joint, the hip or the knee, is more stable? _____

Name two important factors that contribute to the stability of the hip joint

_____ and _____

Name two important factors that contribute to the stability of the knee.

_____ and _____

6. What structural joint changes are common to the elderly? _____

_____

_____

EXERCISE 14

Microscopic Anatomy, Organization and Classification of Skeletal Muscle, and Body Movements

Skeletal Muscle Cells and Their Packaging into Muscles

1. What capability is most highly expressed in muscle tissue? _____

2. Use the items on the right to correctly identify the structures described on the left:

_____ connective tissue ensheathing a bundle of muscle cells	a. endomysium
_____ bundle of muscle cells	b. epimysium
_____ contractile unit of muscle	c. fascicle
_____ a muscle fiber	d. myofiber
_____ thin reticular connective tissue investing each muscle cell	e. myofilament
_____ plasma membrane of the muscle fiber	f. myofibril
_____ a long filamentous organelle with a banded appearance found within muscle cells	g. perimysium
_____ actin- or myosin-containing structure	h. sarcolemma
_____ cord of collagen fibers that attaches a muscle to a bone	i. sarcomere
	j. sarcoplasm
	k. tendon

3. The diagram illustrates a small portion of a muscle myofibril. Using letters from the key, correctly identify each structure indicated by a leader line. Also add a bracket to delineate the extent of one sarcomere.

Key: a.   actin filament   d.   myosin filament
       b.   A band   e.   Z line
       c.   I band

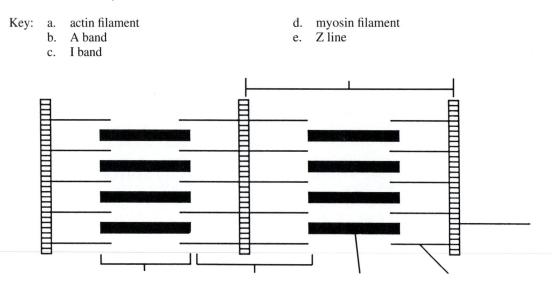

4. Why are the connective tissue wrappings of skeletal muscle important? (Give at least three reasons.)

_____

_____

_____

_____

5. Why are indirect—that is, tendinous—muscle attachments to bone seen more often than direct attachments?

_____

_____

_____

6. How does an aponeurosis differ from a tendon? _____

_____

_____

RS54

The Neuromuscular Junction

Complete the following statements:

The junction between a motor neuron's axon and the muscle cell membrane is called a neuromuscular junction or a __1__ junction. A motor neuron and all of the skeletal muscle cells it stimulates is called a __2__. The axonal terminals of each motor axon have numerous projections called __3__. The actual gap between the axonal terminal and the muscle cell is called a __4__. Within the axonal terminal are many small vesicles containing a neurotransmitter substance called __5__. When the __6__ reaches the ends of the axon, the neurotransmitter is released and diffuses to the muscle cell membrane to combine with receptors there. The combining of the neurotransmitter with the muscle membrane receptors causes the membrane to become permeable to sodium, which results in the influx of sodium ions and __7__ of the membrane. Then contraction of the muscle cell occurs. Before a muscle cell can be stimulated to contract again, __8__ must occur.

1. _____

2. _____

3. _____

4. _____

5. _____

6. _____

7. _____

8. _____

Classification of Skeletal Muscles

1. Several criteria were given relative to the naming of muscles. Match the criteria (column B) to the muscle cell names (column A). Note that more than one criterion may apply in some cases.

    Column A

    _____ gluteus maximus

    _____ adductor magnus

    _____ biceps femoris

    _____ abdominis transversus

    _____ extensor carpi ulnaris

    _____ trapezius

    _____ rectus femoris

    _____ external oblique

    Column B

    a. action of the muscle

    b. shape of the muscle

    c. location of the origin and/or insertion of the muscle

    d. number of origins

    e. location of muscle relative to a bone or body region

    f. direction in which the muscle fibers run relative to some imaginary line

    g. relative size of the muscle

2. When muscles are discussed relative to the manner in which they interact with other muscles, the terms shown in the key are often used. Match the key terms with the appropriate definitions.

    Key: a. antagonist   b. fixator   c. prime mover   d. synergist

    _____ agonist

    _____ postural muscles, for the most part

    _____ reverses and/or opposes the action of a prime mover

    _____ stabilizes a joint so that the prime mover may act at more distal joints

    _____ performs the same movement as the prime mover

    _____ immobilizes the origin of a prime mover

Body Movements

Complete the following statements:

The movable attachment of a muscle is called its __1__ , and its stationary attachment is called the __2__ . Winding up for a pitch (as in baseball) can properly be called __3__ . To keep your seat when riding a horse, the tendency is to __4__ your thighs. In running, the action at the hip joint is __5__ in reference to the leg moving forward and __6__ in reference to the leg in the posterior position. In kicking a football, the action at the knee is __7__ . In climbing stairs, the hip and knee of the forward leg are both __8__ . You have just touched your chin to your chest. This is __9__ of the neck. Using a screwdriver with your arm straight requires __10__ of the arm. Consider all the movements of which the arm is capable. One often used for strengthening all the upper arm and shoulder muscles is __11__ . Movement of the head that signifies "no" is __12__ . Standing on your toes, as in ballet, requires __13__ of the foot. Action that moves the distal end of the radius across the ulna is __14__ . Raising the arms laterally away from the body is called __15__ of the arms. Walking on one's heels is __16__ .

1. _____

2. _____

3. _____

4. _____

5. _____

6. _____

7. _____

8. _____

9. _____

10. _____

11. _____

12. _____

13. _____

14. _____

15. _____

16. _____

EXERCISE 15

Identification of Human Muscles

Muscles of the Head and Neck

1. Using choices from the list at the right, correctly identify muscles provided with leader lines on the diagram.

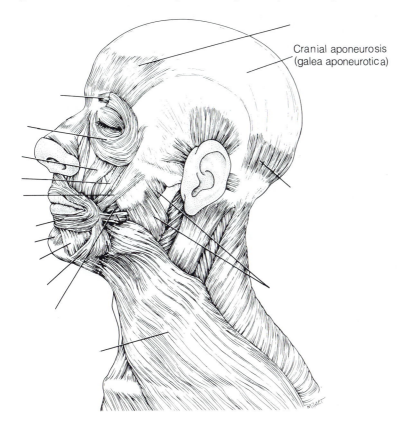

Cranial aponeurosis
(galea aponeurotica)

a. buccinator

b. corrugator supercilii

c. depressor anguli oris

d. depressor labii inferioris

e. epicranius frontalis

f. epicranius occipitalis

g. levator labii superioris

h. masseter

i. mentalis

j. platysma

k. orbicularis oculi

l. orbicularis oris

m. zygomaticus

2. Using the terms provided above, identify the muscles described next.

_____ used in smiling

_____ used to suck in your cheeks

_____ used in blinking and squinting

_____ used in pout (pulls the corners of the mouth downward)

_____ raises your eyebrows for a questioning expression

_____ used to form the vertical frown crease on the forehead

_____ your "kisser"

_____ prime mover to raise the lower jawbone

_____ tenses skin of the neck during shaving

Muscles of the Trunk

1. Correctly identify both intact and transected (cut) muscles depicted in the diagram, using the terms given at the right. (Not all terms will be used in this identification.)

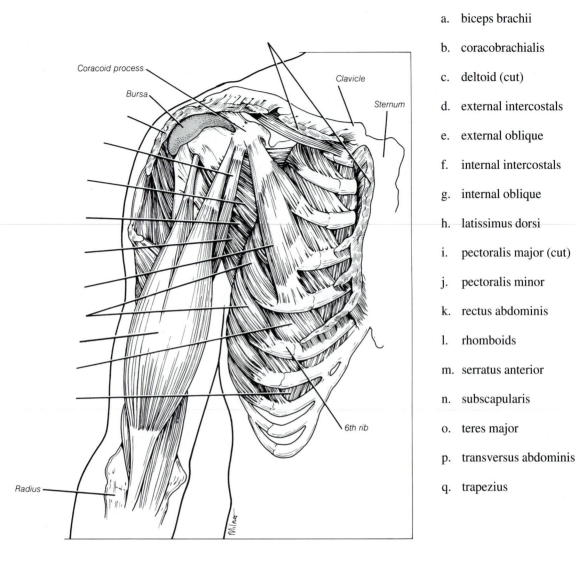

a. biceps brachii

b. coracobrachialis

c. deltoid (cut)

d. external intercostals

e. external oblique

f. internal intercostals

g. internal oblique

h. latissimus dorsi

i. pectoralis major (cut)

j. pectoralis minor

k. rectus abdominis

l. rhomboids

m. serratus anterior

n. subscapularis

o. teres major

p. transversus abdominis

q. trapezius

2. Using choices from the terms provided in question 1 above, identify the major muscles described next:

_____ a major spine flexor

_____ prime mover for pulling the arm posteriorly

_____ prime mover for shoulder flexion

_____ assume major responsibility for forming the abdominal girdle (three pairs of muscles)

_____ pulls the shoulder backward and downward

_____ prime mover of shoulder abduction

_____ important in shoulder adduction; antagonists of the shoulder abductor (two muscles)

_____ moves the scapula forward and downward

_____ small, inspiratory muscles between the ribs; elevate the ribs

_____ extends the head

_____ pull the scapulae medially

Muscles of the Upper Extremity

1. Using terms from the list on the right, correctly identify all muscles provided with leader lines in the diagram. Note that not all the listed terms will be used in this exercise.

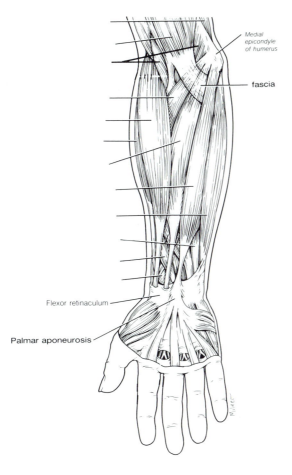

a. biceps brachii

b. brachialis

c. brachioradialis

d. extensor carpi radialis longus

e. extensor digitorum

f. flexor carpi radialis

g. flexor carpi ulnaris

h. flexor digitorum superficialis

i. flexor pollicis longus

j. palmaris longus

k. pronator quadratus

l. pronator teres

m. supinator

n. triceps brachii

2. Use the terms provided in question 1 to identify the muscles described next.

_____ places the palm upward (two muscles)

_____ flexes the forearm and supinates the hand

_____ forearm flexors; no role in supination (two muscles)

_____ elbow extensor

_____ power wrist flexor and abductor

_____ flexes wrist and distal phalanges

_____ pronate the hand (two muscles)

_____ flexes the thumb

_____ extends and abducts the wrist

_____ extends the wrist and digits

_____ flat muscle that is a weak wrist flexor

Muscles of the Lower Extremity

1. Using the terms listed to the right, correctly identify all muscles provided with leader lines in the diagram below. Not all listed terms will be used in this exercise.

a. adductor group

b. biceps femoris

c. extensor digitorum longus

d. flexor hallucis longus

e. gastrocnemius

f. gluteus maximus

g. gluteus medius

h. peroneus brevis

i. peroneus longus

j. rectus femoris

k. semimembranosus

l. semitendinosus

m. soleus

n. tensor fasciae latae

o. tibialis anterior

p. tibialis posterior

q. vastus muscles

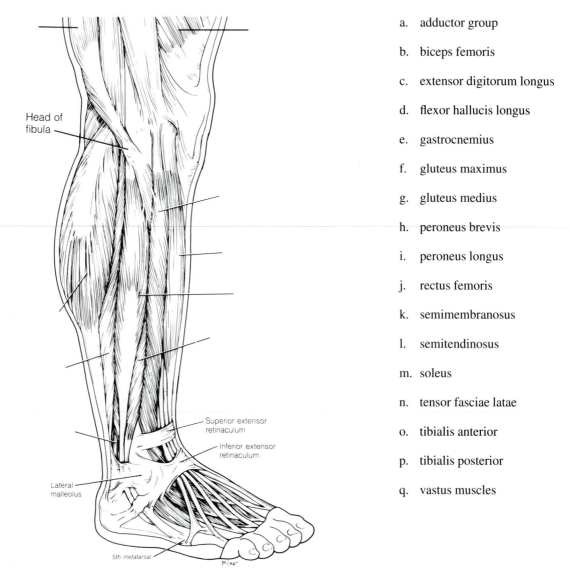

Head of fibula

Superior extensor retinaculum

Inferior extensor retinaculum

Lateral malleolus

5th metatarsal

2. Use the key terms in exercise 1 to respond to the descriptions below.

_____ flexes the great toe and inverts the ankle

_____ lateral compartment muscles that plantar flex and evert the ankle (two muscles)

_____ move the thigh laterally to take the "at ease" stance (two muscles)

_____ used to extend the hip when climbing stairs

_____ prime movers of ankle plantar flexion (two muscles)

_____ major foot inverter

_____ prime mover of ankle dorsiflexion

_____ allow you to draw your legs to the midline of your body, as when standing at attention

_____ extends the toes

_____ extend thigh and flex knee (three muscles)

_____ extends knee and flexes thigh

Muscle Recognition: General Review

1. Identify the numbered muscles in the diagram of the human anterior superficial musculature by matching the number with one of the following muscle names:

_____ orbicularis oris

_____ pectoralis major

_____ external oblique

_____ sternocleidomastoid

_____ biceps brachii

_____ deltoid

_____ vastus lateralis

_____ brachioradialis

_____ frontalis

_____ rectus femoris

_____ pronator teres

_____ rectus abdominis

_____ sartorius

_____ gracilis

_____ flexor carpi ulnaris

_____ adductor longus

_____ palmaris longus

_____ flexor carpi radialis

_____ latissimus dorsi

_____ orbicularis oculi

_____ gastrocnemius

_____ masseter

_____ trapezius

_____ tibialis anterior

_____ extensor digitorum longus

_____ tensor fasciae latae

_____ pectineus

_____ sternohyoid

_____ serratus anterior

_____ adductor magnus

_____ vastus medialis

_____ transversus abdominis

_____ peroneus longus

_____ iliopsoas

_____ temporalis

_____ zygomaticus

_____ coracobrachialis

_____ triceps brachii

_____ internal oblique

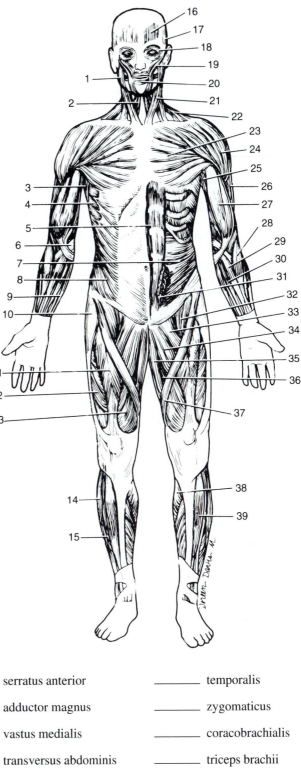

2. Identify each of the numbered muscles in this diagram of the human posterior superficial musculature by matching its number to one of the following muscle names:

_____ gluteus maximus

_____ semimembranosus

_____ gastrocnemius

_____ latissimus dorsi

_____ deltoid

_____ iliotibial tract (tendon)

_____ teres major

_____ semitendinosus

_____ trapezius

_____ biceps femoris

_____ triceps brachii

_____ external oblique

_____ gluteus medius

_____ gracilis

_____ flexor carpi ulnaris

_____ extensor carpi ulnaris

_____ extensor digitorum communis

_____ extensor carpi radialis longus

_____ occipitalis

_____ extensor carpi radialis brevis

_____ sternocleidomastoid

_____ adductor magnus

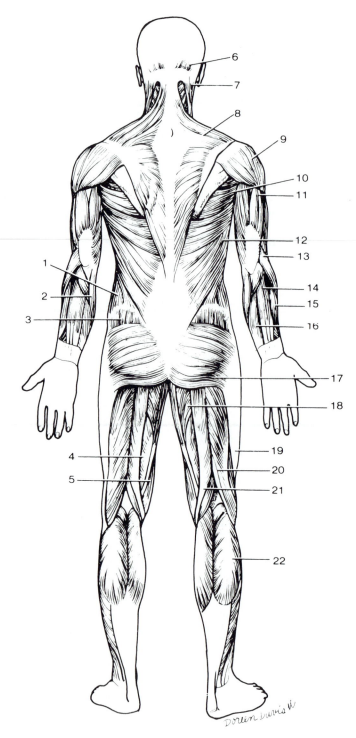

Muscle Descriptions: General Review

1. Identify the muscles described below by completing the statements:

_____ , _____ , and _____
are commonly used for intramuscular injections (three muscles).

The insertion tendon of the _____ group contains a large sesamoid bone, the patella.

The triceps surae insert in common into the _____ tendon.

The bulk of the tissue of a muscle tends to lie _____ to the part of the body it causes to move.

The extrinsic muscles of the hand originate on the _____ .

Most flexor muscles are located on the _____ aspect of the body; most extensors

are located _____ . An exception to this generalization is the extensor-flexor mus-

culature of the _____ .

Dissection and Identification of Fetal Pig Muscles

1. Many human muscles are modified from those of the pig (or any quadruped) as a result of the requirements of an upright posture. The following questions refer to these differences.

How does the human trapezius muscle differ from the pig's? _____

_____

_____

How does the deltoid differ? _____

_____

_____

How does the extent and orientation of the human sartorius muscle differ from its relative position in the pig?

_____

_____

_____

Explain these differences in terms of differences in function. _____

_____

_____

The human rectus abdominis is definitely divided by four transverse tendons. These tendons are absent or difficult to identify in the pig. How do these tendons affect the human upright posture?

_____

_____

_____

EXERCISE 16A

Muscle Physiology (Frog Experimentation)

Muscle Activity

1. The following group of incomplete statements refers to a muscle cell in the resting or polarized state just before stimulation. Complete each statement by choosing the correct response from the key items below.

Key:
    a. Na^+ diffuses out of the cell
    b. K^+ diffuses out of the cell
    c. Na^+ diffuses into the cell
    d. K^+ diffuses into the cell
    e. inside the cell
    f. outside the cell
    g. relative ionic concentrations on the two sides of the membrane

    h. electrical conditions
    i. activation of the sodium-potassium pump, which moves K^+ into the cell and Na^+ out of the cell
    j. activation of the sodium-potassium pump, which moves Na^+ into the cell and K^+ out of the cell

There is a greater concentration of Na^+ _____; there is a greater concentration of K^+ _____. When the stimulus is delivered, the permeability of the membrane at that point is changed; and _____ initiating the depolarization of the membrane. Almost as soon as the depolarization wave has begun, a repolarization wave follows it across the membrane. This occurs as _____. Repolarization restores the _____ of the resting cell membrane. The _____ is (are) reestablished by _____.

2. Number the following statements in the proper sequence to describe the contraction mechanism in a skeletal muscle cell. Number 1 has already been designated.

_____ Acetylcholine is released into the neuromuscular junction by the axonal terminal.

_____ The action potential, carried deep into the cell by the T-system, triggers the release of calcium ions from the sarcoplasmic reticulum.

_____ The muscle cell relaxes and lengthens.

_____ Acetylcholine diffuses across the neuromuscular junction and binds to receptors on the sarcolemma.

_____ The calcium ion concentrations at the myofilaments increase; the myofilaments slide past one another, and the cell shortens.

_____ Depolarization occurs, and the action potential is generated.

_____ The concentration of the calcium ions at the myofilaments decreases as they are actively reabsorbed into the sarcoplasmic reticulum.

3. Muscle contraction is commonly explained by the sliding filament hypothesis. What are the essential points of this hypothesis? _____

_____

_____

4. Relative to your observations of muscle fiber contraction (pp. 155–156):

   a. What percentage of contraction was observed with the solution containing ATP, K^+, and Mg^{2+}? _____%

   With *just* ATP? _____% With *just* Mg^{2+} and K^+? _____%

   b. *Explain* your observations fully. _____

   _____

   c. What zones or bands disappear when the muscle cell contracts? _____

   d. *Draw* a relaxed and a contracted sarcomere below.

Relaxed   Contracted

Induction of Contraction in the Frog Gastrocnemius Muscle

1. Why is it important to destroy the brain and spinal cord of a frog before conducting physiologic experiments on muscle contraction? _____

_____

2. What sources of stimuli, other than electrical shocks, cause a muscle to contract? _____

_____

3. What is the most common stimulus for muscle contraction in the body? _____

4. Name the three phases of the muscle twitch, and describe what is happening during each phase:

_____ , _____

_____

_____ , _____

_____ , _____

5. Use the terms given on the right to identify the conditions described on the left:

_____ sustained contraction without any evidence of relaxation

_____ stimulus that results in no perceptible contraction

_____ stimulus at which the muscle first contracts perceptibly

_____ increasingly stronger contractions in the absence of increased stimulus intensity

_____ increasingly stronger contractions owing to stimulation at a rapid rate

_____ increasingly stronger contractions owing to increased stimulus strength

_____

_____ weakest stimulus at which all muscle cells in the muscle are contracting

a. maximal stimulus

b. multiple motor unit summation

c. subthreshold or subliminal stimulus

d. tetanus

e. threshold stimulus

f. treppe

g. wave summation

6. With brackets and labels, identify the portions of the tracing below that best correspond to three of the phenomena listed in the preceding key. Assume that only the timing of the stimulus has changed.

7. Complete the following statements by writing the appropriate words on the correspondingly numbered blanks at the right.

The "all or none" law applies to skeletal muscle functions at the __1__ level. When a weak but smooth muscle contraction is desired, a few motor units are stimulated at a __2__ rate. Treppe is referred to as the "warming up" process. It is believed that muscles contract more strongly after the first few contractions because the __3__ become more efficient. If blue litmus paper is pressed to the cut surface of a fatigued muscle, the paper color changes to red, indicating low pH. This situation is caused by the accumulation of __4__ in the muscle. Within limits, as the load on a muscle is increased, the muscle contracts __5__ strongly. The refractory period is the time when the muscle cell will not respond to a stimulus because __6__ is occurring.

1. _____

2. _____

3. _____

4. _____

5. _____

6. _____

8. During the experiment on muscle fatigue, how did the muscle contraction pattern change as the muscle began to

    fatigue? _____

    _____

    How long was stimulation continued before fatigue was apparent? _____

    If the sciatic nerve that stimulates the living frog's gastrocnemius muscle had been left attached to the muscle
    and the stimulus had been applied to the nerve rather than the muscle, would fatigue have become apparent

    sooner or later? _____

    Explain your answer. _____

    _____

9. Explain how the weak but sustained (smooth) muscle contractions of precision movements are produced.

    _____

10. What do you think happens to a muscle in the body when its nerve supply is destroyed or badly damaged?

    _____

    _____

11. Explain the relationship between the load on a muscle and its strength of contraction. _____

    _____

    _____

12. The skeletal muscles are maintained in a slightly stretched condition for optimal contraction. How is this accom-

    plished? _____

    Why does overstretching a muscle drastically reduce its ability to contract? (Include an explanation of the events

    at the level of the myofilaments.) _____

    _____

    _____

13. If the length but not the tension of a muscle is changed, the contraction is called an isotonic contraction. In an
    isometric contraction the tension is increased but the muscle does not shorten. Which type of contraction did you

    observe most often during the laboratory experiments? _____

    What is the role of isometric contractions in normal body functioning? _____

    _____

    _____

EXERCISE 16B

Muscle Physiology
(Computerized Simulation)

Electrical Stimulation

1. Complete the following statements.

   A motor unit consists of a __1__ and all the __2__ it innervates. If a single motor unit is stimulated, it will respond in a(n) __3__ fashion, whereas whole muscle contraction is a(n) __4__ response. In order for muscles to work in a practical sense, __5__ is the method used to produce a slow steady increase in muscle force.

   When we see the slightest evidence of force production on a tracing, the stimulus applied must have reached __6__.

   The weakest stimulus that will elicit the strongest contraction that a muscle is capable of is called the __7__, and that level of contraction is called the __8__.

   When the __9__ of stimulation is so high that the muscle tracing shows fused twitch peaks, __10__ has been reached.

1. _____

2. _____

3. _____

4. _____

5. _____

6. _____

7. _____

8. _____

9. _____

10. _____

2. Name and describe what is happening in each phase of the typical muscle twitch.

   (1) _____, _____

   _____

   (2) _____, _____

   (3) _____, _____

   _____

3. What are the two ways in which mode of stimulation can affect the force a muscle produces?

   _____ and _____

   Explain. _____

   _____

   _____

   _____

Isometric Contraction

1. Identify the following conditions by choosing one of the key terms listed on the right.

   Key:

   _____ is generated by muscle tissue when it is being stretched

   a. total force

   _____ requires the input of energy

   b. passive force

   _____ is directly measured by recording instrumentation *before* electrical stimulation

   c. resting force

   _____ is measured by recording instrumentation *during* contraction

   d. active force

2. Using the letters preceeding the following statements, correctly label the area on the given Force-Length curves.

   a. an increase in resting length produced an *increase* in the active force generated

   b. an increase in resting length produced a *decrease* in active force generated

   c. an increase in resting length produced an *increase* in resting force

   H = Help

   F O R C E

   TOTAL FORCE

   ACTIVE FORCE

   RESTING FORCE

   0

   0   TIME   100   14   LENGTH   28

3. Explain what happens to muscle force production at extremes of length (too short or too long).

   Muscle too short: _____

   _____

   Muscle too long: _____

   _____

Isotonic Contraction

1. Assuming a fixed starting length, describe the effect afterload has on the initial velocity of shortening, and explain why.

   _____

   _____

   _____

   _____

2. A muscle has just been stimulated under conditions that will allow both isometric and isotonic contractions. Describe what is happening in terms of length and force.

   Isometric: _____

   _____

   Isotonic: _____

   _____

Terms

Select the condition from column B that most correctly identifies the term in column A.

Column A		Column B	
_____ muscle twitch		a.	response is all or none
_____ wave summation		b.	affects the force a muscle can generate
_____ motor unit summation		c.	a single contraction of intact muscle
_____ resting length		d.	recruitment
_____ afterload		e.	increasing force produced by increasing frequency
_____ initial velocity of shortening		f.	muscle length changing due to relaxation
_____ isotonic shortening		g.	caused by application of maximal stimulus
_____ isotonic lengthening		h.	weight
_____ motor unit		i.	exhibits graded response
_____ whole muscle		j.	high values with low afterloads
_____ tetany		k.	changing muscle length due to active forces

Attach any tracings required by your instructor to the reverse side of this sheet.

EXERCISE 17

Neuron Anatomy
and the Nerve Impulse

1. The cellular unit of the nervous system is the neuron. What is the major function of this cell type?

_____

2. Name four types of neuroglia and list at least four functions of these cells. (You will need to consult your textbook for this.)

Types

_____

_____

_____

_____

Functions

_____

_____

_____

_____

_____

_____

3. Match each statement with a response chosen from the key.

Key: a. afferent neuron   e. ganglion   i. nuclei
      b. association neuron   f. neuroglia   j. peripheral nervous system
      c. central nervous system   g. neurotransmitters   k. synapse
      d. efferent neuron   h. nerve   l. tract

_____ the brain and spinal cord collectively

_____ specialized supporting cells in the CNS

_____ junction or point of close contact between neurons

_____ a bundle of nerve processes inside the central nervous system

_____ neuron serving as part of the conduction pathway between sensory and motor neurons

_____ spinal and cranial nerves and ganglia

_____ collection of nerve cell bodies found outside the CNS

_____ neuron that conducts impulses away from the CNS to muscles and glands

_____ neuron that conducts impulses toward the CNS from the body periphery

_____ chemicals released by neurons that stimulate or inhibit other neurons or effectors

Neuron Anatomy

1. Match the following anatomical terms (column B) with the appropriate description or function (column A).

   Column A

   _____ region of the cell body from which the axon originates

   _____ secretes neurotransmitters

   _____ receptive region of a neuron

   _____ insulates the nerve fibers

   _____ is site of the nucleus and the most important metabolic area

   _____ may be involved in the transport of substances within the neuron

   _____ essentially rough endoplasmic reticulum, important metabolically

   _____ impulse generator and transmitter

   Column B

   a. axon

   b. axonal terminal

   c. axon hillock

   d. dendrite

   e. myelin sheath

   f. neuronal cell body

   g. neurofibril

   h. Nissl bodies

2. Draw a "typical" neuron in the space below. Include and label the following structures on your diagram: cell body, nucleus, Nissl bodies, dendrites, axon, axon collaterals, myelin sheath, and nodes of Ranvier.

3. How is one-way conduction at synapses assured? _____

   _____

4. What anatomical characteristic determines whether a particular neuron is classified as unipolar, bipolar, or multipolar? _____

   Make a simple line drawing of each type here.

   Unipolar neuron   Bipolar neuron   Multipolar neuron

5. Describe how the Schwann cells form the myelin sheath and the neurilemma encasing the nerve processes. (You
    may want to diagram the process.) _____

    _____

    _____

    _____

Structure of a Nerve

1. What is a nerve? _____

    _____

2. State the location of each of the following connective tissue coverings:

    endoneurium _____

    perineurium _____

    epineurium _____

3. What is the value of the connective tissue wrappings found in a nerve? _____

    _____

4. Define *mixed nerve:* _____

    _____

5. Identify all indicated parts of the nerve section.

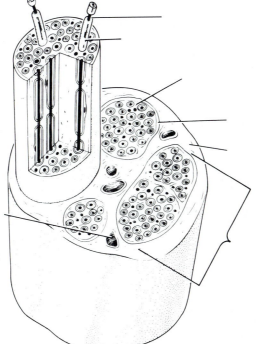

Visualizatior
Oscilloscop

1. What is a stim

2. Explain why tl

   of the stimulu:

3. What was the

   sciatic nerve t

4. When the nerv

   How can this

EXERCISE 18

Neurophysiology of Nerve Impulses

The Nerve Impulse

1. Match each of the terms in column B to the appropriate definition in column A.

   Column A

   _____ period of repolarization of the neuron membrane during which it cannot respond to a second stimulus

   _____ reversal of the resting potential owing to an influx of sodium ions

   _____ period during which potassium ions diffuse out of the neuron owing to a change in membrane permeability

   _____ self-propagated transmission of the depolarization wave along the neuronal membrane

   _____ process during which ATP is used to move sodium out of the cell and potassium into the cell; restores the resting membrane voltage and intracellular ionic concentrations

   Column B

   a. action potential

   b. depolarization

   c. refractory period

   d. repolarization

   e. sodium-potassium pump

2. Respond appropriately to each statement below either by completing the statement or by answering the question raised. Insert your responses in the corresponding numbered blanks on the right.

   1. The cellular unit of the nervous system is the neuron. What is the major function of this cell type?

   2 and 3. What characteristics are highly developed to allow the neuron to perform this function?

   4. Would a substance that decreases membrane permeability to sodium increase *or* decrease the probability of generating a nerve impulse?

   1. _____

   2. _____

   3. _____

   4. _____

3. Why don't the terms *depolarization* and *action potential* mean the same thing? (*Hint:* Under which conditions will a local depolarization *not* lead to the action potential?) _____

   _____

   _____

4. A nerve generally contains many thickly myelinated fibers that typically exhibit nodes of Ranvier. An action potential is generated along these fibers by "saltatory conduction." Use an appropriate reference to explain how saltatory conduction differs from conduction along unmyelinated fibers.

   _____

   _____

   _____

Physic
Stimul

1. Resp
   to the

   1–3.
   sulte
   the s
   tory

   4. '
   effec

   5. '
   perir
   whic
   subje

   6. '
   fer ir

   7.
   were
   ing t
   reco
   trans

2. Desc

   ___

   Does

   durir

   ___

   ___

3. At w

   from

   ___

   ___

   Why

   ___

   ___

EXERCISE 19

Gross Anatomy of the Brain and Cranial Nerves

The Human Brain

1. Match the letters on the diagram of the human brain (right lateral view) to the appropriate terms listed at the left:

_____ frontal lobe

_____ parietal lobe

_____ temporal lobe

_____ precentral gyrus

_____ parieto-occipital sulcus

_____ postcentral gyrus

_____ lateral sulcus

_____ central sulcus

_____ cerebellum

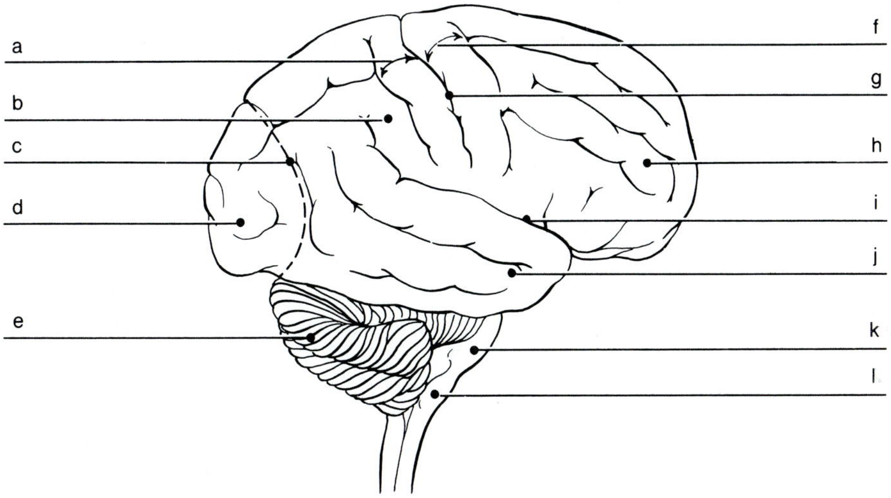

_____ medulla   _____ occipital lobe   _____ pons

2. In which of the cerebral lobes would the following functional areas be found?

auditory area _____   olfactory area _____

primary motor area _____   visual area _____

primary sensory area _____   Broca's area _____

3. Which of the following structures are *not* part of the brain stem? (Circle the appropriate response or responses.)

cerebral hemispheres   pons   midbrain   cerebellum   medulla   diencephalon

4. Complete the following statements by writing the proper word or phrase on the corresponding blanks at the right.

A(n) __1__ is an elevated ridge of cerebral tissue. The convolutions seen in the cerebrum are important because they increase the __2__. Gray matter is composed of __3__. White matter is composed of __4__. A fiber tract that provides for communication between different parts of the same cerebral hemisphere is called a(n) __5__, whereas one that carries impulses to and from the cerebrum from and to lower CNS areas is called a(n) __6__ tract. The lentiform nucleus along with the amygdaloid and caudate nuclei are collectively called the __7__.

1. _____

2. _____

3. _____

4. _____

5. _____

6. _____

7. _____

RS81

5. Identify the structures on the following sagittal view of the human brain by matching the lettered areas to the proper terms at the left:

_____ cerebellum

_____ cerebral aqueduct

_____ cerebral hemisphere

_____ cerebral peduncle

_____ choroid plexus

_____ corpora quadrigemina

_____ corpus callosum

_____ fornix

_____ fourth ventricle

_____ hypothalamus

_____ mammillary bodies

_____ massa intermedia

_____ medulla oblongata

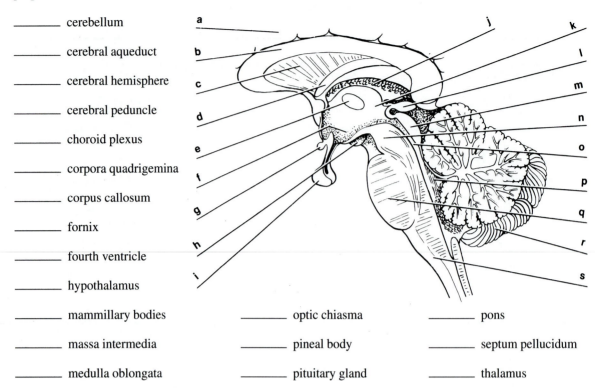

_____ optic chiasma

_____ pineal body

_____ pituitary gland

_____ pons

_____ septum pellucidum

_____ thalamus

6. Using the letters from the diagram in item 5, match the appropriate structures with the descriptions given below:

_____ site of regulation of body temperature and water balance; most important autonomic center

_____ consciousness depends on the function of this part of the brain

_____ located in the midbrain; contains reflex centers for vision and audition

_____ responsible for regulation of posture and coordination of complex muscular movements

_____ important synapse site for afferent fibers traveling to the sensory cortex

_____ contains autonomic centers regulating blood pressure, heart rate, and respiratory rhythm, as well as coughing, sneezing, and swallowing centers

_____ large commissure connecting the cerebral hemispheres

_____ fiber tract involved with olfaction

_____ connects the third and fourth ventricles

_____ encloses the third ventricle

7. Embryologically, the brain arises from the rostral end of a tubelike structure that quickly becomes divided into three major regions. Groups of structures that develop from the embryonic brain are listed below. Designate the embryonic origin of each group as the hindbrain, midbrain, or forebrain.

_____ the diencephalon, including the thalamus, optic chiasma, and hypothalamus

_____ the medulla, pons, and cerebellum

_____ the cerebral hemispheres

8. What is the function of the basal nuclei? _____

_____

9. What is the corpus striatum, and how is it related to the fibers of the internal capsule? _____

_____

_____

10. A brain hemorrhage within the region of the right internal capsule results in paralysis of the left side of the body.

Explain why the left side (rather than the right side) is affected. _____

_____

11. Explain why trauma to the base of the brain is often much more dangerous than trauma to the frontal lobes. (*Hint:* Think about the relative functioning of the cerebral hemispheres and the brain stem structures. Which contain centers more vital to life?)

_____

_____

_____

12. In "split brain" experiments, the main commissure connecting the cerebral hemispheres is cut. First, name this

commissure: _____

Then, describe what results (in terms of behavior) can be anticipated in such experiments. (Use an appropriate reference if you need help with this one!)

_____

_____

_____

_____

_____

Meninges of the Brain

Identify the meningeal (or associated) structures described below:

_____ outermost meninx covering the brain; composed of tough fibrous connective tissue

_____ innermost meninx covering the brain; delicate and highly vascular

_____ structures instrumental in returning cerebrospinal fluid to the venous blood in the dural sinuses

_____ structure that forms the cerebrospinal fluid

_____ middle meninx; like a cobweb in structure

_____ its outer layer forms the periosteum of the skull

_____ a dural fold that attaches the cerebrum to the crista galli of the skull

_____ a dural fold separating the cerebrum from the cerebellum

Cerebrospinal Fluid

Fill in the following flowchart by delineating the circulation of cerebrospinal fluid from its formation site (assume that this is one of the lateral ventricles) to the site of its reabsorption into the venous blood:

Lateral ventricle -------------> _____ -------------> Third ventricle --->

-----------------------------> _____ ------------->_____ --->

_____ -------------> _____

_____ -->

_____ surrounding the brain and cord -------------> Arachnoid villi -------->
(and central canal of the cord)

-----------------------------> _____ containing venous blood

Cranial Nerves

1. Using the terms below, correctly identify all structures indicated by leader lines on the diagram below.

a. abducens nerve (I)

b. accessory nerve (XI)

c. cerebellum

d. cerebral peduncle

e. decussation of the pyramids

f. facial nerve (VII)

g. frontal lobe of cerebral hemisphere

h. glossopharyngeal nerve (IX)

i. hypoglossal nerve (XII)

j. longitudinal fissure

k. mammillary body

l. medulla oblongata

m. oculomotor nerve (III)

n. olfactory bulb

o. olfactory tract

p. optic chiasma

q. optic nerve (II)

r. optic tract

s. pituitary gland

t. pons

u. spinal cord

v. temporal lobe of cerebral hemisphere

w. trigeminal nerve (V)

x. trochlear nerve (IV)

y. vagus nerve (X)

z. vestibulocochlear nerve (VIII)

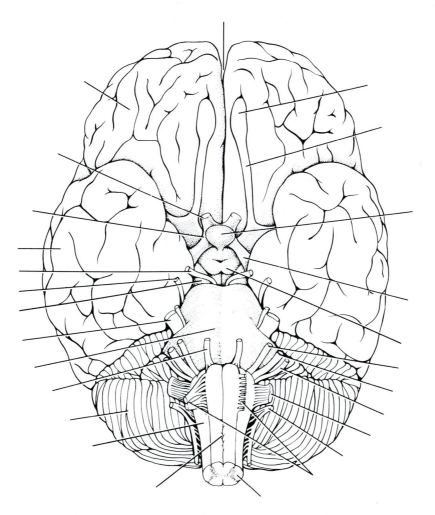

2. Provide the name and number of the cranial nerves involved in each of the following activities, sensations, or disorders:

_____ shrugging the shoulders

_____ smelling a flower

_____ raising the eyelids; focusing the lens of the eye for accommodation; and pupillary constriction

_____ slows the heart; increases the mobility of the digestive tract

_____ involved in Bell's palsy (facial paralysis)

_____ chewing food

_____ listening to music; seasickness

_____ secretion of saliva; tasting well-seasoned food

_____ involved in "rolling" the eyes (three nerves—provide numbers only)

_____ feeling a toothache

_____ reading *Playgirl* or *Playboy* magazine

_____ purely sensory in function (three nerves—provide numbers only)

Dissection of the Sheep Brain

1. In your own words, describe the relative hardness of the sheep brain tissue as observed when cutting into it.

_____

Because formalin hardens all tissue, what conclusions might you draw about the relative hardness and texture of

living brain tissue? _____

2. How does the relative size of the cerebral hemispheres compare in sheep and human brains? _____

_____

What is the significance? _____

_____

3. What is the significance of the fact that the olfactory bulbs are much larger in the sheep brain than in the human

brain? _____

_____

EXERCISE 20   # Electroencephalography

Brain Wave Patterns and the Electroencephalogram

1. Define *EEG*. _____

2. What are the four major types of brain wave patterns? _____

   Match each statement below to a type of brain wave pattern:

   _____ below 4 cps; slow, large waves; normally seen during deep sleep

   _____ rhythm generally apparent when an individual is in a relaxed, nonattentive state with the eyes closed

   _____ correlated to the alert state; usually about 15 to 25 cps

   _____ large, irregular, low-frequency waves; uncommon in adults but common in children

3. What is meant by the term *alpha block*? _____

   _____

   _____

4. List at least four types of brain lesions that may be determined by EEG studies. _____

   _____

5. What is the common result of hypoactivity or hyperactivity of the brain neurons? _____

Observing Brain Wave Patterns

1. How was alpha block demonstrated in the laboratory experiment? _____

   _____

   What was the effect of mental concentration on the brain wave pattern? _____

   _____

   _____

3. What effect on the brain wave pattern did hyperventilation have? _____

   Why? _____

   _____

The Autonomic Nervous System

1. For the most part, sympathetic and parasympathetic fibers serve the same organs and structures. How can they exert antagonistic effects? (After all, nerve impulses are nerve impulses—aren't they?)

   _____

2. Name three structures that receive sympathetic but not parasympathetic innervation.

   _____

   _____

3. The pelvic nerve contains (circle one):

   (a) preganglionic sympathetic fibers   (c) preganglionic parasympathetic fibers

   (b) postganglionic sympathetic fibers   (d) postganglionic parasympathetic fibers

4. The following chart states a number of conditions. Use a check mark to show which division of the autonomic nervous system is involved in each.

Sympathetic Division	Condition	Parasympathetic Division
	Secretes norepinephrine; adrenergic fibers	
	Secretes acetylcholine; cholinergic fibers	
	Long preganglionic axon; short postganglionic axon	
	Short preganglionic axon; long postganglionic axon	
	Arises from cranial and sacral nerves	
	Arises from spinal nerves T_1 through L_3	
	Normally in control	
	"Fight or flight" system	
	Has more specific control (Look it up!)	

5. You are alone in your home late in the evening, and you hear an unfamiliar sound in your backyard. List four physiologic events promoted by the sympathetic nervous system that would aid you in coping with this rather frightening situation:

   _____

   _____

   _____

   _____

   _____

6. Often after surgery, people are temporarily unable to urinate, and bowel sounds are absent. What division of the ANS is affected by the anesthesia? _____

EXERCISE 22

Human Reflex Physiology

The Reflex Arc

1. Define *reflex.* _____

_____

2. Name five essential components of a reflex arc: _____, _____,

_____, _____, and _____

3. In general, what is the importance of reflex testing in a routine physical examination? _____

_____

_____

Somatic and Autonomic Reflexes

1. Use the key terms to complete the statements given below.

    a. abdominal reflex   d. corneal reflex   g. patellar reflex
    b. Achilles jerk   e. crossed extensor reflex   h. plantar reflex
    c. ciliospinal reflex   f. gag reflex   i. pupillary light reflex

Reflexes classified as somatic reflexes include _____, _____, _____, _____, _____, _____,

and _____. Of these, the simple stretch reflexes are _____ and _____, and the superficial cord reflexes

are _____ and _____. Reflexes classified as autonomic reflexes include _____ and _____.

2. In what way do cord-mediated reflexes differ from those involving higher brain centers? _____

_____

Name two cord-mediated reflexes: _____ and _____

_____

Name two somatic reflexes in which the higher brain centers participate: _____

and _____

3. Can the stretch reflex be elicited in a pithed animal? _____

Explain your answer. _____

_____

4. Trace the reflex arc, naming efferent and afferent nerves, receptors, effectors, and integration centers, for the following reflexes:

patellar reflex _____

_____

_____

Achilles reflex _____

_____

_____

5. Three factors that influence the rapidity and effectiveness of reflex arcs were investigated in conjunction with patellar reflex testing—mental distraction, effect of simultaneous muscle activity in another body area, and fatigue.

Which of these factors increases the excitatory level of the spinal cord? _____

Which factor decreases the excitatory level of the muscles? _____

When the subject was concentrating on an arithmetic problem, did the change noted in the patellar reflex indicate

that brain activity is necessary for the patellar reflex or only that it may modify it? _____

_____

6. Name the division of the autonomic nervous system responsible for each of the following reflexes:

ciliospinal reflex _____ salivary reflex _____

pupillary light reflex _____

7. The pupillary light reflex, the crossed extensor reflex, and the corneal reflex illustrate the purposeful nature of reflex activity. Describe the protective aspect of each:

pupillary light reflex _____

corneal reflex _____

crossed extensor reflex _____

_____

_____

_____

_____

8. Was the pupillary consensual response contralateral or ipsilateral? _____

Why would such a response be of significant value in this particular reflex? _____

_____

9. Differentiate between the types of activities accomplished by somatic and autonomic reflexes. _____

    _____

    _____

    _____

10. Several types of reflex activity were not investigated in this exercise. The most important of these are autonomic reflexes, which are difficult to illustrate in a laboratory situation. To rectify this omission, complete the following chart, using references as necessary.

Reflex	Organ involved	Receptors stimulated	Action
Micturition (urination)			
Hering-Breuer			
Defecation			
Carotid sinus			

4. Define *punctate distribution:* _____

_____

5. Several questions regarding general sensation are posed below. Answer each by placing your response in the appropriately numbered blanks to the right.

    1. Which cutaneous receptors are the most numerous?

    2–3. Which two body areas tested were most sensitive to touch?

    4–5. Which two body areas tested were least sensitive to touch?

    6. Which appears to be more numerous—receptors that respond to cold or to heat?

    7–9. Where would referred pain appear if the following organs were receiving painful stimuli— gallbladder (#7), kidneys (#8), and appendix (#9)? (Use your textbook if necessary.)

    10. Where was referred pain felt when the elbow was immersed in ice water during the laboratory experiment?

    11. What region of the cerebrum interprets the kind and intensity of stimuli that cause cutaneous sensations?

1. _____

2. _____

3. _____

4. _____

5. _____

6. _____

7. _____

8. _____

9. _____

10. _____

11. _____

6. Define *adaptation:* _____

_____

7. Why is it advantageous to have pain receptors that are sensitive to all vigorous stimuli, whether heat, cold, or

pressure? _____

Why is the nonadaptability of pain receptors important? _____

_____

8. Imagine yourself without any cutaneous sense organs. Why might this be very dangerous? _____

_____

_____

9. Define *referred pain:* _____

_____

What is the probable explanation for referred pain? (Consult your textbook or an appropriate reference if neces-

sary.) _____

_____

_____

RS98

EXERCISE 24

Special Senses: Vision

Anatomy of the Eye

1. Three accessory eye structures contribute to the formation of tears and/or aid in lubrication of the eyeball. Name each and then name its major secretory product. Indicate which has antibacterial properties by circling the correct secretory product.

Accessory Structures	Product

2. The eyeball is wrapped in adipose tissue within the orbit. What is the function of the adipose tissue?

_____

What seven bones form the bony orbit? (Think! If you can't remember, check a skull or your text.)

_____ _____ _____

_____ _____

_____ _____

3. Why does one often have to blow one's nose after having a good cry? _____

_____

4. Identify the extrinsic eye muscle predominantly responsible for the actions described below.

_____ turns the eye laterally

_____ turns the eye medially

_____ turns the eye up and laterally

_____ turns the eye inferiorly

_____ turns the eye superiorly

_____ turns the eye down and laterally

5. What is a sty? _____

_____

Conjunctivitis? _____

6. Using the terms listed on the right, correctly identify all structures provided with leader lines in the diagram.

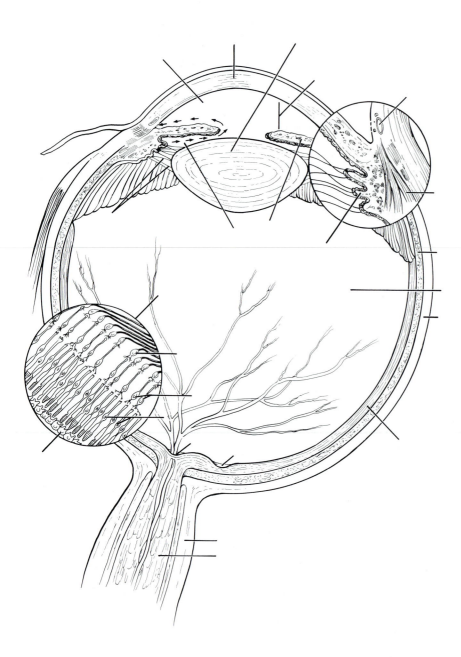

a. anterior chamber

b. anterior segment containing aqueous humor

c. bipolar neurons

d. ciliary body and processes

e. ciliary muscle

f. choroid

g. cornea

h. dura mater

i. fovea centralis

j. ganglion cells

k. iris

l. lens

m. optic disc

n. optic nerve

o. photoreceptors

p. posterior chamber

q. retina

r. sclera

s. scleral venous sinus

t. suspensory ligaments

u. vitreous body in posterior segment

7. Match the key responses with the descriptive statements that follow.

Key: a. aqueous humor
       b. choroid
       c. ciliary body
       d. ciliary processes of
          the ciliary body

       e. cornea
       f. fovea centralis
       g. iris
       h. lens
       i. optic disc

       j. retina
       k. sclera
       l. scleral venous sinus
       m. suspensory ligament
       n. vitreous humor

_____ attaches the lens to the ciliary body

_____ fluid filling the anterior segment of the eye

_____ the "white" of the eye

_____ part of the retina that lacks photoreceptors

_____ modification of the choroid that controls the shape of the crystalline lens

_____ contains the ciliary muscle

_____ drains the aqueous humor from the eye

_____ tunic containing the rods and cones

_____ substance occupying the posterior segment of the eyeball

_____ forms the bulk of the heavily pigmented vascular tunic

_____, _____ smooth muscle structures

_____ area of critical focusing and discriminatory vision

_____ form (by filtration) the aqueous humor

_____, _____, _____,

_____ light-bending media of the eye

_____ anterior continuation of the sclera—your "window on the world"

_____ composed of tough, white, opaque, fibrous connective tissue

8. The iris is composed primarily of two smooth muscle layers, one arranged radially and the other circularly.

   Which of these dilates the pupil? _____

9. You would expect the pupil to be dilated in which of the following circumstances? (Circle the correct response(s).)

   a.   in brightly lighted surroundings   c.   during focusing for near vision

   b.   in dimly lit surroundings   d.   in observing distant objects

10. The intrinsic eye muscles are under the control of which of the following? (Circle the correct response.)

                    autonomic nervous system   somatic nervous system

Dissection of the Cow (Sheep) Eye

1. What modification of the choroid that is not present in humans is found in the cow eye? _____

   _____

   What is its function? _____

   _____

   _____

2. What is the anatomical appearance of the retina? _____

   _____

   At what point is it attached to the posterior aspect of the eyeball? _____

Microscopic Anatomy of the Retina

1. The two major layers of the retina are the epithelial and nervous layers. In the nervous layer, the neuron populations are arranged as follows from the epithelial layer to the vitreous humor. (Circle all proper responses.)

   bipolar cells, ganglion cells, photoreceptors   photoreceptors, ganglion cells, bipolar cells

   ganglion cells, bipolar cells, photoreceptors   photoreceptors, bipolar cells, ganglion cells

2. The axons of the _____ cells form the optic nerve, which exits from the eyeball.

3. Complete the following statements by writing either *rods* or *cones* on each blank:

   The dim light receptors are the _____ . Only _____ are found

   in the fovea centralis, whereas mostly _____ are found in the periphery of the retina.

   _____ are the photoreceptors that operate best in bright light and allow for color vision.

Visual Pathways to the Brain

1. The visual pathway to the occipital lobe of the brain consists most simply of a chain of five neurons. Beginning with the photoreceptor cell of the retina, name them and note their location in the pathway.

   1 _____   4 _____

   2 _____   5 _____

   3 _____   _____

2. Visual field tests are done to reveal destruction along the visual pathway from the retina to the optic region of the brain. Note where the lesion is likely to be in the following cases:

   Normal vision in left eye visual field; absence of vision of right eye visual field: _____

   Normal vision in both eyes for right half of the visual field; absence of vision in both eyes for left half of the visual

   field: _____

3. How is the right optic *tract* anatomically different from the right optic *nerve*? _____

_____

_____

What does this difference result from? _____

_____

Visual Tests and Experiments

1. Match the terms in column B with the descriptions in column A:

Column A	Column B
_____ light bending	a. accommodation
_____ ability to focus for close (under 20 ft) vision	b. astigmatism
_____ normal vision	c. convergence
_____ inability to focus well on close objects (farsightedness)	d. emmetropia
_____ nearsightedness	e. hyperopia
_____ blurred vision due to unequal curvatures of the lens or cornea	f. myopia
_____ medial movement of the eyes during focusing on close objects	g. refraction

2. Complete the following statements:

   In farsightedness, the light is focused __1__ the retina. The lens required to treat myopia is a __2__ lens. The "near point" increases with age because the __3__ of the lens decreases as we get older. A convex lens, like that of the eye, produces an image that is upside down and reversed from left to right. Such an image is called a __4__ image.

   1. _____

   2. _____

   3. _____

   4. _____

3. Use terms from the key to complete the statements concerning near and distance vision.

   Key: a. contracted   b. decreased   c. increased   d. relaxed   e. taut

   During distance vision: The ciliary muscle is ____, the suspensory ligament is ____, the convexity of the lens is ____, and light refraction is ____. During close vision: The ciliary muscle is ____, the suspensory ligament is ____, lens convexity is ____, and light refraction is ____.

4. Explain why vision is lost when light hits the blind spot. _____

5. What is meant by the term *negative afterimage* and what does this phenomenon indicate? _____

_____

_____

_____

RS103

5. Indicate whether the following conditions relate to conduction deafness (C) or sensorineural (central) deafness (S):

_____ can result from the fusion of the ossicles

_____ can result from a lesion on the cochlear nerve

_____ sound heard in one ear but not in the other during bone and air conduction

_____ can result from otitis media

_____ can result from impacted cerumen or a perforated eardrum

_____ can result from a blood clot in the auditory cortex

6. The Rinne test evaluates an individual's ability to hear sounds conducted by air or bone. Which is more indicative of normal hearing? _____

7. Define *nystagmus*. _____

_____

Define *vertigo:* _____

8. The Barany test investigated the effect that rotatory acceleration had on the semicircular canals. Explain *why* the subject still had the sensation of rotation immediately after being stopped. _____

_____

9. What is the usual reason for conducting the Romberg test? _____

_____

Was the degree of sway greater with the eyes open or closed? _____

Why? _____

10. Normal balance, or equilibrium, depends on input from a number of sensory receptors. Name them.

_____

_____

EXERCISE 26

Special Senses: Taste and Olfaction

Localization and Anatomy of Taste Buds

1. Name three sites where receptors for taste are found, and circle the predominant site:

   _____ , _____ , and

   _____

2. Describe the cellular makeup and arrangement of a taste bud. (Use a diagram, if helpful.) _____

   _____

   _____

Localization and Anatomy of the Olfactory Receptors

1. Describe the cellular composition and the location of the olfactory epithelium. _____

   _____

   _____

2. How and why does sniffing improve your sense of smell? _____

   _____

   _____

Laboratory Experiments

1. Taste and smell receptors are both classified as _____ , because they both respond

   to _____

2. Why is it impossible to taste substances with a dry tongue? _____

   _____

3. State the most important sites of the taste-specific receptors, as determined during the plotting exercise in the laboratory:

   salt _____   sour _____

   bitter _____   sweet _____

4. The basic taste sensations are elicited by specific chemical substances or groups. Name them:

   salt _____   sour _____

   bitter _____   sweet _____

4. An anterior view of the heart is shown here. Identify each numbered structure by writing its name on the correspondingly numbered line:

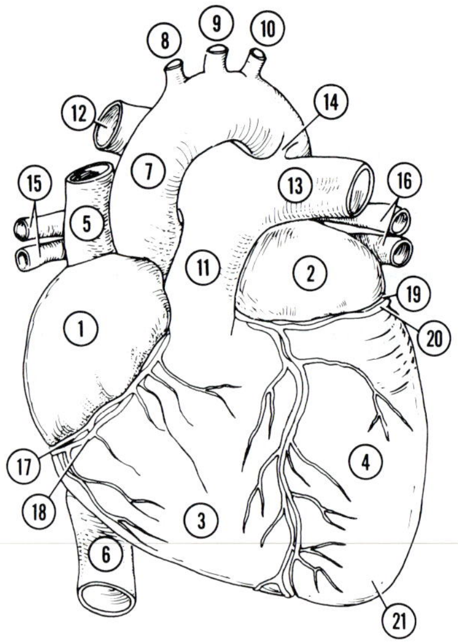

1. _____

2. _____

3. _____

4. _____

5. _____

6. _____

7. _____

8. _____

9. _____

10. _____

11. _____

12. _____

13. _____

14. _____

15. _____

16. _____

17. _____

18. _____

19. _____

20. _____

21. _____

5. What is the function of the valves found in the heart? _prevent back flow of_ _blood_

6. Can the heart function with leaky valves? (Think! Can a water pump function with leaky valves?) _____

7. What is the role of the chordae tendineae? _____

_____

8. Define:

angina pectoris _____

_____

pericarditis _____

RS126

9. Differentiate clearly between the roles of the pulmonary and systemic circulations. _____

_____

_____

10. Complete the following scheme of circulation in the human body:

Right atrium through the tricuspid valve to the _____ through the _____

_____ valve to the pulmonary trunk to the _____

to the capillary beds of the lungs to the _____ to the _____

of the heart through the _____ valve to the _____ through the

_____ valve to the _____ to the systemic arteries to the

_____ of the tissues to the systemic veins to the _____ and

_____ entering the right atrium of the heart.

11. If the mitral valve does not close properly, which circulation is affected? _____

Microscopic Anatomy of Cardiac Muscle

1. How would you distinguish cardiac muscle from skeletal muscle? _____

_____

_____

_____

_____

2. What role does the unique structure of cardiac muscle play in its function? (Note: Before attempting a response, describe the unique anatomy.) _____

_____

_____

_____

_____

4. Discuss the effects of the following on blood vessel diameter (state specifically the blood vessels involved) and rate of blood flow. Then explain the importance of the reaction observed to the general well-being of the body.

local application of cold _____

_____

_____

local application of heat _____

_____

_____

inflammation (or application of HC1) _____

_____

_____

histamine _____

_____

_____

EXERCISE 35

The Lymphatic System and Immune Response

The Lymphatic System

1. Explain why the lymphatic system is a one-way system, whereas the blood vascular system is a two-way system.

   _____

   _____

2. How do lymphatic vessels resemble veins? _____

   How do lymphatic capillaries differ from blood capillaries? _____

   _____

3. What is the function of the lymphatic vessels? _____

   _____

4. What is lymph? _____

5. What factors are involved in the flow of lymphatic fluid? _____

   _____

6. What name is given to the terminal duct draining most of the body? _____

7. What is the cisterna chyli? _____

   _____

   How does the composition of lymph in the cisterna chyli differ from that in the general lymphatic stream?

   _____

8. Which portion of the body is drained by the right lymphatic duct? _____

9. Note three areas where lymph nodes are densely clustered: _____,

   _____, and _____

10. What are the two major functions of the lymph nodes? _____

    _____

11. The radical mastectomy is an operation in which a cancerous breast, surrounding tissues, and the underlying muscles of the anterior thoracic wall, plus the axillary lymph nodes, are removed. After such an operation, the arm usually swells, or becomes edematous, and is very uncomfortable—sometimes for months. Why?

    _____

5. Trace a molecule of oxygen from the external nares to the pulmonary capillaries of the lungs: External nares →

nasal cavity (conchae & nasal mucosa) → nasopharynx → oropharynx → laryngopharynx → larynx → trachea → bronchi → bronchioles → respiratory bronchioles → alveolar ducts → alveolar sacs → alveoli → respiratory membrane

6. What is the function of the pleural membranes? _____

_____

7. Name two functions of the nasal cavity mucosa: *warm, moisten*

8. The following questions refer to the primary bronchi:

Which is longer? *left*   Larger in diameter? *right*   More horizontal? *left*

The more common site for lodging of a foreign object that had entered the respiratory passageways? *right primary bronchus*

9. Match the terms in column B to those in column A.

Column A		Column B
j nerve that activates the diaphragm during inspiration		a. alveoli
h "floor" of the nasal cavity		b. bronchioles
e food passageway posterior to the trachea		c. conchae
d flaps over the glottis during swallowing of food		d. epiglottis
g contains the vocal cords		e. esophagus
l part of the conducting pathway between the larynx and the primary bronchi		f. glottis
i pleural layer lining the walls of the thorax		g. larynx
a site from which oxygen enters the pulmonary blood		h. palate
m autonomic nervous system nerve serving the thoracic region		i. parietal pleura
f opening between the vocal folds		j. phrenic nerve
c increases air turbulence in the nasal cavity		k. primary bronchi
		l. trachea
		m. vagus nerve
		n. visceral pleura

10. What portions of the respiratory system are referred to as anatomical dead space? *respiratory passageways from nasal cavity to bronchioles*

_____

Why? *because they only serve as access or exit routes*

_____

11. Define *external respiration:* _gas exchange (oxygen loading / carbon_ _dioxide unloading (pulmonary circulation)_

  internal respiration: _gas exchange (oxygen unloading /_ _carbon dioxide loading (systemic circulation)_

12. On the diagram below identify alveolar epithelium, capillary endothelium, alveoli, and red blood cells, and bracket the respiratory membrane.

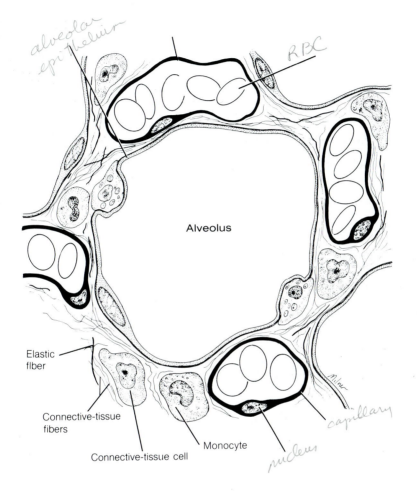

alveolar epithelium

RBC

Alveolus

capillary

nucleus

Elastic fiber

Connective-tissue fibers

Connective-tissue cell

Monocyte

Sheep Pluck Demonstration

1. Does the lung inflate part by part or as a whole, like a balloon? _____

   What happened when the pressure was released? _____

   What type of tissue insures this phenomenon? _____

Examination of Prepared Slides of Lung and Trachea Tissue

1. The tracheal epithelium is ciliated and has goblet cells. What is the function of each of these modifications?

   Cilia? _propel mucus_

   Goblet cells? _produces mucus_

2. The tracheal epithelium is said to be pseudostratified. Why? _____
_____
_____

3. What structural characteristics of the alveoli make them an ideal site for the diffusion of gases?
a single thin layer of squamous epith.

Why does oxygen move from the alveoli into the pulmonary capillary blood? _____
_____
_____

4. If you observed pathologic lung sections, what were the conditions responsible and how did the tissue differ from normal lung tissue?

Slide Type	**Observations**

Dissection of the Respiratory System of the Fetal Pig

1. Are the cartilaginous rings in the pig trachea complete or incomplete? _____

2. How does the number of lung lobes in the pig compare with the number in humans? _____
_____

3. Describe the appearance of lung tissue under the dissection microscope. _____
_____

4. Why did the segment of lung tissue, cut from the fetal pig's lung, *sink* when placed in water? _____
_____
_____

EXERCISE 37

Respiratory System Physiology

Mechanics of Respiration

1. For each of the following cases, check the column appropriate to your observations on the operation of the model lung.

Change	Diaphragm Pushed Up		Diaphragm Pulled Down	
	Increased	Decreased	Increased	Decreased
In internal volume of the bell jar (thoracic cage)		✓	✓	
In internal pressure	✓			✓
In the size of the balloons (lungs)		✓	✓	
In direction of air flow	Into lungs	(Out of lungs)	(Into lungs)	Out of lungs

2. Base your answers to the following on your observations in question 1.

Under what internal conditions does air tend to flow into the lungs? _____ *when pressure* _____

_____

Under what internal conditions does air tend to flow out of the lungs? Explain. _____ *high pressure* _____

_____

3. Activation of the diaphragm and the external intercostal muscles begins the inspiratory process. What results from

the contractions of these muscles, and how is this accomplished? _____

_____

_____

_____

4. What was the approximate increase in diameter of chest circumference during a quiet inspiration?

_____ inches   During forced inspiration? _____ inches

What temporary physiologic advantage does the substantial increase in chest circumference during forced inspi-

ration create? _____

_____

_____

5. The presence of a partial vacuum between the pleural membranes is integral to normal breathing movements. What would happen if an opening were made into the chest cavity, as with a puncture wound?

_____

How is this condition treated medically? _____

Respiratory Volumes and Capacities—Spirometry

1. Write the respiratory volume term and the normal value that is described by the following statements:

volume of air present in the lungs after a forceful expiration _____ ERV exp reserv vl

volume of air that can be expired forcibly after a normal expiration _____ ERV expiratory reserve vol.

volume of air that is breathed in and out during a normal respiration _____ TV Tidal vol.

volume of air that can be inspired forcibly after a normal inspiration _____ IRV inspiratory reserve vol

volume of air corresponding to TV + IRV + ERV _____ VC - vital capacity

2. Record experimental respiratory volumes as determined in the laboratory.

Average tidal volume _____ ml   Average VC _____ ml

Average IRV _____ ml   % predicted VC _____ %

Minute respiratory volume _____ ml/min   FEV, _____ % FVC

Average ERV _____ ml

3. Would your vital-capacity measurement differ if you performed the test while standing? _____ While lying

down? _____ Explain. _____

_____

4. Which respiratory ailments can respiratory volume tests be used to detect? Explain your reasoning.

_____ emphysema① (chronic obstructive pulmon diseases)

chronic bronchitis

_____ ② Restrictive pulmon. diseases

_____ polio

myasthenia gravis

5. Using an appropriate reference, complete the chart below:

		O_2	CO_2	N_2
% of composition of air	Inspired			
	Expired			

Use of the Pneumograph to Determine Factors Influencing Rate and Depth of Respiration

1. Where are the neural control centers of respiratory rhythm? _pons_ _____ and _medulla_

2. Based on pneumograph reading of respiratory variation, what was the rate of quiet breathing?

   Initial testing _____ breaths/min

   Record observations of how the initial pneumograph recording was modified during the various testing procedures described below. Indicate the respiratory rate, and include comments on the relative depth of the respiratory peaks observed.

Test performed	Observations
Talking	
Yawning	
Laughing	
Standing	
Concentrating	
Swallowing water	
Coughing	
Lying down	
Running in place	

3. Student data:

   breath-holding interval after a deep inhalation _____ sec   length of recovery period _____ sec

   breath-holding interval after a forceful expiration _____ sec   length of recovery period _____ sec

   After breathing quietly and taking a deep breath (which you held), was your urge to inspire or expire?

   _____

   After exhaling and then breath holding, was the desire for inspiration or expiration? _____

   Explain these results. (*Hint:* what reflex is involved here?) _____

   _____

4. Observations after hyperventilation: _____

_____

5. Length of breath holding after hyperventilation: _____ sec

   Why does hyperventilation produce apnea or a reduced respiratory rate? _____

_____

_____

6. Observations for rebreathing breathed air: _____

_____

   Why does rebreathing breathed air produce an increased respiratory rate? _____

_____

7. What was the effect of running in place (exercise) on the duration of breath holding? _____

   Explain: _____

_____

8. Relative to the test illustrating the effect of respiration on circulation: *(student data)*

   Radial pulse before beginning test _____ /min   Radial pulse after testing _____ /min

   Relative pulse force before beginning test _____   Relative force of radial pulse after testing _____

   Condition of neck and facial veins after testing _____

   Explain: _____

_____

9. Do the following factors generally increase (indicate with I) or decrease (indicate with D) the respiratory rate and depth?

   increase in blood CO_2 _____   increase in blood pH _____

   decrease in blood O_2 _____   decrease in blood pH _____

   Did it appear that CO_2 or O_2 had a more marked effect on modifying the respiratory rate? _____

10. Sensory receptors sensitive to changes in blood pressure are located where? _____

_____

11. Where are sensory receptors sensitive to changes in O_2 levels in the blood located? _____

_____

12. What is the primary factor that initiates breathing in a newborn infant? _____

_____

RS162

13. Blood CO_2 levels and blood pH are related. When blood CO_2 levels increase, does the pH increase or decrease?

_____ Explain why. _____

_____

_____

Respiratory Sounds

1. Which of the respiratory sounds is heard during both inspiration and expiration? _____

   Which is heard primarily during inspiration? _____

2. Where did you best hear the vesicular respiratory sounds? _____

Role of the Respiratory System in Acid-Base Balance of Blood

1. Define *buffer.* _____

2. How successful was the laboratory buffer (pH 7) in resisting changes in pH when the acid was added?

   _____

   When the base was added? _____

   How successful was the buffer in resisting changes in pH when the additional aliquots (3 more drops) of the acid

   and base were added to the original samples? _____

3. What buffer system operates in blood plasma? _____

   Which of its species resists a *drop* in pH? _____

   Which resists a *rise* in pH? _____

4. Explain how the carbonic acid–bicarbonate buffer system of the blood operates. _____

   _____

   _____

   _____

   _____

   _____

3. Match the items in column B with the descriptive statements in column A.

Column A

_____ structure that suspends the small intestine from the posterior body wall

_____ fingerlike extensions of the intestinal mucosa that increase the surface area for absorption

_____ large collections of lymphoid tissue found in the submucosa of the small intestine

_____ deep folds of the mucosa and submucosa that extend completely or partially around the circumference of the small intestine

_____, _____ regions that break down foodstuffs mechanically

_____ mobile organ that manipulates food in the mouth and initiates swallowing

_____ conduit for both air and food

_____, _____, _____ three structures continuous with and representing modifications of the peritoneum

_____ the "gullet"; no digestive/absorptive function

_____ folds of the gastric mucosa

_____ sacculations of the large intestine

_____ projections of the plasma membrane of a mucosal epithelial cell

_____ valve at the junction of the small and large intestines

_____ primary region of food and water absorption

_____ membrane securing the tongue to the floor of the mouth

_____ absorbs water and forms feces

_____ area between the teeth and lips/cheeks

_____ wormlike sac that outpockets from the cecum

_____ initiates protein digestion

_____ structure attached to the lesser curvature of the stomach

_____ organ distal to the stomach

_____ valve controlling food movement from the stomach into the duodenum

_____ posterosuperior boundary of the oral cavity

_____ site of the hepatopancreatic sphincter through which pancreatic secretions and bile pass

_____ serous lining of the abdominal cavity wall

_____ principal site for the synthesis of vitamin K by microorganisms

_____ region containing two sphincters through which feces are expelled from the body

_____ bone-supported anterosuperior boundary of the oral cavity

Column B

a. anus

b. appendix

c. esophagus

d. frenulum

e. greater omentum

f. hard palate

g. haustra

h. ileocecal valve

i. large intestine

j. lesser omentum

k. mesentery

l. microvilli

m. oral cavity

n. parietal peritoneum

o. Peyer's patches

p. pharynx

q. plicae circulares

r. pyloric valve

s. rugae

t. small intestine

u. soft palate

v. stomach

w. tongue

x. vestibule

y. villi

z. visceral peritoneum

4. Correctly identify all organs depicted in the diagram below.

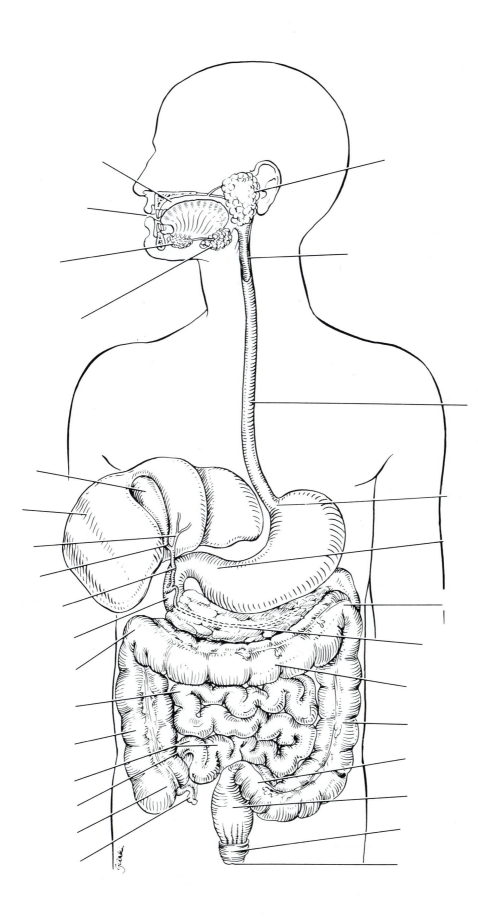

5. You have studied the histologic structure of a number of organs in this laboratory. Three of these are diagrammed below. Identify each.

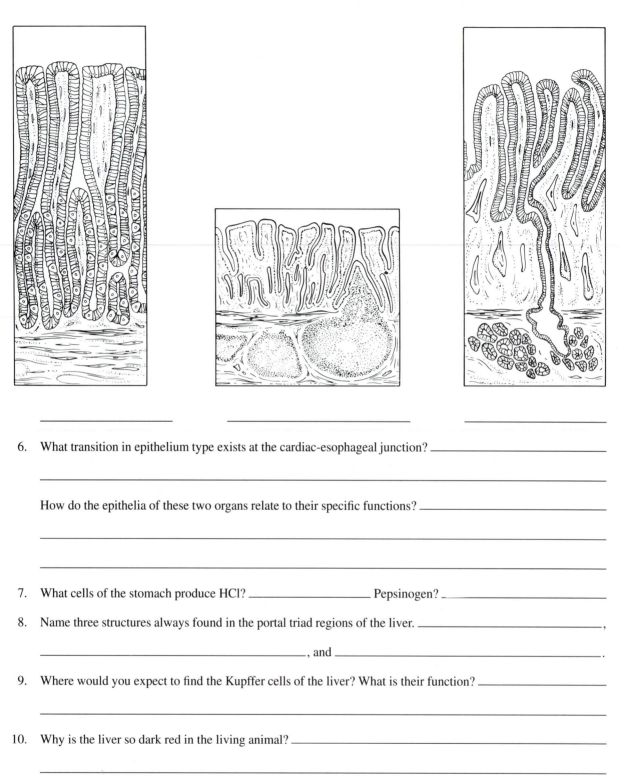

_____   _____   _____

6. What transition in epithelium type exists at the cardiac-esophageal junction? _____

_____

How do the epithelia of these two organs relate to their specific functions? _____

_____

_____

7. What cells of the stomach produce HCl? _____ Pepsinogen? _____

8. Name three structures always found in the portal triad regions of the liver. _____,

_____ , and _____ .

9. Where would you expect to find the Kupffer cells of the liver? What is their function? _____

_____

10. Why is the liver so dark red in the living animal? _____

_____

Accessory Digestive Organs

1. Various types of glands form a part of the alimentary tube wall or duct their secretions into it. Match the glands listed in column B with the function/locations described in column A.

   Column A

   _____ produce mucus; found in the submucosa of the small intestine

   _____ produce a product containing amylase that begins starch breakdown in the mouth

   _____ produces a whole spectrum of enzymes and an alkaline fluid that is secreted into the duodenum

   _____ produces bile that it secretes into the duodenum via the common bile duct

   _____ produce HCl and pepsinogen

   _____ found in the mucosa of the small intestine; produce intestinal juice

   Column B

   a. Brunner's glands

   b. gastric glands

   c. intestinal crypts

   d. liver

   e. pancreas

   f. salivary glands

2. Which of the salivary glands produces a secretion that is mainly serous? _____

3. What is the role of the gallbladder? _____

4. Use the key to identify each tooth area described below.

   _____ visible portion of the tooth *in situ*

   _____ material covering the tooth root

   _____ hardest substance in the body

   _____ attaches the tooth to bone and surrounding alveolar structures

   _____ portion of the tooth embedded in bone

   _____ forms the major portion of tooth structure; similar to bone

   _____ form the dentin

   _____ site of blood vessels, nerves, and lymphatics

   _____ entire portion of the tooth covered with enamel

   Key:
   a. anatomical crown

   b. cementum

   c. clinical crown

   d. dentin

   e. enamel

   f. gingiva

   g. odontoblasts

   h. periodontal ligament

   i. pulp

   j. root

5. In the human, the number of deciduous teeth is _____; the number of permanent teeth is _____.

6. The dental formula for permanent teeth is $\dfrac{2, 1, 2, 3}{2, 1, 2, 3}$

   Explain what this means: _____

   _____

   What is the dental formula for the deciduous teeth?

7. What teeth are the "wisdom teeth"? _____

Dissection of the Digestive System of the Fetal Pig

Several differences between pig and human digestive anatomy should have become apparent during the dissection. Note the pertinent differences between the human and the pig relative to the following structures:

Structure	Pig	Human
Number of liver lobes		
Appendix		
Appearance and distribution of colon		
Presence of round ligament		

STUDENT NAME ____________________

LAB TIME/DATE ____________________

EXERCISE 39

Chemical and Physical Digestion

Part I: Chemical Breakdown of Foodstuffs: Enzymatic Action

1. Match the following definitions with the proper key letters.

   Key: a. catalyst b. control c. enzyme d. substrate

   ____________ increases the rate of a chemical reaction without becoming part of the product

   ____________ provides a standard of comparison for test results

   ____________ biologic catalyst; protein in nature

   ____________ substance on which a catalyst works

2. List three characteristics of enzymes. ____________________

   ____

3. The enzymes of the digestive system are classed as hydrolases. What does this mean? ____________________

   ____

4. Fill in the following chart relative to the various digestive system enzymes encountered in this exercise.

Enzyme	Organ producing it	Site of action	Substrate(s)	Optimal pH

5. Name the end products of digestion for the following types of foods:

   proteins ____________ carbohydrates ____________

   fats ____________ and ____________

6. You used several indicators or tests in the laboratory to determine the presence or absence of certain substances. Choose the correct test or indicator from the key to correspond to the conditions described below:

Key:　a.　IKI (Lugol's iodine)　　　b.　Benedict's solution　　　c.　phenol red　　　d.　biuret test

_____ used to test for the presence of protein, which was indicated by a violet color

_____ used to test for the presence of starch, which was indicated by a blue-black color

_____ used to test for the presence of fatty acids, which was evidenced by a color change from pink to yellow

_____ used to test for the presence of reducing sugars (maltose, sucrose, glucose) as indicated by a blue to red color change

7. In the procedure concerning starch digestion by salivary amylase, how do you explain the fact that neither 0°C incubation nor conditions that involved a preliminary boiling of the enzyme preparation resulted in positive test

results for the digestion of starch? _____

_____

What conclusions can you draw when an experimental sample gives both a positive starch test and a positive

Benedict's test after incubation? _____

_____

Why was 37°C the optimal incubation temperature? _____

Why did very little, if any, starch digestion occur in test tubes 9 and 10? _____

_____

Why was sample #1 completely negative for the presence of sugar?_____

8. In the procedure concerning pepsin digestion of protein, in which test tube did more protein hydrolysis occur?

_____ Why? _____

_____

Why did test tubes 3 and 5 yield negative results for digestion? _____

_____

What functional relationship exists between HCl and pepsin? _____

_____

Pepsin is a protein-digesting enzyme, and the structural material of cells is largely protein. Why doesn't the

stomach digest itself? _____

_____

RS172

9. In the procedure concerning pancreatic lipase digestion of fats and the action of bile salts, how did appearance of test tubes A and B differ? _____

_____

How can you explain this difference? _____

_____

Why did the phenol red indicator change from pink to yellow during the process of fat hydrolysis?_____

_____

_____

Why is bile not considered an enzyme? _____

_____

What role does bile play in fat digestion? _____

_____

10. The three-dimensional structure of a functional protein is altered by intense heat or excesses of pH even though peptide bonds may not break. Such inactivation is called denaturation, and denatured enzymes are nonfunctional.

Explain why. _____

_____

_____

What specific experimental conditions in the various procedures resulted in the denaturation of the enzymes?

_____

_____

11. Pancreatic and intestinal enzymes operate optimally at a pH that is slightly alkaline, yet the chyme entering the duodenum from the stomach is very acid. How is the proper pH for the functioning of the pancreatic-intestinal

enzymes assured? _____

_____

12. Assume you have been chewing a piece of bread for 5 or 6 minutes. How would you expect its taste to change

during this interval? _____

Why? _____

13. Note the mechanism of absorption (passive or active transport) of the following food breakdown products, and indicate by a check mark (√) whether the absorption would result in their movement into the blood capillaries or the lymph capillaries (lacteals).

Substance	Mechanism of absorption	Blood	Lymph
monosaccharides			
fatty acids and glycerol			
amino acids			
water			
Na^+, Cl^-, Ca^{2+}			

14. People on a strict diet to lose weight begin to metabolize stored fats at an accelerated rate. How would this condition affect blood pH? _____

15. Trace the pathway of a ham sandwich (ham = protein and fat; bread = starch) from the mouth to the site of absorption of its breakdown products, noting where digestion occurs and what specific enzymes are involved.

16. Some of the digestive organs have groups of secretory cells that liberate hormones (parahormones) into the blood. These exert an effect on the digestive process by acting on other cells or structures and causing them to release digestive enzymes, expel bile, or increase the mobility of the digestive tract. For each hormone below, note the organ producing the hormone and its effects on the digestive process. Include the target organs affected.

Hormone	Target organ(s) and effects
secretin	
gastrin	
cholecystokinin	

Part II: Food Propulsion Mechanisms

Complete the following statements:

Swallowing, or __1__, occurs in two phases—the __2__ and __3__. One of these phases, the __4__ phase is voluntary. During the voluntary phase, the __5__ is used to push the food into the back of the throat. During swallowing the __6__ rises to insure that its passageway is covered by the epiglottis so that ingested substances don't enter the respiratory passageways. It is possible to swallow water while standing on your head because the water is carried along the esophagus involuntarily by the process of __7__. The pressure exerted by the foodstuffs on the __8__ sphincter causes it to open, allowing the foodstuffs to enter the stomach.

The three major types of movement that occur in the small intestine are __9__, __10__, and __11__. One of these movements, the __12__, acts to continually mix the foods and to increase the absorption rate by moving different parts of the chyme mass over the intestinal mucosa, but has less of a role in moving foods along the digestive tract. Another type of movement seen in the large intestine, __13__, occurs infrequently and acts to move the feces over relatively long distances toward the anus. Three factors that influence the motility of the small intestine are __14__, __15__, and __16__.

1. _____
2. _____
3. _____
4. _____
5. _____
6. _____
7. _____
8. _____
9. _____
10. _____
11. _____
12. _____
13. _____
14. _____
15. _____
16. _____

EXERCISE 40

Anatomy of the Urinary System

Gross Anatomy of the Human Urinary System

1. Complete the following statements:

The kidney is referred to as an excretory organ because it excretes __1__ wastes. It is also a major homeostatic organ because it maintains the electrolyte, __2__, and __3__ balance of the blood.

Urine is continuously formed by the __4__ and is routed down the __5__ by the mechanism of __6__ to a storage organ called the __7__. Eventually, the urine is conducted to the body __8__ by the urethra. In the male, the urethra is __9__ inches long and transports both urine and __10__. The female urethra is __11__ inches long and transports only urine.

Voiding or emptying the bladder is called __12__. Voiding has both voluntary and involuntary components. The voluntary sphincter is the __13__ sphincter. An inability to control this sphincter is referred to as __14__.

1. _____

2. _____

3. _____

4. _____

5. _____

6. _____

7. _____

8. _____

9. _____

10. _____

11. _____

12. _____

13. _____

14. _____

2. What is the function of the fat cushion that surrounds the kidneys in life? _____

_____

3. Define *ptosis.* _____

_____

4. Why is incontinence a normal phenomenon in the child under 1½ to 2 years old? _____

_____

What events may lead to its occurrence in the adult? _____

_____

_____

5. Complete the labeling of the diagram to correctly identify the urinary system organs.

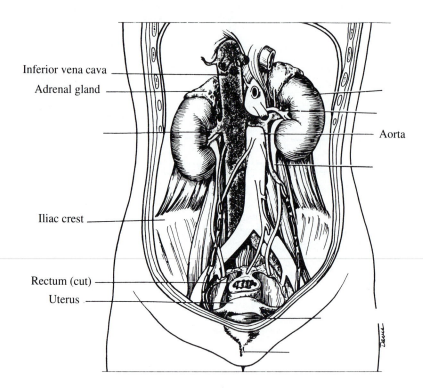

Inferior vena cava

Adrenal gland

Aorta

Iliac crest

Rectum (cut)

Uterus

Gross Internal Anatomy of the Pig or Sheep Kidney

Match the appropriate structure in column B to its description in column A.

Column A

Column B

_____ smooth membrane, tightly adherent to the kidney surface

a. cortex

_____ portion of the kidney containing mostly collecting ducts

b. medulla

_____ portion of the kidney containing the bulk of the nephron structures

c. minor calyx

_____ superficial region of kidney tissue

d. renal capsule

_____ basinlike area of the kidney, continuous with the ureter

e. renal column

_____ a cup-shaped extension of the pelvis that encircles the apex of a pyramid

f. renal pelvis

_____ area of cortical tissue running between the medullary pyramids

Microscopic Anatomy of the Kidney and Bladder

1. Match each of the lettered structures on the diagram of the nephron (and associated renal blood supply) on the left with the terms on the right:

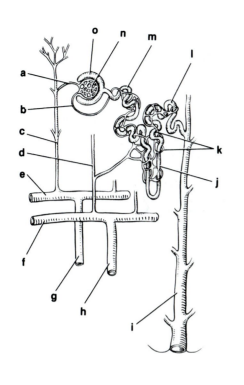

_____ collecting tubule

_____ glomerulus

_____ peritubular capillaries

_____ distal convoluted tubule

_____ proximal convoluted tubule

_____ interlobar artery

_____ interlobular artery

_____ arcuate artery

_____ interlobular vein

_____ efferent arteriole

_____ arcuate vein

_____ loop of Henle

_____ afferent arteriole

_____ interlobar vein

_____ glomerular capsule

2. Using the terms provided in item 1, identify the following:

_____ site of filtrate formation

_____ primary site of tubular reabsorption

_____ secondarily important site of tubular reabsorption

_____ structure that conveys the processed filtrate (urine) to the renal pelvis

_____ blood supply that directly receives substances from the tubular cells

_____ Its inner (visceral) membrane forms part of the filtration membrane

3. Explain *why* the glomerulus is such a high-pressure capillary bed. _____

_____

How does its high pressure condition aid its function of filtrate formation? _____

_____

4. What structural modification of certain tubule cells enhances their ability to reabsorb substances from the filtrate?

_____

5. Explain the mechanism of tubular secretion and explain its importance in the urine formation process. _____

_____

_____

_____

6. Compare and contrast the composition of blood plasma and glomerular filtrate. _____

_____

7. Trace a drop of blood from the time it enters the kidney in the renal artery until it leaves the kidney through the renal vein. Renal artery → _____

_____

_____ → renal vein

8. Trace the anatomic pathway of a molecule of creatinine (metabolic waste) from the glomerular capsule to the urethra. Note each microscopic and/or gross structure it passes through in its travels. Name the subdivisions of the renal tubule. Glomerular capsule → _____

_____

_____ → urethra

9. What is important functionally about the specialized epithelium (transitional epithelium) in the bladder?

_____

_____

Dissection of the Urinary System of the Fetal Pig

1. How does the structure and distribution of the allantoic bladder of the fetal pig differ from the urinary bladder of the human (or that of the adult pig for that matter)? _____

_____

_____

2. What differences in fetal elimination of nitrogenous wastes accounts for the structural differences described above? _____

_____

_____

3. How does the site of urethral emptying in the female pig differ from its termination point in the human female?

_____

_____

_____

EXERCISE 41

Urinalysis

1. What is the normal volume of urine excreted in a 24-hour period? _____

   a. 0.1–0.5 liters　　　b. 0.5–1.2 liters　　　c. 1.0–1.8 liters

2. Assuming normal conditions, note whether each of the following substances would be (a) in greater relative concentration in the urine than in the glomerular filtrate, (b) in lesser concentration in the urine than in the glomerular filtrate, or (c) absent in both the urine and the glomerular filtrate.

   _____ water　　　　　_____ amino acids　　　　_____ urea

   _____ phosphate ions　　_____ glucose　　　　　_____ uric acid

   _____ sulfate ions　　　_____ albumin　　　　　_____ creatinine

   _____ potassium ions　　_____ red blood cells　_____ pus (WBC)

   _____ sodium ions

3. Explain why urinalysis is a routine part of any good physical examination. _____

   _____

4. What substance is responsible for the normal yellow color of urine? _____

5. Which has a greater specific gravity: 1 ml of urine or 1 ml of distilled water? _____

   Explain. _____

   _____

6. Explain the relationship between the color, specific gravity, and volume of urine. _____

   _____

   _____

   _____

7. A microscopic examination of urine may reveal the presence of certain abnormal urinary constituents.

   Name three constituents that might be present if a urinary tract infection exists. _____,

   _____, and _____

8. How does a urinary tract infection influence urine pH? _____

   How does starvation influence urine pH? _____

9. Several specific terms have been used to indicate the presence of abnormal urine constituents. Identify each of the abnormalities described below by inserting a term from the list at the right that names the condition.

_____ presence of erythrocytes in the urine

_____ presence of hemoglobin in the urine

_____ presence of glucose in the urine

_____ presence of albumin in the urine

_____ presence of ketone bodies (acetone and others) in the urine

_____ presence of pus (white blood cells) in the urine

a. albuminuria

b. glycosuria

c. hematuria

d. hemoglobinuria

e. ketonuria

f. pyuria

10. What are renal calculi and what conditions favor their formation? _____

_____

11. All urine specimens become alkaline and cloudy on standing at room temperature. Explain. _____

_____

12. Glucose and albumin are both normally absent in the urine, but the reason for their exclusion differs. Explain the

reason for the absence of glucose. _____

_____

The reason for the absence of albumin. _____

_____

13. Several conditions (both pathologic and nonpathologic) are named below. Using the key provided, characterize the probable abnormal constituents or conditions of the urinary product of each. More than one choice may be necessary to fully characterize the condition in most cases.

a. albumin
b. hemoglobin
c. blood cells

d. glucose
e. ketone bodies
f. bilirubin

g. pus
h. high specific gravity
i. low specific gravity

j. casts

_____ glomerulonephritis

_____ diabetes mellitus

_____ pregnancy, exertion

_____ hepatitis, cirrhosis of the liver

_____ pyelonephritis

_____ gonorrhea

_____ starvation

_____ diabetes insipidus

_____ kidney stones

_____ eating a 5-lb box of candy at one sitting

_____ hemolytic anemias

_____ cystitis (inflammation of the bladder)

14. Name the three major nitrogenous wastes found in the urine. _____,

_____, and _____

15. Explain the difference between organized and unorganized sediments. _____

_____

_____

_____

RS182

EXERCISE 42

Anatomy of the Reproductive System

Gross Anatomy of the Human Male Reproductive System

1. List the two principal functions of the testis: _____

2. Identify all indicated structures or portions of structures on the diagrammatic view of the male reproductive system below.

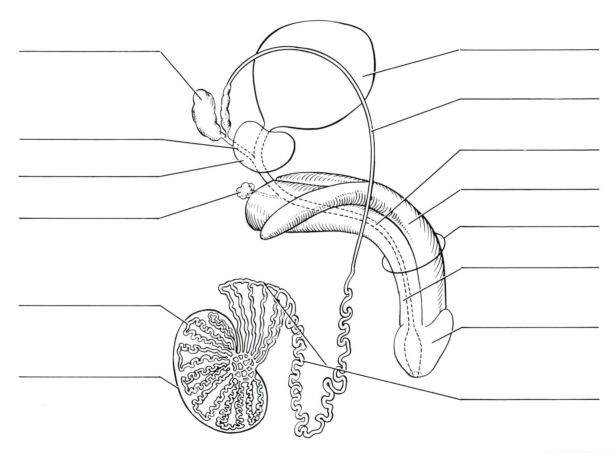

3. A common part of any physical examination of the male is palpation of the prostate gland. How is this accomplished? (Think!) _____

4. How might enlargement of the prostate gland interfere with urination or the reproductive ability of the male?

_____

_____

5. Match the terms in column B to the descriptive statements in column A.

Column A	Column B
_____ copulatory organ/penetrating device	a. bulbourethral glands
_____ site of sperm/androgen production	b. epididymis
_____ muscular passageway conveying sperm to the ejaculatory duct; in the spermatic cord	c. glans penis
_____ transports both sperm and urine	d. membranous urethra
_____ sperm maturation site	e. penile urethra
_____ location of the testis in adult males	f. penis
_____ loose fold of skin encircling the glans penis	g. prepuce
_____ portion of the urethra between the prostate gland and the penis	h. prostate gland
_____ empties a secretion into the prostatic urethra	i. prostatic urethra
_____ empties a secretion into the membranous urethra	j. seminal vesicles
	k. scrotum
	l. testes
	m. vas (ductus) deferens

6. Why are the testes located in the scrotum? _____

_____

7. Describe the composition of semen and name all structures contributing to its formation. _____

_____

_____

8. Of what importance is the fact that seminal fluid is alkaline? _____

_____

9. What structures comprise the spermatic cord? _____

_____

Where is it located? _____

_____

10. Using the following terms, trace the pathway of sperm from the testes to the urethra: rete testis, epididymis, seminiferous tubule, ductus deferens.

_____ → _____ → _____ → _____

11. Using an appropriate reference, define cryptorchidism and discuss its significance.

_____

_____

Gross Anatomy of the Human Female Reproductive System

1. On the diagram of a frontal section of a portion of the female reproductive system seen below, identify all indicated structures.

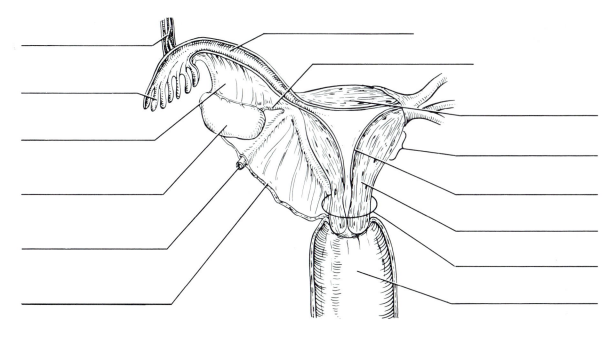

2. Identify the female reproductive system structures described below:

_____ site of fetal development

_____ copulatory canal

_____ "fertilized egg" typically formed here

_____ becomes erectile during sexual excitement

_____ duct extending superolaterally from the uterus

_____ partially closes the vaginal canal; a membrane

_____ produces eggs, estrogens, and progesterone

_____ fingerlike ends of the fallopian tube

3. Do any sperm enter the pelvic cavity of the female? Why or why not? _____

_____

4. What is an ectopic pregnancy, and how can it happen? _____

_____

_____

_____

5. Name the structures composing the external genitalia, or vulva, of the female. _____

_____

_____

6. Put the following vestibular-perineal structures in their proper order from the anterior to the posterior aspect: vaginal orifice, anus, urethral opening, and clitoris.

   Anterior limit: _____ → _____ → _____ → _____

7. Name the male structure that is homologous to the female structures named below.

   labia majora _____   clitoris _____

8. Assume a couple has just consummated the sex act and the male's sperm have been deposited in the woman's vagina. Trace the pathway of the sperm through the female reproductive tract.

   _____

9. Define *ovulation:* _____

10. To describe breast function, complete the following sentences:

   Milk is formed by _____ within the _____ of the breast. Milk

   is then excreted into enlarged storage regions called _____ and then finally through the

   _____.

11. Describe the procedure for self-examination of the breasts. (Men are not exempt from breast cancer, you know!)

   _____

   _____

   _____

   _____

   _____

   _____

Microscopic Anatomy of Selected Male and Female Reproductive Organs

1. The testis is divided into a number of lobes by connective tissue. Each of these lobes contains one to four

   _____ , which converge on a tubular region at the testis hilus called the

   _____ .

2. What is the function of the cavernous bodies seen in the male penis? _____

   _____

   _____

3. Name the three layers of the uterine wall from the inside out.

   _____ , _____ , _____

   Which of these is sloughed during menses? _____

   Which contracts during childbirth? _____

4. What is the function of the stereocilia exhibited by the epithelial cells of the mucosa of the epididymis? _____

   _____

5. On the diagram showing the sagittal section of the human testis, correctly identify all structures provided with leader lines.

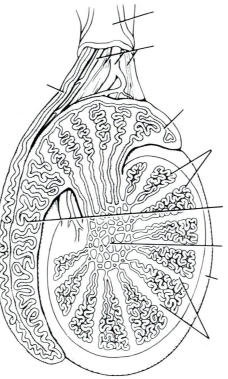

Dissection of the Reproductive System of the Fetal Pig

1. The female pig has a _____ uterus; that of the human female is _____ .

   Explain the difference in structure of these two uterine types. _____

   _____

   _____

2. What reproductive advantage is conferred by the pig's uterine type? _____

   _____

3. Cite differences noted between the pig and the human relative to the following structures:

   uterine tubes or oviducts _____

   _____

   urethral and vaginal openings in the female _____

   _____

   _____

EXERCISE 43

Physiology of Reproduction: Gametogenesis and the Female Cycles

Meiosis

1. The following statements refer to events occurring during mitosis and/or meiosis. For each statement, decide if the event occurs in (a) mitosis only, (b) meiosis only, or (c) both mitosis and meiosis.

_____ dyads are visible

_____ tetrads are visible

_____ product is two diploid daughter cells

_____ product is four haploid daughter cells

_____ involves the phases prophase, metaphase, anaphase, and telophase

_____ occurs throughout the body

_____ occurs only in the ovaries and testes

_____ provides cells for growth and repair

_____ homologues synapse and chiasmata are seen

_____ daughter cells are quantitatively and qualitatively different from the mother cell

_____ daughter cells are genetically identical to the mother cell

_____ chromosomes are replicated before the division process begins

_____ provides cells for replication of the species

_____ consists of two consecutive nuclear divisions, without chromosomal replication occurring before the second division

2. Describe the process of synapsis. _____

_____

3. How does crossover introduce variability in the daughter cells? _____

_____

_____

4. Define *homologous chromosomes*. _____

_____

Spermatogenesis

1. The cell types seen in the seminiferous tubules are listed in the key. Match the correct cell type(s) with the descriptions given below.

Key: a.   primary spermatocyte   c.   spermatogonium   e.   spermatid
         b.   secondary spermatocyte   d.   Sertoli cell   f.   sperm

_____ primitive stem cell   _____ product of meiosis II

_____ haploid   _____ product of spermiogenesis

_____ provides nutrients to   _____ product of meiosis I
                  developing sperm

2. Why are spermatids not considered functional gametes? _____

_____

3. Define *spermatogenesis:* _____

Define *spermiogenesis:* _____

_____

4. Draw a sperm below and identify the *acrosome, head, midpiece,* and *tail.* Then beside each label, note the composition and function of each of these sperm structures.

5. The life span of a sperm is very short. What anatomical characteristics might lead you to suspect this even if you

didn't know its life span? _____

Oogenesis, the Ovarian Cycle, and the Menstrual Cycle

1. The sequence of events leading to germ cell formation in the female begins during fetal development. By the

time the child is born, all the oogonia have been converted to _____ .

In view of this fact, how does the total germ cell potential of the female compare to that of the male?

_____

2. The female gametes develop in structures called *follicles*. What is a follicle? _____

_____

How are primary and vesicular follicles anatomically different? _____

_____

_____

_____

What is a corpus luteum? _____

_____

3. What hormone is produced by the vesicular follicle? _____

By the corpus luteum? _____

4. Use the key to identify the cell type you would expect to find in the following structures.

   Key: a.   oogonium   b.   primary oocyte   c.   secondary oocyte   d.   ovum

   _____ forming part of the primary follicle in the ovary

   _____ in the uterine tube before fertilization

   _____ in the mature vesicular follicle of the ovary

   _____ in the uterine tube shortly after sperm penetration

5. The cellular product of spermatogenesis is four _____; the final product of oogenesis is one

   _____ and three _____. What is the function of this unequal cytoplas-

   mic division seen during oogenesis in the female? _____

   _____

   _____

   What is the fate of the three tiny cells produced during oogenesis? _____

   Why? _____

6. The following statements deal with anterior pituitary and ovarian hormonal interrelationships. Name the hormone(s) described in each statement.

   _____ stimulates ovarian follicles to grow and to produce estrogen

   _____ ovulation occurs after its burstlike release

   _____ and _____ exert negative feedback on
   the anterior pituitary relative to FSH secretion

   _____ stimulates LH release by the anterior pituitary

   _____ stimulates the corpus luteum to produce progesterone and estrogen

   _____ maintains the hormonal production of the corpus luteum in a
   nonpregnant woman

RS191

7. Why does the corpus luteum deteriorate toward the end of the ovarian cycle? _____

_____

8. For each statement below dealing with hormonal blood levels during the female ovarian and menstrual cycles, decide whether the condition in column A is usually (a) greater than, (b) less than, or (c) essentially equal to the condition in column B.

Column A		Column B
_____ amount of estrogen in the blood during menses	↔	amount of estrogen in the blood at ovulation
_____ amount of progesterone in the blood on the fourteenth day	↔	amount of progesterone in the blood on the twenty-third day
_____ amount of LH in the blood during menses	↔	amount of LH in the blood at ovulation
_____ amount of FSH in the blood on day 6 of the cycle	↔	amount of FSH in the blood on day 20 of the cycle
_____ amount of estrogen in the blood on the tenth day	↔	amount of progesterone in the blood on the tenth day

9. Ovulation and menstruation usually cease by the age of _____.

10. What uterine tissue undergoes dramatic changes during the menstrual cycle? _____

11. When during the female menstrual cycle would fertilization be unlikely? _____

_____

12. Assume that a woman could be an "on demand" ovulator like the rabbit, in which copulation stimulates the hypothalamic-anterior pituitary axis and causes LH release, and an oocyte was ovulated and fertilized on day 26 of her 28-day cycle. Why would a successful pregnancy be unlikely at this time?

_____

_____

13. The menstrual cycle depends on events within the female ovary. The stages of the menstrual cycle are listed below. For each, note its approximate time span and the related events in the uterus; and then to the right, record the ovarian events occurring simultaneously. Pay particular attention to hormonal events.

Menstrual Cycle Stage	Uterine Events	Ovarian Events
Menstruation		
Proliferative		
Secretory		

EXERCISE 44

Survey of Embryonic Development

Developmental Stages of the Human

1. Use the key choices to identify the embryonic stage or process described below.

   Key: a. cleavage   c. zygote   e. blastula
                  b. morula   d. fertilization   f. gastrulation

   _____ the event most immediately following sperm penetration

   _____ solid ball of embryonic cells

   _____ process of rapid mitotic cell division without intervening growth periods

   _____ combination of egg and sperm

   _____ process involving cell rearrangements to form the three embryonic germ layers

   _____ embryonic stage in which the embryo consists of a hollow ball of cells

2. What is the importance of cleavage in embryonic development? _____

   _____

   How is cleavage different from mitotic cell division, which occurs late in life? _____

   _____

   _____

3. Explain the importance of gastrulation. _____

   _____

   _____

4. Name the primary germ layers, and describe their relative positions in the embryo.

   _____ , _____

   _____ , _____

   _____ , _____

5. The cells of the human blastula (more commonly called the blastocyst or chorionic vesicle) have various fates. Which blastocyst structures have the following fates?

_____ produces the embryonic body

_____ becomes the chorion and cooperates with uterine tissues to form the placenta

_____ produces the amnion, yolk sac, and allantois

_____ produces the primordial germ cells (an embryonic membrane)

_____ an embryonic membrane that provides the structural basis for the body stalk or umbilical cord

6. What is the function of the amnion and the amniotic fluid? _____

_____

_____

7. Describe the process of implantation, noting the role of the trophoblast cells. _____

_____

_____

8. How many days after fertilization is implantation generally completed? _____ What event in the female menstrual cycle ordinarily occurs just about this time if implantation does not occur? _____

_____

9. What name is given to the part of the uterine wall directly under the implanting embryo? _____

That surrounding the rest of the embryonic structure? _____

10. Using an appropriate reference, find out what *decidua* means and state the definition. _____

_____

How is this terminology applicable to the deciduas of pregnancy? _____

_____

11. Referring to the illustrations and text of "Life Before Birth," answer the following:

Which two organ systems are extensively developed in the *very young* embryo?

_____ and _____

Describe the direction of development by circling the correct descriptions below:

proximal-distal   distal-proximal   caudal-rostral   rostral-caudal

Does bodily control during infancy develop in the same directions? Think! Can an infant pick up a common pin (pincer grasp) or wave his arms earlier? Is arm-hand or leg-foot control achieved earlier?

_____

12. Note whether each of the following organs or organ systems develop from the (a) ectoderm, (b) endoderm, or (c) mesoderm. Use an appropriate reference as necessary.

_____ skeletal muscle   _____ respiratory mucosa   _____ nervous system

_____ skeleton   _____ circulatory system   _____ serosa membrane

_____ lining of gut   _____ epidermis of skin   _____ liver, pancreas

In Utero Development

1. Make the following comparisons between a human and the pregnant dissected animal structures.

Comparison object	Human	Dissected animal
shape of the placenta		
shape of the uterus		

2. Where in the human uterus do implantation and placentation ordinarily occur? _____
_____

3. Describe the function(s) of the placenta. _____
_____
_____

What embryonic membranes has it more or less "put out of business"? _____
_____

4. When does the human embryo come to be called a fetus? _____

5. What is the usual and most desirable fetal position in utero? _____

Why is this the most desirable position? _____
_____
_____
_____

Gross and Microscopic Anatomy of the Placenta

1. Describe fully the gross structure of the human placenta as observed in the laboratory. _____
_____
_____

2. What is the tissue origin of the placenta: fetal, maternal, or both? _____

3. What are the placental barriers that must be crossed to exchange materials? _____
_____

EXERCISE 45

Principles of Heredity

Introduction to the Language of Genetics

1. Match the key choices with the definitions given below.

Key: a. alleles   d. genotype   g. phenotype
     b. autosomes   e. heterozygous   h. recessive
     c. dominant   f. homozygous   i. sex chromosomes

_____ actual genetic makeup

_____ chromosomes determining maleness/femaleness

_____ situation in which an individual has identical alleles for a particular trait

_____ genes not expressed unless they are present in homozygous condition

_____ expression of a genetic trait

_____ situation in which an individual has different alleles making up his genotype for a
particular trait

_____ genes for the same trait that may have different expressions

_____ chromosomes regulating most body characteristics

_____ the more-potent gene allele; masks the expression of the less-potent allele

Dominant-Recessive Inheritance

1. In humans, farsightedness is inherited by possession of a dominant gene. If a man who is homozygous for normal
vision (aa) marries a woman who is heterozygous for farsightedness, what proportion of their children would be

expected to be farsighted? _____%

2. A metabolic disorder called PKU is due to an abnormal recessive gene (p). Only homozygous recessive individuals exhibit this disorder. What percentage of the offspring will be anticipated to have PKU if the parents are Pp

and pp? _____%

3. A man obtained 32 spotted and 10 solid-color rabbits from a mating of two spotted rabbits.

Which trait is dominant? _____ Recessive? _____

What is the probable genotype of the rabbit parents? _____ × _____

4. Assume that the allele controlling brown eyes (B) is dominant over that controlling blue eyes (b) in human beings. (In actuality, eye color in humans is an example of multigene inheritance, which is much more complex than this.) A blue-eyed man marries a brown-eyed woman; and they have six children, all brown-eyed. What is the most likely genotype of the father? _____ Of the mother? _____ If the seventh child had *blue* eyes, what could you conclude about the parents' genotypes? _____

_____

Incomplete Dominance

1. Tail length on a bobcat is controlled by incomplete dominance. The alleles are T for normal tail length and t for tail-less. What name could/would you give to the tails of heterozygous (Tt) cats? _____

How would their tail length compare with that of TT or tt bobcats? _____

2. If curly-haired individuals are genotypically CC, straight-haired individuals are cc, and wavy-haired individuals are heterozygotes (Cc), what percentage of the various phenotypes would be anticipated from a cross between a CC woman and a cc man?

_____ % curly _____ % wavy _____ % straight

Sex-Linked Inheritance

1. What does it mean when someone says a particular characteristic is sex-linked? _____

_____

2. You are a male, and you have been told that hemophilia "runs in your genes." Whose ancestors, your mother's or your father's, should you investigate? _____ Why? _____

_____

_____

3. An $X^C X^c$ female marries an $X^C Y$ man. Do a Punnet square for this match.

What is the probability of producing a color-blind son? _____

A color-blind daughter? _____

A daughter that is a carrier for the color-blind gene? _____

4. Why are consanguineous marriages (marriages between blood relatives) prohibited in most cultures?

_____

_____

Probability

1. What is the probability of having three daughters in a row? _____

2. A man and a woman, each of seemingly normal intellect, marry. Although neither is aware of the fact, each is a heterozygote for the allele for feeblemindedness. Is the allele for feeblemindedness dominant or recessive?

   _____

   What are the chances of their having one feebleminded child? _____

   What are the chances that all of their children (they plan a family of four) will be feebleminded?

   _____

Genetic Determination
of Selected Human Characteristics

1. Look back at your data to complete this section. For each of the situations described here, determine if an offspring with the characteristics noted is possible with the parental genotypes listed. Check (√) the appropriate column.

Parental Genotypes	Phenotype of Child	Possibility	
		Yes	No
Jj × jj	Double-jointed thumbs		
FF × Ff	Straight little finger		
EE × ee	Detached ear lobes		
HH × Hh	Mid-digital hair		
$I^A i \times I^B i$	Type O blood		
$I^A I^B \times ii$	Type B blood		

2. You have dimples, and you would like to know if you are homozygous or heterozygous for this trait. You have six brothers and sisters. By observing your siblings, how could you tell, with some degree of certainty, that you are a heterozygote?

   _____

   _____

   _____

   _____

EXERCISE 46 — Surface Anatomy Roundup

_____ 1. A blow to the cheek is most likely to break what superficial bone or bone part? (a) superciliary arches, (b) the philtrum, (c) zygomatic arch, (d) the tragus.

_____ 2. Rebound tenderness (a) occurs in appendicitis, (b) is whiplash of the neck, (c) is a sore foot from playing basketball, (d) occurs when the larynx falls back into place after swallowing.

_____ 3. The anatomical snuff box (a) is in the nose, (b) contains the styloid process of the radius, (c) is defined by tendons of the flexor carpi radialis and palmaris longus, (d) cannot really hold snuff.

_____ 4. Some landmarks on the body surface can be seen or felt, but others are abstractions that you must construct by drawing imaginary lines. Which of the following pairs of structures is abstract and invisible? (a) umbilicus and costal margin, (b) anterior superior iliac spine and natal cleft, (c) linea alba and linea semilunaris, (d) McBurney's point and midaxillary line, (e) philtrum and sternocleidomastoid.

_____ 5. Many pelvic organs can be palpated by placing a finger in the rectum or vagina, but only one pelvic organ is readily palpated through the skin. This is the (a) nonpregnant uterus, (b) prostate gland, (c) full bladder, (d) ovaries, (e) rectum.

_____ 6. A muscle that contributes to the posterior axillary fold is (a) pectoralis major, (b) latissimus dorsi, (c) trapezius, (d) infraspinatus, (e) pectoralis minor, (f) a and e.

_____ 7. Which of the following is not a pulse point? (a) anatomical snuff box, (b) inferior margin of mandible anterior to masseter muscle, (c) center of distal forearm at palmaris longus tendon, (d) medial bicipital furrow on arm, (e) dorsum of foot between the first two metatarsals.

_____ 8. Which pair of ribs inserts on the sternum at the sternal angle? (a) first, (b) second, (c) third, (d) fourth, (e) fifth.

_____ 9. The inferior angle of the scapula is at the same level as the spinous process of this vertebra: (a) C_5, (b) C_7, (c) T_3, (d) T_7, (e) L_4.

_____ 10. An important bony landmark that can be recognized by a distinct dimple in the skin is (a) posterior superior iliac spine, (b) styloid process of the ulna, (c) shaft of the radius, (d) acromion.

_____ 11. A nurse missed a patient's median cubital vein while trying to withdraw blood and then inserted the needle far too deeply into the cubital fossa. This error could cause any of the following problems, except this one: (a) paralysis of the ulnar nerve, (b) paralysis of the median nerve, (c) bruising the insertion tendon of the biceps brachii muscle, (d) blood spurting from the brachial artery.

_____ 12. Which of these organs is almost impossible to study with the techniques of surface anatomy? (a) heart, (b) lungs, (c) brain, (d) nose.

_____ 13. A preferred site for inserting an intravenous medication line into a blood vessel is (a) medial bicipital furrow on arm, (b) external carotid artery, (c) dorsal venous arch of hand, (d) popliteal fossa.

_____ 14. One listens for bowel sounds with a stethoscope that is placed (a) on the four quadrants of the abdominal wall; (b) in the triangle of auscultation; (c) in the right and left midaxillary line, just superior to the iliac crests; (d) inside the patient's bowels (intestines), on the tip of an endoscope.

15. Define palpation: _____

16. Explain how one locates the proper site for intramuscular injections into:

    (a) Deltoid muscle: _____

    (b) Ventral gluteal site: _____

    _____

    _____

17. Ashley, a pre–physical therapy student, was trying to locate the vertebral spinous processes on the flexed back of her friend Amber, but she kept losing count. Amber told her to check her count against several reliable "guideposts" along the way: the spinous processes of C_7, T_3, T_7, and L_4. Can you describe how to find each of these four particular vertebrae without having to count any vertebrae?

    C_7: _____

    _____

    T_3: _____

    _____

    T_7: _____

    L_4: _____

    _____

18. How does one find the midinguinal point? _____

    _____

19. Locate the standard points of surgical incision for reaching both the appendix and the gallbladder. _____

    _____

    _____

    _____

20. Gregory hit his funny bone. What nerve was hit against what bony process? _____

    _____

21. An athletic trainer was helping a college basketball player find the site of a pulled muscle. The trainer asked the athlete to extend her thigh at the hip forcefully, but she found this action too painful to perform. Then the trainer palpated her posterior thigh and felt some swelling of the muscles there. In simplest terms, which basic muscle

    group was injured? _____

22. Walking to her car after her sixty-fifth birthday party, Mrs. Schultz tripped on ice and fell forward on her outstretched palms. When she arrived at the emergency room, her right wrist and hand were bent like a fork handle. Dr. Jefferson felt that the styloid process of her radius was outside the anatomical snuff box and slightly proximal to the styloid process of the ulna. When he checked her elbow, he found that the olecranon process lay 2 cm proximal to the two epicondyles of the right humerus. Explain all these observations, and describe what had

happened to Mrs. Schultz's limb. _____

_____

_____

_____

_____

The Metric System

Measurement	Unit and Abbreviation	Metric Equivalent	Metric to English Conversion Factor	English to Metric Conversion Factor
Length	1 kilometer (km)	= 1000 (10^3) meters	1 km = 0.62 mile	1 mile = 1.61 km
	1 meter (m)	= 100 (10^2) centimeters = 1000 millimeters	1 m = 1.09 yards 1 m = 3.28 feet 1 m = 39.37 inches	1 yard = 0.914 m 1 foot = 0.305 m
	1 centimeter (cm)	= 0.01 (10^{-2}) meter	1 cm = 0.394 inch	1 foot = 30.5 cm 1 inch = 2.54 cm
	1 millimeter (mm)	= 0.001 (10^{-3}) meter	1 mm = 0.039 inch	
	1 micrometer (μm) [formerly micron (μ)]	= 0.000001 (10^{-6}) meter		
	1 nanometer (nm) [formerly millimicron (mμ)]	= 0.000000001 (10^{-9}) meter		
	1 angstrom (Å)	= 0.0000000001 (10^{-10}) meter		
Area	1 square meter (m²)	= 10,000 square centimeters	1 m² = 1.1960 square yards 1 m² = 10.764 square feet	1 square yard = 0.8361 m² 1 square foot = 0.0929 m²
	1 square centimeter (cm²)	= 100 square millimeters	1 cm² = 0.155 square inch	1 square inch = 6.4516 cm²
Mass	1 metric ton (t)	= 1000 kilograms	1 t = 1.103 ton	1 ton = 0.907t
	1 kilogram (kg)	= 1000 grams	1 kg = 2.205 pounds	1 pound = 0.4536 kg
	1 gram (g)	= 1000 milligrams	1 g = 0.0353 ounce 1 g = 15.432 grains	1 ounce = 28.35 g
	1 milligram (mg)	= 0.001 gram	1 mg = approx. 0.015 grain	
	1 microgram (μg)	= 0.000001 gram		
Volume (solids)	1 cubic meter (m³)	= 1,000,000 cubic centimeters	1 m³ = 1.3080 cubic yards 1 m³ = 35.315 cubic feet	1 cubic yard = 0.7646 m³ 1 cubic foot = 0.0283 m³
	1 cubic centimeter (cm³ or cc)	= 0.000001 cubic meter = 1 milliliter	1 cm³ = 0.0610 cubic inch	1 cubic inch = 16.387 cm³
	1 cubic millimeter (mm³)	= 0.000000001 cubic meter		
Volume (liquids and gases)	1 kiloliter (kl or kL)	= 1000 liters	1 kL = 264.17 gallons	1 gallon = 3.785 L
	1 liter (l or L)	= 1000 milliliters	1 L = 0.264 gallons 1 L = 1.057 quarts	1 quart = 0.946 L
	1 milliliter (ml or mL)	= 0.001 liter = 1 cubic centimeter	1 ml = 0.034 fluid ounce 1 ml = approx. $\frac{1}{4}$ teaspoon 1 ml = approx. 15–16 drops (gtt.)	1 quart = 946 ml 1 pint = 473 ml 1 fluid ounce = 29.57 ml 1 teaspoon = approx. 5 ml
	1 microliter (μl or μL)	= 0.000001 liter		
Time	1 second (s)	= $\frac{1}{60}$ minute		
	1 millisecond (ms)	= 0.001 second		
Temperature	Degrees Celsius (°C)		°F = $\frac{9}{5}$°C + 32	°C = $\frac{5}{9}$(°F − 32)

APPENDIX B Predicted Vital Capacities for Males

Height in centimeters

Age	146	148	150	152	154	156	158	160	162	164	166	168	170	172	174	176	178	180	182	184	186	188	190	192	194
16	3765	3820	3870	3920	3975	4025	4075	4130	4180	4230	4285	4335	4385	4440	4490	4540	4590	4645	4695	4745	4800	4850	4900	4955	5005
18	3740	3790	3840	3890	3940	3995	4045	4095	4145	4200	4250	4300	4350	4405	4455	4505	4555	4610	4660	4710	4760	4815	4865	4915	4965
20	3710	3760	3810	3860	3910	3960	4015	4065	4115	4165	4215	4265	4320	4370	4420	4470	4520	4570	4625	4675	4725	4775	4825	4875	4930
22	3680	3730	3780	3830	3880	3930	3980	4030	4080	4135	4185	4235	4285	4335	4385	4435	4485	4535	4585	4635	4685	4735	4790	4840	4890
24	3635	3685	3735	3785	3835	3885	3935	3985	4035	4085	4135	4185	4235	4285	4330	4380	4430	4480	4530	4580	4630	4680	4730	4780	4830
26	3605	3655	3705	3755	3805	3855	3905	3955	4000	4050	4100	4150	4200	4250	4300	4350	4395	4445	4495	4545	4595	4645	4695	4740	4790
28	3575	3625	3675	3725	3775	3820	3870	3920	3970	4020	4070	4115	4165	4215	4265	4310	4360	4410	4460	4510	4555	4605	4655	4705	4755
30	3550	3595	3645	3695	3740	3790	3840	3890	3935	3985	4035	4080	4130	4180	4230	4275	4325	4375	4425	4470	4520	4570	4615	4665	4715
32	3520	3565	3615	3665	3710	3760	3810	3855	3905	3950	4000	4050	4095	4145	4195	4240	4290	4340	4385	4435	4485	4530	4580	4625	4675
34	3475	3525	3570	3620	3665	3715	3760	3810	3855	3905	3950	4000	4045	4095	4140	4190	4225	4285	4330	4380	4425	4475	4520	4570	4615
36	3445	3495	3540	3585	3635	3680	3730	3775	3825	3870	3920	3965	4010	4060	4105	4155	4200	4250	4295	4340	4390	4435	4485	4530	4580
38	3415	3465	3510	3555	3605	3650	3695	3745	3790	3840	3885	3930	3980	4025	4070	4120	4165	4210	4260	4305	4350	4400	4445	4495	4540
40	3385	3435	3480	3525	3575	3620	3665	3710	3760	3805	3850	3900	3945	3990	4035	4085	4130	4175	4220	4270	4315	4360	4410	4455	4500
42	3360	3405	3450	3495	3540	3590	3635	3680	3725	3770	3820	3865	3910	3955	4000	4050	4095	4140	4185	4230	4280	4325	4370	4415	4460
44	3315	3360	3405	3450	3495	3540	3585	3630	3675	3725	3770	3815	3860	3905	3950	3995	4040	4085	4130	4175	4220	4270	4315	4360	4405
46	3285	3330	3375	3420	3465	3510	3555	3600	3645	3690	3735	3780	3825	3870	3915	3960	4005	4050	4095	4140	4185	4230	4275	4320	4365
48	3255	3300	3345	3390	3435	3480	3525	3570	3615	3655	3700	3745	3790	3835	3880	3925	3970	4015	4060	4105	4150	4190	4235	4280	4325
50	3210	3255	3300	3345	3390	3430	3475	3520	3565	3610	3650	3695	3740	3785	3830	3870	3915	3960	4005	4050	4090	4135	4180	4225	4270
52	3185	3225	3270	3315	3355	3400	3445	3490	3530	3575	3620	3660	3705	3750	3795	3835	3880	3925	3970	4010	4055	4100	4140	4185	4230
54	3155	3195	3240	3285	3325	3370	3415	3455	3500	3540	3585	3630	3670	3715	3760	3800	3845	3890	3930	3975	4020	4060	4105	4145	4190
56	3125	3165	3210	3255	3295	3340	3380	3425	3465	3510	3550	3595	3640	3680	3725	3765	3810	3850	3895	3940	3980	4025	4065	4110	4150
58	3080	3125	3165	3210	3250	3290	3335	3375	3420	3460	3500	3545	3585	3630	3670	3715	3755	3800	3840	3880	3925	3965	4010	4050	4095
60	3050	3095	3135	3175	3220	3260	3300	3345	3385	3430	3470	3500	3555	3595	3635	3680	3720	3760	3805	3845	3885	3930	3970	4015	4055
62	3020	3060	3110	3150	3190	3230	3270	3310	3350	3390	3440	3480	3520	3560	3600	3640	3680	3730	3770	3810	3850	3890	3930	3970	4020
64	2990	3030	3080	3120	3160	3200	3240	3280	3320	3360	3400	3440	3490	3530	3570	3610	3650	3690	3730	3770	3810	3850	3900	3940	3980
66	2950	2990	3030	3070	3110	3150	3190	3230	3270	3310	3350	3390	3430	3470	3510	3550	3600	3640	3680	3720	3760	3800	3840	3880	3920
68	2920	2960	3000	3040	3080	3120	3160	3200	3240	3280	3320	3360	3400	3440	3480	3520	3560	3600	3640	3680	3720	3760	3800	3840	3880
70	2890	2930	2970	3010	3050	3090	3130	3170	3210	3250	3290	3330	3370	3410	3450	3480	3520	3560	3600	3640	3680	3720	3760	3800	3840
72	2860	2900	2940	2980	3020	3060	3100	3140	3180	3210	3250	3290	3330	3370	3410	3450	3490	3530	3570	3610	3650	3680	3720	3760	3800
74	2820	2860	2900	2930	2970	3010	3050	3090	3130	3170	3200	3240	3280	3320	3360	3400	3440	3470	3510	3550	3590	3630	3670	3710	3740

Courtesy of Warren E. Collins, Inc., Braintree, Mass.

APPENDIX B Predicted Vital Capacities for Females

Height in centimeters

Age	146	148	150	152	154	156	158	160	162	164	166	168	170	172	174	176	178	180	182	184	186	188	190	192	194
16	2950	2990	3030	3070	3110	3150	3190	3230	3270	3310	3350	3390	3430	3470	3510	3550	3590	3630	3670	3715	3755	3800	3840	3880	3920
17	2935	2975	3015	3055	3095	3135	3175	3215	3255	3295	3335	3375	3415	3455	3495	3535	3575	3615	3655	3695	3740	3780	3820	3860	3900
18	2920	2960	3000	3040	3080	3120	3160	3200	3240	3280	3320	3360	3400	3440	3480	3520	3560	3600	3640	3680	3720	3760	3800	3840	3880
20	2890	2930	2970	3010	3050	3090	3130	3170	3210	3250	3290	3330	3370	3410	3450	3490	3525	3565	3605	3645	3695	3720	3760	3800	3840
22	2860	2900	2940	2980	3020	3060	3095	3135	3175	3215	3255	3290	3330	3370	3410	3450	3490	3530	3570	3610	3650	3685	3725	3765	3800
24	2830	2870	2910	2950	2985	3025	3065	3100	3140	3180	3220	3260	3300	3335	3375	3415	3455	3490	3530	3570	3610	3650	3685	3725	3765
26	2800	2840	2880	2920	2960	3000	3035	3070	3110	3150	3190	3230	3265	3300	3340	3380	3420	3455	3495	3530	3570	3610	3650	3685	3725
28	2775	2810	2850	2890	2930	2965	3000	3040	3070	3115	3155	3190	3230	3270	3305	3345	3380	3420	3460	3495	3535	3570	3610	3650	3685
30	2745	2780	2820	2860	2895	2935	2970	3010	3045	3085	3120	3160	3195	3235	3270	3310	3345	3385	3420	3460	3495	3535	3570	3610	3645
32	2715	2750	2790	2825	2865	2900	2940	2975	3015	3050	3090	3125	3160	3200	3235	3275	3310	3350	3385	3425	3460	3495	3535	3570	3610
34	2685	2725	2760	2795	2835	2870	2910	2945	2980	3020	3055	3090	3130	3165	3200	3240	3275	3310	3350	3385	3425	3460	3495	3535	3570
36	2655	2695	2730	2765	2805	2840	2875	2910	2950	2985	3020	3060	3095	3130	3165	3205	3240	3275	3310	3350	3385	3420	3460	3495	3530
38	2630	2665	2700	2735	2770	2810	2845	2880	2915	2950	2990	3025	3060	3095	3130	3170	3205	3240	3275	3310	3350	3385	3420	3455	3490
40	2600	2635	2670	2705	2740	2775	2810	2850	2885	2920	2955	2990	3025	3060	3095	3135	3170	3205	3240	3275	3310	3345	3380	3420	3455
42	2570	2605	2640	2675	2710	2745	2780	2815	2850	2885	2920	2955	2990	3025	3060	3100	3135	3170	3205	3240	3275	3310	3345	3380	3415
44	2540	2575	2610	2645	2680	2715	2750	2785	2820	2855	2890	2925	2960	2995	3030	3060	3095	3130	3165	3200	3235	3270	3305	3340	3375
46	2510	2545	2580	2615	2650	2685	2715	2750	2785	2820	2855	2890	2925	2960	2995	3030	3060	3095	3130	3165	3200	3235	3270	3305	3340
48	2480	2515	2550	2585	2620	2650	2685	2715	2750	2785	2820	2855	2890	2925	2960	2995	3030	3060	3095	3130	3160	3195	3230	3265	3300
50	2455	2485	2520	2555	2590	2625	2655	2690	2720	2755	2785	2820	2855	2890	2925	2955	2990	3025	3060	3090	3125	3155	3190	3225	3260
52	2425	2455	2490	2525	2555	2590	2625	2655	2690	2720	2755	2790	2820	2855	2890	2925	2955	2990	3020	3055	3090	3125	3155	3190	3220
54	2395	2425	2460	2495	2530	2560	2590	2625	2655	2690	2720	2755	2790	2820	2855	2885	2920	2950	2985	3020	3050	3085	3115	3150	3180
56	2365	2400	2430	2460	2495	2525	2560	2590	2625	2655	2690	2720	2755	2790	2820	2855	2885	2920	2950	2980	3015	3045	3080	3110	3145
58	2335	2370	2400	2430	2460	2495	2525	2560	2590	2625	2655	2690	2720	2750	2785	2815	2850	2880	2920	2945	2975	3010	3040	3075	3105
60	2305	2340	2370	2400	2430	2460	2495	2525	2560	2590	2625	2655	2685	2720	2750	2780	2810	2845	2875	2915	2940	2970	3000	3035	3065
62	2280	2310	2340	2370	2405	2435	2465	2495	2525	2560	2590	2620	2655	2685	2715	2745	2775	2810	2840	2870	2900	2935	2965	2995	3025
64	2250	2280	2310	2340	2370	2400	2430	2465	2495	2525	2555	2585	2620	2650	2680	2710	2740	2770	2805	2835	2865	2895	2925	2955	2990
66	2220	2250	2280	2310	2340	2370	2400	2430	2460	2495	2525	2555	2585	2615	2645	2675	2705	2735	2765	2800	2825	2860	2890	2920	2950
68	2190	2220	2250	2280	2310	2340	2370	2400	2430	2460	2490	2520	2550	2580	2610	2640	2670	2700	2730	2760	2795	2820	2850	2880	2910
70	2160	2190	2220	2250	2280	2310	2340	2370	2400	2425	2455	2485	2515	2545	2575	2605	2635	2665	2695	2725	2755	2780	2810	2840	2870
72	2130	2160	2190	2220	2250	2280	2310	2335	2365	2395	2425	2455	2480	2510	2540	2570	2600	2630	2660	2685	2715	2745	2775	2805	2830
74	2100	2130	2160	2190	2220	2245	2275	2305	2335	2360	2390	2420	2450	2475	2505	2535	2565	2590	2620	2650	2680	2710	2740	2765	2795

Courtesy of Warren E. Collins, Inc., Braintree, Mass.

Photo Credits

Histology insert photos by Victor Eroschenko, University of Idaho, except as noted. Plate 10: Courtesy of Churchill Livingstone. Plate 20: Carolina Biological Supply Company. Plate 30: Courtesy of Marian Rice.

Anatomy insert photos by Jack Scanlon, Holyoke Community College, except as noted. Beauchene skull: Courtesy of Somso Company/CABISCO.

11.5c, 15.3c, 15.4c, 15.5c, 15.8d, 15.10b, 15.11b, 15.12c, 21.1b: From *A Stereoscopic Atlas of Human Anatomy* by David L. Bassett.

Figure Number	©Credit
2.1b-c, 2.2a-b, 2.3	©Jack Scanlon.
3.1	©Courtesy of Leica Inc.
3.5 ,4.4a-f	©Victor Eroschenko.
5.2	©Richard Megna/Fundamental Photographs.
5.3a	©K.R. Porter/Photo Researchers, Inc.
5.3b	©David M. Phillips/The Population Council, Science Source/Photo Researchers, Inc.
5.3c	©Courtesy of Dr. Mohnadas Narla, Berkeley Livermore Laboratory.
6.3b	©Ed Reschke/Peter Arnold, Inc.
6.3a and c	©Marian Rice.
6.3d-f	©Ed Reschke.
6.3g	©John D. Cunningham/Visuals Unlimited.
6.3h	©Bruce Iverson.
6.4a,c-i	© Ed Reschke.
6.4b	©Marian Rice.
6.4j	©Biology Media/Photo Researchers, Inc.
6.4k-l	©Ed Reschke.
6.5a	©Eric Grave/Photo Researchers, Inc.
6.5b	©Ed Reschke.
6.5c	©Department of Anatomy & Histology, University of California, San Francisco.
6.6	©Ed Reschke.
7.3	©Marian Rice.
7.5	©Victor Eroschenko.
11.6a-b, 11.7	©Richard Hambert, Stanford University.
14.2	©Marian Rice.

Figure Number	©Credit
15.13-15.20	©Jack Scanlon.
17.2 a	From *Tissues and Organs: A Text-Atlas of Scanning Electron Microscopy* by Richard G. Kessel and Randy H. Kardon, W.H. Freeman and Co., © 1979.
19.9 b, 19.10, 19.11b	©Courtesy of Ann Allworth.
20.1a	©Alexander Tsiaras/Photo Researchers, Inc.
21.9	©Jack Scanlon.
24.13	©Courtesy of Christopher S. Sherman, Swedish Hospital Medical Center.
24.04a-c	©Jack Scanlon.
24.12	©Courtesy of Dr. William Spencer.
29.4	©Photo courtesy of Becton-Dichenson Company.
29.6 a-c, 29.7a-d	©Jack Scanlon.
29.8	©Marian Rice.
30.3a-b	©Photo courtesy of Ann Allwaorth.
30.6	©Marian Rice.
32.9b	©Jack Scanlon.
35.4	©Science Photo Library/Photo Researchers, Inc.
36.3	©Victor Eroschenko.
36.5	©Alfred Pasieka/Custom Medical Stock Photo.
36.6	©Photo courtesy of Ann Allworth.
36.7a-b	©Victor Eroschenko.
37.4	©Photo courtesy of Warren E. Collins Company.
38.7a-c, 38.11, 38.12	©Victor Eroschenko.
38.16b, 38.17b	©Jack Scanlon.
40.6a-b	©Victor Eroschenko.
40.7b, 42.9b, 42.10	©Jack Scanlon.